Migration
and
Environment

MIGRATION AND ENVIRONMENT

A Study of the Physical Characteristics of
the Japanese Immigrants to Hawaii
and the Effects of Environment
on their Descendants

By H. L. SHAPIRO

Associate Curator, American Museum of Natural History
Research Professor, University of Hawaii, Lecturer, Columbia University

WITH THE FIELD ASSISTANCE OF

FREDERICK S. HULSE

Issued under the auspices of
the University of Hawaii

OXFORD UNIVERSITY PRESS

LONDON NEW YORK TORONTO

1939

Copyright, 1939, by Oxford University Press, New York, Inc.

— Printed in the United States of America —

ACKNOWLEDGEMENTS

THE field work for this study was begun in the Hawaiian Islands in January 1931. It was completed in Japan, February 1932. During that time over 3,000 individuals submitted to a long, tedious schedule of physical measurements, the purpose of which was often but vaguely defined in their minds. If a few were unwilling to participate, the vast majority displayed a gratifying spirit of co-operation. And although they must remain anonymous, my principal acknowledgements go to them.

The investigation upon which this book reports was carried on under the auspices of the University of Hawaii, supported by the Rockefeller Foundation and encouraged by the American Museum of Natural History. To these institutions I am profoundly grateful.

To David L. Crawford, President of the University of Hawaii, I owe a double debt. His initial interest made this study possible in the beginning and his sustained support carried it through to its completion.

I should like also to express my appreciation to the following Japanese officials for the courtesy and assistance they rendered.

> H.E. Ryuzo Tanaka, Minister of Education in the Minseito Government of 1931.
> H.E. Kenzo Adachi, Minister for Home Affairs in the Minseito Government of 1931.
> H.E. Ichiro Hatoyama, Minister of Education in the Seiyukai Government of 1932.
> H.E. Tokugoro Nakahashi, Minister for Home Affairs in the Seiyukai Government of 1932.
> The Governors of the Prefectures of Fukushima, Niigata and Hiroshima under the Minseito Government.
> The Governors of Yamaguchi, Fukuoka and Kumamoto under the Seiyukai Government.
> The Japanese Consul General at Honolulu.

I am also deeply indebted to Professor Akira Matsumura of the Imperial University of Tokio for his unfailing kindness in smoothing the path of our work in Japan. Valuable service was rendered in the field both by Mr. J. Masuoka of the University of Hawaii and by Mr. Oshima of the

Imperial University of Tokio both of whom aided in the collection of data.

The long and laborious task of statistical computation was ably carried out by Mrs. George Woodbury. The drawing of the graphs I owe to the skill of Mr. Paul Richard. And to Mrs. Bertha Fay and Miss M. Kammerstein I am grateful for assistance in the preparation of the manuscript. I am deeply grateful to Miss Bella Weitzner for her valuable editorial suggestions and to Mr. Frederic Warde who shouldered the arduous burden of seeing this volume through the press. And finally, I wish to thank my wife for her many suggestions and for her labor in reading the proofs.

TABLE OF CONTENTS

LIST OF GRAPHS

Migration
and
Environment

MIGRATION AND ENVIRONMENT

CHAPTER I

Introduction

THE subject of this book may be defined as an inquiry into the consequences of migration and of a change of environment on the physical characteristics of a migrating population. Of this problem two phases in particular will occupy the major share of our attention. One deals with the physical characteristics of the migrant group compared with the original population from which it is derived, or, in other words, with the evidence that the migrant group represents a random or a selected population. The other considers the modifications which a change of environment may produce in the bodily traits of the children of the migrants. More specifically, this investigation is concerned with only one group of migrants, the Japanese, and with the influence of only one environment, the Hawaiian.

Although our subject may be limited in this fashion for the greater convenience of encompassing it, in reality it carries far wider implications than its bare statement might at first suggest. These implications, or at least some of them, may be more adequately discussed in the concluding section of this book, after the data of the present research have been presented. But it does, however, seem appropriate at this stage to sketch in briefly the social setting which lends significance to them.

It is no new observation that the age in which we live is especially characterized by rapidity of communication and ease of travel. The thousands of tourists who annually wander from one continent to another with a speed and a comfort undreamed of a few centuries ago are symbols of a general increase in the mobility of populations. In so far as any social phenomenon can be said to have a precisely datable beginning, this extraordinary acceleration of population movement may be traced back to the Renaissance in Europe. For at that period in European history the questing spirit, freed of its scholastic toils, and stimulated by its tentative but profitable commercial contacts with a vaguely known world, filled a few adventurous men with the desire to explore and 'discover' fabulous lands. Aided by improvements in ship-building and in navigation, the age of 'discovery,' in the egocentric phraseology of Europeans, began brilliantly and continued down to our times. It was a period when the countries of the Old World were brought into ever closer communication and when diverse races of man in both the Old and New World, hitherto unknown to each other, established a variety of contacts. In this epoch population movement and adjustments occurred on a scale new in history. Isolation vanished, and the entire world was exposed to fresh currents. These new geographic vistas, opened by exploration, and the vastly improved means of travel, introduced by science and invention, later provided accessible avenues into which vast hordes of men ventured, driven by various social, economic and individual pressures. Within the last four centuries one swollen stream of millions left Europe to populate the Americas, another of still more millions poured into South Africa and the Antipodes. Multitudes of Negroes were transported from Africa to the plantations of North and South America. Earlier movements of Hindus and Chinese were now resumed in greater number and spread over wider areas. The forgotten pools of Chinese in Southeastern Asia, marking the extent of earlier dispersions, were flooded once more and the overflow reached to the islands of the Pacific and to remote hamlets in America and Europe. In our generation, Chinese have invaded Manchuria in overwhelming numbers and with unprecedented rapidity. Recently the Japanese also have broken their bounds and have reached into the far corners of the earth.

These migrations by no means exhaust the list of peoples who have within our own times spread themselves in vast numbers over great distances. Nor are they unique as a phenomenon. They are symptomatic of a process coeval with mankind. Man has always been migratory, but never before on such a gargantuan scale. The present magnitude of the phenomenon serves to focus our attention on an ancient and significant fact.

But the facility of population movement, even in its present accelerated state, lacks all social meaning, if divorced from its consequences. And in fact, these very consequences are the reasons for our interest in the phenomenon itself.

Our concern here, however, is with only one of the innumerable currents, spiritual, social, economic and biologic, which these wholesale movements set into complex motion. Although biologists have exhibited some interest in the effect of migration on the lower organisms, students of man have lamentably neglected this aspect of their investigations of human biology, even though, as we have seen, migration has always been and is especially now profoundly characteristic of his behavior. Boas, a generation ago, brilliantly demonstrated in a pioneer work,[1] which unfortunately had few followers, that the children of immigrants to the U.S. underwent modifications in stature and cephalic index under the influence of their new environment. The material of his study, however, limited to immigrants and their

1 Changes in Bodily Form of Descendants of Immigrants.—N.Y. 1912.

children, could throw little light on the relationship of the immigrants to the stocks from which they sprang.

The present investigation, which arose from a preceding study on the Chinese and Chinese-Hawaiian, was designed not only to discover what immediate effects a change of environment might produce in the physical habitus of a migrating population—in this case the Japanese born in Hawaii—but also to obtain a control on the physical characteristics of the Japanese immigrants. These ends were achieved both by comparing immigrants with their offspring born and bred in Hawaii and by obtaining for comparison members of the same families in Japan who were raised in the very villages whence the Japanese in Hawaii migrated and who were nurtured under the same conditions which surrounded the immigrants.

Since the question of environment looms so large in this inquiry, some notion of its connotation in this context seems pertinent. Environment, as generally used, is a loose expression to cover the large number of variable factors that constitute the milieu in which an organism exists. In its broadest sense it includes everything outside the individual organism. Although, in human terms, we speak of physical, social, economic, spiritual and intellectual environments beside many others, these are merely subdivisions of the totality of factors material and immaterial which lie outside the organism and sustain or stimulate it. A metaphysician might, perhaps, make no distinction between the environment and the organism. He might conceivably argue that the organism is merely a specialized combination of various elements in the environment and that neither the organism nor the environment may be considered apart from the other.

Accepting, however, the convenient differentiation of environment and organism, we find in nature an infinite variety of environments. In fact what we regard as a constant environment is constant only in its tendency to change. It changes with the seasons, in the succession of night and day and even from minute to minute. It changes in temperature, humidity, barometric pressure, circulation of the atmosphere, solar activity, food supply, water supply, mineral content of the soil, presence and concentration of bacteria, health regulations, culture, and in numerous other ways. Some of these changes are slight and insignificant; others are of presumably greater import. Most of these variables occur in all human environments, although they may differ widely in their particular expression. Recognizing the ever constant change and flux of environment, certain ranges and combinations do form patterns which are distinguishable from each other even though the gradations from one to another are often very fine. Ecologists, for example, divide the earth into a number of areas or zones characterized by special combinations of geologic, geographic, climatic and other physical features. Anthropologists, on the other hand, discern broad cultural differences and classify mankind accordingly. Economists and sociologists likewise make divisions based on their specialized criteria. What precise effect differences in any or all of these variables may exert on the biology of man is practically unknown. Eventually, biologists may be able to determine what factors in the environment are effective in altering the human organism, in exactly what way, and how much variation in a particular environmental factor is responsible for a given modification in the organism. But these refinements of prediction are beyond the present stage of the exploration of the problem, despite some of the achievements of the nutritionists.

It is obvious from this discussion of the complexity of the human environment that a vast number of variables are involved in a change of physical environment and an even greater number where cultural and social differences are involved. The differences between the environment of a Japanese village and life in Hawaii are not only physical and climatic but social and cultural as well. Besides obvious changes in temperature, rainfall, humidity, soil conditions, food supply there are innumerable alterations in cultural and social conditions involving the regulation of health, labor, economics and a multitude of other factors. Since, in the nature of the situation, these factors are beyond exact control, no specific factor may be selected as most significant where so many exhibit marked variations and where the consequences of any one is so inadequately known. For this reason, the environment is here considered as an entity despite the fact already emphasized that it is extremely complex and a resultant of many independent variables. Although it would be extremely desirable to be able to correlate modifications in bodily characteristics with specific environmental forces, in the nature of the data we are unable to make any such deductions. Our immediate problem is rather to demonstrate whether or not bodily modifications do occur under environmental changes, whatever may be the specific environmental factor involved.

CHAPTER II

Methodological and Statistical Considerations

THE data collected for this investigation on the stability of the Japanese physical type are susceptible to a wide variety of classifications, but for the purposes of this study they readily resolve themselves into certain natural groupings. There is the usual dichotomy of sex; there are the various age divisions ranging from early childhood to the end of maturity; and there are the stratifications of socio-economic status. But of special interest is the threefold arrangement of our subjects by birthplace and residence.

All the individuals scrutinized herein are of unmixed Japanese ancestry. Some however were born in Japan and have remained there all their lives, moving within a narrow geographical orbit and marrying into the local population. For them I have coined the term, 'sedentes,' the convenience of which over the tedium of a frequently repeated periphrasis is its own apology.

Secondly, there follows the group composed of those immigrants who on departing from their native Japan have settled in Hawaii. Unfortunately, I have no information on the time elapsed since the individual immigrants reached Hawaii. It is known, however, that most of them entered Hawaii as laborers and were, therefore, past adolescence and very probably in early manhood at the time of their arrival.

The great wave of Japanese immigration to Hawaii got well under way about 1884. Although some concern was expressed by the Japanese over the annexation of Hawaii to the United States in 1898, the movement continued unabated until 1907. In this year the Gentlemen's Agreement went into effect and the number of Japanese immigrants fell off, but the migratory movement did not cease altogether until 1924 with the passage of the Exclusion Act. According to Adams[1] the Japanese born population resident in Hawaii is composed of nearly 90% who have settled there since 1898. Most of those entering before this date returned to Japan on the expiration of their contracts.

Up to 1898 most of the Japanese laborers entered on contract and were assisted in their passage. After this date contract labor for the Japanese was abandoned, and a few years later assisted passages also became illegal.

1 Adams, Romanzo—Interracial Marriage in Hawaii.—N.Y. 1937.

7

The majority of the men came alone, although many brought their wives. The unequal sex ratio thus created was, however, partly corrected by the influx of picture brides who came in great numbers during the second decade of the 20th century.

The third major division of our data consists of the children of Japanese immigrants who have been born and bred in Hawaii. The overwhelming majority of subjects in this group was born after 1900.

This threefold classification, apart from the fundamental division by sex and age, forms the basic pattern of this study, for adherence to such an organization of the data is implicit in the problem. The finer sortings to be discussed later are all made within this tripartite frame, and all comparisons are designed to respect these three major groupings.

Although one of the purposes of this study is the investigation of the influence of a change of environment on the bodily characteristics of the Hawaiian born Japanese, nevertheless knowledge of the antecedent Japanese born type is obviously essential. To measure the extent and direction of modification in the Hawaiian born, it is not enough to seek in the immigrants of the preceding generation the fixed point in the scale of change. The immigrants themselves constitute a transitional population, economically and socially selected and perhaps, to be determined later, physically as well. It can not, therefore, be assumed that the immigrants form a random sample of the original population. We must compare immigrants with sedentes in addition to comparing Hawaiian born with immigrants.

A question of methodology suggests itself at this point. Should the comparison of these three groups be confined to the actual lines of blood succession, with Hawaiian born sons and daughters against their own immigrant parents and sedentes grandparents? Such a suggestion was dismissed in the beginning for several reasons. It was impractical of execution in the field. The expense and time necessary for such an undertaking would have been prohibitive. Moreover it was much to be doubted that an adequate series of grandparents (sedentes) could be secured from ranks heavily depleted by death. Among additional difficulties inherent in this pattern of investigation there were the obvious discrepancies produced by differences in age and the possible influence of secular changes among the Japanese themselves. It seemed on the whole wiser to adopt another plan, since the problem was fundamentally not a comparison of Hawaiian born grandchildren with Japanese born grandparents, but rather an investigation of the deviation, if any, of the Hawaiian born Japanese from what they might have been had they remained in Japan. That this is not merely an academic distinction may be seen from recent data collected in Japan. This material parallels the evidence from other parts of the world that considerable changes are taking place in the bodily development of successive generations of the same population. To eliminate, therefore, the normal age differences between generations and the effects of any general secular changes we determined to make all three 'generation' groups as contemporaneous as possible. We could not succeed completely in this for reasons beyond our control. The Hawaiian born are only just coming into maturity and are scarcely represented in the more advanced age groups, while the immigrants, on the other hand, dating from a period when immigration was unrestricted are mainly in the older age groups.[1]

Although it was not feasible to confine our data to lineal successions only, it was essential to the aim of this study that the genetic control be as complete as possible. To achieve this the sedentes were gathered from among the blood relatives of our subjects measured in Hawaii. The villages from which the immigrants had fared were visited, and with few exceptions we were successful in obtaining candidates for the sedentes series from the very families which had produced the immigrants. For this reason, the sedentes represent in the original environment the present expression of that genetic stock which gave rise to the immigrants and in turn to the Hawaiian born.

After excluding those subjects who for one reason or another fell outside the classificatory limits described above, the working series contained a total of 2,594 subjects, male and female adults and children. Every effort was made to secure as representative a group as possible. Roughly 2.5% of the Japanese population in Hawaii are included in our series. In Japan the only selection consciously followed limited the choice of subjects to the families and the villages of our immigrant and Hawaiian born subjects. It is impossible to estimate what proportion of the total sedentes population is represented in our series of sedentes.

The anthropometric examinations of the subjects of this study were made according to the standards of definition and procedure laid down by Martin.[2] The full field schedule included 43 measurements, 21 indices and 41 observations. Of these the following 28 measurements, 21 indices and 41 observations were employed in the statistical analysis.

1. Weight	8. Upper Leg Length
2. Stature	9. Lower Leg Length
3. Sitting Height	10. Biacromion
4. Trunk Height	11. Cristal Width
5. Upper Arm Length	12. Chest Width
6. Lower Arm Length	13. Chest Depth (omitted in women)
7. Hand Length	14. Head Length

1 Those few immigrants who are in the younger age categories were youths when they entered Hawaii.
2 Martin, Rudolf—Lehrbuch der Anthropologie—2nd ed. Jena. 1928.

15. Head Width	22. Upper Face Height
16. Head Height	23. Nose Height
17. Minimum Frontal Diameter	24. Nose Length
18. Bizygomatic Width	25. Nose Salient
19. Bigonial Width	26. Nose Width
20. Forehead Height	27. Bi-Ocular Width
21. Total Face Height	28. Inter-Ocular Width

And from the above the following indices were calculated:

1. Relative Shoulder Width	12. Breadth-Height
2. Relative Hip Width	13. Cephalo-Facial
3. Shoulder-Hip	14. Fronto-Parietal
4. Relative Sitting Height	15. Zygo-Frontal
5. Relative Trunk Height	16. Zygo-Gonial
6. Thoracic	17. Total Facial
7. Brachial	18. Upper Facial
8. Tibio-Femoral	19. Nasal
9. Inter-Membral	20. Nose Salient-Height
10. Cephalic	21. Nose Length-Height
11. Length-Height	

Observations were taken on the following characters:

Skin Color, inner arm and forehead
Hair: form, texture, color and distribution
Eye Color
Iris Pattern
Sclera
Eye Fold
Axis of Eye
Palpebral Opening
Eyebrows: thickness and concurrency
Forehead: slope and height
Browridges
Glabella
Temporal Hair
Nose: profile, height of bridge
Nasal Root: height and compression
Nasal Tip: thickness and direction
Axis of Nostrils
Lips
Lip Seam
Chin
Ear Lobe: size and attachment
Helix

Because of the comparative nature of this investigation great care had to be exercised to ensure comparability between the various groups of data to be studied. Experience has demonstrated only too often that different investigators of the same populations may achieve varying degrees of divergence in their results. It is well known that the difficulty of taking certain measurements such as nose height and face height often leads to large personal equations. To avoid such complications and to achieve strict comparability all the field work was entrusted to a single investigator. Dr. Frederick S. Hulse is entirely responsible for the very arduous labor which the collection of this series involved. He personally measured and took observations on each subject in the series, his task being lightened only by clerical assistance. This aspect of the investigation was commenced in the Hawaiian Islands in January 1931 and completed in February 1932 in Japan. Factories, canneries, schools, plantations, farms and private homes were invaded in the search for subjects. The generous co-operation which the Japanese community of Hawaii extended to this study was extremely heartening. After six months in the various islands of the Hawaiian group, Dr. Hulse proceeded to Japan where he sought out the villages and families from which his subjects in Hawaii were derived. Here, too, co-operation on the part of the Japanese authorities and private individuals contributed enormously to the success of the undertaking. The more agricultural pursuits of the population in Japan were less adapted for the wholesale collection of subjects. Except at schools where relatively large numbers of children were conveniently grouped, most of the subjects had to be traced to small farms. This meant considerable expenditure of time and energy.

After the data had been collected and the indices had been calculated, each record was transferred to a punch-card according to a code previously determined. The size of these cards imposed a certain limitation on the amplitude of the data which could be utilized so that the class divisions of some measurements had to be grouped into coarser categories than might have been used in hand tabulations. But in no case were the groupings unjustifiably coarse. I mention this because it is possible that a recalculation with finer groupings might yield slightly variant constants, although it is extremely doubtful that such deviations would have statistical validity. Some data which I judged to be least significant had to be omitted altogether because of lack of space on the punch-card.

The benefits derived from highly refined classifications are often counterbalanced in practice by magnified sampling errors created by the smaller numbers of the component groups. The size of the corpus of data and the purposes to which it may be put must be mutually adjusted. Although the present material is large, there is a limit beyond which further subdivision reduces the individual statistical unit to microscopic size and to a proportionate diminution of validity. At the very outset, therefore, we are faced with the problem of sub-classification which is further complicated by the unwieldiness of a threefold comparison. To retain the statistical advantage of a relatively adequate total series and at the same time to subject to detailed analysis whatever relationships may seem apparent, I have chosen the following procedure. I shall first determine the relationships of the total series of sedentes, immigrants and Hawaiian born to each other. These comparisons will be succeeded by inquiries into the influence of age and stature on the resulting observations. Finally, the effects of prefectural origins and socio-economic status on the observed differences will be considered.

To assist the reader in following the successive steps of the ensuing exposition without imposing upon him the necessity of reading the tedious details of statistical analyses, I have furnished certain sections with brief synopses. I have attached these summaries at the beginning rather than at the conclusion of the section in the hope that they might provide a kind of 'life line' in the sea of details which follows.

CHAPTER III

Evidence of Physical Selection in the Japanese Immigrants

A. SYNOPSIS OF THE COMPARISON BETWEEN TOTAL SEDENTES AND TOTAL IMMIGRANTS

In accordance with the plan of procedure previously laid down the purpose of this section will be an examination of the relationship of the total immigrants to the total sedentes. It is essential at the very outset to determine whether the Japanese population which poured into the Hawaiian sugar and pineapple fields during the end of the last century and the beginning of the present was identical with the parental stock in Japan or whether it reflected in its physical traits evidence of selection. It is, of course, true that economic and social factors formed a mesh through which the immigrants were sifted. The landless, the laborers and the poor were recruited for the immigrant army. Economic pressure at home and the prospect of improvement abroad are potent forces which drive men great distances. But there is no evidence that these recruits were specially selected physically. Any able-bodied worker was acceptable to the recruiters.

The statistical bath in which the immigrants and the sedentes are to be immersed reveals what escapes the unassisted notice of the eye bewildered by the complex array of living individuals. Like an image on a developing photographic plate an immigrant type emerges in distinct contrast to the sedentes. The immigrant males are on the average heavier than the sedentes; they have shorter trunks and longer legs; their distal arm segments are longer; their shoulders are wider; their chests are broader but shallower. In the structure of the face and head the immigrant men again reveal profound differences from their parental type. They have higher heads, wider bigonial diameters, longer total and upper face heights, greater dimensions for nose height and length, less salient nasal tips, narrower noses, narrower inter-ocular and wider bi-ocular diameters. These are all statistically significant differentiations.

Corresponding to these changes in bodily and cephalic dimensions a series of modifications in the resultant indicial relationships arise. The immigrants have wider shoulders and narrower hips relative to stature than the sedentes. These alterations in proportions give the immigrants a more

13

V-shaped torso, the shoulder-hip index declining 2.19 units from the average of the sedentes. With this change in the lateral proportions of the trunk, there is a modification in linear relationships. Both the sitting height and the trunk height of the immigrants are relatively shorter. In still another dimension the immigrants reveal a significant differentiation. They have a lower thoracic index, indicating a shallower chest relative to its width. The extremities likewise disclose significant deviations among the immigrants. They have higher brachial and lower inter-membral indices, suggesting thereby that the immigrants have a longer forearm relative to upper arm and a shorter total arm relative to total leg.

In the height of the head relative to its length and breadth the immigrants display an appreciable increase over the sedentes. In the facial proportions the immigrants have relatively wider jaws and longer faces; their noses are proportionately narrower and more salient.

This characterization of the male immigrants corresponds in its principal features with the changes observed in the female immigrants, with, however, certain important differences. Unlike the male, the female immigrants are taller than the sedentes. All the segments of the arm are longer, their heads are wider as well as higher. They have wider faces and their noses are narrower only relative to the increase in nasal length and height. In the proportions of the body the female immigrants are unlike the males in that they disclose no disturbance in the relations of shoulder and hip width either to stature or to each other, their brachial indices are unchanged and their tibio-femoral indices are increased.

The extent of this divergence of the immigrant physical type from its ancestral pattern may be expressed in another, perhaps more comprehensive way. If we arrange the various differences between the two groups according to the size of the x p.e.'s, we obtain a distribution of frequencies of the various degrees of divergence between the series. This has been done in Table 3 and the result is convincing that in the immigrant group we are dealing with a selected population. The preponderance of significant differences is very striking. Out of a total of 29 measurements compared, the immigrant males differ significantly from the sedentes in 21, or in 72.4% of the traits. And in 16 out of 21 indicial comparisons, or in 76.2%, the differences were significant. Such a tendency to diversity confirms the conclusion that the immigrant males are not a random sample of the population represented by the sedentes.

Similarly, the immigrant women also constitute a distinct group related to but not identical with the sedentes population. The distribution of the uncorrected x p.e.'s in Table 6 reveals a departure from the sedentes equivalent in kind if not in degree to the deviation noted among the immigrant males. Out of 28 measurement comparisons the immigrant females depart significantly from the sedentes in 19, or in 67.9%, and out of 20 indicial comparisons 9 or 45.0% yielded significant differences. The immigrant women appear therefore to be somewhat more conservative. Or perhaps it may more exactly be expressed by saying that selection has not been so rigorous among the immigrant women as among the immigrant men.

The immigrant males and females not only vary in the degree of their respective divergence from the sedentes but they also differ to some extent in the specific characters in which these differences are displayed. In Fig. 1 the deviations of the total male and female immigrants from their respective sedentes are plotted from a common base line. In general their courses are quite similar. But some flaws in the perfection of their agreement become visible and necessary to analyse further. In Table 8 the x p.e. of each character is given for both males and females. The immigrant women have significant increases in their means for stature, upper arm length, hip width, head width, bizygomatic diameter and tibiofemoral index, while the immigrant males show no significant change or a significant decrease. On the contrary, the immigrant males, compared with the sedentes, develop significant increases in upper leg length, chest breadth, relative shoulder width and brachial index and significant decreases in sitting height, nose width, nasal salient, inter-ocular width, relative hip width, inter-membral index, nasal index and nose salient-height index, traits for which the females reveal no change or an opposite one.

Such a catalogue, however, over-emphasizes the difference between the sexes in their deviations from the sedentes. If we examine the x p.e.'s carefully, we find that there are in all 48 pairs; and of these the sexes are in agreement as to sign and significance in 28; and they agree in direction of deviation, that is to say in sign, but not in significance in 13 more. Actually in only two characters, cristal or hip width and tibio-femoral index, is the sex difference in x p.e. well marked in both sign and size. In general, therefore, both the males and females in the immigrant group display similar but not exactly equivalent trends in their deviation from their ancestral types.

The slight variation in the male and female patterns of immigrant differentiation is in large part attributable to stature. Whereas the male immigrants developed no essential difference from the male sedentes in total stature, the female immigrants, on the contrary, were 2.52 cm. taller than the female sedentes. This is a highly significant change. Since stature is correlated with many of the body segments we may consequently expect to find that this increase in size among the female immigrants may be a factor in altering their pattern of deviations from that peculiar to the male immigrants.

As an example of the difficulty of comparing the female differences be-

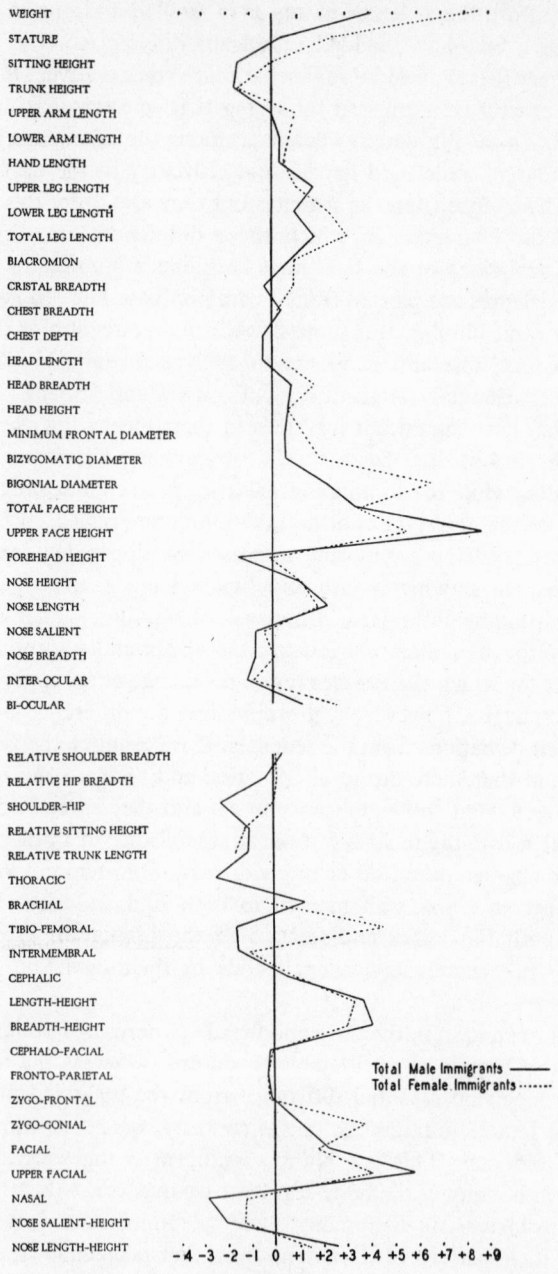

fig. I

Deviations of Total Male and Total Female Immigrants from Their
Respective Sedentes

tween sedentes and immigrants with the male ones, let us examine the sitting height relative and absolute. The relative sitting height of the immigrant women is 1.27 units lower than the same index among the sedentes women. This difference in terms of its probable error reaches the magnitude of 7.06. Such a reduction in the proportion of the sitting height to total height is entirely comparable to the parallel reduction among the immigrant males who have an index one unit lower than that of the sedentes, a difference 7.69 times its probable error. Thus far there is complete agreement between the male and female immigrants. If, however, we contrast the female immigrants with the female sedentes for absolute sitting height, we find that they are equivalent, whereas among the males the immigrants were shorter than the sedentes by a significant margin. It is obvious, therefore, that the changes among the immigrant women must be considered with reference to their increased stature. We may do this either by constant checking with proportional or indicial comparisons or by calculating the regression of specific dimensions on stature wherever the coefficient of correlation justifies this usage.

In Table 7 I have compared the female sedentes and immigrants, the latter being corrected to the stature of the sedentes. We notice that although these comparisons yield somewhat different absolute values from the comparison of the uncorrected series, nevertheless, if these differences are grouped by sign and significance there are but a few major changes. From these various systems of differences and from the comparison of indices we may conclude that on the whole the female immigrants follow the same type of differentiation observed in the immigrant males. Taking into account the increase in stature, the immigrant women display significant differences in the following traits which are paralleled by the significant changes in the immigrant males.

CHARACTERS IN WHICH IMMIGRANTS SHOW SIGNIFICANT DIFFERENCES
FROM SEDENTES

Table 7.

	Males	Females
Weight	increase	increase ?
Sitting Height	decrease	decrease
Trunk Height	decrease	decrease
Upper Arm		increase ?
Lower Arm	increase	increase
Hand	increase	increase
Upper Leg	increase	
Lower Leg	increase	increase
Total Leg	increase	increase
Biacromion	increase	increase ?

CHARACTERS IN WHICH IMMIGRANTS SHOW SIGNIFICANT DIFFERENCES
FROM SEDENTES—*continued*

	Males	Females
Cristal		increase
Chest Width	increase	
Head Length		
Head Width		
Head Height	increase	increase
Minimum Frontal		
Bizygomatic		increase ?
Bigonial	increase	increase
Total Face Height	increase	increase
Upper Face Height	increase	increase
Forehead		
Nose Height	increase	increase
Nose Length	increase	increase
Nose Salient	decrease	decrease
Nose Breadth	decrease	
Inter-Ocular	decrease	decrease ?
Bi-Ocular	increase	increase
Relative Shoulder Width	increase	
Relative Hip Width	decrease	
Shoulder-Hip Index	decrease	
Relative Sitting Height	decrease	decrease
Relative Trunk Height	decrease	decrease
Brachial Index	increase	
Tibio-Femoral Index	decrease	increase
Inter-Membral	decrease	
Cephalic		
Length-Height	increase	increase
Breadth-Height	increase	increase
Cephalo-Facial		
Fronto-Parietal		
Zygo-Frontal		
Zygo-Gonial	increase	increase
Facial	increase	increase
Upper Facial	increase	increase
Nasal	decrease	
Nose Salient-Nose Height	decrease	decrease ?
Nose Length-Nose Height	increase	increase

In several traits, the females actually develop tendencies contrary to those found in the immigrant male series. For example, the increase in arm length among the male immigrants is concentrated in the lower arm and hand thereby elevating the brachial index. The females, on the contrary, display increases in both the upper and lower arm with no alteration in their mutual proportions. Conversely, the females diverge from the males in their disproportionately large addition to the tibial length, thus acquiring a higher tibio-femoral index. In addition to these contrary changes in male and female immigrants, the females are also distinguished from the males in having wider hips, relatively narrower chests and relatively wider noses. The proportionate additions to stature, shoulder width and hip width leave the females unchanged in their relative shoulder width, relative hip width and shoulder-hip width. The male immigrants undergo significant changes in all these proportions.

It appears, therefore, that in the vast majority of traits the female immigrants follow the precedents established by the males in their differentiation from the original stock. That is to say, the female immigrants compared with the sedentes exhibit disproportionate changes similar to those present in immigrant males. In addition the females in a few traits also undergo proportionate changes absent in the males.

B. DETAILED COMPARISON OF TOTAL MALE IMMIGRANTS AND SEDENTES

1. Weight, Bodily Dimensions and Proportions

Let us now turn to the actual figures from which we have concluded that the immigrants represent a statistically selected sampling of their parent stock. The means of the total series of male immigrants and sedentes are listed in Tables 1 and 2 and their differences in Table 3. Here is abundant evidence of divergence between the two groups, which we shall now examine trait by trait.

It should arouse no surprise that the Japanese male immigrant group is 4.2 pounds heavier than the Japanese males in Japan. Bodily weight is not a very good racial character for the very reason that it is a sensitive criterion, other things being equal, of the nutritional level. Whereas the lengths of the bony parts are fixed after the closure of the epiphyses at late adolescence or early maturity, the weight continues to be subject all during life to a variety of environmental and internal factors. Since the immigrants acquired their status as immigrants after growth had been completed, their increased weight, therefore, is a matter of great significance especially since it is associated with the fact that the two groups are practically identical in total stature. It reflects a nutritional factor distinctly favorable to the Japanese resident in Hawaii.

In stature, on the contrary, there is no difference between these groups of males. But stature is a dimension of complex nature, containing within its limits a number of component segments each capable of some degree of independent variation. Consequently each anatomical fraction of stature must be examined in turn. For the sitting height, the immigrant males are shorter than the sedentes males by the significant margin of 1.40 ± .28 cm. The same is true for trunk height alone, where the difference amounts to 1.54 ± .23 cm. As one would expect from their identity in stature the Japanese male immigrants compensate for their shorter trunks by an increase over the sedentes in leg length. The upper leg length for the former is 37.52 cm. as against 35.78 cm. in the latter, a difference of 1.74 cm. which, with reference to its probable error, is significant. The lower leg length, likewise, shows the same reversal but to a lesser degree, the immigrants being only .94 cm. longer in this dimension. Taking the entire leg length, we discover that the immigrants are 1.80 cm. longer than their compatriots in Japan. We see, therefore, a dichotomy in the stature: the trunk against the legs. In the trunk, the immigrant males are shorter than the sedentes, and, in the leg, they are longer. Since the plus difference is roughly equal to the minus one, total stature is the same for both groups.

The arm segments in the two groups are less decisive in their differences. In the upper arm, the two groups are practically identical. In the lower arm the immigrant males are longer by .35 cm., a difference exactly thrice its own probable error. The increase in the hand lengths of the immigrants although absolutely small—.33 cm.—becomes of still greater significance because of its excess of 5.5 times its probable error. The arm, therefore, shows a progressive lengthening in the immigrants from the proximal to the distal segment.

The lateral dimension of the shoulder girdle is expressed by the biacromial width. The immigrant males are .75 cm. wider at this point than are the sedentes. The difference, moreover, by the test of significance is a valid one. At the other end of the trunk, in the width of the hips, there is no real difference between these groups.

The chest diameters, width and depth, of the immigrants differ in opposite directions from the sedentes. In the breadth of the chest the immigrants are wider by .40 cm.; in the depth they are shallower by .33 cm. Both these differences approximate three times their own errors.

We have noted in comparing the sedentes with the immigrants that while the two groups are indistinguishable in certain absolute dimensions, in others they are distinctly divergent. But without reference to other bodily dimensions these similarities or deviations tell us little of the body proportions. Let us, therefore, examine the body indices, the relationships of these absolute dimensions to each other. Indices, constituted as they are of two variables, may show greater or less deviations than either constituent factor, depending on whether the differences in the factors are both positive, both minus or of opposite signs. It follows therefore that significant differences may appear for indices where there are none for the single dimensions or vice versa.

The relative shoulder width is the index of the biacromial width in terms of total stature. The absolutely wider shoulders of the immigrants have increased their relative shoulder width significantly. If the shoulder widths are taken not with reference to stature but to the trunk heights the relatively wider shoulders of the immigrant males stand out even more sharply against the sedentes. This intensification of proportional difference in the two groups is the result of a combined decrease in trunk height and increase in shoulder width in the immigrant group.

The proportion of hip width to stature was also calculated and the resultant index dropped .34 units among the immigrants, a difference which is just large enough to be significant although the decrease in absolute hip width was not. Moreover, if the trunk height is taken as the dimension of reference the picture is reversed and the immigrant group emerges with relatively wider hips since their trunks are shorter than those of the Japanese in Japan.

The proportion of shoulder to hip width definitely differs in the two series, the immigrants having relatively narrower hips in relation to their shoulders than have the sedentes, who are in this respect rather more rectangular and more Mongoloid in proportions.

As one might anticipate from the absolute diameters, the relative sitting height and trunk height of the immigrants are decisively lower than we find among the sedentes. The shorter trunks and longer legs of the former account for this.

The thoracic index illustrates rather well the enhanced indicial effect of opposite changes in the component dimensions. This index is calculated by dividing the chest width into the chest depth times 100. Now the chest width of the immigrant males is .40 cm. wider than that of the sedentes, a plus difference about 3 times its probable error. The chest depth of the immigrants is, on the contrary, less—a minus difference of .33 cm. also only about 3 times its probable error. But in calculating the index the direction of narrow chestedness is multiplied to the extent that the immigrant group is 2.40 units less than the sedentes—a divergence which amounts to 6 times its probable error.

The lower segment of the arm is significantly longer in relation to the humeral length among the immigrants than among the sedentary Japanese. But their positions are reversed for the tibio-femoral index. Although the immigrants are distinguished from the Japanese in Japan by longer legs, the increase in the upper leg is greater than in the lower thereby lowering the indicial relation of the segments. The difference, however, is not, by the test of the probable error, a significant one.

The increase in leg length among the immigrants has also resulted in a definite shift in the proportion of the arm to the leg, thereby lowering the inter-membral index of the immigrants compared with the sedentes.

2. Head and Face and Their Indices

A comparison of the immigrant males with the male sedentes reveals no significant difference in head length or in head width. But in the height of the head, from tragion to vertex, the immigrants are distinctly higher. The width of the anterior portion of the head embraced in the minimum frontal diameter is essentially the same in both series.

Examining now the facial dimensions of the two Japanese groups under consideration, we again find evidences of homogeneity in certain traits and intimations of diversity in others. The differences for bizygomatic diameter and the forehead height are within the bounds of three times the probable error of the difference and are, therefore, probably insignificant. The bigonial diameter, the face heights, the nose height and length, and the bi-ocular are, however, significantly larger and the nose salient, the nose width and the inter-ocular significantly smaller in the immigrants.

In the various proportions of the head and face, we again discover evidence of a differentiation of the immigrants from the sedentes. In the length-height and breadth-height indices of the cranial vault, and in the zygo-gonial, facial, upper facial and nose length-height indices the immigrants undergo a significant increase while in the nasal and nose salient-height indices they reveal a significant decrease. There are, however, no differences between the two groups in the cephalic, cephalo-facial, fronto-parietal and zygo-frontal indices. Thus of 12 cephalic and facial indices 8 are significantly different and 4 are similar in both series. It should be noticed, however, that the facial and nasal indices, which constitute most of the divergent indices, are the result of a general lengthening of the face of the immigrants. Therefore the divergencies between the two groups are somewhat overweighted and the fundamental similarities which do exist are masked.

C. DETAILED COMPARISON OF TOTAL FEMALE IMMIGRANTS AND SEDENTES

1. Weight, Bodily Dimensions and Proportions

The Japanese females fall into the same categories as the males. There are the women born and reared in Hawaii, those who arrived in Hawaii as immigrants and the control group of sedentes obtained in Japan. Following the procedure adopted for the corresponding males, we shall first examine the relationships between the total female immigrants and sedentes as disclosed in Tables 4, 5 and 6 and Fig. 1.

The bodily weight of the immigrant women is $8\frac{1}{2}$ pounds heavier than that of the sedentes, an excess which goes even beyond that found among the males of the same categories.

Unlike the immigrant males, who exceed the sedentes in weight but are identical in stature, the immigrant women are significantly superior to the sedentes women in both weight and stature. The stature of the immigrant women is 2.52 cm. greater than among Japanese women, a margin that is 5.6 times its own probable error. It is difficult to explain this difference in the sexes. In the sitting height also the immigrant men and women show distinct differences in their relation to the sedentary groups in Japan. Whereas the male immigrants have a shorter sitting height than the sedentes, the immigrant females are the same as the sedentes in this regard. But this difference is more apparent than real, for the sitting height index reveals the fact that with reference to their statures, both the immigrant men and the immigrant women have relatively shorter sitting heights than the sedentes.

The same fundamental pattern repeats itself in the reduced trunk height of the immigrant women, who thereby closely parallel the immigrant males. The mean of the immigrant women for this character is 49.56 cm., a value which is 1.40 cm. less than the mean of the sedentes. Taken in conjunction with the superior stature of the immigrant women it forms a relative trunk height of 33.27 which is 1.66 cm. less than the corresponding relationship in the sedentes and 9.76 times its probable error.

Again in the dimensions and proportions of the leg and its component segments, the immigrant women occupy a position similar to the males. That is to say, the immigrant women have longer upper and lower leg segments than have their 'sisters' in Japan. The difference, however, in the upper leg is just below three times its own probable error which, in view of the increased stature of the immigrant women, would probably be reduced still further were this difference adjusted for the discrepancy in stature. The superiority, however, of the immigrant women in the length of tibia is so great that it not only would survive a correction for stature but it also contributes to make the entire leg length significantly longer than the corresponding dimension in the sedentes. This disproportionate tibial increase succeeds in adding 4.65 units to the tibio-femoral index of the immigrant women, an increment of significant size.

The upper arm length, the lower arm length and the hand length are all significantly greater among the immigrant women than in the sedentes. Among the immigrant males, on the contrary, we found a significant difference only in the lower arm and the hand length. But these pronounced increases of the immigrant women over their controls may be accounted for

[handwritten margin note, right:] but since women are taller we should expect an increase in upper leg so it is not fair to say there is a variation here, unless

[handwritten note, bottom:] the upper leg has been increased considerably. making correction for what the leg should measure and comparing it with what it does measure, we find only a very slight variation.

in part by the increase in stature, which is positively correlated with arm length. Although the tendency is far less marked in the immigrant women than in immigrant males, the increase in the distal arm segment appears to be relatively the most significant. No change, however, occurs in the brachial index.

The relatively greater increase in the leg length than in the arm length of the immigrant women serves to lower their inter-membral index, but not significantly.

The width of the shoulders, measured from the acromia, shows a significant increase among immigrant women. The increase is not, however, as striking as the corresponding one among immigrant males, owing to the fact that there has been a proportionate elevation of stature in the former. This is well illustrated by comparing the shoulder breadths relative to stature. Here we find that while the immigrant men are still significantly wider shouldered than the sedentes, the immigrant women are identical with their relatives in Japan. But if the shoulder width is taken with reference to the trunk height, the immigrant women agree with the immigrant men in possessing relatively wider shoulders.

Immigrant women have a mean cristal width of 29.98 cm., which is .88 cm. greater than the mean of the sedentes and 4.19 times its own probable error. The immigrant men, on the contrary, have a mean cristal width which is smaller than the mean of the males in Japan, but the difference, however, is less than is demanded by the test of significance. This discrepancy between the sexes appears, however, to be the result of the increase in stature among the immigrant women. Bearing in mind the superiority of the immigrant women in stature, it is not, therefore, surprising to find that their relative hip width is the same as that of the sedentes women. If proportional hip width is calculated in terms of trunk height, the immigrant women instead of being similar to the sedentes have on the contrary relatively much wider hips, a result which is similar to what was found to be the case among the males. The shoulder-hip index, on the contrary, remains undisturbed among the immigrant women, whereas the immigrant males suffered a very significant drop in this proportion.

It was not feasible for obvious reasons to measure the chest depth among Japanese women. Consequently the breadth is the only measure of the chest taken on the females. In this dimension there were no noteworthy distinctions between the immigrant women and those in Japan. The males, however, exhibited a difference favorable to the immigrants.

2. Head and Face and Their Indices

There is no essential difference between the two female groups in the maximum length of the cephalic vault. The very slight superiority of the immigrant women amounts only to .42 mm., a magnitude which is not significant and may be accounted for by the greater stature of these women. In this identity of immigrants and sedentes the women follow the men.

In the width of the head there is, however, a suspicion of a definite tendency toward expansion among the immigrant women who have a mean head width 1.74 mm. greater than that of the sedentes. This is a difference that just exceeds three times its own probable error. The immigrant men also had wider heads than the sedentes but not to a significant degree.

The resulting cephalic index of the immigrant women is expectedly higher than the mean for the sedentes. The difference, however, is only .84 units and not significant.

Not only in breadth of head but in the height as well the immigrants of both sexes reveal a significant accretion. The immigrant women are .61 cm. higher headed than those in Japan. Although the error is large, owing to the technical uncertainty of this measurement, the difference remains a significant one. The indices of cephalic height, both length-height and breadth-height, are, by virtue of this immoderate increase in absolute head height among immigrant women, greater than the corresponding proportions among the women in Japan. The slightly increased head length and head width of the immigrant women have, however, operated to keep these indicial differences from assuming proportions much beyond three times the probable error of the difference.

The breadth of the forehead, as measured by the minimum frontal diameter, is among the immigrant women but slightly larger than among the women in Japan. The difference of 1.29 mm. is apparently a largish one, but the error is of considerable size and nullifies the statistical reality of the discrepancy. In this statistical approximation of the two groups of women in their mean frontal diameters, the situation is comparable to that among the males. It is worthy of note that the slightly if not significantly wider brows of the immigrants are wholly consistent with their relatively wider heads.

The last sentence contains the explanation for the agreement we may note in both series for the fronto-parietal index. The structural relationship between the width of the forehead and the width of the head remains unchanged, even though the absolute values of these dimensions among the immigrant women are larger than among the sedentes.

Continuing, we next discover that the immigrant women have a mean face width, the bizygomatic diameter, which is 1.98 mm. wider than that for the sedentes. Moreover, this is a difference which is 3.67 times its probable error. Among the males there is no statistically valid difference in this dimension. But the face width in reference to the head width, expressed by the cephalo-facial index, yields a negligible difference between

Mean face width = bizygomatic diameter

the two groups, both male and female. Equally insignificant are the differences in both groups and sexes for the zygo-frontal index, which is determined by the breadths of the face and of the forehead. In other words, in
spite of a probably significant increase in face width among the immigrant
women, there does not seem to be any disturbance in their identity with
the women of Japan in the indicial relationships of face width to head
width and forehead width.

Perhaps some may see an association between the determination necessary to immigration and the massive jaws of the immigrant women. Without, however, subscribing to such an interpretation, it must be emphasized
that one of the most significant differences between immigrant women and
the women of Japan is to be found in the bigonial diameter. This measurement is taken with its limiting points as the external angles of the lower jaw
formed by the ramus and the body of the mandible. The mean for Japanese
women is 102.41 mm. The mean for the immigrant women is 109.07 mm.
The difference, therefore, equals 6.66 ± .55 mm. which amounts to exactly
12.11 times the probable error. Such an excess is unquestionably significant
and rarely occurs between groups that may be regarded as intimately related. The males of the corresponding populations exhibit a trend that is
similar in kind if not in degree. Among the immigrant males the mean bigonial diameter is 2.25 mm. greater than among the sedentes and this difference is 5.36 times its own probable error.

It follows from this that the facial proportions of the immigrants which
involve the bigonial diameter will reflect a startling divergency from the
basic pattern of the Japanese type. In fact the zygo-gonial index, the proportion between the face width and bigonial diameter, of the immigrant
women is 3.88 greater than in the women of Japan and this difference is
resolved into 10.49 times its own probable error. In other words the divergency in bigonial diameter is not in harmony with the change in bizygomatic width. It represents an eccentric deviation which is difficult to
explain.

Similarly, the dimensions of the face height, and the segments thereof,
also betray an unprecedented alteration among the immigrant women. The
upper face height (nasion to alveon), total face height (nasion to gnathion),
the anatomic face height and the nose height, in the order named, are greater
in the immigrant women than in the sedentes. The deviations are 5.62 mm.
for upper face height, 3.54 mm. for total face height, and 1.20 mm. for nose
height. In each case, the difference exceeds more than thrice the probable
error; in the upper face height 10.22 times, in total face height 5.53 times
and in nose height 3.43 times. Without stopping at this point to examine
their inter-relationships more carefully, it seems reasonable to suppose that
a single factor is basic to this uniform tendency toward lengthened facial

(ratio?)

Bigonial diameter = from corner of jaw to opposite
corner of jaw (st. line)

Zygo - gonial index = face width / bigonial diam

and nasal heights among the immigrants, for the same thing is to be seen in the males. The area of major modification is in the alveolar portion of the maxilla or upper jaw. The reason for this conclusion is that in both immigrant males and females the differences in the upper face heights are far and away greater than in either the total face height or in the nose height. And since the nose height, which forms a part of upper face height, is relatively more similar in both immigrants and sedentes, it necessarily follows that the alveolar portion of the upper face height is the area of principal change.

The lengthening of the total face height in the immigrant women is sufficient to offset their wider faces and to produce a mean facial index only 1.80 units greater than in the sedentary women. This increase is 3.46 times its probable error. Especially telling is the increase of upper face height on the upper facial index. Here the addition of indicial units amounts to 4.11 which in turn equals 9.13 times the probable error of the difference.

Before discussing the nasal index we must first consider the nasal breadths of both groups of women. The mean of the immigrant women is 33.22 mm. and that of the women in Japan is 33.18 mm. There is, therefore, no difference in the crude means. The immigrant males on the contrary showed a definite if small decrease in the width of the nose.

Although the nasal height of the immigrant women showed a distinct increase, it is impossible to regard the relative narrowing of the nasal index among them—amounting to a decrease of 1.20—as a statistically valid one for in this case the probable error involved is very high and consequently increases enormously the limits of insignificance.

The standard measurements of the nose are usually two: the nose height from nasion to the juncture of the septum with the upper lip, and nose width at the maximum expansion of the alae. In addition to these, there were added two others, intended to define the character of the nose more specifically. What we have called the nose length, in contradistinction to the nose height, is the distance from nasion to the nasal tip as seen in profile. The nasal tip is not always easily distinguishable especially if that portion of the nasal prominence is depressed. That condition, however, rarely offered difficulties among the Japanese. The nasal salient was also taken in order to measure the elevation of the nose at its lower level. The points employed were the tip as defined for nasal length and the base of the nose as taken for nasal height. I am not altogether sure that the personal equation involved in taking these two measurements may not be too large to be overlooked. In their defense in this present use of them I might add that since all the measurements were taken by one individual, the error is at least a constant one.

Since the nose length is to a large degree a function of the nose height it should occasion no surprise to find that the immigrant women in this dimension as in nose height exceed the women of Japan. In fact the difference in this case is perhaps slightly more significant statistically. The relationship between these two dimensions of the nose, its height and its length, shows an alteration among the immigrant women. The relatively greater increase in their nasal length has resulted in a closer approximation of the nose height and nose length with an index that is significantly higher than that of the sedentes. A similar shift was observed among the immigrant males. The salient of the nose, however, shares with breadth a greater degree of stability. Although the nose of the immigrant women is less prominent there does not appear to be any appreciable statistical difference in this character between the two series of females. But this slightly reduced salient becomes of much more significance when taken in proportion to the increased nasal height. The slight decrease of the one dimension combined with the significant increase in the other yield an index that is lower among the immigrant women than among the sedentes. The difference however is just short of three times its own probable error.

Returning to the nobler part of the face, we find practically an identity between the means for the height of the forehead. The distance between the inner corners of the eyes is measured by the inter-ocular distance, the mean of which is smaller among the immigrant women than among the sedentes. It is not, however, a real difference, statistically speaking. It should be noted, nevertheless, that the deviation is in the same direction as among male immigrants. The bi-ocular width taken from the outer corners of the eyes shows a reversal. In this dimension the immigrant women are significantly wider, thereby agreeing with the immigrant males. It appears, thus, that the immigrants both male and female have wider palpebral diameters than the sedentes. By subtracting the inter-ocular width from the bi-ocular and dividing by two, we obtain the palpebral width of eye. For the immigrant women it is 34.5 mm. and for the Japanese women in Japan 32.7.

Immigrant women have wider eye widths (length of eye)

CHAPTER IV

The Physical Changes in the Hawaiian Born

A. SYNOPSIS OF COMPARISONS OF TOTAL HAWAIIAN BORN WITH TOTAL IMMIGRANTS AND TOTAL SEDENTES

HAVING examined the immigrants in relation to the sedentes and having found them constituting a distinct sub-group characterized by significant departures from the Japanese type, we may now proceed to the consideration of the Japanese males born and bred in Hawaii. The questions to be answered here are these. Do the Hawaiian born continue the trend of differentiation established by their immigrant parents, thereby solidifying the significance of the immigrant deviation? Or do they revert to the sedentes type, thus suggesting a phenotypical origin for the immigrant variations? Or do they reveal their own characteristic modifications perhaps to be associated with their new environment? What are the relationships of these modifications to those of the immigrant parents and to the character of the sedentes?

I have already indicated the tentative conclusions to be drawn from the comparison of the total series of sedentes with the total immigrants. I have pointed out that the statistical evidence of the differentiation of the Japanese immigrants is too overwhelming to be the effect of chance. Since the male immigrants to a very large extent entered Hawaii as contract labor, they must have been at least in early manhood if not somewhat older. Consequently, their physical development would have been completed before they left Japan. I have, therefore, suggested that the differences which the immigrants exhibit in comparison with the sedentes indicate that they were a selected portion of the particular universe represented by the sedentes. There is no evidence that this selection of the immigrants was consciously designed. On the contrary, it is probable that some factor or complex of factors had operated unconsciously in this process of selection. I reserve for a later section the more complete discussion of this interesting question.

The third grouping of the Japanese includes all those who have been born in Hawaii. From the nature of the events already described, this group contains only the Hawaiian born children of Japanese immigrants. The second generation to be born in Hawaii has not yet come to maturity and consequently plays no part in our series.

29

When the Hawaiian born are aligned with the immigrants and the sedentes, new developments are at once apparent. Not only do the Hawaiian born differ from the sedentes, as might be expected from the selection among the immigrants, but they show divergencies from the immigrants as well. In Table 10 the comparison between Hawaiian born and immigrant males is presented. The differences together with their probable errors occupy the first column, followed by a column devoted to the values representing the x p.e.'s obtained by dividing the probable error into the difference. The values of x p.e. which are equal to or larger than three are taken to be significant. It will be seen at once that such significant differences are very numerous. Of 29 listed differences in measurements, 16, or 55.2%, were three or more times their probable error, and in 10, or 34.5%, were six or more times. In the indices the divergence is only slightly reduced. Of a total of 21 indicial comparisons the differences were three or more times their probable errors in 9 instances, or in 42.9%, and in 5, or 23.8%, of the cases the difference was six or more times the probable error.

Similarly the Hawaiian born and immigrant females are compared in Table 13, and again the number of significant discrepancies is large. Summarizing the x p.e.'s in this table, we note that in 13 out of 28 measurements, or in 46.4%, the differences are three or more times their probable errors, and in 9 out of 20 indicial comparisons, or in 45%, the differences exceed three or more times their probable errors.

Even greater than the division between Hawaiian born and immigrants is the differentiation of the Hawaiian born compared with the sedentes. Following the procedure adopted in comparing Hawaiian born and immigrants, we may study the differences between Hawaiian born and sedentes males in Table 11. That the increase of significant deviations is considerable may be seen from the bare statement of their summary. Of the 29 measurable characters, 23, or 79.3%, showed differences between Hawaiian born and sedentes males, which equalled or exceeded thrice the probable error. In the indices, 19 out of 21, or 90.5% showed differences of three or more times the probable error. The proportion of differences in both measurements and indices which equal or exceed six times the probable error is correspondingly higher in the comparison of Hawaiian born and sedentes.

The females (see Table 14), also, yield evidence of the greater gap between Hawaiian born and sedentes than between Hawaiian born and immigrants. For example, 19 out of 28, or in 67.9%, of the differences, the difference equals or exceeds thrice its own probable error, and in 16 out of 20, or in 80% of the indices, the differences are three or more times their probable errors. In 39.3% of the measurements and in 45% of the indices, the differences reach or exceed the sixth multiple of their probable errors.

Statistical Summary of the Differentiation of Sedentes,
Immigrants and Hawaiian Born

The percentage of significant differences to total number of comparisons
is given below. The percentage of significant indicial differences is distinguished from the percentage of significant measurement differences by
the use of parentheses.

MALES

	Sedentes	Immigrants	Hawaiian Born
Sedentes	——	72.4% (76.2%)	79.3% (90.5%) *indicis*
Immigrants	72.4% (76.2%)	——	55.2% (42.9%)
Hawaiian Born	79.3% (90.5%)	55.2% (42.9%)	——

FEMALES

	Sedentes	Immigrants	Hawaiian Born
Sedentes	——	67.9% (45.0%)	67.9% (80.0%)
Immigrants	67.9% (45.0%)	——	46.4% (45.0%)
Hawaiian Born	67.9% (80.0%)	46.4% (45.0%)	——

Table 13

The above summary, however, discloses the importance of orientation. If we hold the Hawaiian born as the pivotal point and compare first the immigrants and then the sedentes with them, we discern a vastly greater divergence between the Hawaiian born and the sedentes than between the Hawaiian born and the immigrants. On the contrary if the sedentes become the base line for comparison then the successive deviations of immigrants and Hawaiian born are of the same order except for the somewhat greater indicial differentiation of the Hawaiian born.

The extent, therefore, of the divergence between these three groups is abundantly clear. But this does not tell us very much about the character of the differentiation which has taken place. I now wish to compare the kind of change which has occurred among the immigrants with that characteristic of the Hawaiian born.

Before proceeding, however, to the inspection of the graphic representations of our data, let us pause to distinguish between the two varieties of quantitatively significant differences. In a three dimensional body such as the human organism, the various parts and diameters of each individual form a complex of mutual adjustments peculiar in its details to itself. Yet these reciprocal accommodations, despite the individuality of their resolutions, do conform to general principles of growth and development. It follows, therefore, that every dimension has one or more associated diameters usually in another plane to which it stands in a definite architectural relationship. Two such dimensions, one expressed in terms of the other, form an index. Where both components of an index change proportionately in the same direction it follows that the indicial relationship remains the same. Such changes, no matter how great the differences may be quantitatively, we may refer to in the present connection as proportionate.[1]

On the other hand, where the two components of an index undergo sufficiently different alterations, or where one changes and the other remains undisturbed, the indicial relationship is no longer the same, and consequently the changes in the components are disproportionate. One may liken these two types of changes, on the one hand, to the proportionate reduction or magnification wrought by the pointing device of the sculptor and, on the other, to the distortions produced by an imperfect glass.

Returning once more to the analysis of the changes among the immigrants and Hawaiian born we may see in Figs. 2 and 3 the direction of the differentiation which these two male groups have taken.

The base line represents the means of the sedentes, the solid line the deviations of the immigrants, and the broken line the deviations of the Hawaiian born. With a few exceptions, to be mentioned presently, the im-

1 The phenomenon of differential growth might well alter the significance of 'proportionate' as defined above.

Index = defined

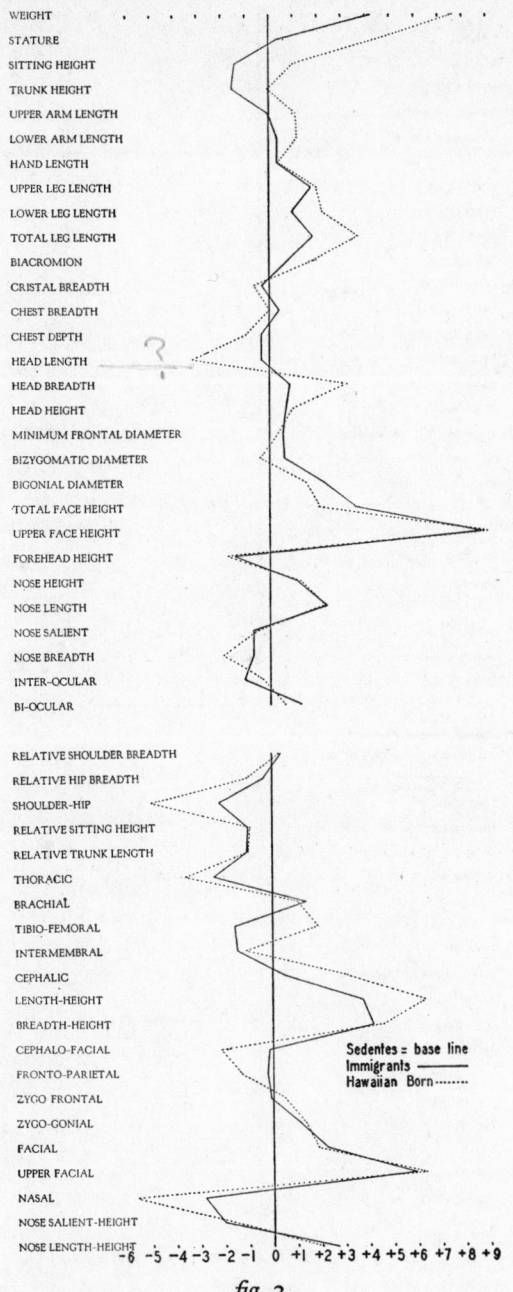

WEIGHT
STATURE
SITTING HEIGHT
TRUNK HEIGHT
UPPER ARM LENGTH
LOWER ARM LENGTH
HAND LENGTH
UPPER LEG LENGTH
LOWER LEG LENGTH
TOTAL LEG LENGTH
BIACROMION
CRISTAL BREADTH
CHEST BREADTH
CHEST DEPTH
HEAD LENGTH
HEAD BREADTH
HEAD HEIGHT
MINIMUM FRONTAL DIAMETER
BIZYGOMATIC DIAMETER
BIGONIAL DIAMETER
TOTAL FACE HEIGHT
UPPER FACE HEIGHT
FOREHEAD HEIGHT
NOSE HEIGHT
NOSE LENGTH
NOSE SALIENT
NOSE BREADTH
INTER-OCULAR
BI-OCULAR

RELATIVE SHOULDER BREADTH
RELATIVE HIP BREADTH
SHOULDER-HIP
RELATIVE SITTING HEIGHT
RELATIVE TRUNK LENGTH
THORACIC
BRACHIAL
TIBIO-FEMORAL
INTERMEMBRAL
CEPHALIC
LENGTH-HEIGHT
BREADTH-HEIGHT
CEPHALO-FACIAL
FRONTO-PARIETAL
ZYGO FRONTAL
ZYGO-GONIAL
FACIAL
UPPER FACIAL
NASAL
NOSE SALIENT-HEIGHT
NOSE LENGTH-HEIGHT

Sedentes = base line
Immigrants ——
Hawaiian Born ········

-6 -5 -4 -3 -2 -1 0 +1 +2 +3 +4 +5 +6 +7 +8 +9

fig. 2

Deviations of Immigrant and Hawaiian Born Males from Male Sedentes

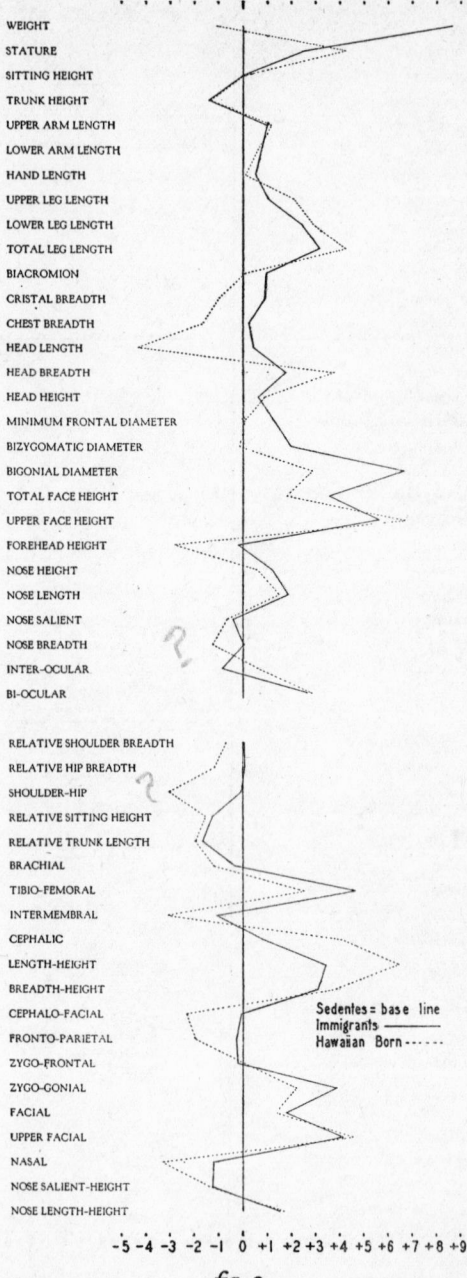

WEIGHT
STATURE
SITTING HEIGHT
TRUNK HEIGHT
UPPER ARM LENGTH
LOWER ARM LENGTH
HAND LENGTH
UPPER LEG LENGTH
LOWER LEG LENGTH
TOTAL LEG LENGTH
BIACROMION
CRISTAL BREADTH
CHEST BREADTH
HEAD LENGTH
HEAD BREADTH
HEAD HEIGHT
MINIMUM FRONTAL DIAMETER
BIZYGOMATIC DIAMETER
BIGONIAL DIAMETER
TOTAL FACE HEIGHT
UPPER FACE HEIGHT
FOREHEAD HEIGHT
NOSE HEIGHT
NOSE LENGTH
NOSE SALIENT
NOSE BREADTH
INTER-OCULAR
BI-OCULAR

RELATIVE SHOULDER BREADTH
RELATIVE HIP BREADTH
SHOULDER-HIP
RELATIVE SITTING HEIGHT
RELATIVE TRUNK LENGTH
BRACHIAL
TIBIO-FEMORAL
INTERMEMBRAL
CEPHALIC
LENGTH-HEIGHT
BREADTH-HEIGHT
CEPHALO-FACIAL
FRONTO-PARIETAL
ZYGO-FRONTAL
ZYGO-GONIAL
FACIAL
UPPER FACIAL
NASAL
NOSE SALIENT-HEIGHT
NOSE LENGTH-HEIGHT

Sedentes = base line
Immigrants ———
Hawaiian Born ------

-5 -4 -3 -2 -1 0 +1 +2 +3 +4 +5 +6 +7 +8 +9

fig. 3

Deviations of Immigrant and Hawaiian Born Females from Female Sedentes

migrants are especially distinguished from the sedentes by disproportionate changes, whereas the Hawaiian born, compared with immigrants, show principally proportionate changes correlated with a general increase in size. There are also exceptions to this generalization which will appear later.

To clarify these distinctions, let us consider the behavior of such fundamental body relationships as the sitting height or the trunk height index. The male immigrants disclose a significant reduction from the male sedentes in their sitting height and trunk height, but since they are identical with the sedentes in stature, we note a compensatory increase in the leg lengths. Thus although these two groups are approximate in total height, the immigrants drop an index unit in the relative sitting height and relative trunk height.

The Hawaiian born males compared with the male immigrants, likewise reveal noteworthy changes in these characters, but of a totally different nature. Here we observe that the stature of the Hawaiian born is 4.11 cm. greater than that of the immigrants, that not only the sitting height and trunk height have increased, but the legs, also, have lengthened. The relative sitting height and the relative trunk height of the Hawaiian born, therefore, have not undergone any significant alteration from the means of the immigrants. The differences which occur between Hawaiian born and immigrants in these characters are all correlated with increases dependent on a general increase in size with a more or less harmonious preservation of proportion. It is worthy of comment that the increase in the absolute trunk and sitting height lengths of the Hawaiian born close in the gap which the immigrants created. In fact, the Hawaiian born and the sedentes show no difference at all in trunk height, and in sitting height the Hawaiian born are actually longer. But this closer agreement between Hawaiian born and sedentes than between Hawaiian born and immigrants is of little value divorced from its context. Hence it is clear that the male immigrants differ from the male sedentes in proportion and dimension, that the Hawaiian born males maintain this difference in proportion despite a closer approximation to the sedentes in dimension. The various fluctuations of the dimensions under consideration do produce agreements and disagreements which, however, are of little diagnostic value without reference to the total complex of traits involved.

Similarly, the widening of the shoulders of the male immigrants produces among them a significant increase in the relative shoulder width. But the continued increase of the shoulders among the Hawaiian born males yields, on the contrary, no real change in proportion since it is associated with an accession in stature.

Of nine bodily proportions used herein the male immigrants show significant changes from the sedentes in eight. It is evident that as far as the body dimensions are concerned, the male immigrants, in general, show disproportionate changes from the male sedentes.

The Hawaiian born males on the other hand, reveal mainly proportionate modifications from the immigrants in their body diameters. In the 9 body indices the Hawaiian born differ from the immigrants in only 3. Disproportionate changes occur only exceptionally. For example, there is a tendency, of less than significant degree however, toward a narrower hip width among the Hawaiian born even though the stature is higher and the trunk is longer and wider at the shoulders. This single disharmonic change is responsible for two of the three disproportionate indicial differences mentioned above. A similar disharmonic change in the Hawaiian born males occurs in the narrowing and flattening of the chest.

In the diameters and proportions of the head and face, the immigrants continue to show principally disproportionate changes from the sedentes in their higher heads, wider bigonial diameters, higher total and upper faces, longer, narrower and less salient noses, narrower inter-ocular diameters and wider bi-ocular diameters. These differences are all reflected in the significant deviations of the indices of which they form a part. Of the 12 cephalic and facial indices the immigrants show changes from the sedentes in 8. No significant change occurs in the remaining 4 indices nor in the components thereof.

The Hawaiian born, contrary to their tendency to merely proportionate increases in their body dimensions, disclose in the head and face a series of disproportionate or disharmonic differences. For example, despite a large and significant increase in stature the Hawaiian born have significantly shorter head lengths than the immigrants. The head width, however, is correspondingly greater and the head height slightly larger. These changes increase the cephalic index by 2.60 units and the length-height index by 2.54 units. The considerable addition to the head width and a not quite statistically significant tendency in the opposite direction in the face width produce a marked drop in the cephalo-facial index. Similarly, the fronto-parietal index is lowered largely because of the disproportionate increase in head width. Another significant change in proportion appears in the considerably reduced nasal index of the Hawaiian born. This difference is largely the consequence of a relatively enormous reduction in nasal width emphasized by the stability of the nose height. In the nose length-nose height index we find a barely significant decrease, although here the changes in the component diameter are not significant.

Thus in 6 of the 12 cephalic and facial indices the Hawaiian born males display disproportionate changes from the immigrant males. The other 6 indices remain unchanged, but 3 are undisturbed because no changes occurred in the component diameters and 3 are proportionate according to previous definition. These latter are breadth-height index in which both head breadth and height received additions, facial index in which both total face height and bizygomatic width suffered reductions and upper face index in which both dimensions again reveal parallel losses.

Returning once more to Fig. 2 in which these changes are all displayed, it is possible to appreciate the tenor of the group changes and modifications which have taken place. We see the wide fluctuations of the immigrant profile against the sedentes base line. We note, to mention only a few, minus deviations for sitting height and trunk height, and positive ones for the leg lengths, the bigonial diameter and the upper face height. Then for the indices and proportions the profile of the immigrants again discloses sharp fluctuations from the sedentes base line. All these, except for the few exceptions previously commented upon, are changes in kind and therefore disproportionate.

Tracing now the profile of the deviations of the Hawaiian born, we are immediately impressed by the similarity of its outline to that of the immigrants, although they are separated from each other by the difference in magnitude of the absolute means. But in head length, in head width, and in nose breadth and in the indices of which they are component members, the two groups draw apart. Summing up these remarks, we can merely repeat what has already been stated in various ways. The immigrants appear to be a selected group in which the differences from the original stock, the sedentes, are mainly disproportionate ones. In the Hawaiian born these disproportionate differences of the immigrants are maintained and even intensified, thereby converting them into proportionate changes from immigrants to Hawaiian born. Besides these differences, the Hawaiian born also reveal new tendencies toward disproportionate change particularly manifest in the vault and nose.

When we turn to the Hawaiian born females in Fig. 3 we notice at once that they, like the Hawaiian born males, have been modified from the immigrant pattern. They have added to their stature, decreased their shoulder, chest and hip widths. They have become shorter and wider headed. With the exception of the upper face height, the inter- and bi-ocular width, their facial diameters are all smaller, but this diminution only reaches a significant degree in the bizygomatic width, bigonial diameter, forehead height and nose breadth.

The effect of these alterations in dimension may be seen in the indices and relative proportions. The relative shoulder width, hip width and shoulder-hip index all decrease noticeably. The slight decrease in arm length coupled with a moderate increase in leg length yields in the Hawaiian born females a significantly lower inter-membral index. In the head and face, also, the changes in dimensions have produced significant modifications in the resultant indices. We may see these in the increased cephalic and length-height index, and in the decreased cephalo-facial, fronto-parietal and zygo-gonial indices.

In their deviations the Hawaiian born females do not, however, by any means all follow the direction taken by the immigrants. To particularize, the Hawaiian born females show decreases from the immigrant means in hand length, biacromion, cristal width, chest width, head length, bizygo-matic diameter, bigonial diameter, forehead height and nose width, and increases in inter-ocular width. These are all measurements in which the immigrant females revealed changes contrary to the above or none at all. Only the additions to the stature and head width of the Hawaiian born females agree with similarly significant increases in the immigrant females. In other words, of the twelve significant differences in the measurements of the Hawaiian born compared with the immigrants, nine are minus and three plus. All the nine minus differences between Hawaiian born and im-migrants are contrary to the sign of the corresponding difference of the immigrants and sedentes, and in addition, one of the three plus differences (inter-ocular width) is contrary to the direction of immigrant deviation.

Similarly, the significant deviations in the Hawaiian born indices are mainly minus (seven out of nine) and contrary to the trend in the immi-grants.

In Fig. 4 the deviations of the Hawaiian born males and females from their respective immigrants are compared graphically. It is clear from the close parallelism of their deviations that both sexes undergo similar changes in the Hawaiian born generation.

B. DETAILED COMPARISON OF TOTAL SERIES OF HAWAIIAN BORN MALES WITH IMMIGRANTS AND SEDENTES

1. Weight, Bodily Dimensions and Proportions

The corresponding means of these three groups may be found in Tables 1, 2 and 9. The x p.e. differences are listed in Tables 10 and 11. The first discrepancy to be observed between the Hawaiian born, on the one hand, and the immigrants and sedentes, on the other, is an age differ-ence. Between the Hawaiian born and the immigrants there is a gap of 14.45 years, and between the Hawaiian born and the sedentes 9.4 years. Although these differences are much greater than the corresponding one between immigrants and sedentes, I shall omit temporarily a discussion of their possible influence on the total means. Following, therefore, the pat-tern of analysis adopted for the previous comparisons, I shall consider first the total group means without specific reference to age.

The increase of weight among the immigrants is carried still further in

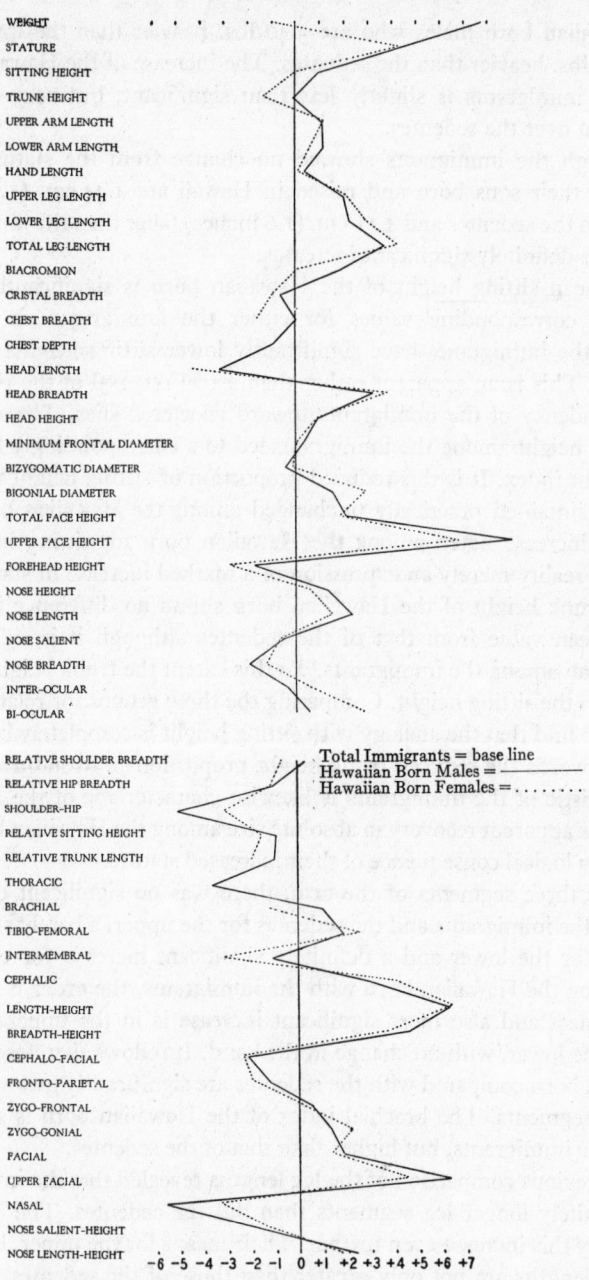

fig. 4

*Deviation of Total Hawaiian Born Males and Total Hawaiian Born Females
from their respective Immigrants*

the Hawaiian born males who are 3.40 lbs. heavier than the immigrants and 7.60 lbs. heavier than the sedentes. The increase of the Hawaiian born over the immigrants is slightly less than significant, but very definitely significant over the sedentes.

Although the immigrants showed no change from the stature of the sedentes, their sons born and raised in Hawaii are 4.44 cm. (1.7 inches) taller than the sedentes and 4.11 cm. (1.6 inches) taller than the immigrants. These are definitely significant increases.

The mean sitting height of the Hawaiian born is significantly greater than the corresponding values for either the immigrants or sedentes, whereas the immigrants have significantly lower sitting heights than the sedentes. This is an apparent rather than a real reversal of the previously noted tendency of the immigrants toward shorter bodies. The reduction in sitting height among the immigrants led to a correspondingly lower sitting height index. It is this reduced proportion of sitting height to stature that is maintained practically unchanged among the Hawaiian born. The absolute increase noted among the Hawaiian born for sitting height becomes in reality merely an expression of a marked increase in stature.

The trunk height of the Hawaiian born shows no difference in its absolute mean value from that of the sedentes although it is significantly longer than among the immigrants. To this extent the trunk height is comparable to the sitting height. Comparing the three groups for relative trunk height we find that the analogy with sitting height is completely borne out. In other words the reduced trunk height proportionate to stature which is characteristic of the immigrants is likewise characteristic of the Hawaiian born. The apparent recovery in absolute size among the Hawaiian born thus becomes a logical consequence of their increased stature.

Of the three segments of the arm, there was no significant difference between the immigrants and the sedentes for the upper, a barely significant increase for the lower and a definitely significant increase for the hand. Comparing the Hawaiian born with the immigrants, the order is reversed. The greatest and also most significant increase is in the upper arm, the next in the lower, with no change in the hand. It follows therefore that the Hawaiian born compared with the sedentes are significantly greater in each of these segments. The brachial index of the Hawaiian born is similar to that of the immigrants, but higher than that of the sedentes.

The previous comparison of the leg lengths revealed that the immigrants had definitely longer leg segments than did the sedentes. The Hawaiian born carry this increase even further. Their means for the upper, lower and total leg lengths are not only greater than those of the sedentes, but they are also greater than the means of the immigrants. But whereas the elongation of the leg among the immigrants was rather greater in the upper than in the lower, among the Hawaiian born the continuation of this increase in leg length is confined almost entirely to the lower leg. As a result the Hawaiian born show a significant increase over the immigrants in the tibio-femoral index. This difference between the immigrants and the Hawaiian born in their respective increases in the leg segments is suggestive. In the case of the immigrants the increases represented an alteration in a fundamental proportion without a change in stature. The trunk decreased in inverse ratio to the increase in the leg length so that the immigrants compared with the sedentes were distinguished by relatively and absolutely shorter bodies and longer legs. In the case of the Hawaiian born the relation of trunk to legs remains unchanged from the parental immigrant pattern. The leg increase is merely proportionate to a general increase in body size. This latter is a homogeneous change and conforms with the observation that with a continued increase in size the tibia tends to grow faster than the femur. Such a differential would explain the marked increase of the tibio-femoral index of the taller Hawaiian born.

The shoulder width in its gross dimension is significantly different in each of the three groups of Japanese. Narrowest among the Japanese sedentes it becomes widest among the Hawaiian born. But this dimension read in terms relative to stature undergoes a somewhat different modification. No difference for relative shoulder width is apparent between the Japanese immigrants and those born in Hawaii and both these derivative groups are strikingly altered when compared with the parental group in Japan. It is clear therefore that the change in shoulder proportions is already established among the immigrants and is maintained among the Hawaiian born. The wider shoulder relative to stature which characterizes both the immigrants and the Hawaiian born is intensified if the shoulder width is referred to the trunk height instead of to stature.

Although the differences between sedentes and immigrants and between immigrants and Hawaiian born in hip width fall somewhat short of statistical significance, there can be no doubt from other considerations that the hip width both absolutely and relatively to stature, to shoulder width and to trunk height becomes narrower as one proceeds from the Japanese sedentes to the immigrants and to the Hawaiian born. The accumulative effect builds up a significant decrease in the hip width of the Hawaiian born who are .62 cm. narrower than the sedentes. The difference amounts to 4.77 times its own probable error. A comparison of all three series for hip width relative to stature (relative hip width) and to shoulder width (shoulder-hip index) adequately demonstrates that the decreases in relative hip width and shoulder-hip index among the immigrants, as compared with the sedentes, continue significantly in the same direction among the Hawaiian born.

We previously discovered that the Japanese immigrants deviated from the sedentes in having a wider and shallower chest with a significantly lower index. The Hawaiian born reveal a mixed tendency. On the one hand the chest width reverts to a value equivalent to that for the sedentes, in spite of increased stature; and on the other the chest depth is even shallower than that for the immigrants. But since the change in chest depth is proportionately greater than that for chest width, the thoracic index of the Hawaiian born exhibits a significant reduction from the level of the immigrants which in turn represented a reduction from the sedentes population. In other words the Hawaiian born continue to deviate significantly toward a condition of flat chestedness which was already clearly adumbrated among the immigrants.

2. Head and Face and Their Indices

The changes in the cephalic dimensions and proportions of the Hawaiian born are especially distinctive. The reduction in head length occurs quite unheralded, nothing in the sedentes or the immigrants having presaged this modification. Almost as great as the decrease in head length is the compensatory increase in head width of the Hawaiian born. The consequence of these modifications emerges clearly in the cephalic index. Whereas both sedentes and immigrants have similar means, the Hawaiian born move abruptly toward an increased brachycephaly. The latter show additions of 2.6 and 3.10 index units over the immigrants and the sedentes respectively.

Unlike the alterations in the head width and head length, the change in head height of the Hawaiian born is a continuation of a trend first apparent among the immigrants. We have already found in the immigrants a large and significant addition to the head height. The additional increase to the head height of the Hawaiian born is less pronounced.

Compared with immigrants the Hawaiian born have significantly higher length-height indices as a result of divergent trends in the component dimensions. In the breadth-height index, on the contrary, the parallel changes in both breadth and height yield no appreciable difference. It should be observed, however, that breadth-height index of the Hawaiian born maintains the significant increase over the sedentes which the immigrants first established.

There are no real differences between any of the three groups in the dimension of the minimum frontal diameter, but the very real increase in head width among the Hawaiian born produces among them a significant reduction of the fronto-parietal index from the immigrant and sedentes means.

The means for the bizygomatic diameter reveal no significant change in the immigrants or in the Hawaiian born from the Japanese population in

Japan. As in the fronto-parietal index, the increase in head width of the Hawaiian born has also reduced their cephalo-facial index to a degree significantly lower than the mean index for either the immigrants or the sedentes who are identical for this index. The zygo-frontal index, however, reveals no significant change, except for a slight increase among the Hawaiian born.

The expansion of the bigonial width notable in the immigrants suffers a slight recession among the Hawaiian born toward the level of the sedentes. The reduction, however, is not sufficient to prevent the Hawaiian born from continuing, like the immigrants, to be distinguished by significantly wider jaws than are the Japanese sedentes. A comparison of the relationship of the bigonial to the face width likewise pairs the immigrants and the Hawaiian born against the sedentes whose zygo-gonial index is significantly lower than those for the two derivative groups.

Between the Japanese sedentes on the one hand and the immigrants and Hawaiian born on the other, exists a profound contrast in the length of the face. Both the total face length and the upper face length have increased in the derivative groups. In fact the increases from the sedentes in upper face length in terms of x p.e. are the largest of any change found in these comparisons. Although the immigrants and the Hawaiian born have deviated from the sedentes in the same direction and although these two groups are identical in the upper face height, the Hawaiian born are significantly lower than the immigrants in total face height. But the total face height of the Hawaiian born, however, remains significantly higher than the mean for the sedentes. We may, then, conclude that the tendency toward elongation of the face is definitely characteristic of the derivative groups of immigrants and Hawaiian born, that it is most pronounced in the upper face, that it is present in the total face to a lesser degree. It is obvious that the respective face indices will reflect these modifications in the facial lengths. Actually the indices follow the same pattern as do the face heights, that is to say both the Hawaiian born and the immigrants have significantly higher total and upper face indices than the sedentes. The differences between the Hawaiian born and the immigrants are negligible.

Although the decrease in the forehead height of the immigrants was not found sufficiently large to be called significant, it is noteworthy that the Hawaiian born show the *same* tendency to a lower forehead which, in comparison with the sedentes, becomes significantly lower.

The factor, whatever it may be, which is responsible for the increased face heights among the immigrants and the Hawaiian born is apparently also effective in the nose length and height. With no significant difference between themselves, the Hawaiian born and immigrants both have greater dimensions than the sedentes. The increase is more evident for the nose length than for the height but in both the differences are significant.

The nasal projection or salient suffers a significant shortening among the immigrants and the Hawaiian born, as compared with the sedentes. Although the Hawaiian born have a somewhat greater mean than the immigrants, the difference is negligible.

The nasal breadth likewise has undergone a significant reduction in the immigrants and Hawaiian born. As a matter of fact the narrowing of the nose appears progressively greater as one proceeds from sedentes to immigrants to Hawaiian born. The minus difference being in each case significant.

The nasal index naturally reflects the changes in the nasal dimensions of the immigrants and the Hawaiian born. Their longer and narrower noses yield indices that are much lower than that for the sedentes. In fact, as in nose width, the reduction of nasal index is progressive from the sedentes to the Hawaiian born. In nasal width and nasal index, therefore, the immigrants and the Hawaiian born show similar changes from the sedentes.

The projection of the nasal tip relative to the distance from nasion to the base of the nose (nose height) is similar among the immigrants and the Hawaiian born and in both significantly less than among the Japanese sedentes.

The relationship of the nose length and nose height indicates the degree of upward tilt of the nasal tip. Both the immigrants and the Hawaiian born have significantly higher indices than the sedentes which together with their consistently lower nasal salients indicate clearly enough that the retroussé nose of the Japanese has become less tilted among the two derivative groups. It should be mentioned that the nose length-nose height index of the Hawaiian born is slightly nearer the sedentes mean than is the immigrant mean. In fact the difference between the immigrants and the Hawaiian born is exactly three times its own probable error.

The inter-ocular distance among the immigrants shows a significant reduction, but among the Hawaiian born the mean returns to a value only slightly less than that of the sedentes.

Bi-ocular differences occur between the sedentes and the immigrants. The Hawaiian born are intermediate but the differences are negligible.

C. DETAILED COMPARISON OF TOTAL SERIES OF HAWAIIAN BORN FEMALES WITH IMMIGRANTS AND SEDENTES

1. Weight, Bodily Dimensions and Proportions

The means of the total Hawaiian born females are given in Table 12, and their comparisons with the total immigrants and sedentes in Tables 13 and 14.

The Hawaiian born females of our series are approximately $14\frac{1}{2}$ years younger than either the immigrants or sedentes. Although this is a considerable age difference, I shall reserve for a later section its possible effects on the following comparisons. For the present all series will be regarded as of equivalent ages.

In weight the Hawaiian born women are significantly lighter than their immigrant mothers, who on the contrary were very definitely heavier than the sedentes. This is an apparent reversal of trend in the Hawaiian born back to the original level. It would be of interest to know whether the Hawaiian born women have adopted the practice of many American women of controlling their figures by rigorous diets.

The stature of the Hawaiian born women exceeds that of the immigrants by a significant margin, thereby greatly accentuating a change already discernible in the immigrant women themselves. It is worth recalling here that among the males the first change in stature appeared not in the male immigrants but in their children born in Hawaii.

Despite an increased stature, the Hawaiian born women reveal no proportionate increase in the sitting height or in trunk height. In fact, all three groups are identical in absolute sitting height. In trunk height the Hawaiian born and the immigrants are equal and both are significantly shorter than the sedentes. If these dimensions are read against their respective statures, a clearer picture emerges and reveals a sharp reduction among the immigrant women of their relative sitting and trunk heights. This trend toward relatively shorter bodies tapers off in the Hawaiian born women. By virtue of an increase over the immigrants in stature and of no alteration in sitting or in trunk height the Hawaiian born women have slightly shorter bodies relative to stature. But their difference from the immigrants is not statistically important.

The legs, on the contrary, are longer in the immigrants and Hawaiian born than in the sedentes. The tendency is carried somewhat further in the Hawaiian born women than in the immigrants, but as in the trunk and sitting height the difference between Hawaiian born and immigrants does not exceed thrice its probable error.

In this primary proportion of the total body—the relation of trunk to legs, the males and females are in accord. They both show in the immigrants a profound alteration toward shorter trunks and longer legs. They both maintain and to a more limited extent intensify the alteration of the proportions in the Hawaiian born generation.

It is a general assumption that with increase in stature the increase in leg length is proportionately greater than in the trunk and that in the legs themselves greater in the tibia than in the femur. The tibio-femoral index which is a measure of the proportion of the lower to the upper leg shows in the immigrant women a significant increase over the sedentes, thus bearing out the common belief. But in the next generation, in the Hawaiian born, the index fails to make an advance to higher levels despite the concomitant addition to stature. Actually it drops only slightly below the mean of the immigrants, but sufficiently to diminish the significance of its superiority over the mean of the sedentes. Thus on the one hand, the stature increase of the immigrants brings about disproportionate increases in the leg segments, and, on the other hand, the addition to the stature of the Hawaiian born leaves the proportion of the leg segments unchanged, or at most, but slightly altered.

These shifts in the tibio-femoral index among the females are the antithesis of the corresponding movements in the males. Among the latter, the index falls slightly in the immigrants and in the Hawaiian born jumps forward above the means of the immigrants and the sedentes.

I am at a loss to account satisfactorily for the unexpected results of a comparison of the arm segments. For the upper arm length the Hawaiian born and the immigrant females are in fair agreement and both are significantly longer than the sedentes. Again in the lower arm segment the accordance between Hawaiian born and immigrants is fairly close and both once more are longer than the sedentes. Up to this point the parallelism with the progression of trunk height is close, and since the arms may be correlated with the trunk there is no problem but rather a corroboration of the inter-relation of bodily parts. But in the hand length the Hawaiian born are so much smaller than the immigrants that they practically revert to the dimensions of the sedentes. It is curious to observe that the same tendency is apparent to a lesser degree among the males. It is necessary to reserve comment on the possibility of a functional explanation until the data on occupation are presented.

Like the tibio-femoral index of the leg, the brachial index of the arm measures the proportion of the lower segment (the radius) to the upper (the humerus). In the three series there is a steady but small decline in the index as one moves from sedentes to immigrants to Hawaiian born. The piling up of these successive minus differences results in a significant difference between the Hawaiian born and the sedentes.

The relative size of the arm in relation to the leg is expressed in the intermembral index. As might be expected from the progressively increasing length of the legs, this index falls among the immigrants and even more definitely among the Hawaiian born.

In the transverse diameters of the trunk, i.e. the biacromion, the cristal width and the chest diameter, the Hawaiian born women are not only significantly smaller than their immigrant mothers, but in cristal and chest width significantly smaller than the sedentes as well, despite their greater stature. It is true that the absolute trunk height of the Hawaiian born women is shorter than the sedentes, but so also is the same dimension in the immigrants who nevertheless exceeded the sedentes in all these three lateral diameters.

The narrowness of the trunk of Hawaiian born women is also emphasized in the relative shoulder width and the relative hip width. In these proportions the Hawaiian born have significantly smaller indices, whereas both the immigrant and sedentes women are identical.

Comparing the Hawaiian born with the immigrants for the shoulder-hip index, we discover at once that the decrease in the hip width of the Hawaiian born is relatively much greater than the decrease in shoulder width. The index drops about 3 index units and is definitely significant. It is interesting to note that between the sedentes and immigrants despite differences in absolute dimensions no change occurred in proportion.

2. Head and Face and Their Indices

In no character is the modification in the Hawaiian born more unexpected than in the head length. Although no intimation of this change is discernible in the immigrant women, the Hawaiian born women show a shrinkage of 4.74 mm. from the average head length of the immigrants and of 4.32 mm. from the sedentes. This is a change that is exactly comparable to that already pointed out among males.

The analogy with the males continues in the other two diameters of the cranial vault. In the head breadth, the Hawaiian born women surpass the immigrants and the sedentes, and in the head height they are again greater. But both these changes in Hawaiian born women are adumbrated in the increases in the immigrant women.

These changes in cephalic dimensions have precise consequences in the indices or proportions of the cephalic vault. In the length-breadth or cephalic index, the Hawaiian born depart from the immigrants and sedentes. Whereas the latter two groups are at the upper limits of mesocephaly the Hawaiian born are frankly brachycephalic. In the length-height index, the means of the three groups are ranged in an increasing series. The lowest are the sedentes who also have the lowest head heights; then with a significant addition to the mean come the immigrants whose head length is the same as the sedentes but whose head height has increased; finally the Hawaiian born with another addition to the index as a result of both a shorter and a higher head than the two previous groups. In the third index, the breadth-height, the Hawaiian born and the immigrants pair off against the sedentes. The mean indices of the former are not only higher than those of the sedentes but are roughly equal, since the increases in head breadth and head height are equivalent although of differing amounts.

The lateral dimensions of the 'face' behave uniformly. In the minimum frontal, the bizygomatic and the bigonial diameters, the immigrants maintain consistent increases over the sedentes. And in all three the Hawaiian born show recessions toward the original values of the sedentes. In the bigonial diameter, however, the recession of the Hawaiian born is not quite great enough to wipe out their statistical superiority over the sedentes.

The indices of which the above three dimensions are a part, clarify the character of the changes that have occurred in both the immigrants and the Hawaiian born. Although the immigrants have added to their head width and face width, they remain identical with the sedentes in the relation of head width to face width (cephalo-facial index). The Hawaiian born, however, because they have undergone an increase in head width and a decrease to the level of the sedentes in face width do reveal a significant drop in this index. Similarly for the fronto-parietal index the proportionate changes in the component measurements of the immigrants have not altered this ratio significantly, whereas a definite decrease does occur among the Hawaiian born. In the zygo-frontal index all three groups remain the same despite alterations in the absolute dimensions of frontal and bigonial diameters. Finally, in the zygo-gonial index, the proportion of the lower jaw width to face width, the most significant change occurs among the immigrant women because of a disproportionately large increase in the width of their lower jaws. There is a significant recession in this index however, among the Hawaiian born, among whom nevertheless it continues to remain significantly greater than among the sedentes.

Of all the bewildering modifications heretofore singled out, only a few are more significant in a statistical sense than those in the lengths of the face, both total and upper face. The increases in both these dimensions first appear among the immigrants and they are retained in the Hawaiian born generation. The same alignment is repeated in the total facial and upper facial indices. That is, the Hawaiian born and the immigrants are distinguished from the sedentes by virtue of definite increases in the upper and total facial indices.

The height of the forehead among the Hawaiian born women suffers a sharp and definite constriction compared with the immigrant and sedentes women who are practically identical in this character.

Without reference to the parallel changes in the face heights the similar but less striking changes in the nose height and length might assume less significance than they deserve. In both these measurements the immigrant women show a considerable elongation compared with the sedentes. And in both the Hawaiian born suffer a slight reduction. Although this reduction is not statistically significant in either case it does serve to restore the deviation of the nose height of the Hawaiian born women within the limits of insignificance with respect to the sedentes. But in the nose length they remain significantly longer than the sedentes.

In nose breadth, on the contrary, the Hawaiian born women in contrast to the immigrants and sedentes, reveal a definite narrowing. Among the males there was a similar progressive constriction in the nose breadth from sedentes to immigrants to Hawaiian born.

The effect of the changes in nose height and nose breadth on the nasal index are apparent. There is a progressively smaller index, or expressed differently the nose becomes relatively narrower from sedentes to Hawaiian born. Although the decrease for each stage is within the limits of thrice the probable error of the difference, yet the final difference between Hawaiian born and sedentes is large enough to leap over the three-bar barrier of significance. The same progression is found magnified among the corresponding males.

In the salience of the nasal tip there are constant reductions at each step from the sedentes to the Hawaiian born women. These are small but at their end points significant. The reflections of these modifications in the absolute diameters of the nose are shown in the nose salient-height index which measures the relative elevation of the nasal tip. Again we find a gradually less prominent nose among the immigrants and Hawaiian born. Although in actual figures the Hawaiian born continue on the path laid down by the immigrants, the difference between them is too slight to be more than chance.

One other nasal index helps to define the proportions of the nose. This is the nose length-height index in which the length is defined in terms of the nose height. In this proportion the Hawaiian born and the immigrants agree. They both have noses that are more nearly equal in length from nasion to tip and from nasion to base. In other words the nose of the sedentes is more retroussé, wider and shorter.

The slight difference between the three groups of Japanese women for the inter-ocular width does not appear to have any special meaning. Except for the increase in this width among the Hawaiian born over the immigrants, the discrepancies are not of real importance.

With bi-ocular width the situation is quite different. Here the Hawaiian born preserve the significant increase achieved by the immigrant women.

CHAPTER V

Prefectural Sub-Divisions of the Total Series

A. SYNOPSIS OF PREFECTURAL COMPARISONS

JAPAN proper is divided for administrative purposes into 3 urban and 43 rural prefectures. The rural prefecture is called a *ken* and is further divided into sub-prefectures, towns and districts. In size these prefectures range from the urban prefectures, the smallest of which contains only 690 square miles, to the largest of the rural prefectures, Iwate, which embraces 5,359 square miles. The prefecture may roughly be compared with our county.

Only a small number of prefectures have contributed to the general stream of migration to Hawaii, and of these still fewer have had a large share in the movement. Numerically the most important contingents have come from the following prefectures.

Prefecture	Area—sq.mi.
Hiroshima	3,103.84
Yamaguchi	1,324.34
Fukuoka	1,894.14
Kumamoto	2,774.20
Niigata	4,914.55
Fukushima	5,042.57

Hiroshima and Yamaguchi are contiguous and occupy the southern-most part of the main island of Hondo. The immigrants in our series from these two prefectures come mainly from Aki, a sub-division of Hiroshima, and from Suwo in Yamaguchi, bordering on Aki. Aki and Suwo likewise furnish the major portion of our sedentes.

Continuing from Yamaguchi across the narrow channel which divides Hondo from its neighboring island, Kyushu, we come next to the prefectures of Fukuoka and Kumamoto.

Niigata and Fukushima are geographically separated from the preceding cluster of prefectures. They are situated in the northern part of central Hondo and are among the largest in size.

All these prefectures by number and geography fall into four groups: namely, Hiroshima, Yamaguchi, Kyushu (including Fukuoka and Kumamoto) and 'Other Japan' (including Niigata and Fukushima). Each of the three master series was susceptible to this additional division by prefecture. The classificatory criteria were the birthplaces of both parents. If one parent was born in a different prefecture than the other, their offspring was not included in the seriations. Actually the casualties from this species of disability were relatively few, although they were greatest among the Hawaiian born males indicating perhaps a tendency toward extra-prefectural marriage among the immigrants.

The sedentes, immigrants and Hawaiian born of each prefectural grouping were intimately related by blood. All the adults in the total series of sedentes had relatives in Hawaii, and practically all were related to subjects included in the series of immigrants and Hawaiian born. No village was visited in Japan that had not contributed to our series of Japanese obtained in Hawaii.

The exigencies of field work made it impossible to secure exactly equivalent numbers or proportions of each prefecture in each of the three master series. Consequently, as the following demonstrates, each of the three master series varies from the others in the proportion of subjects from any one prefecture.

DISTRIBUTION OF MALES BY BIRTHPLACE OF PARENTS

Prefecture	Yamaguchi		Hiroshima		Kyushu		'Other Japan'	
	No.	%	No.	%	No.	%	No.	%
Sedentes	36	23.68	68	44.74	22	14.47	26	17.11
Immigrants	35	21.88	48	30.00	41	25.63	36	22.50
Hawaiian Born	53	41.73	36	28.35	32	25.20	6	4.72

DISTRIBUTION OF FEMALES BY PREFECTURE

Prefecture	Yamaguchi		Hiroshima		Kyushu		'Other Japan'	
	No.	%	No.	%	No.	%	No.	%
Sedentes	16	20.78	27	35.06	18	23.38	16	20.78
Immigrants	18	23.08	28	35.90	16	20.51	16	20.51
Hawaiian Born	24	30.38	22	27.85	17	21.52	16	20.25

Such a distribution suggests the possibility that the observed changes in the immigrants and Hawaiian born might be the consequences not so much of selection and modification as the resultants of varying numerical representation of initial prefectural differences.

Before we can feel assured, therefore, of the validity of the preceding generalizations, the data must be analysed still further. In this section the total series will be broken down into prefectural units which may then be compared with each other and with the total series of which they are a part. We shall seek principally to determine (1) if the various prefectural groups of sedentes constitute recognizably distinct sub-types, (2) if they do, to ascertain what influence their numerical representation in the total series of immigrants and Hawaiian born might have, (3) whether or not the sedentes, immigrant and Hawaiian born phases of each prefectural group repeat the pattern in which the total series arrange themselves.

Tables 15–18 contain the means of the male sedentes grouped by prefecture. In Tables 19–22 each prefectural group of sedentes is compared with the means for the total group of sedentes. The results of these comparisons are given in Table 23, showing the actual distributions of x p.e.'s. On the whole the agreements are fair, much better for the Hiroshima and Yamaguchi sedentes than for the sedentes from Kyushu and 'Other Japan.' In fact, the two latter prefectures give evidence of a slight but definite tendency to form distinct local varieties of the sedentes type. Such a result is not unexpected from a geographical point of view. The subjects in the Yamaguchi and Hiroshima groups are from neighboring districts, whereas the Kyushu and the 'Other Japan' series are the most widely separated geographically.

The comparisons of the sedentes of each prefecture with the total sedentes are summarized in the following table. These figures represent the percentage of significant differences to total number of differences.

SUMMARY COMPARISON OF MALE PREFECTURAL SEDENTES
WITH TOTAL MALE SEDENTES

Prefecture	No.	Percentage of Significant Differences	
		Measurements	Indices
Hiroshima	68	6.9	14.3
Yamaguchi	36	6.9	9.5
Kyushu	22	24.1	33.3
'Other Japan'	26	20.7	28.6

In addition to comparing each prefectural group of sedentes with the total series, I have also compared in Tables 24–29 and in Fig. 5 each prefecture with the other three. The distributions of the x p.e.'s resulting from these calculations are given in Table 30 and summarized below by percentage of significant differences. In the following table the first number represents the percentage of significant differences in the measurements, the number in parentheses being the percentage of significant differences in the indices. The perusal of these figures confirms and clarifies the preceding comparisons. The sedentes from 'Other Japan' are the most deviant,

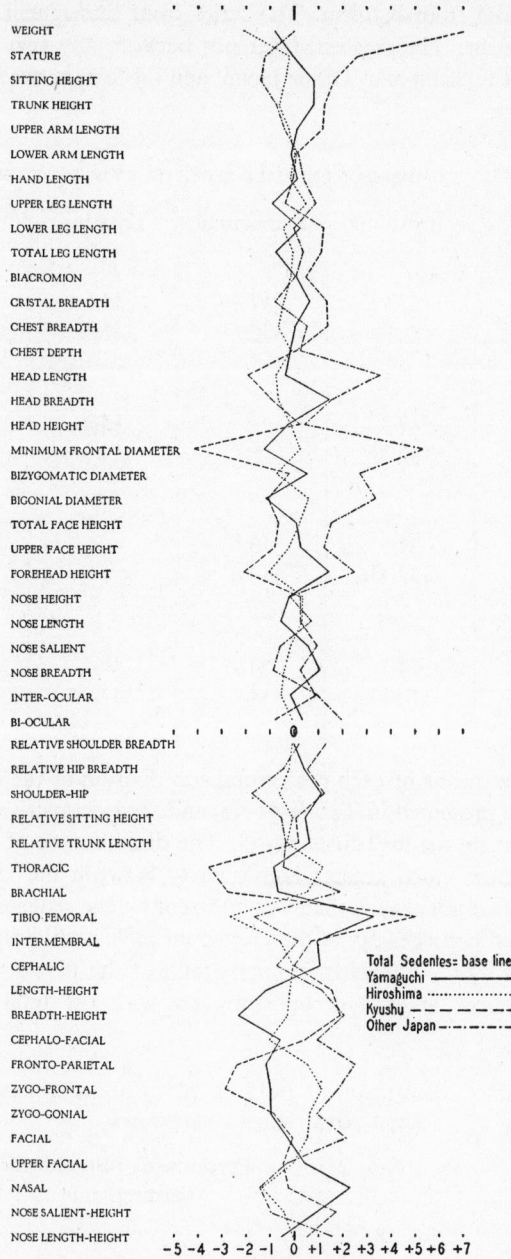

WEIGHT
STATURE
SITTING HEIGHT
TRUNK HEIGHT
UPPER ARM LENGTH
LOWER ARM LENGTH
HAND LENGTH
UPPER LEG LENGTH
LOWER LEG LENGTH
TOTAL LEG LENGTH
BIACROMION
CRISTAL BREADTH
CHEST BREADTH
CHEST DEPTH
HEAD LENGTH
HEAD BREADTH
HEAD HEIGHT
MINIMUM FRONTAL DIAMETER
BIZYGOMATIC DIAMETER
BIGONIAL DIAMETER
TOTAL FACE HEIGHT
UPPER FACE HEIGHT
FOREHEAD HEIGHT
NOSE HEIGHT
NOSE LENGTH
NOSE SALIENT
NOSE BREADTH
INTER-OCULAR
BI-OCULAR
RELATIVE SHOULDER BREADTH
RELATIVE HIP BREADTH
SHOULDER-HIP
RELATIVE SITTING HEIGHT
RELATIVE TRUNK LENGTH
THORACIC
BRACHIAL
TIBIO-FEMORAL
INTERMEMBRAL
CEPHALIC
LENGTH-HEIGHT
BREADTH-HEIGHT
CEPHALO-FACIAL
FRONTO-PARIETAL
ZYGO-FRONTAL
ZYGO-GONIAL
FACIAL
UPPER FACIAL
NASAL
NOSE SALIENT-HEIGHT
NOSE LENGTH-HEIGHT

Total Sedentes= base line
Yamaguchi ————
Hiroshima ·················
Kyushu — — — —
Other Japan —·—·—·—

−5 −4 −3 −2 −1 0 +1 +2 +3 +4 +5 +6 +7

fig. 5
Deviations of Male Sedentes by Prefecture

followed by those from Kyushu. The series from Yamaguchi appears to be the least variant. The greatest difference between any two prefectures occurs between Kyushu and 'Other Japan' and the least between Yamaguchi and Kyushu.

SUMMARY COMPARISON OF MALE SEDENTES BY PREFECTURE

	Hiroshima	Yamaguchi	Kyushu	'Other Japan'
Hiroshima	——	17.2 (38.1)	34.5 (38.1)	24.1 (14.3)
Yamaguchi	17.2 (38.1)	——	13.8 (14.3)	24.1 (52.4)
Kyushu	34.5 (38.1)	13.8 (14.3)	——	48.2 (42.9)
'Other Japan'	24.1 (14.3)	24.1 (52.4)	48.2 (42.9)	——

Similarly the means of each prefectural sub-division of the male immigrant series are presented in Tables 31–34, and their comparisons with the total immigrant means in Tables 35–38. The distributions of the x p.e.'s in Table 39 show much greater homogeneity between the various male immigrant prefectural groups than was apparent for the sedentes.

The increased homogeneity of the immigrant prefectural groups is made further evident by the following summary table of the percentages of significant differences of each group compared with the total immigrant series.

SUMMARY COMPARISON OF MALE PREFECTURAL IMMIGRANTS
WITH TOTAL MALE IMMIGRANTS

Prefecture	No.	Percentage of Significant Differences Measurements	Indices
Hiroshima	48	0	4.8
Yamaguchi	35	13.8	33.3
Kyushu	41	3.4	14.3
'Other Japan'	36	0	4.8

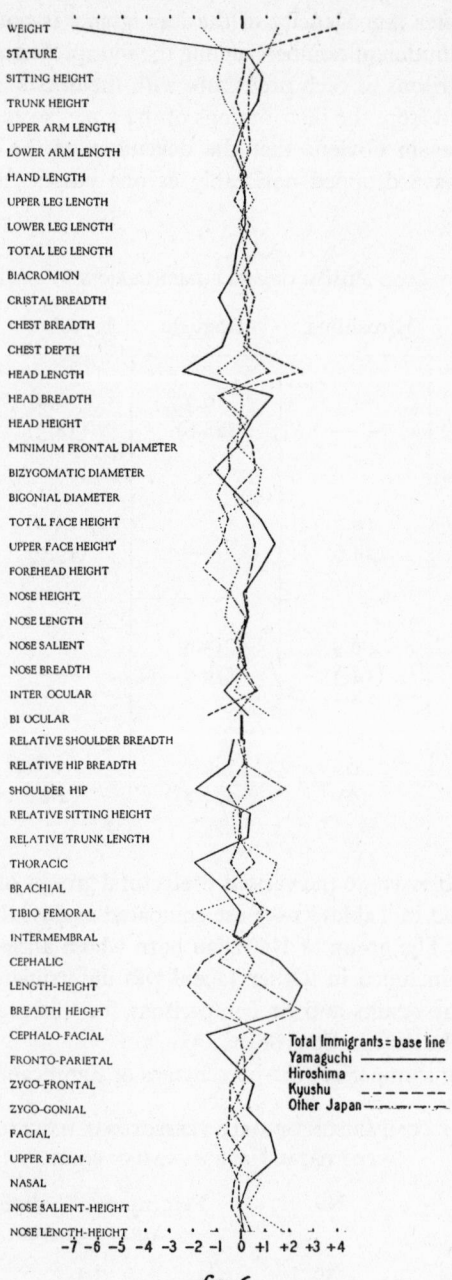

WEIGHT
STATURE
SITTING HEIGHT
TRUNK HEIGHT
UPPER ARM LENGTH
LOWER ARM LENGTH
HAND LENGTH
UPPER LEG LENGTH
LOWER LEG LENGTH
TOTAL LEG LENGTH
BIACROMION
CRISTAL BREADTH
CHEST BREADTH
CHEST DEPTH
HEAD LENGTH
HEAD BREADTH
HEAD HEIGHT
MINIMUM FRONTAL DIAMETER
BIZYGOMATIC DIAMETER
BIGONIAL DIAMETER
TOTAL FACE HEIGHT
UPPER FACE HEIGHT
FOREHEAD HEIGHT
NOSE HEIGHT
NOSE LENGTH
NOSE SALIENT
NOSE BREADTH
INTER OCULAR
BI OCULAR
RELATIVE SHOULDER BREADTH
RELATIVE HIP BREADTH
SHOULDER HIP
RELATIVE SITTING HEIGHT
RELATIVE TRUNK LENGTH
THORACIC
BRACHIAL
TIBIO FEMORAL
INTERMEMBRAL
CEPHALIC
LENGTH-HEIGHT
BREADTH HEIGHT
CEPHALO-FACIAL
FRONTO-PARIETAL
ZYGO-FRONTAL
ZYGO-GONIAL
FACIAL
UPPER FACIAL
NASAL
NOSE SALIENT-HEIGHT
NOSE LENGTH-HEIGHT

Total Immigrants = base line
Yamaguchi ——————
Hiroshima ·············
Kyushu   – – – – – –
Other Japan —··—··—··—

-7 -6 -5 -4 -3 -2 -1 0 +1 +2 +3 +4

fig. 6

Deviations of Male Immigrants by Prefecture

That the greater homogeneity of the immigrants is not the effect of a more even distribution of numbers among the four prefectures may be seen from the comparisons of each prefecture with the others in Tables 40–45 and in Fig. 6 and from the distributions of the x p.e.'s presented in Table 46. Here it is again obvious that the deviations of the prefectures one from another have dropped noticeably as one passes from sedentes to immigrants.

SUMMARY COMPARISON OF MALE IMMIGRANTS BY PREFECTURE

	Hiroshima	Yamaguchi	Kyushu	'Other Japan'
Hiroshima	——	10.3 (28.6)	6.9 (14.3)	0 (0)
Yamaguchi	10.3 (28.6)	——	13.8 (19.0)	20.7 (23.8)
Kyushu	6.9 (14.3)	13.8 (19.0)	——	0 (4.8)
'Other Japan'	0 (0)	20.7 (23.8)	0 (4.8)	——

Finally in Tables 47–50 the various prefectural groups of Hawaiian born are presented and in Tables 51–53 are compared against the total series of Hawaiian born. The group of Hawaiian born whose ancestors came from the prefectures included in 'Other Japan' was unfortunately too small to yield trustworthy results and no comparisons for this group were made. Table 54 gives the distributions of the x p.e.'s.

The following summarizes the percentages of significant differences.

SUMMARY COMPARISON OF MALE PREFECTURAL HAWAIIAN BORN
WITH TOTAL MALE HAWAIIAN BORN

Prefecture	No.	Percentage of Significant Differences	
		Measurements	Indices
Hiroshima	36	3.4	4.8
Yamaguchi	53	0	4.8
Kyushu	32	0	0

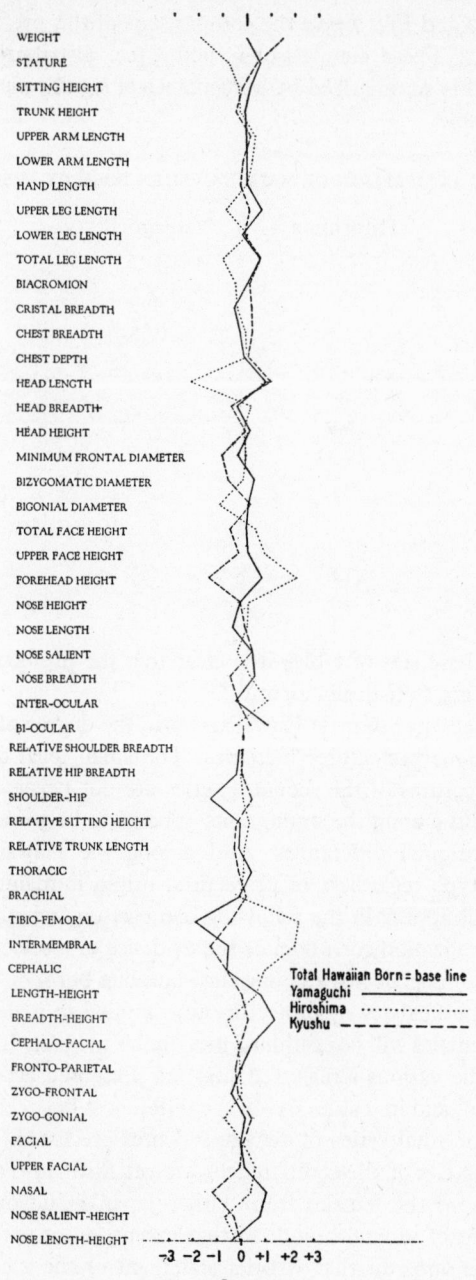

WEIGHT
STATURE
SITTING HEIGHT
TRUNK HEIGHT
UPPER ARM LENGTH
LOWER ARM LENGTH
HAND LENGTH
UPPER LEG LENGTH
LOWER LEG LENGTH
TOTAL LEG LENGTH
BIACROMION
CRISTAL BREADTH
CHEST BREADTH
CHEST DEPTH
HEAD LENGTH
HEAD BREADTH
HEAD HEIGHT
MINIMUM FRONTAL DIAMETER
BIZYGOMATIC DIAMETER
BIGONIAL DIAMETER
TOTAL FACE HEIGHT
UPPER FACE HEIGHT
FOREHEAD HEIGHT
NOSE HEIGHT
NOSE LENGTH
NOSE SALIENT
NOSE BREADTH
INTER-OCULAR
BI-OCULAR
RELATIVE SHOULDER BREADTH
RELATIVE HIP BREADTH
SHOULDER-HIP
RELATIVE SITTING HEIGHT
RELATIVE TRUNK LENGTH
THORACIC
BRACHIAL
TIBIO-FEMORAL
INTERMEMBRAL
CEPHALIC
LENGTH-HEIGHT
BREADTH-HEIGHT
CEPHALO-FACIAL
FRONTO-PARIETAL
ZYGO-FRONTAL
ZYGO-GONIAL
FACIAL
UPPER FACIAL
NASAL
NOSE SALIENT-HEIGHT
NOSE LENGTH-HEIGHT

Total Hawaiian Born = base line
Yamaguchi ————————
Hiroshima ....
Kyushu — — — — — —

−3 −2 −1 0 +1 +2 +3

fig. 7

Deviations of Male Hawaiian Born by Prefecture

Tables 55–57 and Fig. 7 give the comparisons of the prefectural groups with each other. These comparisons yield x p.e. distributions shown in Table 58 which is summarized by percentages of significant differences in the following table.

SUMMARY COMPARISON OF MALE HAWAIIAN BORN BY PREFECTURE

	Hiroshima	Yamaguchi	Kyushu
Hiroshima	——	6.9 (9.5)	3.4 (4.8)
Yamaguchi	6.9 (9.5)	——	0 (0)
Kyushu	3.4 (4.8)	0 (0)	——

From both these sets of tables it is clear that the prefectural groups of Hawaiian born are statistically identical.

From male sedentes to male Hawaiian born, the degree of homogeneity among the various prefectures increases. The small local differences between the prefectures of the sedentes series are not perpetuated. In fact, the general trend among the immigrants appears to be toward conformity regardless of original differences. And among the Hawaiian born this uniformity of type regardless of prefectural origin is maintained and intensified. It will appear in the following comparisons whether or not this statistical generalization corroborates the evidence of a selected immigrant type modified homogeneously among the Hawaiian born.

The preceding analysis by prefecture was applied to males only. In the following the females will be examined in a similar manner. In Tables 59–62 the means of the various female sedentes are presented according to prefecture of origin, and in Tables 63–66 the differences between each of these groups with the total series of female sedentes are listed. The distributions of the x p.e.'s of these differences are set forth in Table 67. In all these comparisons the females from 'Other Japan' stand out as the most divergent group of sedentes, and, to that extent, agree with the male sedentes from the same district. A brief statement of the x p.e. differences in terms of the percentage of significant differences is given in the following table.

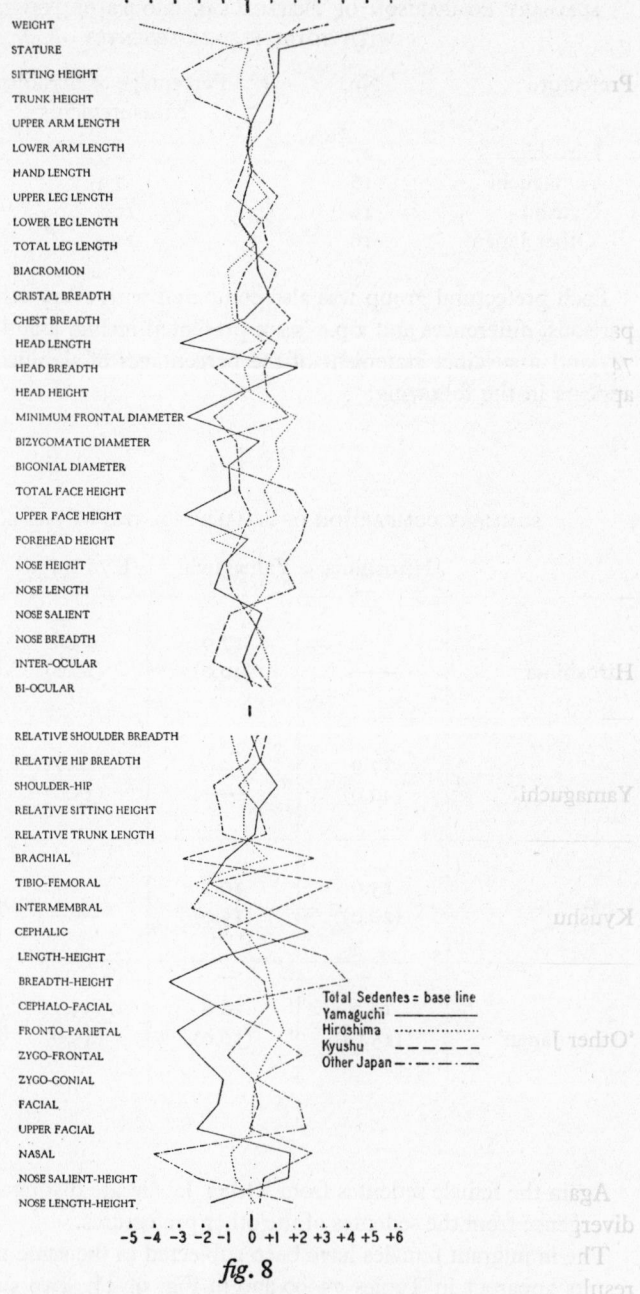

WEIGHT
STATURE
SITTING HEIGHT
TRUNK HEIGHT
UPPER ARM LENGTH
LOWER ARM LENGTH
HAND LENGTH
UPPER LEG LENGTH
LOWER LEG LENGTH
TOTAL LEG LENGTH
BIACROMION
CRISTAL BREADTH
CHEST BREADTH
HEAD LENGTH
HEAD BREADTH
HEAD HEIGHT
MINIMUM FRONTAL DIAMETER
BIZYGOMATIC DIAMETER
BIGONIAL DIAMETER
TOTAL FACE HEIGHT
UPPER FACE HEIGHT
FOREHEAD HEIGHT
NOSE HEIGHT
NOSE LENGTH
NOSE SALIENT
NOSE BREADTH
INTER-OCULAR
BI-OCULAR

RELATIVE SHOULDER BREADTH
RELATIVE HIP BREADTH
SHOULDER-HIP
RELATIVE SITTING HEIGHT
RELATIVE TRUNK LENGTH
BRACHIAL
TIBIO-FEMORAL
INTERMEMBRAL
CEPHALIC
LENGTH-HEIGHT
BREADTH-HEIGHT
CEPHALO-FACIAL
FRONTO-PARIETAL
ZYGO-FRONTAL
ZYGO-GONIAL
FACIAL
UPPER FACIAL
NASAL
NOSE SALIENT-HEIGHT
NOSE LENGTH-HEIGHT

Total Sedentes = base line
Yamaguchi ————
Hiroshima ....
Kyushu – – – –
Other Japan – · – · –

-5 -4 -3 -2 -1 0 +1 +2 +3 +4 +5 +6

fig. 8

Deviations of Female Sedentes by Prefecture

SUMMARY COMPARISON OF PREFECTURAL GROUPS OF FEMALE SEDENTES
WITH TOTAL FEMALE SEDENTES

Prefecture	No.	Percentage of Significant Differences	
		Measurements	Indices
Hiroshima	27	10.7	10.0
Yamaguchi	16	7.1	20.0
Kyushu	18	10.7	10.0
'Other Japan'	16	21.4	40.0

Each prefectural group was also compared with every other. The comparisons, differences and x p.e.'s are presented in Fig. 8 and in Tables 68–74, and a succinct statement of the percentages of significant differences appears in the following.

SUMMARY COMPARISON OF FEMALE SEDENTES BY PREFECTURE

	Hiroshima	Yamaguchi	Kyushu	'Other Japan'
Hiroshima	——	17.9 (40.0)	25.0 (20.0)	14.3 (15.0)
Yamaguchi	17.9 (40.0)	——	10.7 (15.0)	28.6 (50.0)
Kyushu	25.0 (20.0)	10.7 (15.0)	——	35.7 (45.0)
'Other Japan'	14.3 (15.0)	28.6 (50.0)	35.7 (45.0)	——

Again the female sedentes from 'Other Japan' are distinguished by their divergence from the sedentes of the other prefectures.

The immigrant females have been subjected to the same treatment with results apparent in Tables 75–90 and in Fig. 9. The two summary tables which follow support the greater detail of the extended tables.

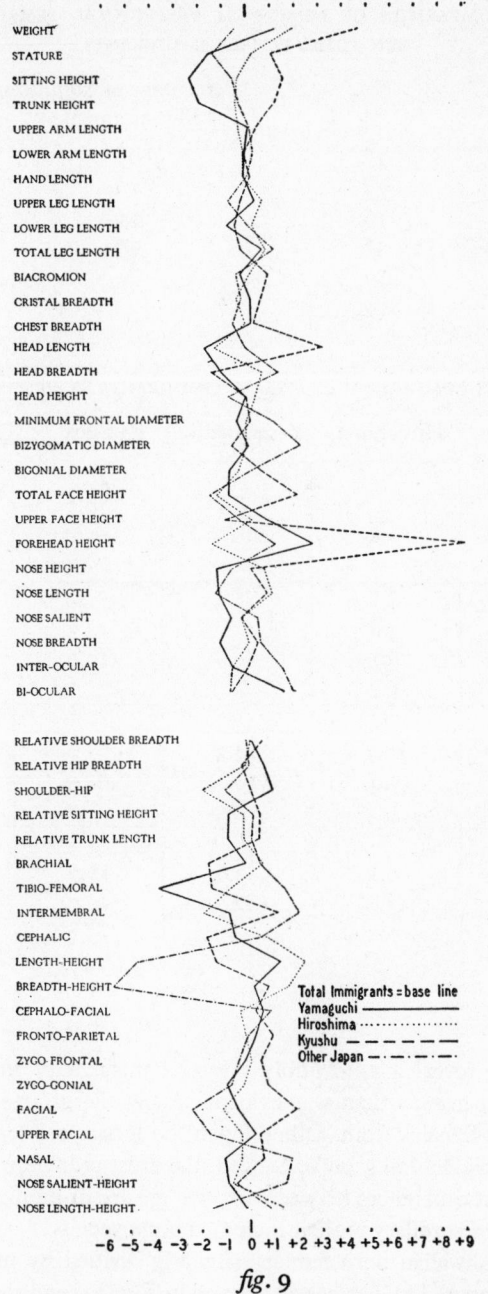

WEIGHT
STATURE
SITTING HEIGHT
TRUNK HEIGHT
UPPER ARM LENGTH
LOWER ARM LENGTH
HAND LENGTH
UPPER LEG LENGTH
LOWER LEG LENGTH
TOTAL LEG LENGTH
BIACROMION
CRISTAL BREADTH
CHEST BREADTH
HEAD LENGTH
HEAD BREADTH
HEAD HEIGHT
MINIMUM FRONTAL DIAMETER
BIZYGOMATIC DIAMETER
BIGONIAL DIAMETER
TOTAL FACE HEIGHT
UPPER FACE HEIGHT
FOREHEAD HEIGHT
NOSE HEIGHT
NOSE LENGTH
NOSE SALIENT
NOSE BREADTH
INTER-OCULAR
BI-OCULAR

RELATIVE SHOULDER BREADTH
RELATIVE HIP BREADTH
SHOULDER-HIP
RELATIVE SITTING HEIGHT
RELATIVE TRUNK LENGTH
BRACHIAL
TIBIO-FEMORAL
INTERMEMBRAL
CEPHALIC
LENGTH-HEIGHT
BREADTH-HEIGHT
CEPHALO-FACIAL
FRONTO-PARIETAL
ZYGO-FRONTAL
ZYGO-GONIAL
FACIAL
UPPER FACIAL
NASAL
NOSE SALIENT-HEIGHT
NOSE LENGTH-HEIGHT

Total Immigrants = base line
Yamaguchi ——————
Hiroshima ················
Kyushu — — — — —
Other Japan — · — · — ·

−6 −5 −4 −3 −2 −1 0 +1 +2 +3 +4 +5 +6 +7 +8 +9

fig. 9

Deviations of Female Immigrants by Prefecture

SUMMARY COMPARISON OF IMMIGRANT PREFECTURAL FEMALE GROUPS
WITH TOTAL FEMALE IMMIGRANTS

Prefecture	No.	Percentage of Significant Differences	
		Measurements	Indices
Hiroshima	28	0	0
Yamaguchi	18	7.1	0
Kyushu	16	3.6	0
'Other Japan'	16	3.6	10.0

SUMMARY COMPARISON OF FEMALE IMMIGRANTS BY PREFECTURE

	Hiroshima	Yamaguchi	Kyushu	'Other Japan'
Hiroshima	——	3.6 (0)	10.7 (5.0)	7.1 (15.0)
Yamaguchi	3.6 (0)	——	14.3 (10.0)	3.6 (10.0)
Kyushu	10.7 (5.0)	14.3 (10.0)	——	10.7 (10.0)
'Other Japan'	7.1 (15.0)	3.6 (10.0)	10.7 (10.0)	——

These tables reveal a perceptibly greater homogeneity among the various immigrant groups than was evident among the groups of sedentes. The immigrant females from 'Other Japan' no longer are separated from the rest of the prefectural groups. Indeed, the great reduction in the number of significant differences between any two groups of immigrant females may be taken as a corollary to their increased homogeneity.

Finally the Hawaiian born females similarly divided by prefecture are defined and compared in Tables 91–106 and in Fig. 10, and the summaries of their significant differences are tabulated in the following tables.

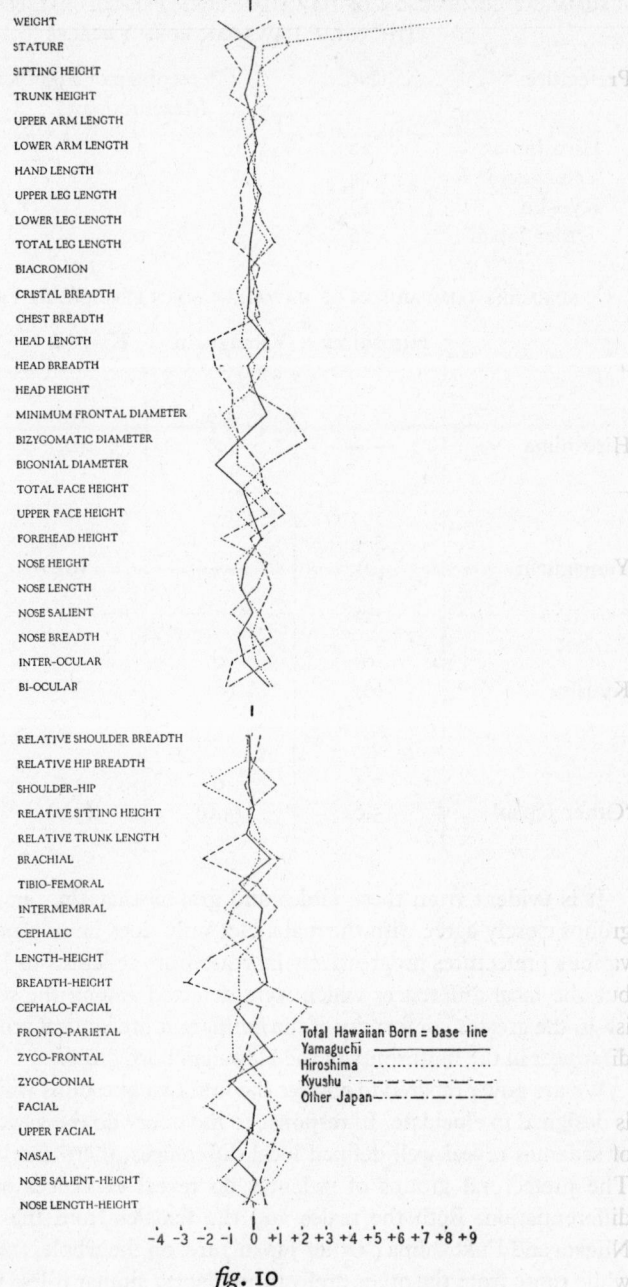

fig. 10

Deviations of Hawaiian Born Females by Prefecture

SUMMARY COMPARISON OF HAWAIIAN BORN PREFECTURAL FEMALE GROUPS
WITH TOTAL HAWAIIAN BORN FEMALES

Prefecture	No.	Percentage of Significant Differences	
		Measurements	Indices
Hiroshima	22	3.6	0
Yamaguchi	24	0	0
Kyushu	17	3.6	0
'Other Japan'	16	0	5.0

SUMMARY COMPARISON OF HAWAIIAN BORN FEMALES BY PREFECTURE

	Hiroshima	Yamaguchi	Kyushu	'Other Japan'
Hiroshima	—	3.6 (0)	0 (0)	7.1 (5.0)
Yamaguchi	3.6 (0)	—	0 (0)	0 (5.0)
Kyushu	0 (0)	0 (0)	—	3.6 (5.0)
'Other Japan'	7.1 (5.0)	0 (5.0)	3.6 (5.0)	—

It is evident from these tables and graphs that the female prefectural groups closely agree with the male. Not only does homogeneity among the various prefectures progressively increase from sedentes to Hawaiian born, but the local differences which were detected among the sedentes diminish in the greater conformity of the immigrant prefectural groups and finally disappear in the uniformity of the Hawaiian born groups.

We are now prepared to answer the first two questions which this section is designed to elucidate. In response to the query do the various prefectures of sedentes reveal well defined local differences, there can be little doubt. The prefectural groups of sedentes do reveal evidences of geographical differentiation. Both the males and the females from the prefectures of Niigata and Fukushima ('Other Japan') are, on the whole, the most deviant, while those from the other prefectures display similar if less well developed degrees of divergency.

But these geographical sub-types are of little importance, if it can be shown that they have not effected the changes observed in the immigrants and the Hawaiian born. For the prefectural differentiation of the sedentes to have influenced the purported trends of the immigrants, for example, it is necessary to demonstrate that these trends are not the product of deviations shared by all the immigrant prefectural groups but are the result of a fortuitous overweighting in the immigrant series of a particular prefecture which has remained identical with its sedentes phase. Another possibility which must be considered envisages a profound differentiation between the sedentes and the immigrants of a single prefecture which, if sufficiently represented in the immigrant series, might overshadow and even conceal the absence of any change in the other three groups.

Now I believe that both these hypothetical eventualities are eliminated by the phenomenon brought out clearly in the above tables. The fact that, despite initial differentiation among the prefectural groups of sedentes, the immigrants and the Hawaiian born of the same prefectures move toward ever greater identity with each other indicates one thing: the prefectural groups of immigrants and of Hawaiian born pursue mutually convergent courses regardless of their divergent origins. Each prefecture in its three phases of sedentes, immigrants and Hawaiian born passes through virtually similar stages. The gaps between these stages are determined more by the deviation of the preceding than the succeeding phase. This follows from the successively narrower range of prefectural variation. It will be apparent later in the detailed prefectural comparisons that the differentiated sedentes followed by the closer knit immigrants lead to inevitable discrepancies in the degree of difference between sedentes and immigrants of the various prefectures. This, however, need not be taken to indicate conflict or contradiction in the results of the prefectural comparisons.

At the risk of belaboring a self-evident point, I have made various computations to check the legitimacy of this deduction. I have calculated the deviation of each prefectural group of sedentes from the total immigrant series to determine which of them revealed any initial tendency to vary in the direction of the immigrants. These deviations together with their significance in terms of their probable errors are listed in Tables 107–111. From these figures the following percentages are calculated. They represent the percentage of significant deviations in measurements and in indices of each male prefectural group of sedentes from total male immigrants.

Males	Percentage of Significant Differences	
	Measurements	Indices
Yamaguchi Sedentes	62.07	71.43
Total Immigrants		
Hiroshima Sedentes	48.28	61.90
Total Immigrants		
Kyushu Sedentes	51.72	71.43
Total Immigrants		
'Other Japan' Sedentes	27.59	19.05
Total Immigrants		

The female sedentes have been subjected to a similar analysis with similar results. Each prefectural group of sedentes was compared with the total immigrant group. These comparisons are given in Tables 112–116. In the following table the percentages of significant differences only are listed.

Females	Percentage of Significant Differences	
	Measurements	Indices
Yamaguchi Sedentes	50.00	60.00
Total Immigrants		
Hiroshima Sedentes	46.43	40.00
Total Immigrants		
Kyushu Sedentes	57.14	50.00
Total Immigrants		
'Other Japan' Sedentes	39.29	25.00
Total Immigrants		

The above figures at once suggest that the sedentes from 'Other Japan' are the least deviant from the total immigrants. If we compare each group of sedentes, male and female, with its corresponding group of immigrants, as has been done in Tables 117–121, 130–134, we again find both the male and female sedentes from 'Other Japan' with the fewest differences of a significant order. In other words the sedentes from 'Other Japan' tend to anticipate the type characteristic of the immigrants. Moreover, the indicial resemblance of the sedentes from 'Other Japan' to the immigrants is greater than the similarity in absolute diameters.

This tendency of one group of sedentes to approximate the immigrant type combined with a slight increase in its representation in the total immigrant series need not, however, lead to the conclusion that this group is accountable for the deviation of the total immigrants from the total sedentes. If we study the preceding comparisons of the immigrant prefectural groups we find that the immigrants from 'Other Japan' are very similar not only to the total series of immigrants but to the various prefectural sub-divisions thereof. Furthermore the repetition of the same pattern of immigrant differentiation within each prefecture contributes to the support of its validity. Finally the prefectural means are pooled to obtain the total un-weighted means in which the effect of varying numerical representation is eliminated. These show differences of the same order as between the weighted series. The unweighted means are given in Tables 145, 146. Their differences may be compared in the same table with those for the weighted totals already presented. From these considerations, therefore, we must conclude that the immigrants represent a differentiated population which appears to be more common among the sedentes of 'Other Japan' than in any of the other prefectures.

If we now turn our attention to tracing the course of each prefectural group through the three phases of sedentes, immigrants and Hawaiian born, we may note at least one phenomenon which they all show in common with the corresponding total series (see Tables 117–144). The differences between each pair of successive phases exceed by far the deviations normally expected from random samplings of the same population. In other words, the selection of the immigrant type is repeated in each of the prefectural groups; and the modification of the Hawaiian born is also reaffirmed by each prefectural comparison. Some variation in the degree of this progressive phenomenon might be anticipated from the large number of variables involved and in actuality is found. The Yamaguchi, the Hiroshima, the Kyushu and the 'Other Japan' immigrants all vary slightly from each other in the amount of deviation they exhibit in relation to their particular group of sedentes. To a lesser extent, because of increased homogeneity, this is true when the Hawaiian born are compared with the immigrants.

B. ANALYSIS OF MALE PREFECTURAL GROUPS

1. Sedentes and Immigrants

In comparing the male immigrants of each prefecture with their respective sedentes (see Tables 117–121), I found a bewildering diversity in the degree of deviation which each immigrant group exhibited for a specific character. Unanimity of behavior at first appeared to be absent. This diversity in the sedentes-immigrant pattern arises from the markedly different degrees of homogeneity which these two groups exhibit. In other words each prefectural group of immigrants seeks to conform with the immigrant type regardless of the particular deviation of its associated group of sedentes from the total sedentes. Such a situation, therefore, tends to confusion in reading the successive sedentes-immigrant prefectural comparisons.

But if all the prefectural comparisons are anchored to a common base line then what formerly appeared chaotic now assumes a gratifying regularity. I have shown this graphically in Figs. 11–14. The base line for each comparison is plotted from the means of the total group of sedentes. Against this common factor I have compared by prefecture the sedentes and immigrants. This method has the double advantage of comparing immigrants and sedentes by prefecture and of relating the position of each prefectural group of sedentes to the total series of which it is a part. Contrast the profiles of the various groups of sedentes with those of the immigrants, and immediately the immigrants emerge as homogeneous groups and the sedentes as relatively heterogeneous ones. Generalizing from these graphs we are justified in concluding that the actual *degree of difference* between any pair is largely controlled by the position of the sedentes but that the *position* of an immigrant group is determined by conformity to a pattern characteristic of all immigrants regardless of their prefectural origin. Certain fluctuations from the expected pattern do occur among the immigrant groups, but they are normal variations and with few exceptions do not exceed three times their probable errors.

The same phenomenon may also be demonstrated by graphing the immigrants and sedentes of each prefecture against a base line represented by the total immigrants. Here the deviations of the immigrants are small and approximate a straight line while the sedentes vary widely according to their individual patterns. I have not reproduced these graphs since they essentially restate what the figures already make clear.

The importance of the ensuing analysis justifies, I believe, a detailed report of it in spite of the danger of adding to the already great complexity of these comparisons. I shall, therefore, consider now the immigrants and sedentes by prefecture. Before proceeding however, I should like to illustrate the kind of anomaly which arises in these comparisons. An earlier comment indicated that the deviations of some of these prefectural pairs contradict others. For example, the Kyushu male immigrants are shorter in stature, sitting height and trunk height than the corresponding Kyushu sedentes. Whereas the male immigrants from 'Other Japan' are taller in stature and are only very slightly different in sitting and trunk height from their sedentes. In spite of these differences from their sedentes both the Kyushu and the 'Other Japan' immigrants are practically identical. These differences arise from the divergencies in the position of the respective

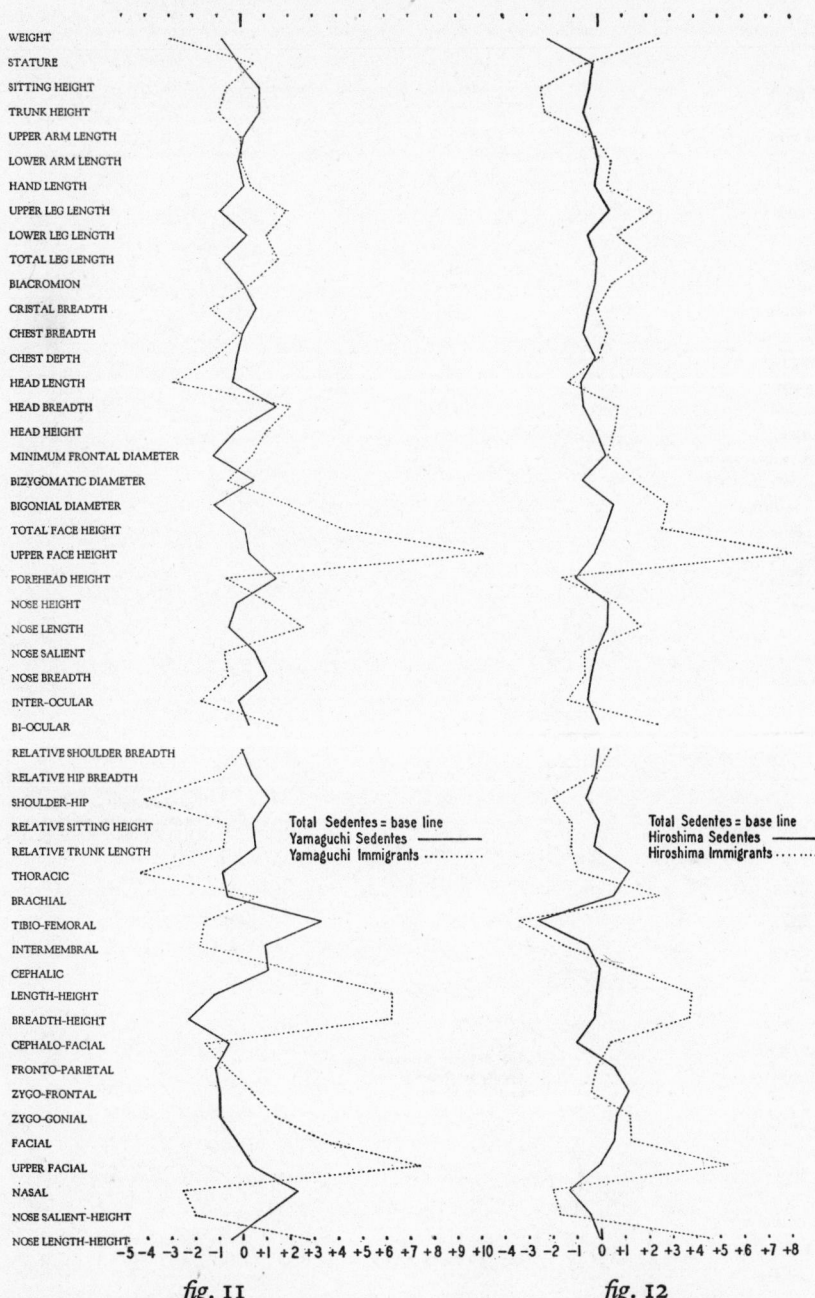

fig. II

Deviation of Yamaguchi Male Immigrants from Yamaguchi Male Sedentes

fig. I2

Deviation of Hiroshima Male Immigrants from Hiroshima Male Sedentes

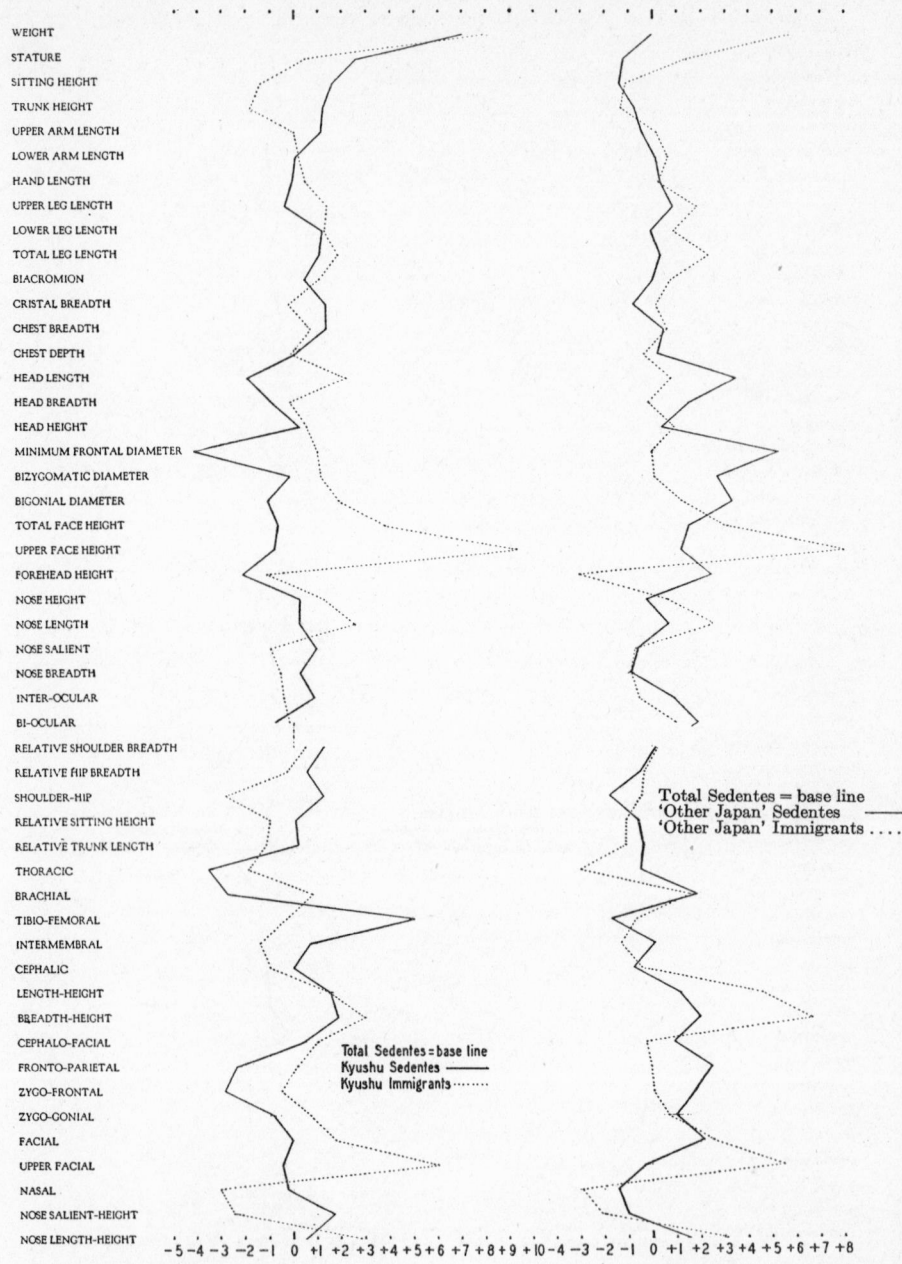

WEIGHT
STATURE
SITTING HEIGHT
TRUNK HEIGHT
UPPER ARM LENGTH
LOWER ARM LENGTH
HAND LENGTH
UPPER LEG LENGTH
LOWER LEG LENGTH
TOTAL LEG LENGTH
BIACROMION
CRISTAL BREADTH
CHEST BREADTH
CHEST DEPTH
HEAD LENGTH
HEAD BREADTH
HEAD HEIGHT
MINIMUM FRONTAL DIAMETER
BIZYGOMATIC DIAMETER
BIGONIAL DIAMETER
TOTAL FACE HEIGHT
UPPER FACE HEIGHT
FOREHEAD HEIGHT
NOSE HEIGHT
NOSE LENGTH
NOSE SALIENT
NOSE BREADTH
INTER-OCULAR
BI-OCULAR
RELATIVE SHOULDER BREADTH
RELATIVE HIP BREADTH
SHOULDER-HIP
RELATIVE SITTING HEIGHT
RELATIVE TRUNK LENGTH
THORACIC
BRACHIAL
TIBIO-FEMORAL
INTERMEMBRAL
CEPHALIC
LENGTH-HEIGHT
BREADTH-HEIGHT
CEPHALO-FACIAL
FRONTO-PARIETAL
ZYGO-FRONTAL
ZYGO-GONIAL
FACIAL
UPPER FACIAL
NASAL
NOSE SALIENT-HEIGHT
NOSE LENGTH-HEIGHT

Total Sedentes = base line
Kyushu Sedentes ———
Kyushu Immigrants ·······

Total Sedentes = base line
'Other Japan' Sedentes ———
'Other Japan' Immigrants ....

−5 −4 −3 −2 −1 0 +1 +2 +3 +4 +5 +6 +7 +8 +9 +10 −4 −3 −2 −1 0 +1 +2 +3 +4 +5 +6 +7 +8

fig. 13

*Deviation of Kyushu Male Immigrants
from Kyushu Male Sedentes*

fig. 14

*Deviation of 'Other Japan' Male Immi-
grants from 'Other Japan' Male Sedentes*

sedentes, not from any conflict among the immigrants in their conformity to type.

In general the male immigrants are identical with the total male sedentes in stature. They likewise all reveal a definite tendency toward shorter sitting and trunk heights and toward longer leg length than the sedentes. Moreover, the relative proportions of sitting height and trunk height show a constant decline among each prefectural group of male immigrants. These changes are consistent both absolutely and relatively and agree with the alterations already pointed out for the total series of male immigrants. It is interesting to observe that absolutely each of the immigrant groups has increased more in the upper leg than in the lower.

Although the various male immigrant groups are contradictory in their deviations from their sedentes in the three arm segments they nevertheless all agree very closely among themselves and in their relation to the total series of sedentes. They show no change in the upper arm, a tendency toward increased lower arms only in the Hiroshima and 'Other Japan' immigrants and a definite increase in the head lengths of all groups of immigrants.

The proportion of the lower to the upper arm, the brachial index, undergoes rather wide fluctuations among the four groups of sedentes. The Kyushu sedentes have relatively the shortest forearms and the other extreme is held by the sedentes of 'Other Japan.' The mean range represented is from 76.04 to 80.66. The corresponding immigrant groups, on the other hand, are in no case significantly different from each other; they all show a constant trend toward higher indices indicating a relative increase in the length of the forearm.

Similarly, the tibio-femoral index varies widely and significantly among the sedentes, whereas among the respective immigrants the range of means is very considerably reduced. But unlike the brachial index the tibio-femoral shows a consistent trend toward a lower index among the immigrants.

The graphic and statistical comparisons of the prefectural groups also confirm the change in the inter-membral index among the immigrants. They have relatively longer legs than arms and their alteration in this proportion is overwhelmingly apparent.

Although the increases in shoulder width in the immigrant groups over their respective sedentes are not all significant, nevertheless their consistency is impressive. In each case the immigrants have wider shoulders than their sedentes and in one case significantly. They all fall within a narrow range.

The cristal width, on the other hand, reveals a contradictory situation. Except for the Yamaguchi immigrants the cristal width falls at the midpoint of the average of the sedentes means, but among the Yamaguchi immigrants there is a decided decrease.

As might be expected, the relative shoulder width among the immigrants is slightly higher than was the case for the sedentes, but the increases are small. It hardly needs repeating that the range of the sedentes means surpasses the range of the immigrants. The relative hip index among the immigrants of each prefecture is lower than for the total sedentes. Where the mean of the prefectural sedentes is greater than the average for the total series, the decrease among the corresponding immigrants is large and significant. On the contrary, where the prefectural sedentes have lower indices than the total mean there is no statistically significant change among the immigrants.

The shoulder-hip index undergoes a marked decline among the immigrant groups. This decrease is statistically most significant when the respective sedentes fall above the average for the total series. Among the immigrants from 'Other Japan' the mean is higher than for the other three groups and it also represents an increase over the corresponding sedentes mean. This apparent exception may be explained, however, by the fact that the mean for the sedentes of 'Other Japan' approaches the average of the immigrants more nearly than the means of any other sedentes group thereby increasing the probability that the respective immigrants fall insignificantly above the prefectural sedentes mean.

The immigrants of each prefecture show a definite tendency in the alteration of their chest proportions. The thoracic index, in comparison with the total sedentes, is consistently lower, indicating a shallower chest among the immigrants. The actual decreases in the thoracic indices of the prefectural immigrants are statistically large, although in the Kyushu pair there is an actual increase for the immigrants. But, as in the case of the shoulder-hip index of the immigrants from 'Other Japan,' this increase is the result of the close approximation of the Kyushu sedentes' mean to that characteristic of the immigrants.

Without the clarity afforded by these changes in chest proportions, the means of the chest diameters alone would be confusing. In only two prefectural groups are the immigrants significantly wider-chested than their respective sedentes and in one they are practically identical with the sedentes. Moreover only in one instance are the immigrants notably shallower for the chest depth although they all show minor changes in that direction. But in every group the immigrants consistently conform to a pattern in which the chest depth is relatively narrower and the width relatively greater than among the sedentes.

Although the graphs show wide deviations in head length, these striking departures from the base line are in part the result of an innately greater range of variation in head length. The measure of this may be seen in the probable errors of the various head lengths. The reader, in considering the comparisons for this dimension must, therefore, take account of this factor. Actually the head lengths of the total series of immigrants and of sedentes were discovered to be practically identical. But a first glance at the corresponding means taken by prefectures seems to disclose fairly large deviations between immigrants and sedentes. In three instances the prefectural immigrants are shorter headed than their sedentes and in the fourth they are longer. But in only one, however, is the difference significant. The various prefectural sedentes vary significantly from each other as do the prefectural immigrants. Moreover, the immigrants show no consistency among themselves in their relation to the total group of sedentes. It seems, therefore, reasonable to conclude that the head length undergoes no statistically valid modification among the immigrants. The apparently enormous divergencies displayed in the graphs may be attributed to normal variations in the sampling process.

Similarly the fluctuations in the head width, although less violent, are expressions of normal variability rather than indications of a pattern of change. None of the immigrant groups depart significantly from the base line, nor do the variations in the head widths of the sedentes fall into consistent relationships with those of the immigrants. In three group comparisons the immigrants are wider headed and in one they are narrower. For no prefectural pair is the difference between immigrants and sedentes of significant magnitude. There does not appear, therefore, to be any real difference in head width between sedentes and immigrants.

The head height shows a definite increase among the immigrant groups. Each series of prefectural immigrants are higher headed than the sedentes, in two instances significantly. These immigrant means are all above the mean for the total series of sedentes.

The indices derived from these vault dimensions behave as might be anticipated from the relationships of the constituent measurements. In the cephalic index no consistent nor significant alteration is discernible in any of the prefectural immigrants. Their differences from their respective sedentes fall within the limits of thrice the probable error.

The situation, on the contrary, becomes definite with regard to the length-height and breadth-height indices because of the consistent increase in the head height of the immigrants. In both these indices the immigrants stand forth by their significant additions. The mean of each group of immigrants is superior to the average of the total sedentes; each prefectural pair shows an increase among the immigrants except in the length-height index of the Kyushu sedentes and immigrants. This exception, however, illustrates the point that where no difference occurs it may be the result of a deviation of the sedentes in the direction of the immigrant means.

The minimum frontal diameters of the various groups of immigrants show no change from the average of the total sedentes. But on comparing the immigrants with their respective sedentes, the immigrants from Kyushu display a large plus difference and the immigrants from 'Other Japan' a corresponding minus one. These differences, however, are the consequences of large deviations on the part of the sedentes from Kyushu and 'Other Japan.' The respective immigrants, as is obvious, conform to the general immigrant pattern.

The principal difference in the fronto-parietal index between the various immigrants and the corresponding sedentes is that the latter vary more widely than the former. None of the immigrant groups are significantly different from each other or from the total series of sedentes.

Although the Hiroshima immigrants are significantly greater than the sedentes of the same prefecture in the width of the face and the immigrants of 'Other Japan' are significantly narrower than their sedentes, these contradictory relationships indicate not a complementary difference between the two groups of immigrants but a disparity between the sedentes. As a matter of fact, none of the immigrant groups shows any significant deviations from each other in face width. The immigrants, in general, can not be said to manifest any definite tendency toward differentiation from the sedentes in the width of the face.

The cephalo-facial index, also, remains essentially unchanged among the immigrants.

The comments on the fronto-parietal index are appropriate to the zygo-frontal. The difference between the prefectural pairs of immigrants and sedentes are functions of the divergencies found among the sedentes. The immigrants are homogeneous and agree closely with the total mean for the sedentes.

In the width of the lower jaw, the bigonial diameter, the immigrant groups show significant increases over the sedentes collectively and, with one exception, individually. Only among the immigrants of 'Other Japan' is there a decrease from the mean of the corresponding sedentes, but the graph explains this apparent reversal. Actually the sedentes from 'Other Japan' differ from the remaining groups of sedentes by deviating in the direction represented by the immigrants, so that the immigrants of that prefecture, while having wider jaws than sedentes in general, are narrower in relation to their atypical sedentes.

The zygo-gonial index of the various immigrant groups, as a result of the consistent increase of the bigonial width among them, falls above the general average of all sedentes, and except in the case of 'Other Japan,' above the group sedentes.

The spectacular change in the length of the face among the immigrants, which was emphasized earlier, is borne out by the prefectural comparisons. The increase in the total face height, and especially in the upper face height, is characteristic of each group of immigrants. The corresponding facial indices likewise partake of this increase so that the conclusion is inevitable that the immigrants are particularly characterized by an increased face height and a relatively longer face.

The forehead height of the immigrants tends to be somewhat lower than that of the sedentes, although the decrease in height is not especially great.

The dimensions and proportions of the nose also show uniform differences among all the immigrant groups. Compared with the total sedentes and with the prefectural sedentes, the immigrants have longer and higher, less salient, and narrower noses. Moreover, the means of these various immigrants are noteworthy in their homogeneity. The indices derived from these measurements share in these changes, that is, the immigrant groups have lower nasal indices and noses less salient in relation to height.

Finally the immigrants show a consistent tendency toward narrower inter-ocular widths and except for the Kyushu immigrants toward wider bi-ocular diameters.

I have analysed at some length the relationships of the immigrants of the various prefectures to each other, to their respective sedentes, and to the master series of sedentes. The results of this analysis confirm the previous comparisons of total sedentes and total immigrants, even though among the various inter-prefectural comparisons of immigrants and sedentes some showed an apparently contrary trend. These exceptions, however, proved to be the result not of a lack of consistency in the pattern of the immigrant type but of a heterogeneity among the diverse prefectural groups of sedentes. In fact, the tables and graphs of the immigrants by prefectures serve to reaffirm the existence of an immigrant type, distinct from the sedentes from whom they are derived.

2. Immigrants and Hawaiian Born

If we now compare in Tables 122–125 the male immigrants with the male Hawaiian born by prefecture as we have the sedentes and the immigrants, we see at once that we are confronted with a quite different relationship. In the first place, the patterns of the immigrant and Hawaiian born prefectural types represented by graphic profiles are much more similar than were the corresponding sedentes and immigrants. But not only are the differences of a lesser degree but the courses of the profiles of the immigrants and Hawaiian born run more often in parallel lines than did those of the sedentes and immigrants. We may pursue in Figs. 15–17 the alignment of immigrant and Hawaiian born. The reader will note the ab-

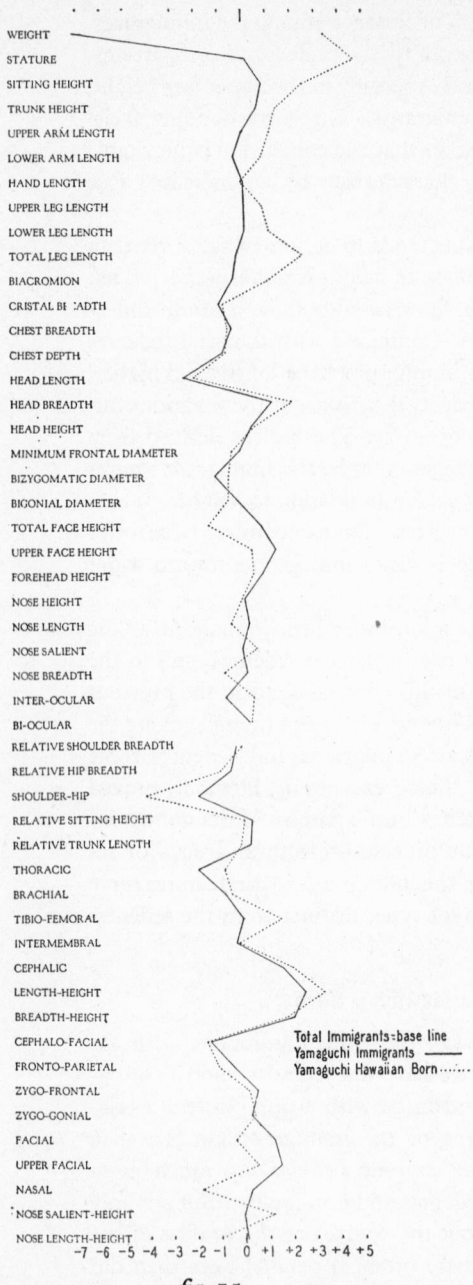

WEIGHT
STATURE
SITTING HEIGHT
TRUNK HEIGHT
UPPER ARM LENGTH
LOWER ARM LENGTH
HAND LENGTH
UPPER LEG LENGTH
LOWER LEG LENGTH
TOTAL LEG LENGTH
BIACROMION
CRISTAL BREADTH
CHEST BREADTH
CHEST DEPTH
HEAD LENGTH
HEAD BREADTH
HEAD HEIGHT
MINIMUM FRONTAL DIAMETER
BIZYGOMATIC DIAMETER
BIGONIAL DIAMETER
TOTAL FACE HEIGHT
UPPER FACE HEIGHT
FOREHEAD HEIGHT
NOSE HEIGHT
NOSE LENGTH
NOSE SALIENT
NOSE BREADTH
INTER-OCULAR
BI-OCULAR
RELATIVE SHOULDER BREADTH
RELATIVE HIP BREADTH
SHOULDER-HIP
RELATIVE SITTING HEIGHT
RELATIVE TRUNK LENGTH
THORACIC
BRACHIAL
TIBIO-FEMORAL
INTERMEMBRAL
CEPHALIC
LENGTH-HEIGHT
BREADTH-HEIGHT
CEPHALO-FACIAL
FRONTO-PARIETAL
ZYGO-FRONTAL
ZYGO-GONIAL
FACIAL
UPPER FACIAL
NASAL
NOSE SALIENT-HEIGHT
NOSE LENGTH-HEIGHT

Total Immigrants=base line
Yamaguchi Immigrants ———
Yamaguchi Hawaiian Born ·······

-7 -6 -5 -4 -3 -2 -1 0 +1 +2 +3 +4 +5

fig. 15

*Deviation of Yamaguchi Hawaiian Born
Males from Yamaguchi Male Immigrants*

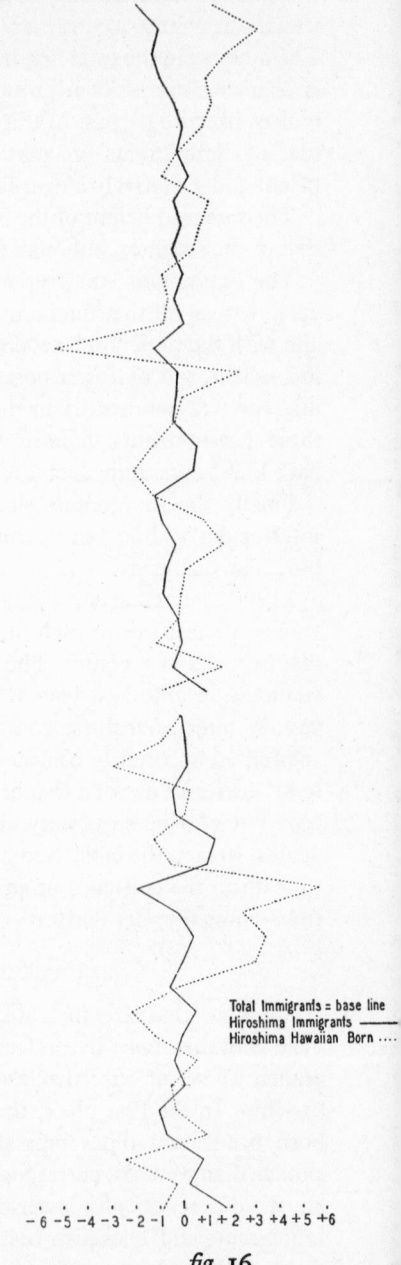

Total Immigrants = base line
Hiroshima Immigrants ———
Hiroshima Hawaiian Born ·······

-6 -5 -4 -3 -2 -1 0 +1 +2 +3 +4 +5 +6

fig. 16

*Deviation of Hiroshima Hawaiian B
Males from Hiroshima Male Immigrants*

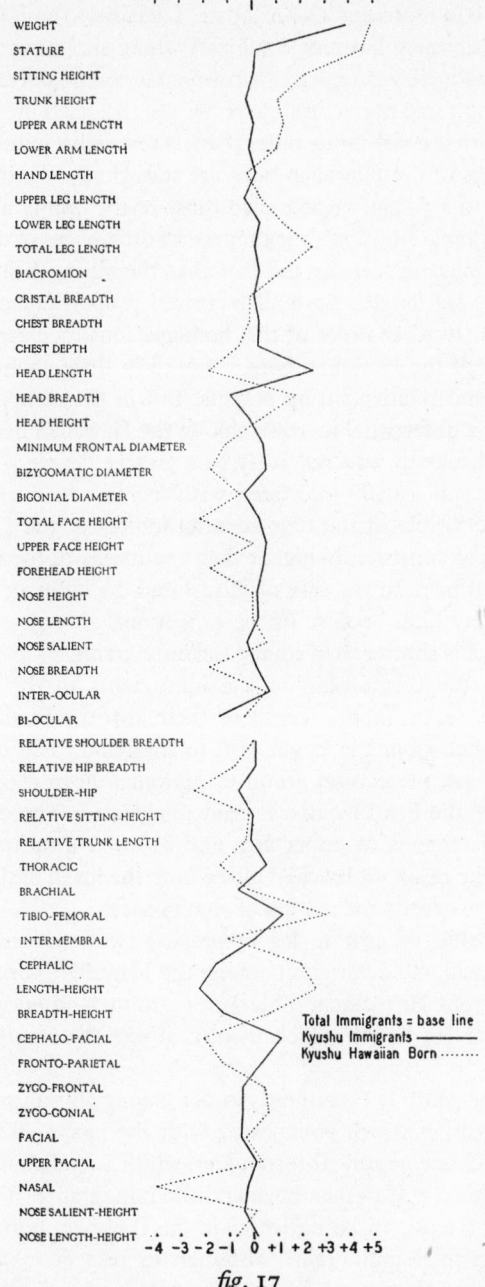

WEIGHT
STATURE
SITTING HEIGHT
TRUNK HEIGHT
UPPER ARM LENGTH
LOWER ARM LENGTH
HAND LENGTH
UPPER LEG LENGTH
LOWER LEG LENGTH
TOTAL LEG LENGTH
BIACROMION
CRISTAL BREADTH
CHEST BREADTH
CHEST DEPTH
HEAD LENGTH
HEAD BREADTH
HEAD HEIGHT
MINIMUM FRONTAL DIAMETER
BIZYGOMATIC DIAMETER
BIGONIAL DIAMETER
TOTAL FACE HEIGHT
UPPER FACE HEIGHT
FOREHEAD HEIGHT
NOSE HEIGHT
NOSE LENGTH
NOSE SALIENT
NOSE BREADTH
INTER-OCULAR
BI-OCULAR
RELATIVE SHOULDER BREADTH
RELATIVE HIP BREADTH
SHOULDER-HIP
RELATIVE SITTING HEIGHT
RELATIVE TRUNK LENGTH
THORACIC
BRACHIAL
TIBIO-FEMORAL
INTERMEMBRAL
CEPHALIC
LENGTH-HEIGHT
BREADTH-HEIGHT
CEPHALO-FACIAL
FRONTO-PARIETAL
ZYGO-FRONTAL
ZYGO-GONIAL
FACIAL
UPPER FACIAL
NASAL
NOSE SALIENT-HEIGHT
NOSE LENGTH-HEIGHT

Total Immigrants = base line
Kyushu Immigrants ———
Kyushu Hawaiian Born ·······

-4 -3 -2 -1 0 +1 +2 +3 +4 +5

fig. 17

Deviation of Kyushu Hawaiian Born Males from Kyushu Male Immigrants

sence of a graph to represent 'Other Japan.' I decided to omit this since there were only six Hawaiian born male subjects whose ancestry could be traced to the provinces included under this rubric. Confining ourselves therefore to the remaining three prefectural pairs, we see that each prefectural group of Hawaiian born is consistently taller than its respective immigrants. These superior statures of the Hawaiian born are statistically significant, ranging from 4.14 cm. to 4.50 cm. greater than those of the immigrants. Although these are remarkable additions, they represent differences of degree and not of kind. This may be seen by the fact that the sitting height, the trunk height, and the leg lengths have all increased proportionately among the Hawaiian born. Further proof of this homogeneous increase of the major body segments of the Hawaiian born is found in their unchanged relative trunk heights and relative sitting heights. But in the component parts of the leg there is a differential increase among the Hawaiian born. The lower leg increases absolutely and relatively to a greater degree than the upper leg, a phenomenon usually associated with increase in total stature. The effect of this is visible in the tibio-femoral indices of the Hawaiian born groups which are consistently higher than the means of the immigrants of each prefectural pair. In the case of Hiroshima the index of the Hawaiian born is especially high because of the exceptional shortness of the upper leg which in fact is shorter than among the immigrants.

Contrary to the relationship of the immigrants to the sedentes, the Hawaiian born reveal in the length of their arm segments a decreasing amount of change from the upper arm to the hand. The upper and the lower arm in each prefectural group of Hawaiian born show distinct increments, while the hand lengths remain unchanged. The differences between these increments to upper arm and to lower arm are sufficient to lower slightly the resultant brachial index from the mean of the total immigrants but not to exceed the margin of significance.

The relationship of arm to leg, expressed by the inter-membral index, shows considerable variation among the Hawaiian born, particularly among those from Hiroshima. This latter group is atypical in having a shortened upper leg length which in turn affects the length of the total leg.

The shoulder width is consistently wider among all groups of Hawaiian born, a modification which is expected with the increased stature found among them. Consequently the shoulder width in relation to stature is identical in both the Hawaiian born and the immigrants. The hip width, on the contrary, tends to be narrower in the Hawaiian born groups compared with the total immigrants, although in respect to the individual groups of immigrants the tendency is mixed. Such a reversal produces among the Hawaiian born narrower hips relative to stature and to the shoulder width. In both these indices the modifications of proportion are decisive.

Previously in comparing the total series of Hawaiian born with the total group of immigrants, the former were found to have smaller chest dimensions and shallower thoracic proportions than the latter. This was all the more remarkable in that the increased size of the Hawaiian born favored the expectation of a larger if not a relatively deeper chest. Returning to our comparisons of Hawaiian born and immigrants by prefecture, we find a repetition of this pattern. Each group of Hawaiian born reveals a tendency toward narrower chests, a still more definite change toward shallower chests and consequently a lower thoracic index. In the case of Yamaguchi there is an apparent exception, for here the Hawaiian born show no change from the immigrants. But closer inspection reveals that the Yamaguchi immigrants have anticipated the changes characteristic of the Hawaiian born. We have, therefore, a situation in which the Yamaguchi Hawaiian born agree with the other groups of Hawaiian born but statistically is undifferentiated from its immigrant group.

The diameters of the cephalic vault of the Hawaiian born display, in general, profound alterations from the dimensions of the immigrants. The greatest change is in the marked decrease in the head length of the Hawaiian born. Contrariwise, the head width is greatly expanded. A slight but consistent increase in head height also occurs. These cephalic modifications, equally apparent in the total series of Hawaiian born, are consistent and convincing in the prefectural comparisons between Hawaiian born and immigrants. The apparent exception in the Yamaguchi group is merely another illustration of what has already been pointed out. The absence of a significant change here is the result of the atypical position of the Yamaguchi immigrants. Their deviation from their total group mean is in the direction taken by the Hawaiian born. Consequently, the Yamaguchi Hawaiian born, although conforming to its total group means, is also practically identical with the Yamaguchi immigrants.

As a consequence of the changes in the cephalic dimensions of the Hawaiian born, the cephalic proportions likewise undergo significant modifications. The Hawaiian born groups are more brachycephalic than the immigrants. They are also relatively higher headed. The breadth-height index, however, does not follow any consistent change. Its variations in the Hawaiian born groups fall within the normal limits of the immigrants. The lack of any profound change in the cephalic and length-height indices of the Yamaguchi Hawaiian born is explained by previous comments on their cephalic diameters. This analysis of the cephalic vault by prefectures supports the results of the comparisons by total series.

As in the case of the total Hawaiian born compared with the total immigrants, the prefectural groups of Hawaiian born show a slight but insignificant change in minimum frontal diameter from the averages of the associated groups of immigrants.

The fronto-parietal index of the various Hawaiian born groups registers the effect of the quite large increment in head width. The Hawaiian born groups are exceptionally homogeneous in this index. They are all lower than the immigrant groups individually and collectively.

Comparing the Hawaiian born and the immigrants by prefecture, we find a definite tendency on the part of the former toward narrower face widths. The apparent exception in the case of Yamaguchi finds its explanation in the position of the Yamaguchi immigrants which here approximates the Hawaiian born. In this reduction of face width, the individual Hawaiian born groups follow the direction indicated by the total series. As a result of these decreases in face width combined with noteworthy increases in the head width the Hawaiian born groups display cephalo-facial means which are significantly lower than the corresponding ones for the immigrant groups.

Although both the bizygomatic width and the minimum frontal diameter of the Hawaiian born have suffered slight decreases, the reduction in the former dimension is relatively greater. This results in giving the Hawaiian born groups slightly higher zygo-frontal indices than the immigrants. The superiority of the Hawaiian born, however, is statistically significant neither by prefectural comparison nor by total series.

The bigonial diameter in the various Hawaiian born groups is slightly narrower than in the corresponding immigrants. The difference is of no statistical importance although it is consistent. The zygo-gonial index does not appear to have undergone any fixed modification among the Hawaiian born.

In the height of the forehead the Hawaiian born groups show equally great minus and plus fluctuations from the means of the immigrants, but in neither case have they any statistical validity. The innate variability of this character is among the highest on our list, judged by the standard deviation and the probable error. The fluctuations, therefore, seem most reasonably to be a function of a large inherent variability.

It was in the length of the total and upper face that the immigrants departed most decisively from their sedentes. Among the Hawaiian born groups, however, it is doubtful whether or not a real deviation from the immigrants can be detected. Although in relation to the total series of immigrants, each of the Hawaiian born groups has a slightly shorter total face length, the decrease is not significant save in the case of the Kyushu Hawaiian born. Moreover, none of the Hawaiian born groups is significantly shorter faced than the respective immigrants. In the upper face there is no significant or even consistent difference between the two groups.

The facial indices, likewise, show no valid statistical deviations among the Hawaiian born groups.

In the dimensions of the nose the Hawaiian born and the immigrant groups are much alike, except in the nasal width. In this dimension the narrowing previously observed in the immigrants is carried even further among the Hawaiian born. The effect of this decrease in nasal width is carried over into the nasal index which in the Hawaiian born becomes significantly lower.

The relationship of nose salient to the nasal height is unchanged in the Hawaiian born. But in the proportion of nose length to nose height there appears to be some indication of a slight change among the Hawaiian born in the decrease of the relative length of the nose.

For inter-ocular width each Hawaiian born group is greater than the mean of the total series of immigrants, but only significantly in the case of Kyushu. In comparison with the respective immigrant groups the trends are mixed partly owing to deviations among the immigrant groups. The bi-ocular width can not be said to show in the Hawaiian born any consistent trend from the means of the immigrants.

C. ANALYSIS OF FEMALE PREFECTURAL GROUPS

1. Sedentes and Immigrants

Turning now to the comparison of female sedentes, immigrants and Hawaiian born within each prefectural grouping, we may follow each progression in Tables 130–144 and in Figs. 18–25. The distributions of the x p.e.'s in these tables make it abundantly clear that the differences between sedentes and immigrants, immigrants and Hawaiian born, and sedentes and Hawaiian born within each prefecture are of a much higher order than the horizontal differences between any two prefectural groups of sedentes, immigrants or Hawaiian born. To this extent the progressive changes revealed in the total series are corroborated in the component prefectural sub-divisions.

If the graphs presented in Figs. 18–21 are examined in detail, the following pattern becomes evident. The local groups of immigrant women are heavier and tend to have slightly greater statures than their respective sedentes. The absolute sitting height and trunk length which in the immigrant males showed a definite movement toward decreased dimensions, here displays a variable tendency dependent on the degree of increase in stature, with the result that some prefectural groups of immigrant women have greater sitting heights and trunk lengths than their sedentes while others have shorter ones. When, however, we examine the relative sitting height and relative trunk length the female conformity to the male pattern

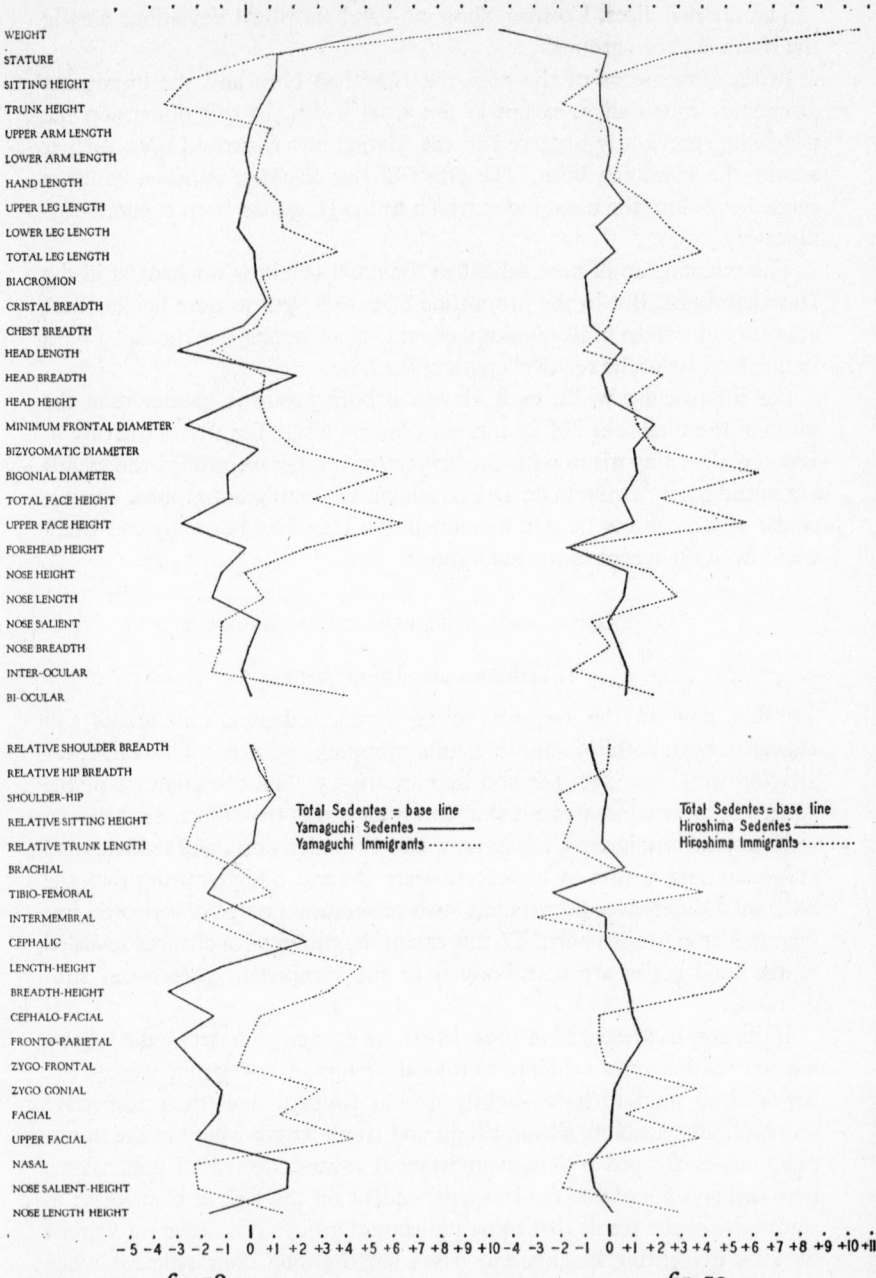

WEIGHT
STATURE
SITTING HEIGHT
TRUNK HEIGHT
UPPER ARM LENGTH
LOWER ARM LENGTH
HAND LENGTH
UPPER LEG LENGTH
LOWER LEG LENGTH
TOTAL LEG LENGTH
BIACROMION
CRISTAL BREADTH
CHEST BREADTH
HEAD LENGTH
HEAD BREADTH
HEAD HEIGHT
MINIMUM FRONTAL DIAMETER
BIZYGOMATIC DIAMETER
BIGONIAL DIAMETER
TOTAL FACE HEIGHT
UPPER FACE HEIGHT
FOREHEAD HEIGHT
NOSE HEIGHT
NOSE LENGTH
NOSE SALIENT
NOSE BREADTH
INTER-OCULAR
BI-OCULAR

RELATIVE SHOULDER BREADTH
RELATIVE HIP BREADTH
SHOULDER-HIP
RELATIVE SITTING HEIGHT
RELATIVE TRUNK LENGTH
BRACHIAL
TIBIO-FEMORAL
INTERMEMBRAL
CEPHALIC
LENGTH-HEIGHT
BREADTH-HEIGHT
CEPHALO-FACIAL
FRONTO-PARIETAL
ZYGO-FRONTAL
ZYGO GONIAL
FACIAL
UPPER FACIAL
NASAL
NOSE SALIENT-HEIGHT
NOSE LENGTH HEIGHT

Total Sedentes = base line
Yamaguchi Sedentes ———
Yamaguchi Immigrants ·········

Total Sedentes = base line
Hiroshima Sedentes ———
Hiroshima Immigrants ·········

-5 -4 -3 -2 -1 0 +1 +2 +3 +4 +5 +6 +7 +8 +9 +10 -4 -3 -2 -1 0 +1 +2 +3 +4 +5 +6 +7 +8 +9 +10 +11

fig. 18   *fig. 19*

Deviation of Yamaguchi Female Immigrants from Yamaguchi Female Sedentes   *Deviation of Hiroshima Female Immigrants from Hiroshima Female Sedentes*

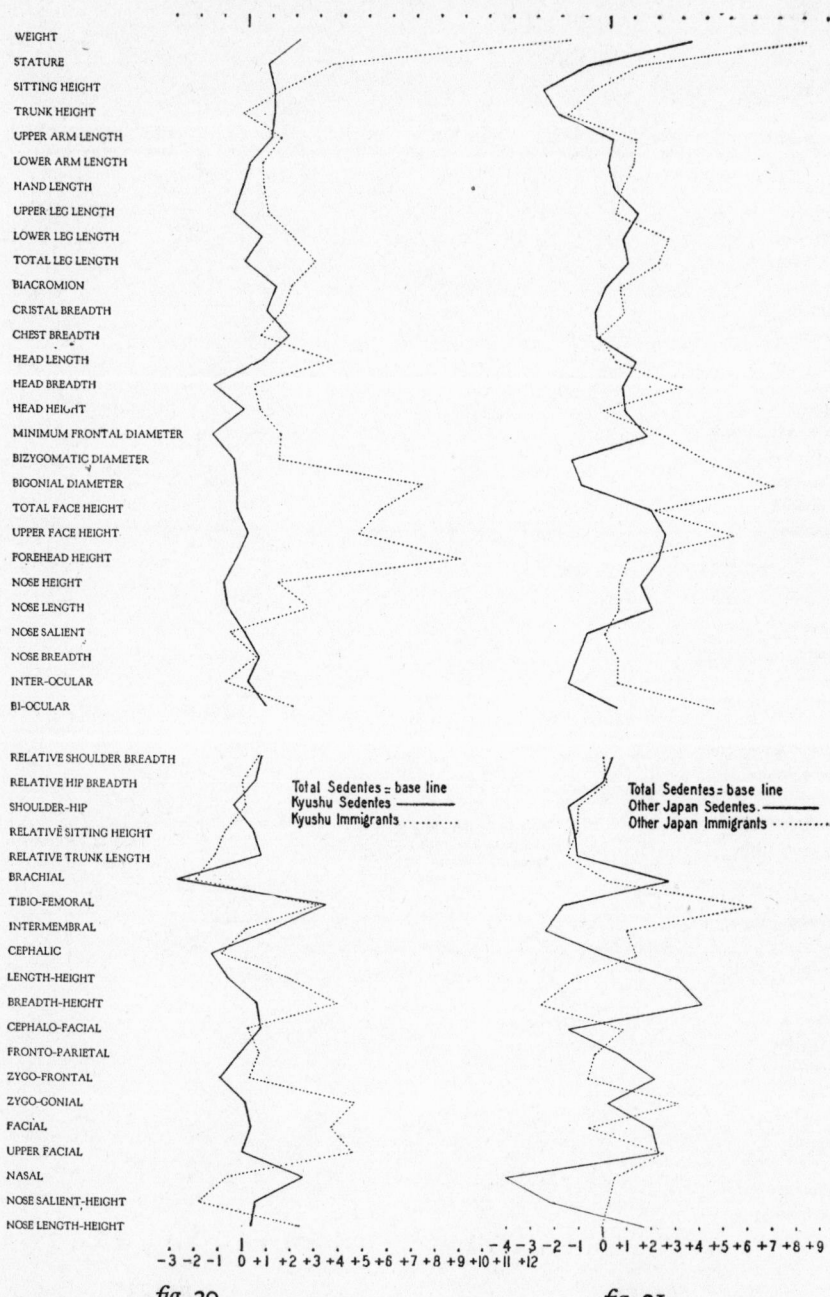

WEIGHT
STATURE
SITTING HEIGHT
TRUNK HEIGHT
UPPER ARM LENGTH
LOWER ARM LENGTH
HAND LENGTH
UPPER LEG LENGTH
LOWER LEG LENGTH
TOTAL LEG LENGTH
BIACROMION
CRISTAL BREADTH
CHEST BREADTH
HEAD LENGTH
HEAD BREADTH
HEAD HEIGHT
MINIMUM FRONTAL DIAMETER
BIZYGOMATIC DIAMETER
BIGONIAL DIAMETER
TOTAL FACE HEIGHT
UPPER FACE HEIGHT
FOREHEAD HEIGHT
NOSE HEIGHT
NOSE LENGTH
NOSE SALIENT
NOSE BREADTH
INTER-OCULAR
BI-OCULAR

RELATIVE SHOULDER BREADTH
RELATIVE HIP BREADTH
SHOULDER-HIP
RELATIVE SITTING HEIGHT
RELATIVE TRUNK LENGTH
BRACHIAL
TIBIO-FEMORAL
INTERMEMBRAL
CEPHALIC
LENGTH-HEIGHT
BREADTH-HEIGHT
CEPHALO-FACIAL
FRONTO-PARIETAL
ZYGO-FRONTAL
ZYGO-GONIAL
FACIAL
UPPER FACIAL
NASAL
NOSE SALIENT-HEIGHT
NOSE LENGTH-HEIGHT

Total Sedentes = base line
Kyushu Sedentes ————
Kyushu Immigrants ....

Total Sedentes = base line
Other Japan Sedentes ————
Other Japan Immigrants ··········

-3 -2 -1 0 +1 +2 +3 +4 +5 +6 +7 +8 +9 +10 +11 +12

-4 -3 -2 -1 0 +1 +2 +3 +4 +5 +6 +7 +8 +9

fig. 20

fig. 21

Deviation of Kyushu Female Immigrants from Kyushu Female Sedentes

Deviation of 'Other Japan' Female Immigrants from 'Other Japan' Female Sedentes

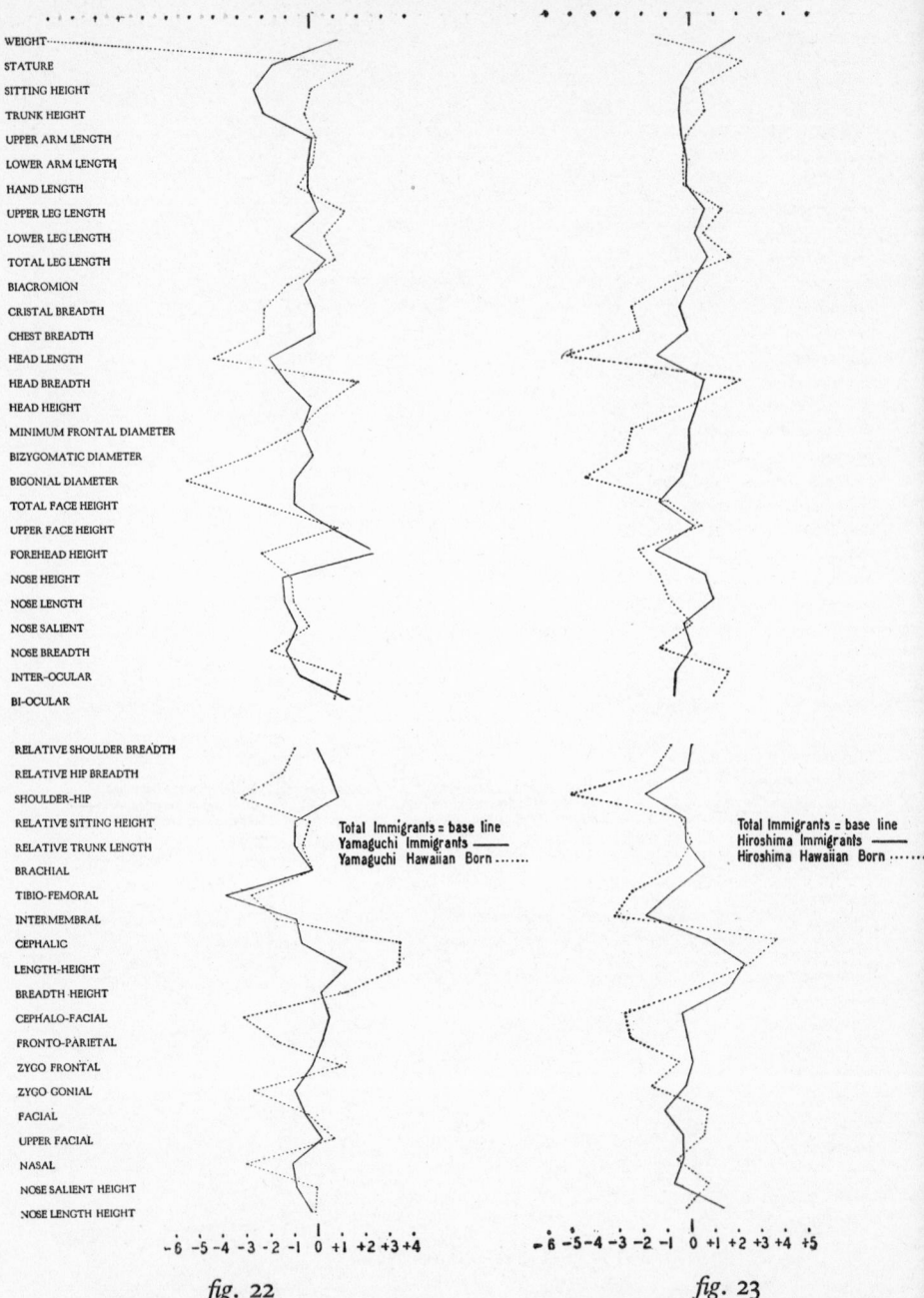

fig. 22

Deviation of Yamaguchi Hawaiian Born Females from Yamaguchi Immigrant Females

fig. 23

Deviation of Hirsohima Hawaiian Born
Females from Hiroshima Immigrant Females

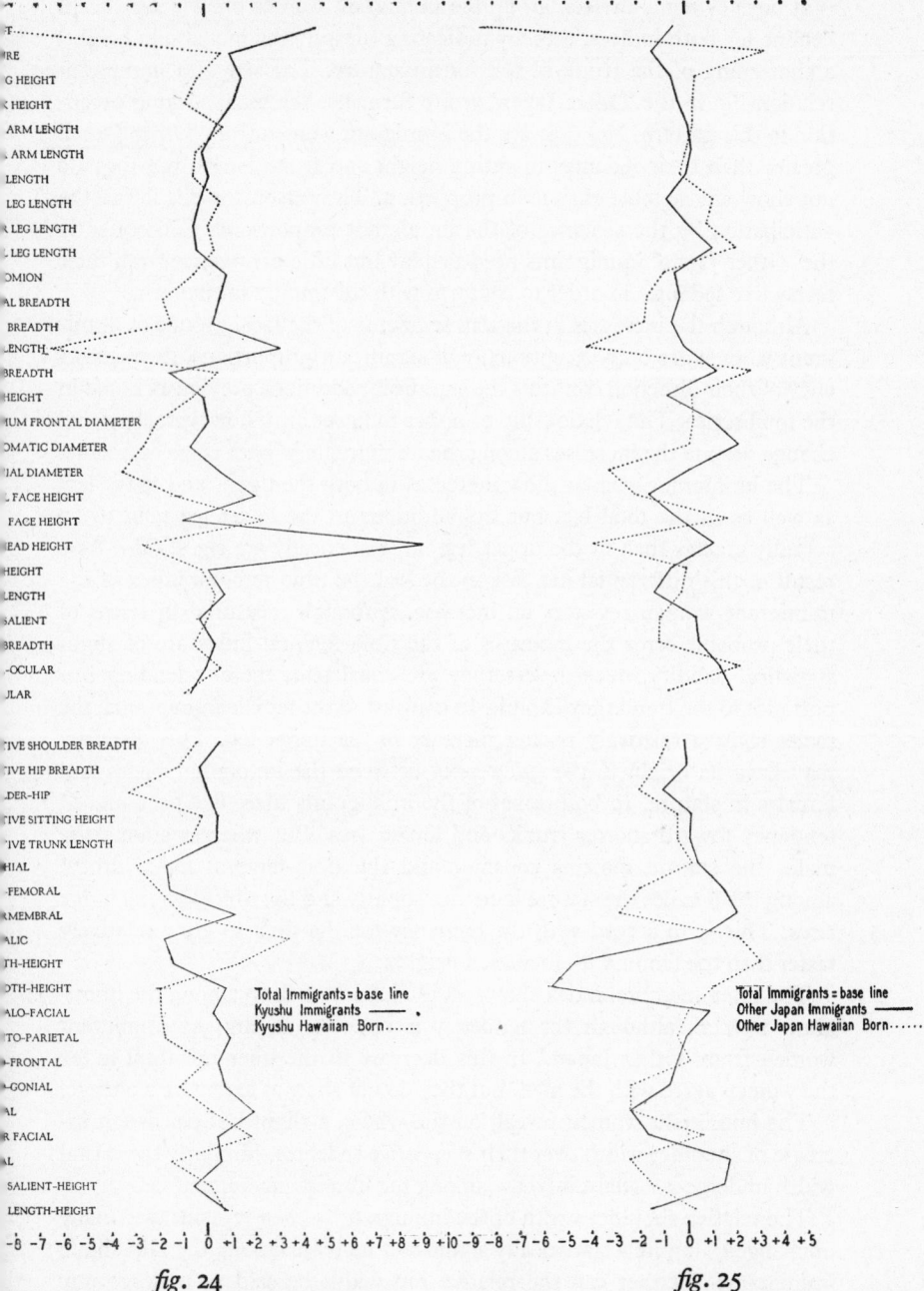

T
RE
G HEIGHT
K HEIGHT
ARM LENGTH
ARM LENGTH
LENGTH
LEG LENGTH
LEG LENGTH
LEG LENGTH
OMION
AL BREADTH
BREADTH
LENGTH
BREADTH
HEIGHT
IUM FRONTAL DIAMETER
OMATIC DIAMETER
IAL DIAMETER
FACE HEIGHT
FACE HEIGHT
EAD HEIGHT
HEIGHT
LENGTH
SALIENT
BREADTH
OCULAR
ULAR

IVE SHOULDER BREADTH
IVE HIP BREADTH
DER-HIP
IVE SITTING HEIGHT
IVE TRUNK LENGTH
HIAL
FEMORAL
RMEMBRAL
ALIC
TH-HEIGHT
OTH-HEIGHT
ALO-FACIAL
TO-PARIETAL
FRONTAL
GONIAL
AL
R FACIAL
AL
SALIENT-HEIGHT
LENGTH-HEIGHT

Total Immigrants = base line
Kyushu Immigrants ——— .
Kyushu Hawaiian Born.......

Total Immigrants = base line
Other Japan Immigrants ———
Other Japan Hawaiian Born.......

-8 -7 -6 -5 -4 -3 -2 -1 0 +1 +2 +3 +4 +5 +6 +7 +8 +9 +10 -9 -8 -7 -6 -5 -4 -3 -2 -1 0 +1 +2 +3 +4 +5

fig. 24

fig. 25

viation of Kyushu Hawaiian Born Fe-
les from Kyushu Immigrant Females

Deviation of 'Other Japan' Hawaiian Born
Females from 'Other Japan' Immigrant
Females

is at once evident. In each group the immigrant women show a significant decline for both indices, thereby indicating (despite the increase in height) a shortening of the trunk in relation to stature. The sedentes-immigrant relationship in the 'Other Japan' group furnishes the most striking exception to this pattern. Not only are the immigrant women from 'Other Japan' greater than their sedentes in sitting height and trunk length but they do not show any notable change in proportion. The reason for this lies in the anticipation by the sedentes of the immigrant proportions. Consequently the 'Other Japan' immigrants need display but little divergence from their respective sedentes in order to conform with the immigrant pattern.

Although the increases in the arm segments of the local groups of immigrant women are only exceptionally of significant proportions, the consistency of their direction confirms the significant additions previously noted in the total series. The relationship of upper to lower arm, however, shows no change despite the increases among the immigrants in both these segments.

The immigrant women show increases in both the upper and lower leg, as well as in the total leg, but the additions to the lower leg tend to be actually greater than to the upper leg and statistically are significant. As a result of this differential increase in the leg, the tibio-femoral index of the immigrant women registers an increase. Although measured in terms of their probable error the increases of the tibio-femoral index are of slight statistical validity, nevertheless they are consistent, thereby lending importance to the trend they exhibit. In contrast to the female immigrants, the males show a relatively greater increase in the upper leg. This disparity may have its origin in the differences between the immigrant males and females in stature. In both sexes of the immigrants there is a pronounced tendency toward shorter trunks and longer legs. But whereas among the males the stature remains constant and the tibio-femoral index drops, among the females the stature increases slightly and the tibio-femoral index rises. This is in accord with the tendency for the tibia to grow relatively faster than the femur with increased heights.

The inter-membral index shows an inclination to drop among the immigrant women, although the tendency is opposite among the immigrant women from 'Other Japan.' In this decrease in the inter-membral index the women agree with the men, but they do not show as extensive a change.

The immigrant women reveal, on the whole, a slight but consistent increase of shoulder width over their respective sedentes. Similarly the cristal width undergoes a slight increase among the immigrant women.

The relative shoulder width of the immigrant women remains essentially unchanged, despite a statistically significant increase among the Hiroshima immigrants. Neither can the relative hip width be said to undergo any definite alteration in the immigrant women. It follows, therefore, that the relationship of shoulder to hip likewise remains fixed among the immigrant women.

These female immigrant proportions of the shoulder and hip to stature and to each other show tendencies contrary to those displayed among the male immigrants. The differences are brought about by the slight increases in stature and hip width among the female immigrants in contrast to the slight decrease and unchanged stature of the male immigrants.

The chest width appears to remain unchanged among the various groups of immigrant women despite some minor fluctuations.

The statistically insignificant variations of the head length of the female immigrant groups from their respective sedentes fall into no significant pattern. In head width, however, each group of immigrant women is invariably greater than the total and with one exception the respective local groups of sedentes. The one exception occurs for Yamaguchi. An examination of the Yamaguchi graph discloses that the Yamaguchi sedentes are eccentric in head width. The increases in head width do not, however, reach significant size in any prefectural pair. Head height, however, in the various prefectural groups of immigrant women except in those from 'Other Japan' do disclose well defined increases over their sedentes.

The slightly increased head widths of the immigrant women effect no marked change in the cephalic indices. With the exception of Yamaguchi, the prefectural immigrants reveal only slight increases. The Yamaguchi immigrants, on the contrary, decrease in cephalic index almost to the conventional point of significance, but this may be read not as a significant departure of the Yamaguchi immigrants from the means of their cogeners but as a marked deviation on the part of the Yamaguchi sedentes.

The length-height and breadth-height indices increase in each group of immigrant women except in the group from 'Other Japan.' The increases in both indices of the Yamaguchi and in the length-height of the Hiroshima immigrants are significant.

The minimum frontal diameter increases significantly in the Yamaguchi immigrant women and to a lesser degree in the immigrants from Kyushu and 'Other Japan.' Although the Hiroshima immigrants have slightly narrower minimum frontal diameters than their sedentes, nevertheless they have wider diameters than the total series of sedentes. The consistency therefore of this trend if not its magnitude supports the recognition of a slight expansion in the minimum frontal diameter of the immigrant women.

The effect of variation in the local groups of sedentes on these comparisons is well displayed in the fronto-parietal index. The Yamaguchi immigrants show a significant increase, the Hiroshima immigrants a significant decrease and the Kyushu and 'Other Japan' immigrants minor differences only. The first two differences may be explained by the large deviations, respectively negative and positive, on the part of the sedentes. Actually the immigrant groups are all closely grouped about the mean for the total series of sedentes. In view of these facts, it can not be unequivocally affirmed that the immigrants display any consistent trend toward change in their fronto-parietal index. Nor does the statistical significance of the differences in the Yamaguchi and Hiroshima comparisons effect the present problem.

Although the expansion of the bizygomatic width among the immigrant women attains statistical significance only in the case of 'Other Japan,' the unanimity of increase in each local group falls in with the significant increase in the total series of immigrant women.

The cephalo-facial indices of the immigrant groups remain essentially similar to the mean of the total sedentes women, although in the case of Yamaguchi the immigrants show a significant rise over the sedentes. Taking all the local pairs no definite trend is discernible. The differences may be discounted by the heterogeneity of the sedentes.

Similarly the zygo-frontal index of the immigrant women shows no definite alteration despite conflicting variations among the prefectural pairs.

In the bigonial diameter we encounter a prodigious expansion among all the local groups of immigrant women. Although the male immigrants likewise exhibited an increase in bigonial diameter, they fell far behind the women in the extent of this modification.

As a result of the disproportionate increase in bigonial diameter, the zygo-gonial index undergoes a marked increase in the immigrant groups of women, individually and collectively.

One of the most significant differences between the male sedentes and immigrants occurs in the height of the face. Here, too, among the immigrant females we discern a parallel increase in both total and upper face height. The increase in the upper face, however, is absolutely greater and statistically more significant than the addition to the total face. The lack of any appreciable increase in the total face height of the immigrant women from 'Other Japan' appears to be the result of a deviation of the 'Other Japan' sedentes toward the level of the immigrants.

Even though the bizygomatic diameter has expanded in the immigrant women, this expansion has not been proportionate to the increase in the face height. Consequently we find that there is a disproportionate modification in both facial indices of the immigrant women. The upper facial index however increases more definitely than does the total facial index. Indeed, in the comparisons for the total facial index the immigrants from 'Other Japan' display an actual decrease in the total facial index. In this instance we may remember that the immigrants from 'Other Japan' had exceptionally large increases in the bizygomatic diameter and the corresponding sedentes deviated toward the immigrant means in face height. This conjunction may be regarded as accidental or as indicative of a peculiarity of the subjects from 'Other Japan.'

In spite of the impressive addition to the forehead height of the Kyushu immigrant women, the character of the deviations among the other immigrant groups merely serves to emphasize the eccentricity of the Kyushu immigrants and to support the absence of any significant modification in forehead height.

The extension of the upper face, so notable both in the male and female immigrants, seems to have influenced the nose height of which it is a part and the nose length as well. In the Yamaguchi, Hiroshima and Kyushu groups the immigrant women have greater nose heights and nose lengths than the sedentes. The contrary is true for the immigrant women from 'Other Japan,' but this decrease is not so much an expression of a tendency toward shorter noses among the immigrants as it is a marked superiority of the local sedentes over the means of the total series of sedentes.

Aside from 'Other Japan' each prefectural pair display a definite trend to greater increase in nose length than in nose height among the immigrants. The consequence of this disproportionate increase is manifested in the nose length-nose height index in which the immigrant women show an advance over the sedentes.

The salient of the nose of the immigrant women shows some tendency toward a reduction, but again the immigrant women from 'Other Japan' form an exception. The extensions of nasal height and the slight decrease in nasal salient combine to produce significant decreases in the nose salient-nose height index in all the immigrant groups except in that from 'Other Japan.'

No consistent or significant change is perceptible in the breadth of the nose among the immigrant women, but by virtue of a modest increase in nasal height a slight tendency toward lower nasal indices finds expression in the three immigrant groups which have shown parallel changes in relation to their sedentes. The immigrant women from 'Other Japan' as in other nasal dimensions and proportions constitute an exception.

For the inter-ocular and bi-ocular widths the immigrant women have narrower diameters in the former and wider ones in the latter.

2. Immigrants and Hawaiian Born

The preceding analysis of female immigrant-sedentes comparisons by prefecture confirms in all essential points the results obtained from similar comparisons of the total series. There still remains the consideration of the Hawaiian born females grouped according to prefecture of origin.

In Tables 135–139 the various Hawaiian born groups of females arranged by prefecture are compared with their respective immigrant groups. The differences between these diverse pairs are graphed in Figs. 22–25 as in the preceding ones; that is, both the Hawaiian born and the immigrants of the same prefecture are plotted against a base line of total immigrants.

The graphs indicate that the Hawaiian born females, regardless of prefecture of origin, are much lighter in weight than their immigrant groups. Bearing in mind the considerable age discrepancy between Hawaiian born and immigrants, one might justifiably question the reality of this reduction in weight. But on examining the age tables we find confirmation of the reduced weight of Hawaiian born women contrasted with immigrant women. Then comparing the two groups for the decade from 20 to 30 years, we again find the Hawaiian born are appreciably less in weight. Perhaps we are confronted here with the effect of culture contact and the adoption by the Hawaiian born women of American fashions in dieting for slimness of figure.

The stature of the Hawaiian born groups enjoys an increase of varying statistical significance except in the case of the Kyushu Hawaiian born. This group is very slightly shorter than the Kyushu immigrants and at the same time taller than the mean for the total immigrants. In this connection it is perhaps worthy of notice that the Kyushu immigrants are taller than any other immigrant group.

Parallel to these increases in stature run the increases in the sitting and trunk heights of the Hawaiian born with the consequent result that the relative sitting heights and relative trunk heights remain unchanged. This change in the absolute dimensions of a proportion which itself remains undisturbed I have previously called proportionate. I have already emphasized a similar proportionate change in the male Hawaiian born groups. It is interesting to observe that the Hawaiian born Kyushu group is exceptional once more in that the sitting and trunk heights undergo reductions rather than increases with a moderate tendency toward lower relative sitting and trunk heights. This apparent reversal of trend in a single group is, however, more apparent than real. For if we consult Fig. 10 and Tables 100–105 wherein the various Hawaiian born prefectures are compared, we find in these characters no significant deviation of the Kyushu Hawaiian born from the other groups. Moreover, a close study of the comparative behavior of the Hawaiian born and immigrants from Kyushu emphasizes the importance of the deviations of the Kyushu immigrants in reading the position of the Kyushu Hawaiian born.

If we compare the results of these prefectural comparisons with those from the study of the total series and the age series, certain discrepancies are at once noticeable. In the total series the Hawaiian born females are significantly taller than the immigrants but show no change in trunk and sitting height. The disproportion, however, is not sufficiently great to do more than slightly lower the relative sitting and trunk heights.

The Hawaiian born females of 20–29 years of age compared with immigrants of equivalent age reveal in the former a slight increase in stature, a greater increase in sitting height, and, again a slight increase in trunk height. The effect of these modifications on the body proportions is enough to produce a significant increase in the relative sitting height of the Hawaiian born but only a slight rise in relative trunk height. In the age series, contrary, therefore, to the results of the prefectural comparisons there is some indication of a disproportionate increase in sitting height among Hawaiian born females.

Little, if any, change from the dimensions of the immigrants is discernible in the upper and lower arm lengths of the various Hawaiian born groups. In other words, the Hawaiian born maintain the slight increases in length previously observed in comparing immigrants with sedentes. The hand length, on the contrary, of two Hawaiian born groups (Yamaguchi and Kyushu) has undergone a significant decrease from the means of the respective sedentes. And in all the Hawaiian born groups the mean hand length shows some reduction. This reduction in hand length also appears when each Hawaiian born group is plotted against the total immigrant series. As additional indications of this modification, similar changes may be cited in the total and age series.

From the absence of significant change in the lengths of the upper and lower arm among the Hawaiian born, it follows that the brachial index likewise will reveal no marked swing from the means of the various immigrant groups. Actually, the Hawaiian born and immigrants from Yamaguchi are identical. In each of the other three pairs a slight drop in the brachial index appears, but in no case is it a significant one.

The above discussion on the stature and trunk height leads us to anticipate definite, if not significant, increases in the leg lengths of the Hawaiian born groups. These we do in reality find. In the total series of Hawaiian born females similar increases are apparent, but their significance is enhanced by the smaller probable errors. The means of the 20–29 year groups in the age series, however, yield no support for an increase in total leg length of however slight a degree. This contradiction follows from the previous observations of a disproportionate increase in sitting height in the Hawaiian born of the 20–29 year old group.

The proportion of tibia to femur undergoes no alteration in the Hawaiian born prefectural groups, thereby agreeing closely with the total series.

The slight increases in the leg lengths of the diverse Hawaiian born prefectural groups, combined with the absence of change or slight decreases in the arm lengths, yield lower inter-membral indices in each Hawaiian born group. These decreases, however, are worthy of particular comment, not because of their statistical validity, but because of the consistency of their trend. Not only are the means of the Hawaiian born groups lower than their respective sedentes, however slightly, but in each case they are also lower than the total immigrant mean. The decrease in the total series of Hawaiian born is, however, large enough to reach significance.

The three following dimensions, biacromion, chest breadth and cristal width, are measures of the width of the body at various levels from shoulder to hip. And at each we find a definite reduction in the Hawaiian born. This narrowing down of the torso of the Hawaiian born females is exceptionally consistent in each comparison, for age, prefecture or total series. The graphs of the prefectural comparisons clearly demonstrate the unanimity of this trend among Hawaiian born who are, in each prefectural pair, narrower than both their respective immigrants and the total immigrants. In general, the reduction in shoulder width is less significant statistically than are the decreases in chest and hip width.

Not only is the reduction of the shoulder width less in terms of probable error than that of the hip width, but in absolute size as well there is a differential narrowing at these levels. This is apparent in the indices of these dimensions. In both shoulder and hip the reductions in the Hawaiian born are sufficient to lower both relative shoulder breadth and relative hip breadth significantly, but the decrease in relative hip breadth is greater. This disproportionate decrease is evident from the marked decline in the shoulder-hip index. Examination of the total series confirms these modifications in the proportions of the Hawaiian born females.

Turning now to the cephalic and facial measurements and proportions, we find a striking alteration in the cephalic dimensions of the Hawaiian born. They have invariably shorter and broader heads than the immigrants. To this extent our findings agree with the results from comparisons of the total series. The significance, however, of these modifications in the prefectural comparisons are statistically of less validity, but their consistency is sufficiently impressive. Moreover, in each prefectural comparison the deviations of the Hawaiian born are consistent not only in relation to their respective immigrants but to the total immigrants as well.

The homogeneity of behavior of the Hawaiian born in head length and breadth changes does not extend to head height. For example, the total series of Hawaiian born has moderately, but not significantly, higher heads than the immigrants. Among the diverse prefectural groups of Hawaiian born, on the other hand, some have slightly higher heads than the immigrants, others have slightly lower ones and the relationship of these to the base line of total immigrants is equally mixed. In other words, the statistically insignificant increase in the head height of the total series is not carried out consistently in the prefectural comparisons.

The indices derived from these cephalic dimensions of the Hawaiian born prefectural groups behave according to expectation. The cephalic indices of the Hawaiian born groups are significantly greater than those of the corresponding immigrants or of the total series. Thus far the prefectural Hawaiian born agree with the total and age series. But in the comparisons of length-height and breadth-height indices they part company. The prefectural groups of Hawaiian born in general display no significant change from their respective immigrants, whereas the total series of Hawaiian born have significantly greater length-height and breadth-height indices. On examining the prefectural groups more closely we may discern a certain trend in the length-height index which brings it into greater conformity with the total series. This trend lies in the consistency of the positions of the various Hawaiian born prefectural groups in relation to the total immigrants. Although their superiority over their corresponding prefectural immigrants is significant only for 'Other Japan,' each group of Hawaiian born is superior to the total series of immigrants.

Although the slight reduction of the minimum frontal diameter visible in the Hawaiian born of each prefectural group nowhere reaches significant proportions, nevertheless the fact that these very minor decreases are associated with a significant increase in head width serve to lower to some degree the fronto-parietal index in all four prefectural groups of Hawaiian born and in two instances, significantly. The pattern is identical in the total series.

In each prefectural group of Hawaiian born females we encounter a bizygomatic breadth diminished from the mean of the corresponding immigrants. These decreases, however, are not of significant proportions and only derive a certain validity from their consistency with each other and with the total series. But in combination with the considerable increases in head width they yield cephalo-facial indices which, except for 'Other Japan,' are significantly lower than those of the immigrants of the corresponding prefectures. Comparing these prefectural comparisons with those for the total and age series, we again discover a close similarity.

The proportionate decreases in both the minimum frontal and bizygomatic diameters of the diverse Hawaiian born groups result in leaving these groups unchanged in the zygo-frontal index. These conclusions also follow closely the comparisons of the total and age series.

The refinement, or to avoid gratuitous connotations, the narrowing of the face of the Hawaiian born which was evident in the minimum frontal and bizygomatic diameters is made completely consistent by the definite and the statistically satisfactory reduction in the bigonial diameter. This bigonial reduction is not only characteristic of the various prefectural groups of Hawaiian born, but in the total series it is the most notable statistical modification. It is of more than passing interest to recall that the lateral dimensions of the trunk undergo parallel decreases among the Hawaiian born. Moreover, this narrowing down of the face of the Hawaiian born runs contrary to the expansion in the head width.

In spite of the fact that all three lateral diameters of the face of the Hawaiian born females are reduced in dimension from those of the immigrants and that for the minimum frontal and the bizygomatic diameters these decreases are proportionate to each other, we find that the bigonial, in relation to the bizygomatic diameter, has suffered a disproportionate decrease. This may readily be seen in the comparisons for the zygo-gonial index. It is true that the reductions of this index in each prefectural group of Hawaiian born females from the corresponding immigrant means nowhere attain statistical validity, but by their accumulative effect and by their constancy below both the individual and total immigrant means they carry considerable weight. To this should be added the fact that the total series also displays a significant decrease in the zygo-gonial index.

The deviations of the Hawaiian born groups from their respective immigrants in the total and upper face heights are, statistically speaking, negligible. But before we dismiss them as unimportant, it is worth noting that in relation to the total immigrant means the Hawaiian born groups invariably have smaller total and greater upper face heights. Furthermore, we should recall at this point that the total series of Hawaiian born also shows a slight tendency toward smaller total face and larger upper face heights. I am, therefore, inclined to regard the statistically negligible changes in the prefectural groups of Hawaiian born as indicative of a real, if slight, trend.

From their effect on the total facial and upper facial indices, it is apparent that the slight changes in total face and upper face heights of the Hawaiian born are very slight indeed. None of the differences between Hawaiian born and immigrant by prefecture are significant. The deviations of the Hawaiian born groups from corresponding immigrants or from total immigrants show no consistent pattern for facial index. For the upper face index, however, the diverse Hawaiian born groups are consistent in that they are all higher than their corresponding immigrants and the total immigrant series. These observations on the facial and upper facial index of the prefectural groups also apply to the comparisons of the total series.

On examining the Hawaiian born and immigrants by prefecture, a well defined tendency appears for the diverse Hawaiian born groups to have lower foreheads. In the Kyushu series of Hawaiian born the forehead height drops 11.69 mm. which is 7.35 times its probable error. A similar reduction in the forehead height of the total series of Hawaiian born was previously observed. It will, of course, occur to the reader that this superiority of immigrant over Hawaiian born may be an effect of time for the immigrants are older than the Hawaiian born. When, however, we compare the Hawaiian born and immigrants of the same age, we find a repetition of this phenomenon, although the difference measured by the probable error is not as great.

Turning now to the various dimensions and proportions of the nose, we find that in the nose height and length the Hawaiian born groups are, in general, similar to the respective immigrants. When deviations occur, they are inconsistent as well as statistically insignificant. The slight reductions in the nose height and length of the total series of Hawaiian born are likewise of negligible degree.

It follows, therefore, that no real change in the nose length-nose height proportion would be expected in the various Hawaiian born groups. None, in fact, is found.

Similarly, the nasal salient remains essentially unchanged in the Hawaiian born prefectural groups. The nose salient-nose height proportion as a consequence is undisturbed.

The only indication of modification in the nasal dimensions of the Hawaiian born occurs in the nasal breadth. Each prefectural group of Hawaiian born have narrower noses than their corresponding immigrants. Although these decreases are, in general, insignificant, among the Hiroshima Hawaiian born the decrease does reach statistical significance. But more important is the homogeneity of the behavior of the various Hawaiian born groups. Each prefectural group of Hawaiian born has a narrower nose than its respective immigrant and total immigrant series. This nasal constriction among the Hawaiian born assumes, however, a much more significant aspect in the total series.

Although each Hawaiian born prefectural group has, according to expectation, a more leptorrhine nose than the immigrants, the drop in the mean index is minimized in significance by the magnitude of the accompanying probable error. These absolutely and relatively narrower noses of the Hawaiian born appear to acquire more status as significant modifications from their consistency than from the magnitude of their decrease in width.

The distance between the inner corners of the eyes—the inter-ocular distance—is increased among the Hawaiian born females. The magnitude of this increase is statistically significant only among the Hiroshima Hawaiian born, but each prefectural group of Hawaiian born exceeds both their respective immigrants and the total series of immigrants. Similar increases have already been observed in the total and age series of Hawaiian born.

The bi-ocular distance—the distance between the outer corners of the eyes—shows, on the contrary, no consistent nor significant change.

CHAPTER VI

Age Changes

THE bland and comforting assumption that after the attainment of maturity and before the onset of senility differences in age are of slight importance can no longer be regarded as axiomatic. Recent investigations of age changes during maturity have abundantly demonstrated that the period of maturity, instead of being a static resting phase after the completion of adolescent growth and before the onset of senescence, is in fact dynamic with subtle adjustments. The dimensions both of the body and of the head undergo changes throughout life. Some of these changes are infinitesimal during maturity; others during the same time span are considerable; and all proceed at a slower tempo than characterizes the changes during the earlier period of active growth. But although the changes during maturity are small compared with the rapid alterations of youth, the former continue for a longer duration of time.

Up to now we have treated our series as though they were strictly comparable in age. With that as a working assumption we have drawn from the preceding comparisons the concept of a selected immigrant group and of an Hawaiian sub-type, based on immigrant selection and modified by environment. But in actuality the sedentes, immigrants and Hawaiian born are not exactly comparable either in frequency of age groups or in average age. It becomes imperative, therefore, for the reasons briefly outlined above to re-examine these series and to determine whether or not the existing differences in age are accountable for the results obtained.

To make each of the three series comparable in age I divided them into decades. The resulting age distributions for each series are presented in the table on page 105.

It is at once observable that the three series differ radically in their age composition. The immigrants compared with the other series are more heavily weighted in the older decades. More than three-quarters of the Hawaiian born, on the contrary, are less than 30 years old. The reason is obvious. The generation of Japanese born in Hawaii is only just entering into maturity and it has consequently a paucity of individuals over 30 years

FREQUENCY DISTRIBUTIONS OF AGE GROUPS

Males

Age	Sedentes	Immigrants	Hawaiian Born
20–29	71	34	144
30–39	35	42	40
40–49	34	59	4
50–59	19	36	
60–64	13	7	
Total	172	178	188

Females

Age	Sedentes	Immigrants	Hawaiian Born
20–29	28	19	81
30–39	20	32	7
40–49	26	23	2
50–59	12	14	
60–64	5	1	
Total	91	89	90

of age. It follows from this concentration of the Hawaiian born in the first decade that if a particular character were associated with definite, progressive age changes, its total mean would be influenced by this overweighting of the younger age group.

The situation is similar for the female series. Whereas the first decade contains 81 of the Hawaiian born females, the second includes a mere 7, the third only 2 and the fourth and fifth none. The female immigrants and sedentes are rather more evenly distributed. But because the numbers are reduced no age group of female sedentes or immigrants is completely satisfactory as regards size. I have, therefore, in the following comparisons concentrated on the males, omitting entirely the female series.

Fortunately the numbers in the male age groups are more satisfactory. But here too certain omissions were necessary. Although the tables contain the complete array of age means, the graphs make use of only the first two decades of the Hawaiian born males, the first four of the male immigrants and all age groups of the male sedentes although the final period from 60 to 64 is but meagrely represented.

Since the curve of the adult Hawaiian born males is defined by only two points, the decades 20–29 and 30–39, its abbreviated course occasionally appears somewhat erratic. To orientate more securely not only this curve but that of the male sedentes as well, I have attached the curves of the adult sedentes and Hawaiian born males to those of the respective children. These latter are represented by Hawaiian born and sedentes male children from five years up to the beginning of the adult series at 20 years. There is no series of immigrant children because the immigrants are all adult. The reader will find these combined curves of male children and male adults in Figs. 26–75. The statistics from which these graphs were prepared unfortunately must be omitted for lack of space. The age distribution of the male children is given in the following table.

AGE DISTRIBUTION OF MALE CHILDREN

Age	Sedentes	Hawaiian Born
4–5	1	23
6–7	78	84
8–9	85	94
10–11	72	95
12–13	63	85
14–15	74	109
16–17	73	89
18–19	84	66
Total	530	645

I have avoided in the following analysis any discussion of age changes for their own sake. I hope to deal with them on another occasion. Here my purpose has been to test the validity of observed differences and similarities between the three total series of sedentes, immigrants and Hawaiian born by eliminating the effects of age variations. On the whole it seemed to me that the numbers in the various age groups neither warranted nor could support intricate mathematical treatment. I have, therefore, preferred to hold consistency as worthy of serious consideration even in the absence of statistical significance.

The obvious conclusion, after comparing the various series by corresponding age, is that age discrepancies have had little influence in producing the characteristic patterns formed by the total series. The extent of the agreement between the total series and the age comparisons may be roughly expressed in a percentage. Immigrants and sedentes, Hawaiian born and immigrants, and Hawaiian born and sedentes are each compared in 50 characters, making in all 150 comparisons. For each of these 150 trait comparisons we have two results, one obtained statistically from the total seriations, the other deduced from age curves. These may be in complete agreement, in partial agreement, in partial disagreement or in total disagreement. By calculating the percentages of each of these four kinds of agreements or disagreements, we may obtain a general conception of the degree to which the age and total seriations support each other. In no case were there any complete disagreements by which is meant significant or definite changes in opposite directions. Complete agreement occurred for 78% of the 150 traits and partial agreement in 14%. Partial disagreements, where a significant change was recorded by one method and no significant change by the other, was present in only 8% of the traits. It appears, therefore, that for 92% of the traits the results of the two methods of comparison were in complete or partial agreement. This seems to me abundant confirmation of the main outlines of our previous analyses, especially when the numerous variables are taken into consideration.

In the following table I have summarized the point by point comparisons of total and age seriations. All the changes indicated are taken to be significant except where a question mark follows in which case the change is appreciable but either insignificant by the strictest statistical criteria or inconsistent in the age curves. The absence of notable or significant change is represented simply by a line.

Although in general the age comparisons do confirm the previous conclusions drawn from the total seriations, nevertheless for certain traits discrepancies occur which suggest a reconsideration of tentative conclusions. In part these discrepancies are caused by the different tempo of the age changes during maturity, thus altering the relative position of the curves to each other; in part, by the fluctuations created by reduced numbers for the decadal means; and in part by the fact that the abbreviated curve of the Hawaiian born is compared with curves of longer spans which undergo shifts in late maturity. In some instances the adjustments made necessary by the age analyses are of very minor import; in a few the upset is rather more profound. The greatest number of the latter occur in the Hawaiian born-immigrant comparisons and the fewest in the immigrant-sedentes. A careful inspection of the following table discloses 12 instances in which significant changes are reduced to insignificance or insignificant differences magnified into significance.

Only one definite change occurs in the immigrant-sedentes pattern of differences. The significant reduction in the hip width of the total group of immigrants is not borne out by the age comparisons.

For the Hawaiian born-immigrant relationship the age comparisons suggest 7 corrections. Although the total means recorded no difference in hand length, the age curves reveal a slight but consistent increase among the Hawaiian born, thereby bringing the hand length into closer harmony with the changes observed for the other segments of the arm. The decreases in the chest width and depth noted in the total means of the Hawaiian born are disclosed as consequences of changes in the immigrants in later age groups unrepresented in the brief age curve of the Hawaiian born. Similarly the drop in the head height that takes place in the latter part of the immigrant age curve has lowered their total mean significantly below the Hawaiian born average. Actually no difference is discernible between the two

Measurement	Immigrants compared with Sedentes by — Total Series	Age	Hawaiian Born compared with Immigrants by — Total Series	Age	Hawaiian Born compared with Sedentes by — Total Series	Age
Weight	heavier	heavier	heavier ?	heavier	heavier	heavier
Stature	—	—	taller	taller	taller	taller
Sitting Height	shorter	shorter	greater	greater	greater	—
Trunk Height	shorter	shorter	greater	greater	—	—
Upper Arm Length	longer	longer	longer	longer	longer	longer
Lower Arm Length	longer	longer	longer	longer	longer	longer
Hand Length	longer	longer	—	longer	longer	longer
Upper Leg Length	longer	longer	longer	—	longer	longer
Lower Leg Length	longer	longer	longer	longer	longer	longer
Total Leg Length	longer	longer	longer	longer	longer	longer
Shoulder Width	wider	wider	wider	wider	wider	wider
Cristal Width	narrower ?	narrower	narrower ?	—	narrower	—
Chest Width	wider	wider ?	narrower	—	—	—
Chest Depth	less	less	less	—	less	less
Head Length	—	—	shorter	shorter	shorter	shorter
Head Width	wider ?	wider ?	wider	wider	wider	wider
Head Height	higher	higher	higher	—	higher	higher
Minimum Frontal Diameter	—	—	—	—	—	—
Bizygomatic Diameter	—	—	narrower ?	—	—	—
Bigonial Diameter	wider	wider	—	—	wider	wider ?
Total Face Height	higher	higher	shorter	shorter	higher	—

	1	2	3	4	5	6
Upper Face Height	higher	higher	—	—	higher	higher
Forehead Height	lower?	lower	—	—	lower	lower
Nose Height	greater	greater	—	greater?	greater	greater
Nose Length	longer	longer	—	longer?	longer	longer
Nose Salient	less	less	—	—	less	less
Nose Breadth	narrower	narrower	narrower	—	narrower	narrower
Inter-Ocular Width	narrower	narrower?	wider	—	—	—
Bi-Ocular Width	wider	wider	—	—	—	—
Index						
Relative Shoulder Width	higher	higher	—	—	higher	higher
Relative Hip Width	lower	—	lower	lower?	lower	lower
Shoulder-Hip	lower	lower	lower	lower	lower	lower
Relative Sitting Height	lower	lower	—	—	lower	lower
Relative Trunk Height	lower	lower	—	—	lower	lower
Thoracic	higher	lower	lower?	—	lower	lower
Brachial	lower?	higher	—	—	higher	higher
Tibio-Femoral	lower?	lower?	higher	higher	higher?	higher
Inter-Membral	lower	lower	—	—	lower	lower
Cephalic	—	—	higher	higher	higher	higher
Length-Height	higher	higher	higher	higher?	higher	higher
Breadth-Height	higher	higher	—	—	higher	higher
Cephalo-Facial	—	—	lower	lower	lower	lower
Fronto-Parietal	—	—	lower	lower?	lower?	lower?
Zygo-Frontal	—	—	higher?	—	higher?	—
Zygo-Gonial	higher	higher?	—	—	higher	higher

[Continued]

TABLE—*continued*]

Index	Immigrants compared with Sedentes by		Hawaiian Born compared with			
			Immigrants by		Sedentes by	
	Total Series	Age	Total Series	Age	Total Series	Age
Facial	higher	higher	—	lower	higher	higher
Upper Facial	higher	higher	—	lower ?	higher	higher
Nasal	lower	lower	lower		lower	lower
Nose Salient-Nose Height	lower	lower	—	—	lower	lower
Nose Length-Nose Height	higher	higher	lower	lower ?	higher	higher

series in the age groups in which both are represented. The nose breadth provides a parallel example. Here the Hawaiian born and immigrants are closely similar during the first two decades of maturity, but the nose breadth of the latter increases rapidly thereafter, raising their total mean above that of the Hawaiian born. The evidence, therefore, reveals no real change. In the inter-ocular width it is the marked decrease in the later decades of the immigrants which produces the false impression in the total means that the Hawaiian born have wider diameters than the immigrants. The total means for facial index yielded no significant difference, yet it is apparent from the age curves that the Hawaiian born tend to have lower indices than the immigrants at equivalent decades.

Finally, four emendations are required in the relationship of Hawaiian born to sedentes. In the sitting height the superiority of the total Hawaiian born mean is not corroborated by the age analysis. It is true that in the first decade the Hawaiian born have significantly greater sitting heights than the sedentes but in the next decade they are significantly lower. Similarly in the first decade of the age series the Hawaiian born are significantly narrower in cristal width than the sedentes, but are very slightly wider in the second decade. We can not, consequently, accept without qualification the implications of these total means. It should, however, be pointed out that the Hawaiian born boys are consistently narrower in hip width than are the sedentes.

The total face height presents a different situation. Here the eccentricity of the sedentes in the second decade strikes a discordant note in what otherwise would be a satisfactory interval. To clarify this I should add that in the first decade the Hawaiian born have significantly greater face heights than the sedentes which agrees with the earlier growth curves, but in the second decade the sedentes show an atypical increase which raises their mean for that period above the corresponding one for the Hawaiian born. Thereafter the sedentes subside to a position in line with the former level. Now, although the age curves except at one point strongly suggest the correctness of the conclusion drawn from the total series, namely that the Hawaiian born have greater total face heights than the sedentes, the reversal which occurs in the second decade introduces an element of doubt as to the reliability of the suggested increase.

In the relative hip width we see an example of the influence of age in enhancing a slight difference into a significant one. In the first two decades the age graphs reveal the Hawaiian born closing up the gap present during the earlier growth phase. Actually the superiority of the sedentes over the Hawaiian born becomes very slight by the beginning of maturity. But since the sedentes continue to increase all through maturity whereas the Hawaiian born are lacking in the later decades, the total mean of the sedentes significantly outstrips that of the Hawaiian born.

B. DETAILED COMPARISON OF MALE SEDENTES, IMMIGRANTS AND
HAWAIIAN BORN BY AGE[1]

Weight

The increase in weight characteristic of the middle aged in European populations appears to be absent among the Japanese males of all three groups. There is even a rapid decline in weight among the male sedentes after 39 years. Although the individual differences between the three groups are not statistically significant, the relationships between them in each adult decade are perfectly consistent with those of the total series. The Hawaiian born males are the heaviest, the immigrants are next and the sedentes are the lightest.

The superiority of the Hawaiian born over the sedentes extends backward only to the 16–17 year age level. Before that age the sedentes boys are slightly heavier than or equivalent to the Hawaiian born boys.

Stature

The slopes of the stature curves of the male adults indicate that stature progressively declines after the 20–29 decade. Among both the Hawaiian born and the sedentes the 18–19 year olds are the tallest of any age group. This does not necessarily mean that the 18–19 year olds represent the actual peak in the growth of stature. In all probability that eminence is attained in the early twenties, but it is not apparent here since the age intervals for adults are expanded from two years to decades, thereby masking the transition. Moreover, the progressive increase in the average stature for each successive generation which has been observed not only in Europe but in Japan as well may account for the peak at 18–19 years and the apparently sharp shrinkage in height during maturity.

It is evident from the graphs of growth in stature that the curve for the adult male sedentes is rather erratic during early maturity. The excessive drop in the 20–29 decade is probably due to inadequate sampling. Were the sedentes adjusted to fit its dominant curve, they would be slightly taller than the immigrants in the first two decades of maturity. Actually they fall below the immigrants in the first, third and fourth decades. The differences are however not very large. The superiority of the Hawaiian born over the immigrants is as definite as it is over the sedentes. In the latter comparison the Hawaiian born are consistently taller in each age group back to the 8–9 year level. At 6–7 years, on the contrary, the sedentes boys are taller than their contemporaries among the Hawaiian born.

1 Illustrative graphs for the ensuing discussion will be found at the end of this chapter.

Sitting Height

The decisively shorter sitting height of the adult male immigrants compared with the sedentes which occupied our interest in the earlier comparisons is again emphasized in these age groups. The difference would be even more striking if the mean of the sedentes for the 20–29 year decade were raised to fit the contour of the complete curve. The Hawaiian born male adults agree with the previous comparisons in their increase over the immigrants in sitting height. In the relationship of the Hawaiian born and sedentes, however, we encounter a contradiction. The total series of adult Hawaiian born yielded a mean significantly greater than that for the total series of sedentes. In the first decade of maturity the Hawaiian born have definitely greater sitting heights than the sedentes, but the positions are reversed in the second decade. This reversal is apparently caused by the earlier onset of reduction in sitting height among the Hawaiian born. Comparing the Hawaiian born and sedentes children we find that the sedentes have greater sitting heights before the 12–13 year level, but after that period the more rapid growth of the Hawaiian born places them considerably in advance of the sedentes. In other words, because of the longer period of growth in sitting height among the sedentes they are able to overtake the Hawaiian born and surpass them by the second decade of maturity.

Trunk Height

The trunk height repeats in all essentials the relationships observed for sitting height. Here also the adult male immigrants are shorter trunked than the sedentes, and the Hawaiian born males are longer than the immigrants. To this extent the graph confirms the comparison of the total series. But the equivalence of Hawaiian born and sedentes in the comparison of the total series actually occurs only during the first decade of maturity. Thereafter the sedentes surpass the Hawaiian born. Among the children we find a repetition of the curves for sitting height. Up to the 14–15 year level the sedentes have longer trunks, but thereafter the Hawaiian born exceed them. Again, we note that the longer continued growth in trunk height among the sedentes permits them eventually to overtake the Hawaiian born during the second decade of maturity.

Upper Arm Length

In general the curves for the upper arm lengths by decades agree with the results obtained from the total series. Thus, there is no consistent difference between the male immigrants and sedentes whereas the Hawaiian born males have longer upper arms than either the immigrants or sedentes.

The increased arm length of the Hawaiian born in comparison with the sedentes is maintained all through the growth period. The adult differences, therefore, are merely a continuation of childhood ones.

Lower Arm Length

In this middle segment of the total arm, we find that the Hawaiian born males again are longer than the sedentes and immigrants, but the immigrants now are intermediate between the sedentes and Hawaiian born.

Similarly the Hawaiian born boys are consistently superior in lower arm length to the sedentes.

Hand Length

In this distal segment of the arm the Hawaiian born adults continue to maintain a superiority over both the sedentes and the immigrants, while the immigrants are intermediate to Hawaiian born and sedentes. It should be observed that these differences although consistent are very small.

The superiority of the Hawaiian born adults over the sedentes has its counterpart throughout the entire growth period.

These comparisons of the age curves of the various arm segments may be said to confirm only to a limited extent the preceding results drawn from the total series. The progressive tendency toward increase from the upper arm to hand which was previously noted among the immigrants is less definite when studied by decades. The opposite trend among the Hawaiian born of successively less significant increases over the levels of the immigrants is, however, in large measure corroborated.

Upper Leg Length

In the length of the thigh the adult sedentes are definitely shorter than the immigrants and the Hawaiian born. These two latter, however, are not consistently different from each other. To this extent these curves fulfil the expectations derived from the study of the total series, but among the Hawaiian born and sedentes boys the relationship is reversed. Among them the sedentes are throughout most of the growth curve superior to the Hawaiian born. At the 8–9 year level the sedentes first jump ahead and they gradually increase their thigh length over the Hawaiian born until a maximum is reached at 16–17 years. Intimation of the renewal of the superiority of the Hawaiian born appears at the 18–19 year level. The greater thigh length of the adult Hawaiian born appears to be the result of a more sustained period of growth in this body segment.

Lower Leg Length

Again the analysis of the adult series by decades bears out the conclusions drawn from the total series. The sedentes have the shortest lower leg lengths, followed by the immigrants and finally by the Hawaiian born with the largest. The children confirm this relationship between the Hawaiian born and sedentes, the Hawaiian born boys having definitely longer tibiae at every age level. This pattern of tibial expansion follows closely the progressive increments in stature from the sedentes to the Hawaiian born.

Total Leg Length

The total leg lengths of the adults agree with the preceding curves. The greatest leg lengths are found among the Hawaiian born and the shortest in the sedentes. The immigrants are intermediate. Among the children, the Hawaiian born boys exceed the sedentes at every stage except at the 16–17 year level.

The increase of the adult Hawaiian born over the sedentes is more pronounced in lower leg length than in the upper leg.

Biacromion

Despite their shorter trunks, both the Hawaiian born and the immigrants exceed the longer trunked sedentes in shoulder width. The Hawaiian born are also wider than the immigrants.

Up to the 16–17 year level, on the contrary, the Hawaiian born boys have narrower shoulders than the sedentes, but from then on by virtue of greater growth increments they surpass the sedentes.

Cristal Width

The relationships between the adult groups for hip width are not entirely consistent. The immigrants, it is clear, have narrower hips than the sedentes although the total means were not significantly different. But the Hawaiian born, who in the 20–29 year decade show an added decrease in hip width, in the 30–39 year period reveal an accession to their cristal width sufficient to overleap the immigrants and even slightly exceed the sedentes. This is also contradictory to the wide discrepancy between the Hawaiian born and sedentes boys, for all during their growth period the Hawaiian born boys are definitely narrower in hip width. It is, therefore, impossible to decide from the brief span of the curve of the adult Hawaiian born whether the increase in width in the decade from 30 to 39 represents a departure from the true curve through insufficient sampling or whether the Hawaiian born have a longer continued growth than the other groups.

The conclusion drawn from the total series that the Hawaiian born have narrower hips than the sedentes can only be applied to the children. In adults the evidence for such a deduction is uncertain. On the other hand, the slight difference between the immigrants and sedentes appears to be confirmed.

Chest Breadth

During the first two decades of maturity no real difference occurs between the three groups in their breadth of chest. Thereafter the immigrants show a tendency toward wider chests. The Hawaiian born boys at 6–7 years of age are distinctly narrower in chest width than the sedentes, but the average diameters of these two groups show a progressively increasing trend towards approximation until at 18–19 years and thereafter to the end of the second decade of maturity they are practically identical. We may conclude that the Hawaiian born only show a differentiation during childhood when their chests are narrower than those of the sedentes and that all the adults are identical during the first two decades of maturity. To the extent that the total means seemed to indicate a significant decrease in chest width among the Hawaiian born from the average of the immigrants the present evidence must be taken as contradictory. All that can be said of adult differentiation is that the immigrants appear to display a tendency in their third and fourth decades of maturity toward a wider chest than the sedentes.

Chest Depth

Contrary to the results of the comparisons of the total series the immigrants and Hawaiian born are not essentially different in chest depth during at least the first 20 years of maturity. They both, however, are shallower in this dimension than are the sedentes. Moreover, the sedentes are consistently deeper chested than the Hawaiian born at all stages of childhood and youth.

Head Length

The comparison of the curves of head length reveals that the immigrants, because of fairly large fluctuations which alternately recede from and approach the curve of the sedentes, are difficult to assess in relation to the sedentes. If any difference exists at all, it would seem to be small. The Hawaiian born, on the contrary, are not only shorter headed than the immigrants in the adult stage, but are also decisively shorter headed than the sedentes throughout childhood and during maturity.

Head Width

The marked differentiation in head width which has been previously emphasized is clearly confirmed in the graph of the means by age groups. The Hawaiian born are not only wider headed than the sedentes at every age level from 6 to 40 but they are also wider than the immigrants during the first two decades of maturity for which they are comparable. The immigrants, although consistently wider headed than the sedentes, are superior by too slight a margin to merit distinction.

Head Height

In the height of the head, the immigrants are clearly greater than the sedentes even though they both coincide at the 50–59 year decade, largely because the sedentes at this point show an abnormally high peak in their curve. The Hawaiian born, however, are identical with the immigrants although we found that their total mean was significantly greater. This appears to have been the result of a decline in head height among the immigrants after the second decade, an age period unrepresented in the Hawaiian born series. The Hawaiian born are also higher headed than the sedentes both in maturity and in childhood.

Minimum Frontal Diameter

The total means of the adult males revealed no deep seated difference between any of the three groups of Japanese for the minimum frontal diameter. Nor do the analyses by decades present any more substantial evidence of differentiation. The lines of the immigrants and sedentes cross each other at every decade. And the Hawaiian born run close to the sedentes and cross the line of the immigrants.

In the early ages the Hawaiian born are slightly narrower than the sedentes up to 12–13 years, but from 14–15 years they are wider.

Bizygomatic Diameter

The reversal of the Hawaiian born from being the widest faced in the first decade to being the narrowest in the next decade and the closeness of the sedentes and immigrants, except in the 50–59 year decade, give little basis for assuming the existence of real difference between these three groups. As for the Hawaiian born and sedentes during the early age levels the divergencies are very slight and hardly significant.

Bigonial Diameter

We find in the curves for the bigonial diameter that the immigrants are definitely and unvaryingly wider in this diameter than the sedentes. This superiority over the sedentes appears to be in part maintained among the Hawaiian born, at least in the first decade, and would appear more certain in the second if the curve for this group followed more definitely the slope characteristic of the other two. The wider bigonial diameter among the adult Hawaiian born is consistently preserved throughout the childhood period.

Total Face Height

Although the total means represented the immigrants as deviating most widely from the sedentes and the Hawaiian born as being significantly lower in total face height than the immigrants and higher than the sedentes, the analysis by decade does not completely support these deductions. The immigrants do emerge as longer faced than the sedentes and Hawaiian born, but the last named are not consistently different from the sedentes. The erratic character of the curve of the Hawaiian born just before maturity and of the curve of the sedentes during the second decade of maturity mask effectively any difference which might exist. Therefore, although the Hawaiian born during puberty and through the first decade of manhood are longer faced than the sedentes, they drop behind in the second decade of maturity.

Upper Face Height

In this dimension there is less confusion. The disparity between the sedentes and the immigrants on the one hand and the Hawaiian born on the other is so great that no doubt can be entertained that the difference is real. Moreover, the greater upper face length of the Hawaiian born over the sedentes is also characteristic in the earlier age periods. Although in the 20–29 year decade the Hawaiian born show an additional increase over the immigrants, by the virtual cessation of growth in the next decade they forfeit their lead over the immigrants.

Forehead Height

Although the greater height of the forehead of the sedentes as compared with the immigrants seems firmly established, the true relation of the Hawaiian born to these two antecedent groups is less clear. For example, the Hawaiian born exceed the immigrants by a wide margin in the first decade but fall slightly behind in the second. In relation to the sedentes, the Hawaiian born in the adult period have lower foreheads, but in puberty and youth they have higher ones. It should be noted that the curve of the Hawaiian born children is excessively erratic. So far as reliance can be placed on these curves, they suggest certain modifications of the conclusions drawn from the total means. The decrease in forehead height among the immigrants, compared with sedentes, seems to be more definite than the statistical significance of the difference allowed. This decrease from the forehead height of the sedentes is shared by the Hawaiian born adults, in spite of their reversal of position during puberty, which may be explained by the erratic course of their curve due to a greater variability in this dimension.

Nose Height

The progression in the increase of nose height is greatest from the sedentes to the immigrants; the further addition to the nose height of the Hawaiian born is slight and perhaps statistically negligible. The total means displayed a similar succession of increases in nasal height. In comparing Hawaiian born and sedentes it is interesting to observe that the ultimately greater height of the nose of the Hawaiian born commences late in youth. Not until the 16–17 year level do the Hawaiian born overtake the sedentes who by an earlier onset of accelerated growth had surpassed them all through childhood and puberty. Evidence of a late acceleration in growth occurs also in the total and upper face height and in the nasal length.

Nasal Length

These curves repeat the pattern shown in the nasal heights. Although the immigrants enjoy an even greater increment over the sedentes in nose length than in nose height, the Hawaiian born, at least in the first decade, again show a slight tendency to a further elongation of the nose. And in the earlier age period the Hawaiian born also attain their first supremacy over the sedentes at the 16–17 year level as they did in nose height.

Nose Salient

The relative lengths of the nose salient form a consistent pattern with the nasal heights and lengths. It follows that the shorter the nose length in relation to nose height, the longer the distance from the tip of the nose to the juncture of the septum with the lip, provided that the angle that the line of the nose length makes on the nose height does not differ. Actually the difference between nose length and nose height is greatest among the sedentes (see the nose height-nose length index) and in consequence we find that they have the greatest nose salients. Moreover, it is worth noting that at the point where the curve of the nasal length of the Hawaiian born rises above that of the sedentes, the nose salient falls below.

The positions, therefore, of the three groups with respect to nose salient become clarified. The sedentes have the greatest and the immigrants and Hawaiian born are in close agreement.

Nose Width

The immigrants and the Hawaiian born by decades are about equal in nasal breadth, although the total means seemed to indicate a continuation of the nasal constriction first evident in the immigrants. This discrepancy is brought about by the fact that the mean of the immigrants includes the later decades of their maturity when a strong tendency appears toward increase in nasal breadth. This trend is so strong that they actually surpass the previously wider nosed sedentes. The narrower nose of the Hawaiian born compared with the sedentes is consistently prophesied throughout the earlier growth period.

Inter-Ocular Width

The paths which the inter-ocular widths of sedentes and immigrants pursue with age are erratic. In the first decade of maturity the sedentes are moderately wider than the immigrants. In the succeeding decade, however, these positions are reversed because of a drop in the mean of the sedentes and a corresponding rise among the immigrants. Thereafter, however, the sedentes and immigrants return to their earlier positions which become increasingly separated in the third and fourth decades. It is apparent from this graph that the significant reduction observed in the inter-ocular width of the total immigrants is in large measure the consequence of the significant gap which occurs in the latter part of maturity. On the whole despite the contradiction in the second decade the tendency of the immigrants toward narrower inter-ocular widths seems more than fortuitous.

The Hawaiian born adults, however, offer no evidence for concluding that they differ essentially from either immigrants or sedentes, although the Hawaiian born boys have wider diameters than the sedentes up to the final biennium.

Bi-Ocular Width

The immigrants have consistently wider bi-ocular diameters than the sedentes but the curve of the Hawaiian born crosses both and is reduced from being widest in one decade to being narrowest in the next. In the curve for the antecedent age period the Hawaiian born have greater bi-ocular widths from the 6–7 year level up to the 16–17 year period but thereafter the relationship is reversed.

Relative Shoulder Breadth

Although the total means disclosed no difference between immigrants and Hawaiian born in their respective increases from the sedentes in relative shoulder width, the age curves do reveal a tendency in the second decade for this increase among the Hawaiian born to exceed that of the immigrants. It is difficult to know how much weight to allow this trend since the margin of gain over the immigrants is not significant.

It is interesting to note that up to the 16–17 year level the Hawaiian born boys have relatively as well as absolutely narrower shoulders than the sedentes, but thereafter they rapidly forge ahead.

Relative Hip Width

Although the statistics of the total series gave no significance to the slight decrease among the immigrants in absolute hip width, they did seem to point to a consistently narrower hip in relation to stature. The curves for relative hip width can, however, be said to support only incompletely that conclusion. In the first decade the immigrants actually have greater relative hip widths than the sedentes and thereafter are only appreciably below the sedentes during the 40–49 year decade. As for the Hawaiian born it is true that in the course of their limited span the relative hip width is lower than that of the sedentes and even the immigrants, and that all during childhood the Hawaiian born boys are significantly lower than the sedentes, but the discrepancy during maturity is slight and can be regarded only as suggestive.

Shoulder-Hip Index

The progressive decline from sedentes to Hawaiian born in the total means for the shoulder-hip index is repeated in the age curves. This is a result readily predictable from the relationships of the three groups with regard to the component dimensions. Moreover, the relatively greater shoulder to hip width of the adult Hawaiian born is merely an extension of a relationship previously displayed in the earlier growth stages.

Relative Sitting Height

In each decade of maturity the immigrants fall definitely below the sedentes in relative sitting height. In doing so they repeat the difference already observed for the total series. Considering next the Hawaiian born, we discover that they also confirm the indications of their total series by closely agreeing with the immigrants. I have previously pointed out that although the Hawaiian born are taller and have longer sitting heights than the immigrants, nevertheless the proportion remains unaltered.

During childhood the Hawaiian born boys have relatively lower sitting heights until they reach puberty when they temporarily surpass the sedentes only to fall back again in reaching adulthood.

Relative Trunk Height

The curves of sedentes, immigrants and Hawaiian born for relative trunk height repeat in all essentials the respective courses of those for relative sitting height and to that extent reaffirm the results of the total group comparisons. Again the adult Hawaiian born and immigrants are identical and both have shorter relative trunk heights than the sedentes. And in childhood the Hawaiian born have shorter relative trunk heights than the sedentes except at puberty.

Thoracic Index

The previous comparison of the total means seemed to point to a progressive decline in the thoracic index from sedentes to Hawaiian born. But checking this pattern with the age curves we find that in this instance the total means are misleading because of the extraordinary degree of age change in the thoracic index. From the high values of early childhood the thoracic index falls very rapidly reaching its nadir at 16–19 years. All during maturity the index climbs as steeply back to the initial levels. It follows from such an age curve that a total mean embracing only a part of it will be unrepresentative. Such is the case for the Hawaiian born adults who are largely concentrated in the ages from 20 to 39 years, consequently yielding a total mean below its theoretical value for the entire adult age span. For this reason the total mean of the Hawaiian born falls below that of the immigrant and drops excessively below that of the sedentes. On comparing these three groups by comparable decades we find that the immigrants reveal a consistent decrease from the sedentes and that the Hawaiian born show a slight but statistically insignificant tendency to revert to the upper level of the sedentes.

During the growth period both the sedentes and the Hawaiian born show a profound drop at puberty. Their curves cross each other at the beginning and toward the end of puberty. The movement back toward a higher value which appears to be characteristic of maturity begins earlier in the sedentes and thereby gives them their margin over the Hawaiian born.

Brachial Index

The proportion of lower to upper arm length undergoes an increase from the sedentes to the immigrants. At one point—the decade from 40–49 years—the sedentes overlap the immigrants, but aside from this single exception the immigrants have relatively longer forearms. This might have been forecast from the fact that the immigrants showed a tendency toward elongated forearms in comparison with the sedentes. The Hawaiian born, however, reveal no additional increase in the brachial index. In fact, they have insignificantly lower indices than the immigrants. Both immigrants and Hawaiian born, therefore, are distinguished from the sedentes by their higher brachial indices.

The increase in brachial index among the Hawaiian born over the sedentes is maintained throughout the growth period. The difference is actually greater during this earlier growth period than it is in the later decades of maturity.

Tibio-Femoral Index

Although the total mean of the immigrants almost attains a significant reduction from that of the sedentes in the tibio-femoral index, actually the curves of the age means reveal that in the 20–29 year decade they have somewhat higher indices than the sedentes. In the next three decades, however, the immigrants have much reduced indices, but combined with large probable errors so that the significance of this decline is rather diminished. This situation is produced by the slightly greater increase among the immigrants in the upper leg than in the lower leg length, although both leg segments are significantly greater in the immigrants than in the sedentes.

As for the Hawaiian born, they have higher indices than the immigrants and the sedentes, but only significantly higher than the immigrants in the 30–39 year decade and significantly higher than the sedentes in the 20–29 year decade. The relatively greater increase in the lower leg of the Hawaiian born as compared with the relatively greater increase in the upper leg among the immigrants tends to produce a reversal in the respective groups when contrasted with sedentes.

Glancing backward to the growth curves of the sedentes and Hawaiian born, we see the curves of the sedentes and Hawaiian born widely spaced except at both ends, where they approach each other. At the 6–7 year level the sedentes have slightly higher indices and at the 18–19 year level the Hawaiian born are less than one index unit higher. At all intervening ages the indices of the Hawaiian born are significantly higher. It seems reasonable to suppose that these terminal exceptions are eccentric to the major trend of the curves. We may conclude, therefore, that in both the children and the adults the Hawaiian born are distinguished from the sedentes by a higher tibio-femoral index.

Inter-Membral Index

Although the reduction of the inter-membral index of the immigrants does not attain statistical significance except at the second decade of maturity yet this relatively large decrease, maintained consistently as it is through four decades, does lend substance to the significant decrease in the total mean of the immigrants. Similarly the Hawaiian born show a comparable if not quite as large a decrease from the sedentes.

The decline in the inter-membral index of the Hawaiian born and the immigrants compared with the sedentes merely implies that the leg has become longer in relation to the arm length. This fact can be verified absolutely from the charts of arm and leg lengths. But these charts also show another fact of great interest. Whereas the arm segments of Hawaiian born children and adults are alike in their increased length over the sedentes, the leg lengths differ. In the upper leg length the Hawaiian born do not exceed the sedentes until the 18–19 year old level. The effect of this on the total leg length reduces the gains of the Hawaiian born in the lower leg and produces a curve for total leg length which is but very slightly superior to that of the sedentes during childhood and explodes into a significant spacing only at maturity. The graphic consequences of these differential and compensated curves are to be seen in the reversal in childhood of the Hawaiian born adult superiority of inter-membral index. The reading of the graphs and the tables, therefore, indicates that during growth the sedentes have lower indices, therefore relatively longer legs than arms, but in maturity it is the Hawaiian born group that usurps this position.

Cephalic Index

The slight but indecisive decrease in immigrant head length and increase in head breadth has yielded among the immigrants a cephalic index which is slightly higher, consequently more brachycephalic, than that of the sedentes. The increase, however, is not significant though it is consistent, and at the third and fourth decades the difference from the sedentes is negligible.

The Hawaiian born, however, are indisputably wider headed and shorter headed and their cephalic index is consequently equally decisive in its increase over both the immigrants and the sedentes.

The differentiation of Hawaiian born and sedentes in the cephalic index is also maintained throughout the period of growth. At each age level the Hawaiian born boys have higher indices than the sedentes.

Length-Height Index

Although the immigrants coincided with the Hawaiian born in a significant increase over the sedentes in the height of the head, their irregular and very slight decrease from the sedentes in head length has produced a length-height index which occupies a wavering middle position between the low index of the sedentes and the high index of the Hawaiian born. During the first two decades the immigrants are significantly above the sedentes and only slightly below the Hawaiian born, during the next two decades they decline to a position only slightly above the sedentes. This causes some confusion in relating the results of the comparison of the total means to this analysis by decades. In the total mean of the immigrants these decadal fluctuations are balanced and yield a value significantly higher than the sedentes and significantly lower than the Hawaiian born, whereas the graph shows a split allegiance to both the sedentes and the Hawaiian born.

The Hawaiian born, however, are definitely superior to the sedentes in the length-height index, although their relationship to the immigrants is ambiguous. Moreover the vastly higher index of the Hawaiian born over the sedentes is characteristic of the entire preceding growth period.

Breadth-Height Index

The justification for this detailed age analysis is well illustrated by the breadth-height index. In comparing the total means of the three master series, the Hawaiian born appeared to have the highest indices, followed very closely by the immigrants with the sedentes significantly lower than the two preceding groups. Actually the graph of these groups by decades uncovers a rather different relationship. The immigrants are still significantly higher, except at their terminal decade, than the sedentes, but they also have higher indices than the Hawaiian born, although the difference is slight. This perhaps minor contradiction of the reading of the total means is readily explainable. The breadth-height index of the immigrants pursues a falling course with age so that in the later decades the immigrants are roughly three units lower than in the first decade. The Hawaiian born likewise show a falling index, but the curve, extending only over two decades, does not fall to the same degree exhibited by the immigrants. Consequently the longer span of the falling curve of the immigrants produces naturally a total mean which is lower than that of the Hawaiian born even though in actuality the curve of the immigrants never crosses that of the Hawaiian born. It is, of course, conjectural that the Hawaiian born curve might have continued to decline had the data been at hand for its extension into the later decades, but nevertheless the actual evidence shows the Hawaiian born with a slightly lower index than the immigrants.

As far as the data permit we can only conclude that the immigrants and Hawaiian born show no real difference and that they both have significantly higher breadth-height indices than the sedentes.

As for the Hawaiian born, the higher breadth-height index which they possess in maturity compared with corresponding sedentes is likewise preserved throughout the preceding growth period.

Cephalo-Facial Index

In studying the changes in the cephalo-facial index, we find among the immigrants no consistent change from the sedentes. In the first two decades they have slightly lower indices but in the third decade they are identical with and in the fourth slightly superior to the sedentes. The Hawaiian born, however, show a decided trend away from both immigrants and sedentes in the direction of lower indices. This pattern is, of course, the resultant of the changes already observed in the component measurements, and is very largely the consequence of the greatly expanded head width specifically characteristic of the Hawaiian born.

The lower cephalo-facial index of the Hawaiian born adults is also present among the children who are slightly but consistently inferior in this regard to the sedentes children.

Fronto-Parietal Index

The comparison of immigrants with sedentes reveals no alteration in the proportions of the minimum frontal diameter to the head width. The Hawaiian born, because of their increased head width, have a relatively narrower forehead than the immigrants and sedentes. The difference, however, is of significant proportions only in the first decade. In the second decade all three groups are statistically well within the limits of significance. The evidence, therefore, is inconclusive that the Hawaiian born have lower fronto-parietal indices since it is impossible to judge whether the direction of the Hawaiian born curve represents a movement in maturity toward the level of the sedentes and immigrants or whether it is fortuitous. It is worth noting that the total means render the division between the Hawaiian born, on the one hand, and the sedentes and immigrants, on the other, as far more decisive than it is in fact.

In so far as the evidence of the growth curves is pertinent, it bears witness to the existence of a distinction between Hawaiian born and sedentes. The former, except at the 16–17 year level, are ponderably lower than the sedentes in the fronto-parietal index.

Zygo-Frontal Index

The absence of any homogeneous difference between immigrants and sedentes for the zygo-frontal index might have been forecast from the similar lack of consistent deviation in the bizygomatic and minimum frontal diameters. In this there is agreement between the results of the comparison by total means and by age decades.

The Hawaiian born also can not be unequivocally separated from the sedentes, even though their curve in the second decade takes a marked upward direction away from both sedentes and immigrants. This separation, although graphically striking, does not quite reach the security of statistical significance. Moreover, it can be explained by relatively insignificant divergent deviations in bizygomatic and minimum frontal diameters.

The comparison of the growth curves of the Hawaiian born and sedentes boys discloses the fact that the tendency, uncertain as it may be, for the Hawaiian born adults to possess higher zygo-frontal indices arises as early as the 16–17 year old level. Previous to the 14–15 year stage the sedentes have the higher index.

Zygo-Gonial Index

Although in the first decade of maturity the immigrants have significantly higher zygo-gonial indices than the sedentes, the rapidly rising index among the sedentes closes in the gap until in the fourth decade the two groups are identical. Thereafter the sedentes fall precipitously to their initial level.

Unfortunately the immigrants and the sedentes can not be compared for the final age group. It is manifestly impossible to know from the present data whether this approximation of the two groups in the fourth decade is fortuitous or not. All that can be profitably said is that the immigrants, at least in the earlier decades, reveal a tendency toward high zygo-gonial indices.

As for the Hawaiian born, they are similar to the immigrants for the two decades covered by their data. Consequently the Hawaiian born have significantly higher indices than the sedentes. This superiority of the Hawaiian born over the sedentes is supported by the relationship between the corresponding immature groups. The Hawaiian born boys have higher indices at each age level and most of these differences are significant.

Facial Index

The remarkable difference between the total immigrants and sedentes in the proportions of the face is thoroughly confirmed in the graphs by decades. In each decade the immigrants have higher total face indices than the sedentes, with the most significant difference occurring in the first decade. Since the two groups are relatively alike for face width, it is obvious that the greater face heights of the immigrants are responsible for their marked tendency toward higher total facial indices.

The movement of the immigrants toward a higher total facial index suffers a decline among the Hawaiian born, who in the first decade are both significantly above the sedentes and insignificantly below the immigrants. In the second decade they are exactly midway between sedentes and immigrants and insignificantly different from either.

The Hawaiian born have significantly higher total facial indices than the sedentes not only in the first decade of maturity, but they also have higher indices during growth except for the period of puberty when the sedentes temporarily surpass them. This pubertal reversal seems to have its origin in a contemporaneous spurt in the growth of the total face among the sedentes boys.

Upper Facial Index

The disparity between sedentes and immigrants in facial proportions is even more definite in the upper facial index than in the total facial index. In the former index, the immigrants are roughly six index units above the sedentes. The degree of this discrepancy is far beyond the statistical requirements for significance. The same degree, even slightly increased, of superiority is maintained by the Hawaiian born, who while hardly above the immigrants, are consequently significantly superior to the sedentes. It merely remains to point out that the Hawaiian born boys have higher upper facial indices than the sedentes at each age.

Nasal Index

Although in the earlier decades of maturity the immigrants have significantly lower nasal indices than the sedentes, the immigrants in the third decade show a sharp increase which, continuing into the next decade, raises them to the level of the sedentes. This rapid change in the nasal proportions of the immigrants is the direct consequence of a large increase of the nasal width which begins in the third decade. The same tendency toward relatively wider noses in the later age period is also present in the sedentes, but among them its manifestation is most evident a decade later than among the immigrants. This difference in the time of the onset of nasal widening may account for the overlapping of sedentes and immigrants in the fourth decade.

The Hawaiian born carry the relative narrowing of the nose even beyond the immigrants. Although the total mean index of the Hawaiian born is significantly lower than that of the immigrants, the difference becomes insignificant when they are compared by decades. In comparison with the sedentes, however, the Hawaiian born are at least as decisively narrower nosed as the immigrants. Since the curve of the Hawaiian born ends at the 30–39 year decade it is impossible to know whether or not this curve, also, would follow the precedent of the immigrants by an age change in the nasal index sufficient to lift them to the level of the sedentes.

The curves of the Hawaiian born and sedentes boys reveal very erratic courses. We observe that the sedentes have higher indices at 6–7 years, fall far below the Hawaiian born boys from 8–13 years, and again for the years 16–19 rise above the Hawaiian born. But this uncertainty in the relationship of these two groups is somewhat misleading. The graph of the nose widths show that the Hawaiian born boys consistently have narrower noses than the sedentes. But in the nose height the Hawaiian born do not establish their lead over the sedentes until the end of the growth period. It is, therefore, the slower growth in nose height among the Hawaiian born boys and not a wider nose that assigns them to a higher indicial category than the sedentes during the major part of their growth span.

Nose Salient-Height Index

The relative projection of the nasal tip may be estimated from the nose salient-height index and from the nose length-height index. In the nose salient-height index the salient is measured against the nasal height. The immigrants reveal a distinct reduction in the relative prominence of the nasal salient. No other sequel could have been anticipated from the fact that the immigrants not only have greater nasal heights but lower nasal salients. Similarly the Hawaiian born in relation to the sedentes present a reduction in nasal salience. The extent of this reduction goes a little beyond the average of the immigrants, but not significantly.

The Hawaiian born boys, however, first show intimations of the adult reduction only as late as 18–19 years. Before that they are either far above the sedentes or only insignificantly so. Again this anomalous situation can be partly explained by the slower growth of nasal height among the Hawaiian born boys. But part of the tremendous superiority of the Hawaiian born boys at the 14–15 year level must be attributed to an eccentric peak in the growth curve of nose salient which occurs at the same age.

Nose Length-Height Index

The longer the nose length is in relation to nose height, the higher the resulting length-height index becomes. Both the immigrants and the Hawaiian born enjoy an increase over the sedentes in this index, although the Hawaiian born display a secondary tendency of uncertain significance to revert to the lower indices characteristic of the sedentes.

It is interesting to observe that the Hawaiian born during their growth period do not reveal their later divergence from the sedentes until they reach the 18–19 year level. Similarly, in nasal height and nasal length the Hawaiian born lag behind the sedentes until the same age.

This increase in the nose length-height index of the Hawaiian born and immigrants is structurally linked with the decrease in absolute and relative saliency of the nose among both these groups. It is, therefore, apparent that the immigrants and Hawaiian born have less retroussé noses than the sedentes.

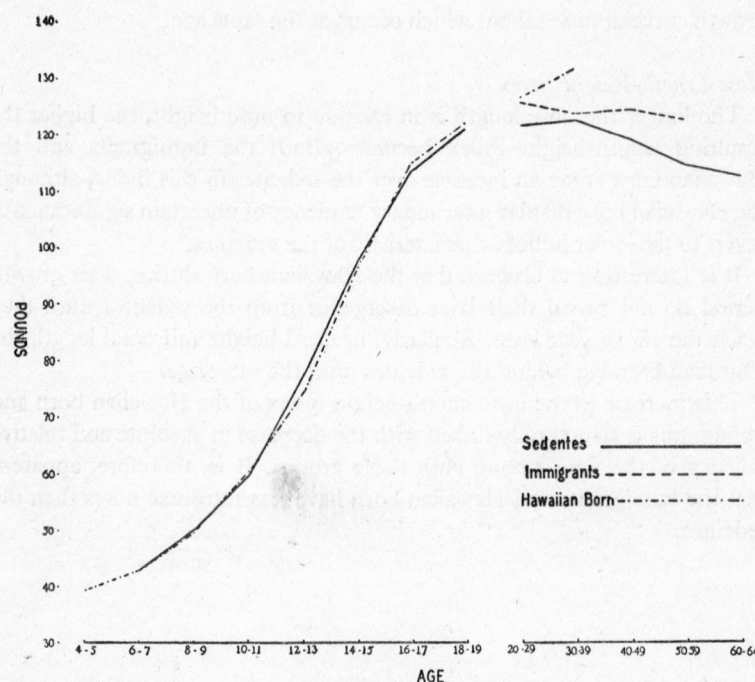

fig. 26

Age Changes in the Weight of Males

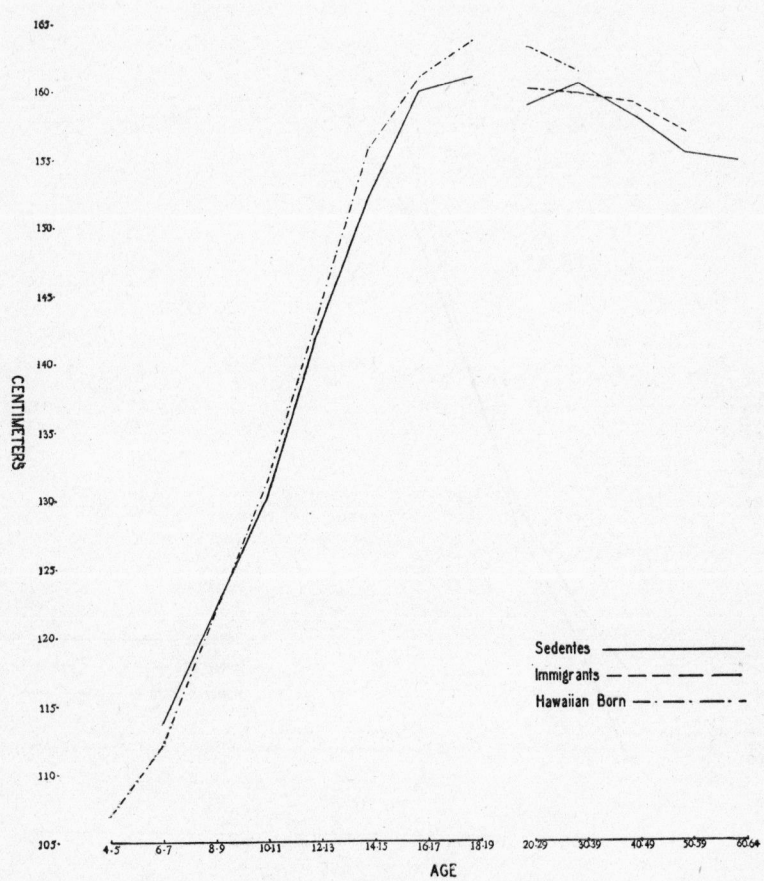

fig. 27

Age Changes in the Stature of Males

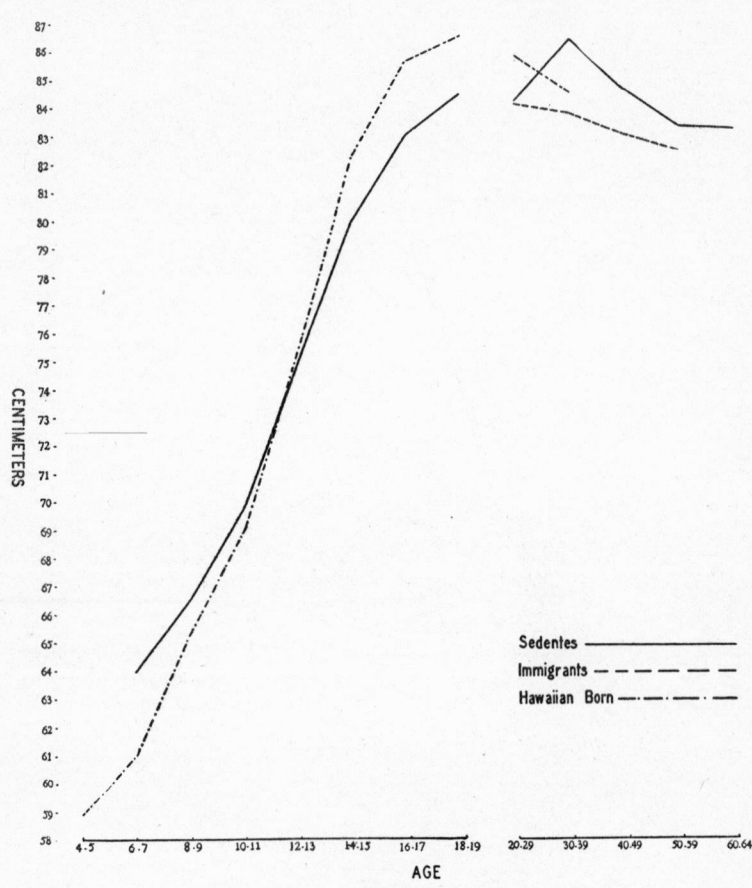

fig. 28

Age Changes in the Sitting Height of Males

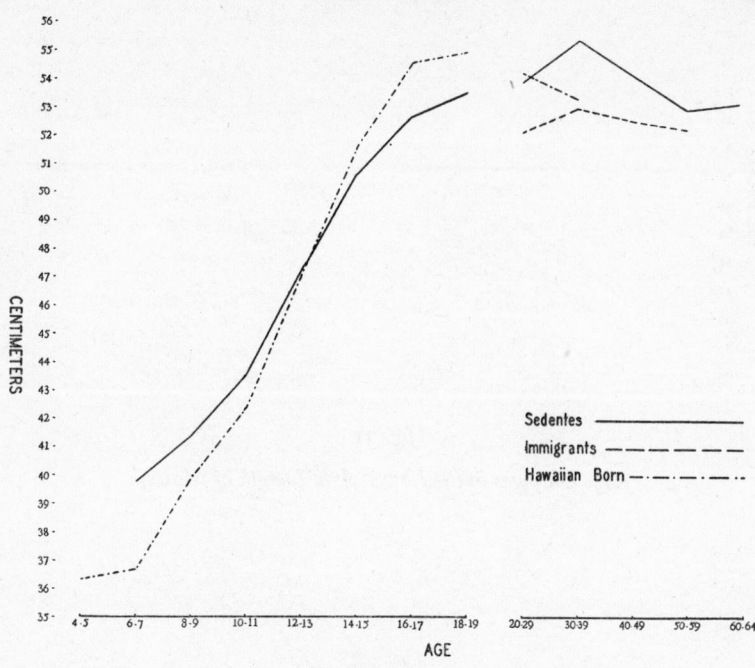

fig. 29

Age Changes in the Trunk Height of Males

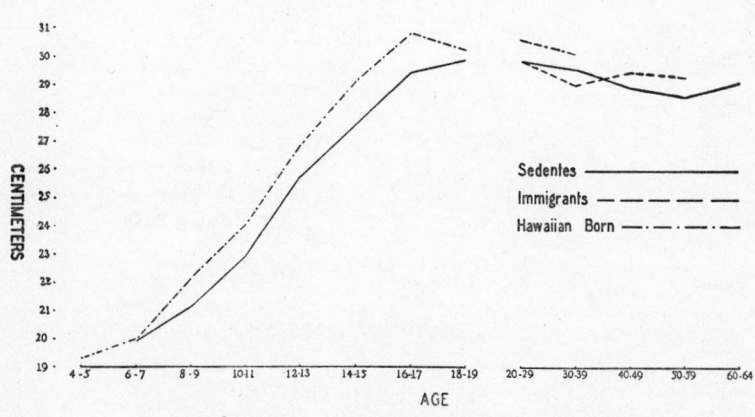

fig. 30

Age Changes in the Upper Arm Length of Males

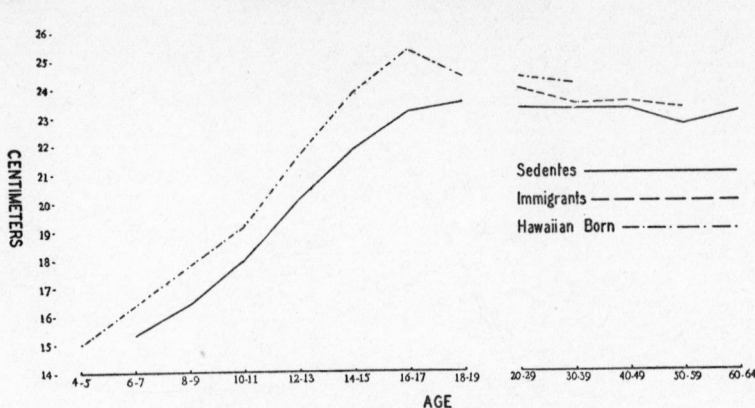

fig. 31

Age Changes in the Lower Arm Length of Males

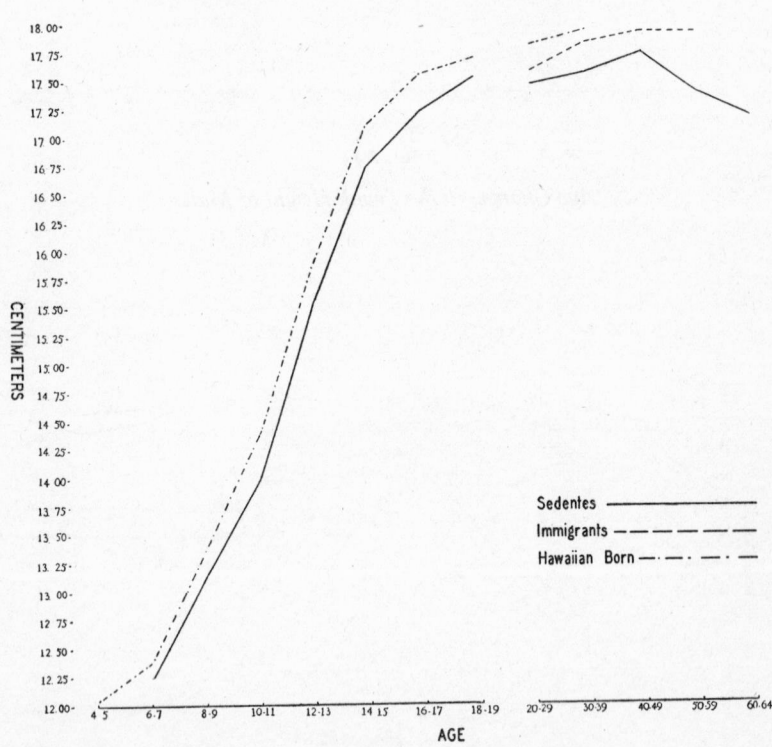

fig. 32

Age Changes in the Hand Length of Males

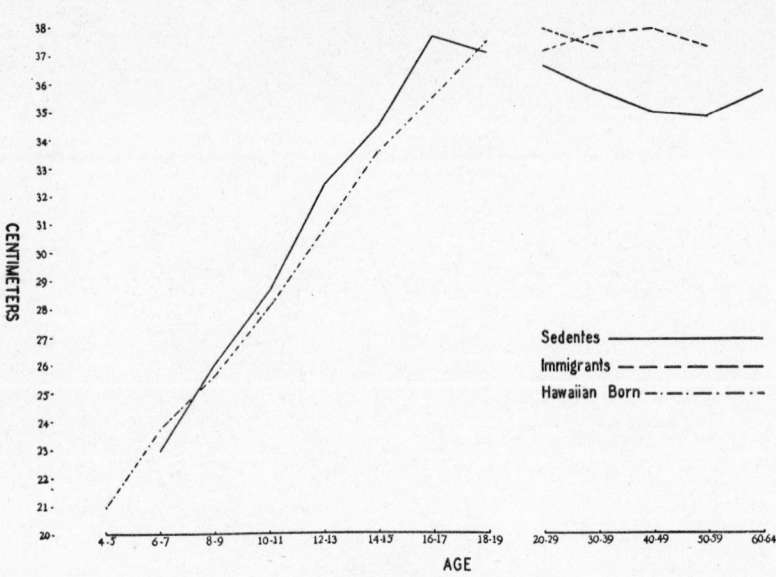

fig. 33

Age Changes in the Upper Leg Length of Males

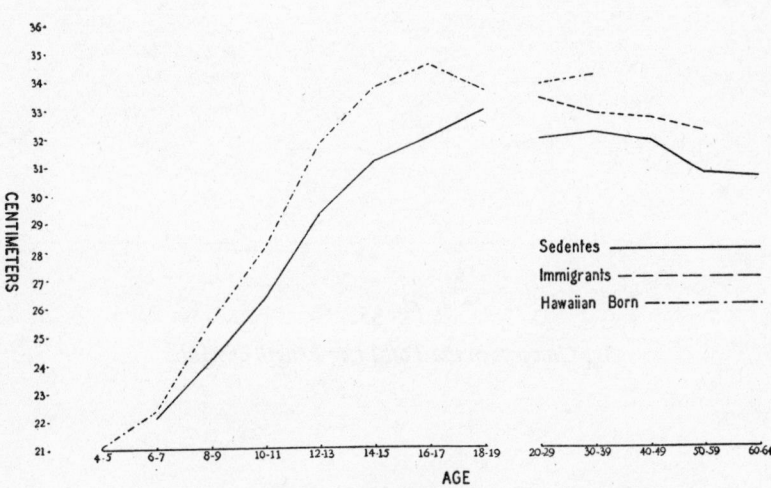

fig. 34

Age Changes in the Lower Leg Length of Males

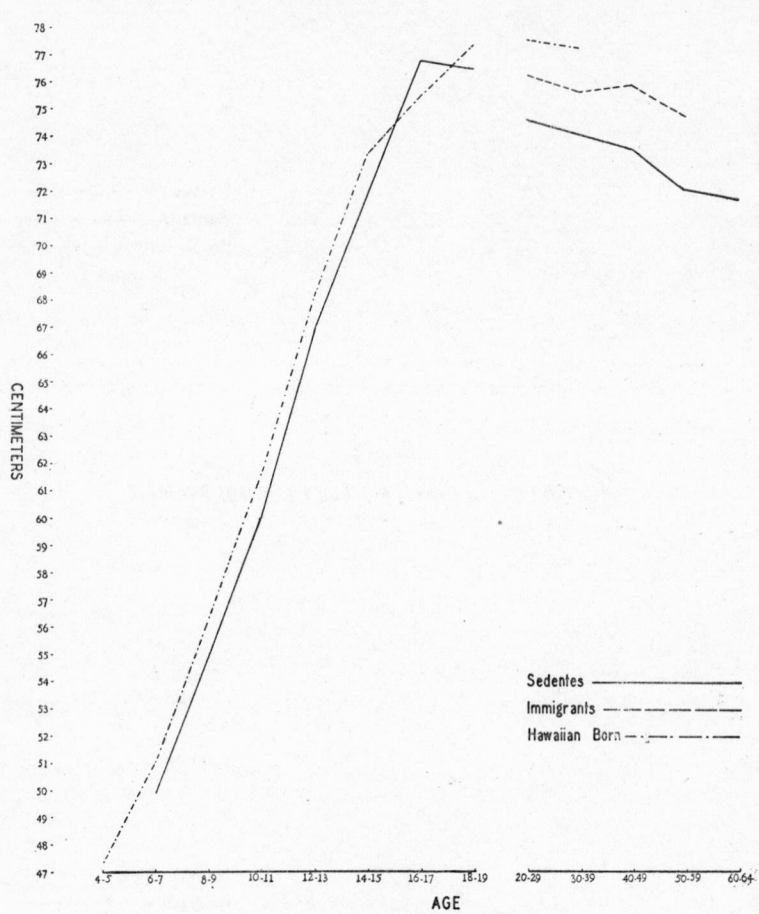

fig. 35

Age Changes in the Total Leg Length of Males

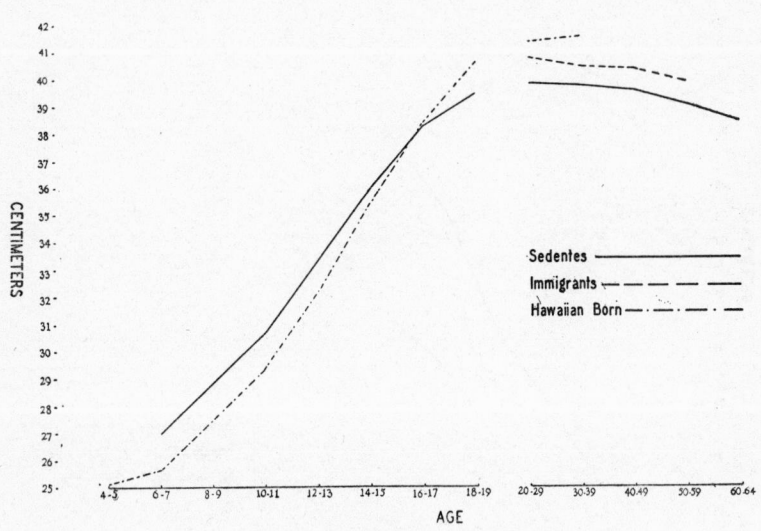

fig. 36

Age Changes in the Biacromial Width of Males

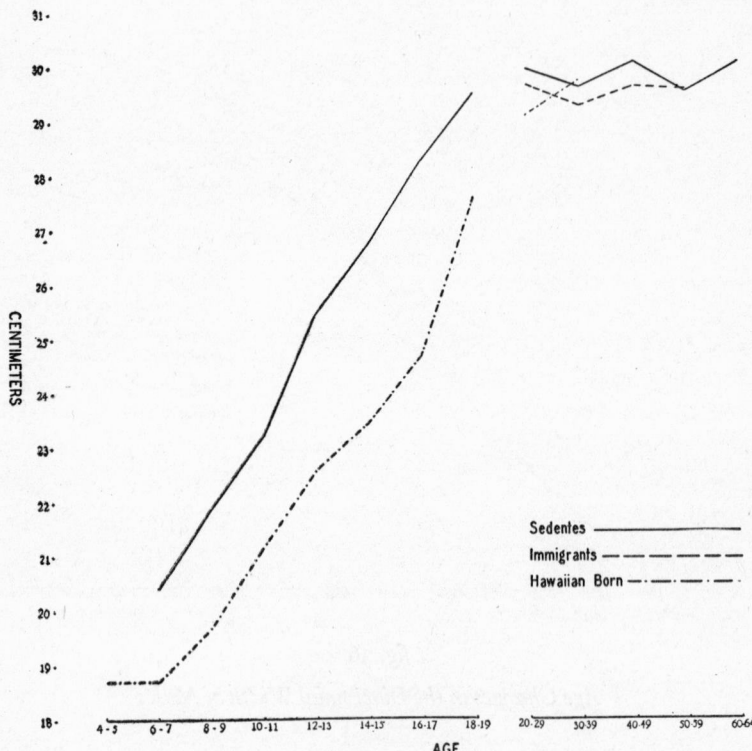

fig. 37

Age Changes in the Cristal Breadth of Males

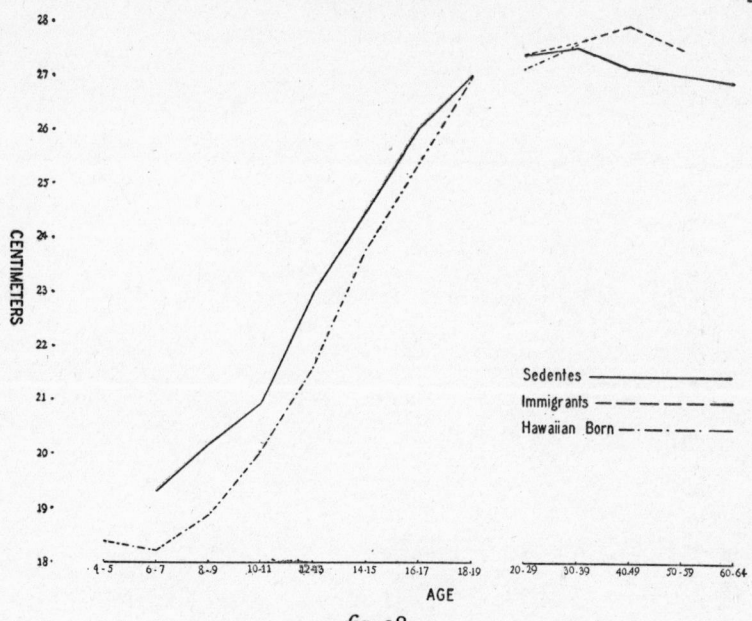

fig. 38

Age Changes in the Chest Breadth of Males

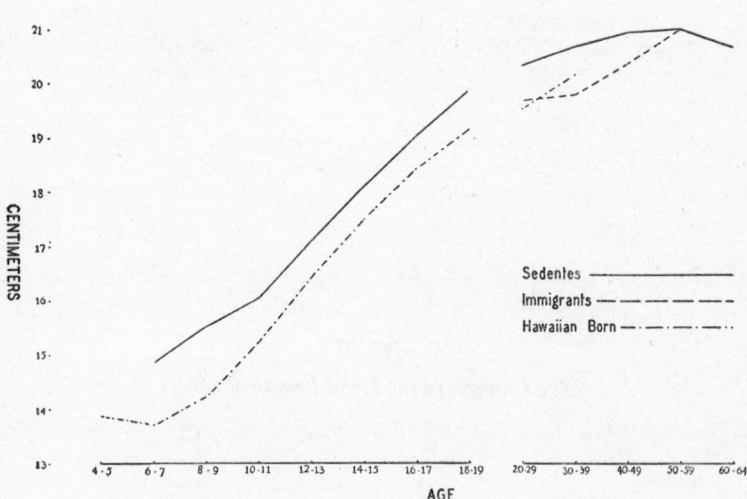

fig. 39

Age Changes in the Chest Depth of Males

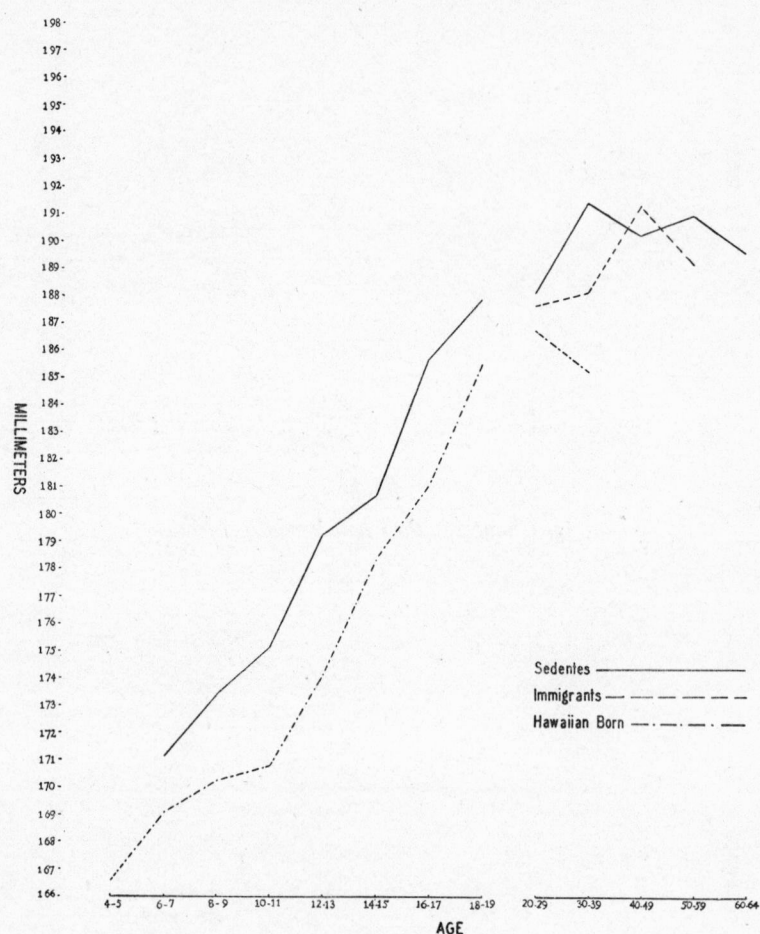

fig. 40

Age Changes in the Head Length of Males

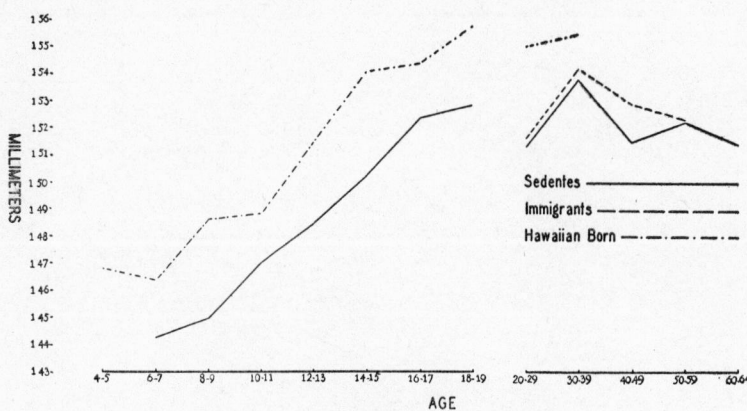

fig. 41

Age Changes in the Head Breadth of Males

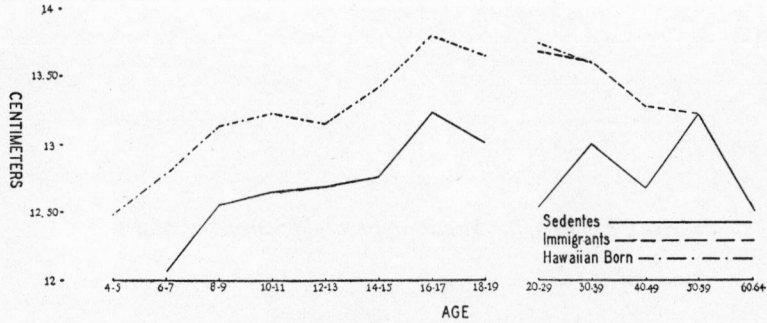

fig. 42

Age Changes in the Head Height of Males

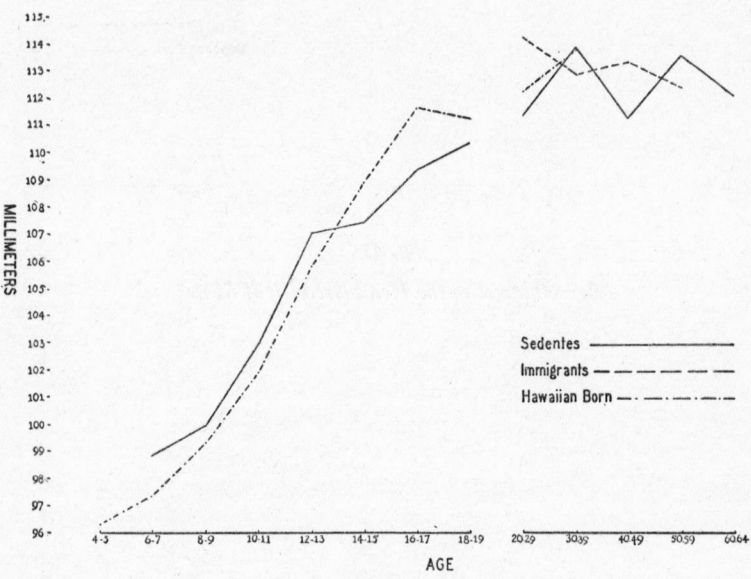

fig. 43

Age Changes in the Minimum Frontal Diameter of Males

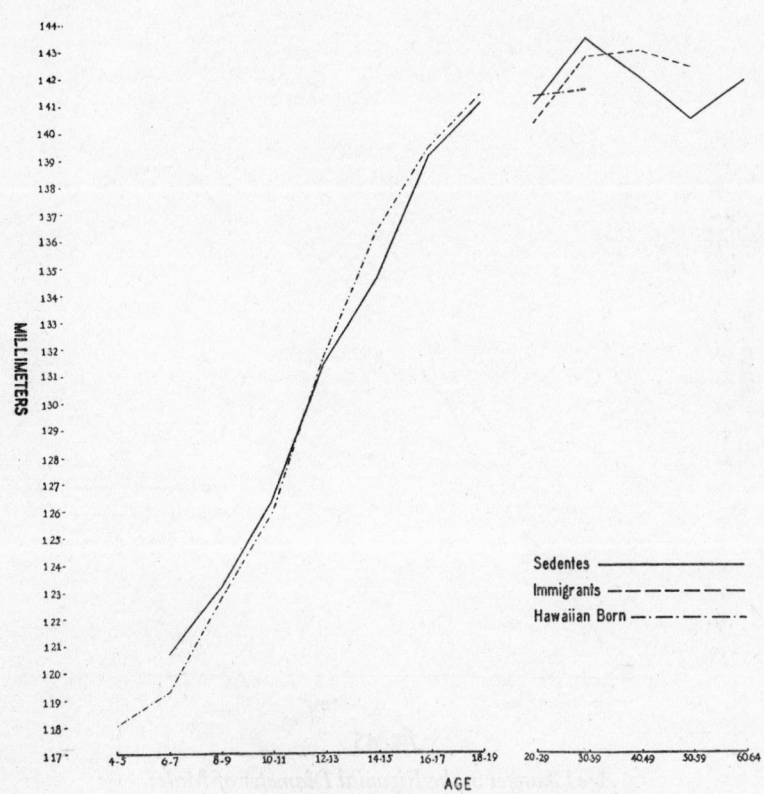

MILLIMETERS

Sedentes ————————
Immigrants — — — — — —
Hawaiian Born — · — · — · —

AGE

fig. 44

Age Changes in the Bizygomatic Diameter of Males

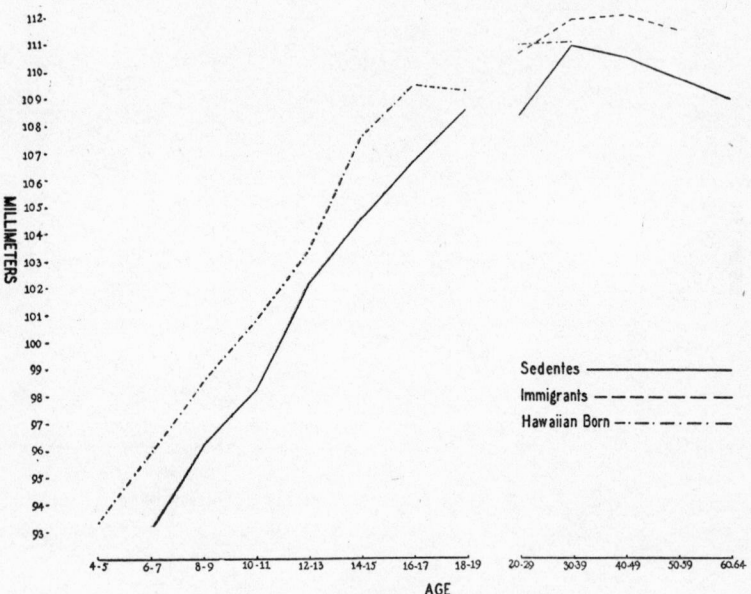

fig. 45

Age Changes in the Bigonial Diameter of Males

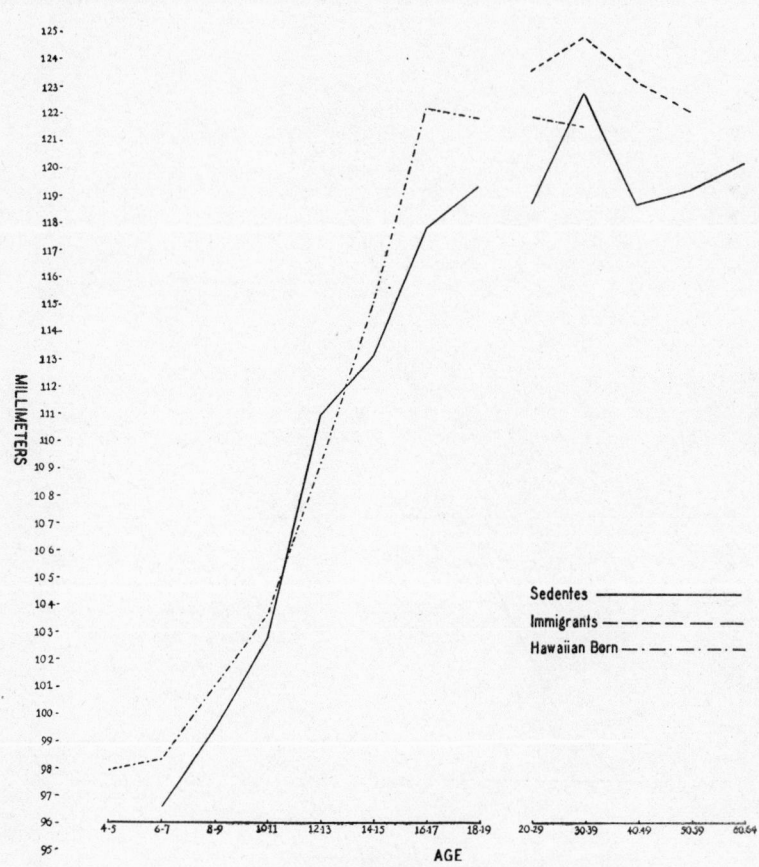

fig. 46

Age Changes in the Total Face Height of Males

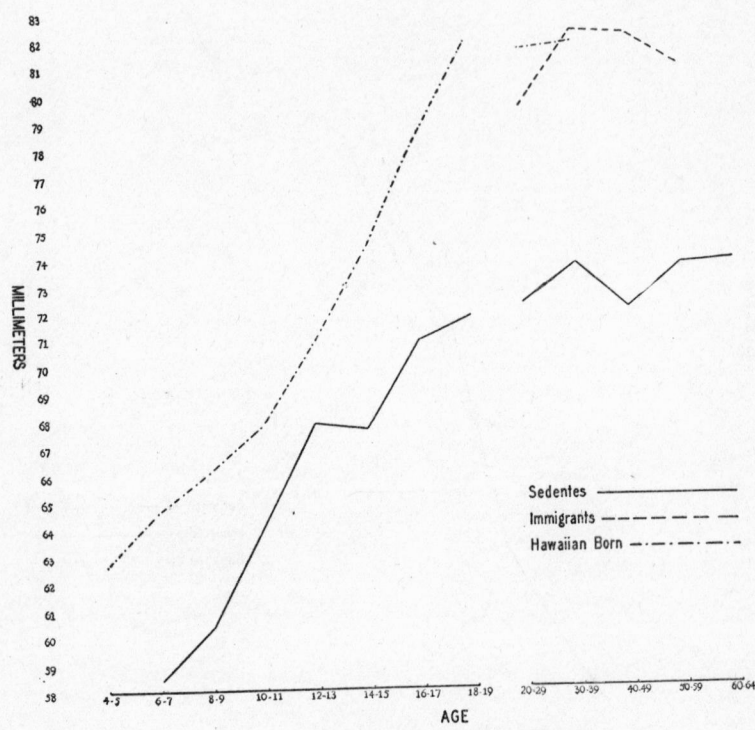

fig. 47

Age Changes in the Upper Face Height of Males

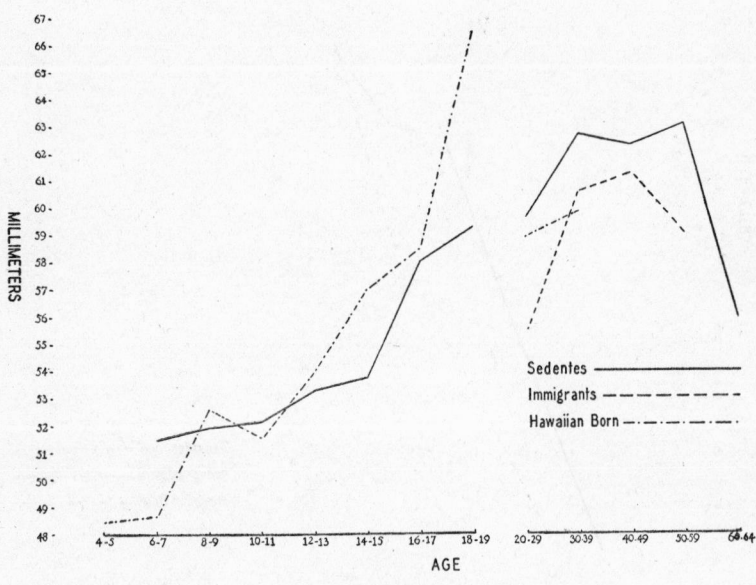

fig. 48

Age Changes in the Forehead Height of Males

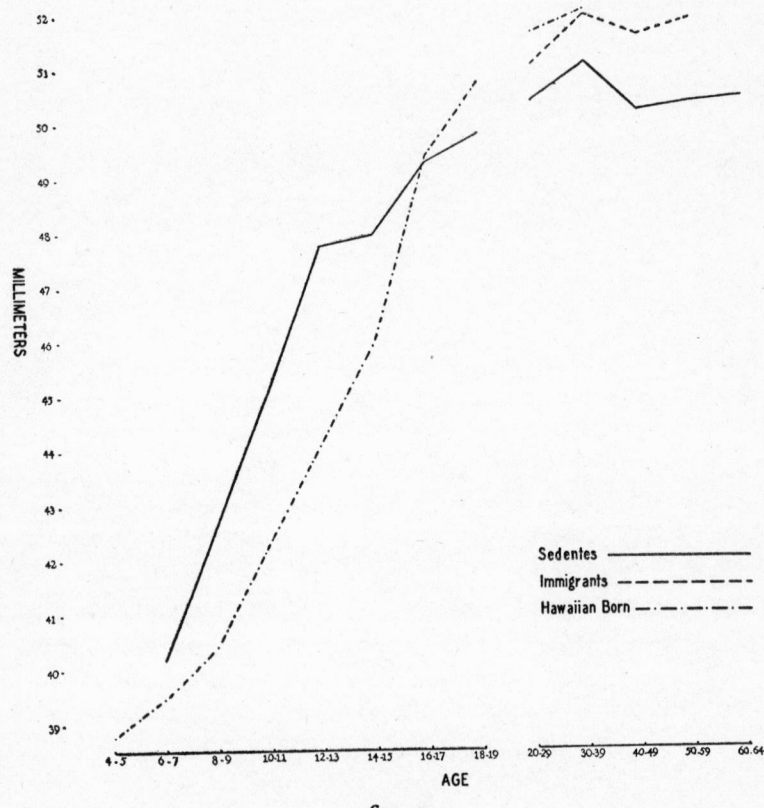

fig. 49

Age Changes in the Nose Height of Males

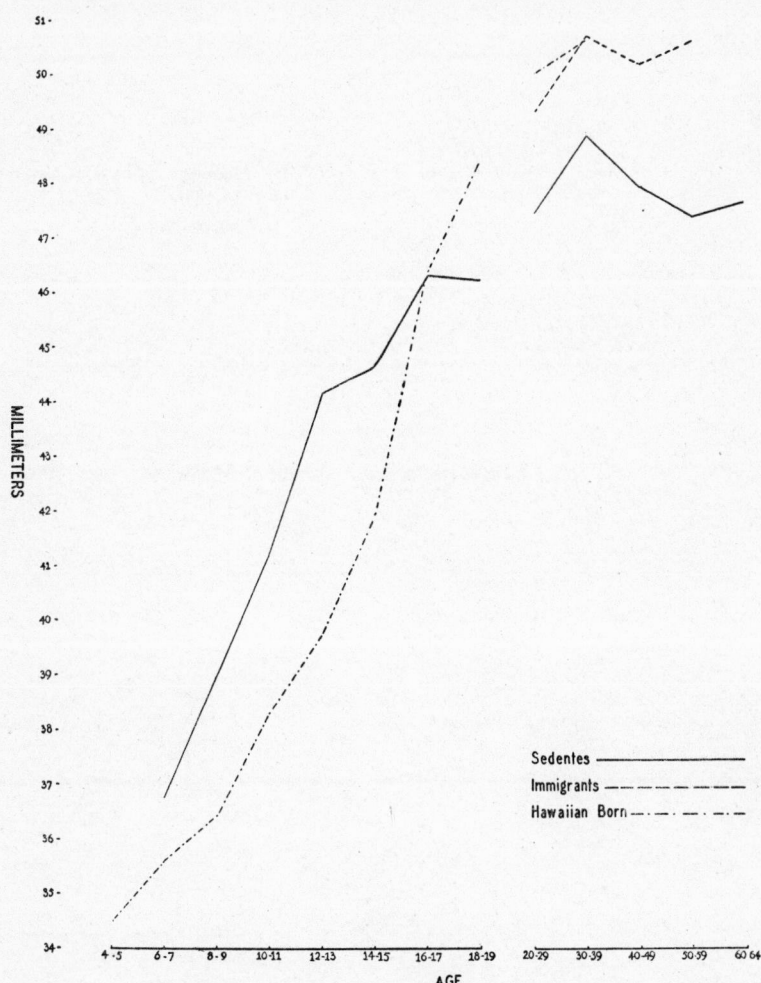

fig. 50

Age Changes in the Nose Length of Males

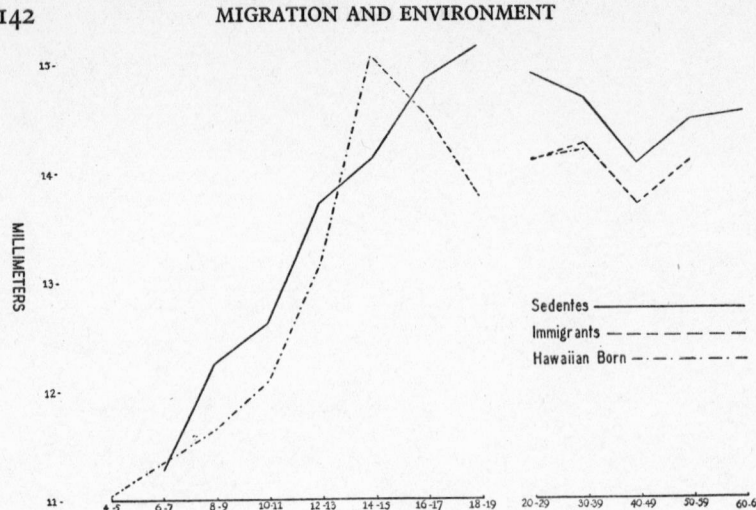

fig. 51

Age Changes in the Nose Salient of Males

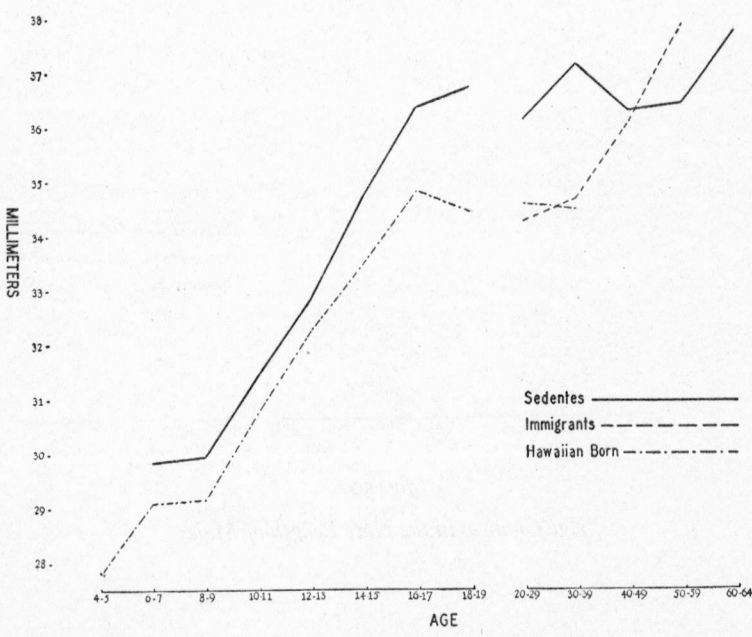

fig. 52

Age Changes in the Nose Breadth of Males

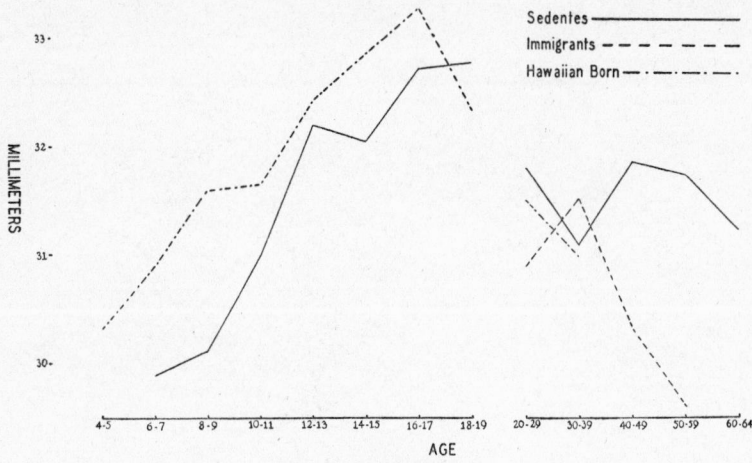

fig. 53

Age Changes in the Inter-Ocular Width of Males

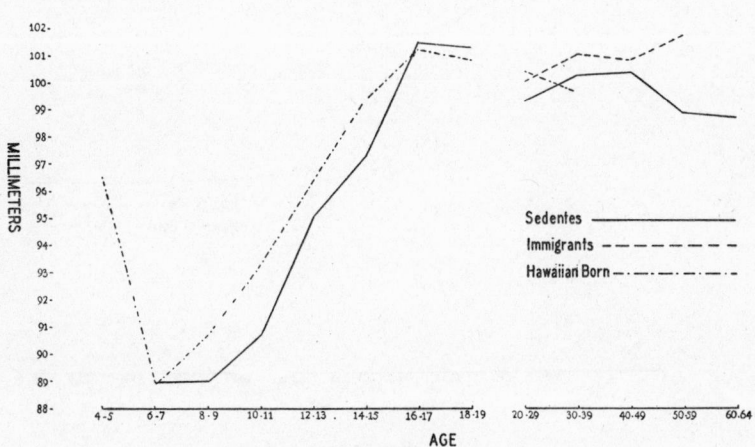

fig. 54

Age Changes in the Bi-Ocular Width of Males

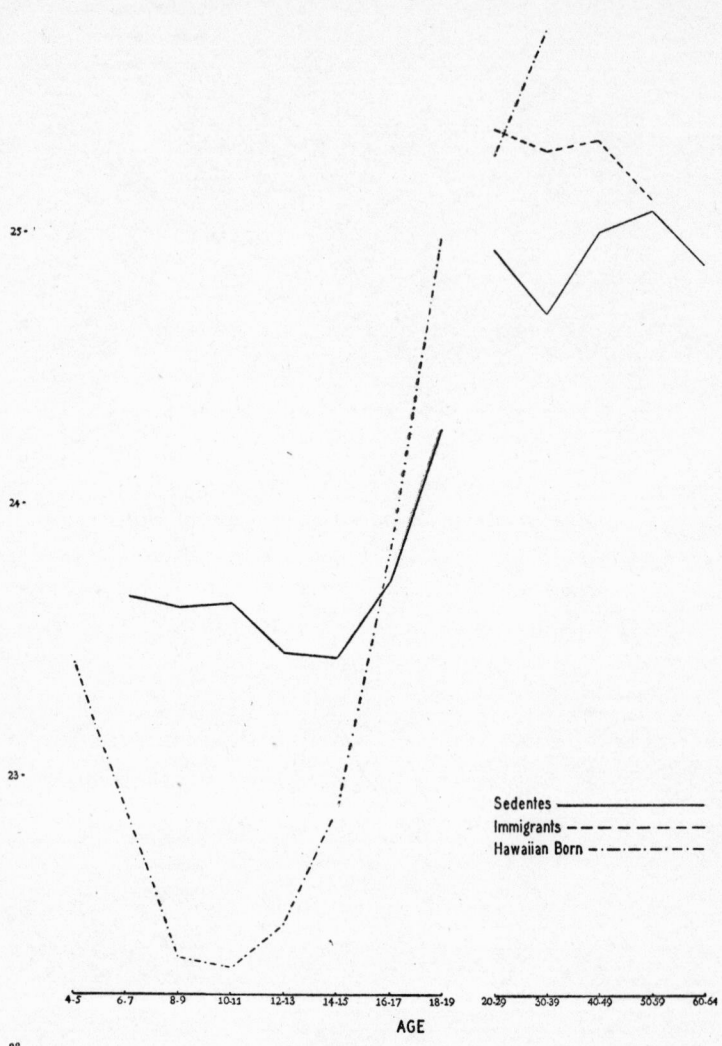

fig. 55

Age Changes in the Relative Shoulder Breadth of Males

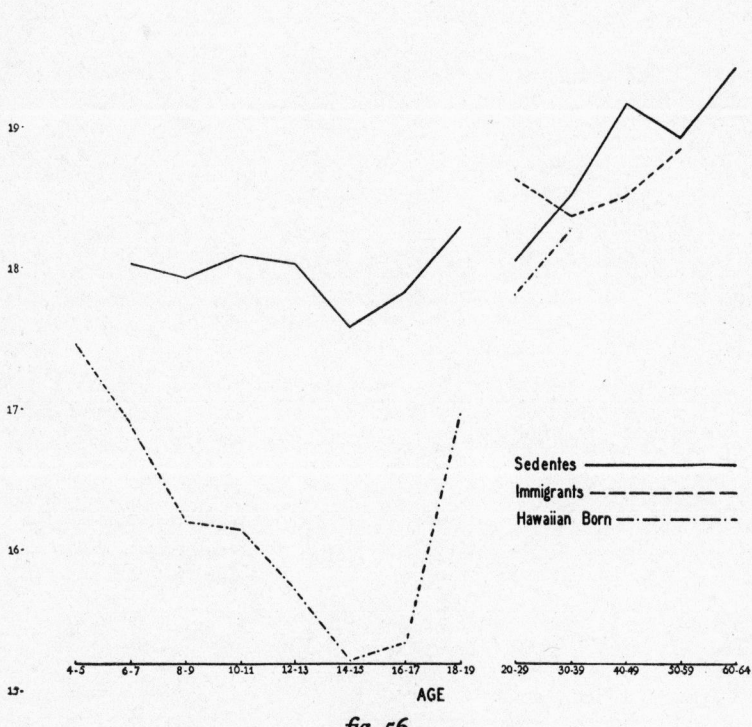

fig. 56

Age Changes in the Relative Hip Breadth of Males

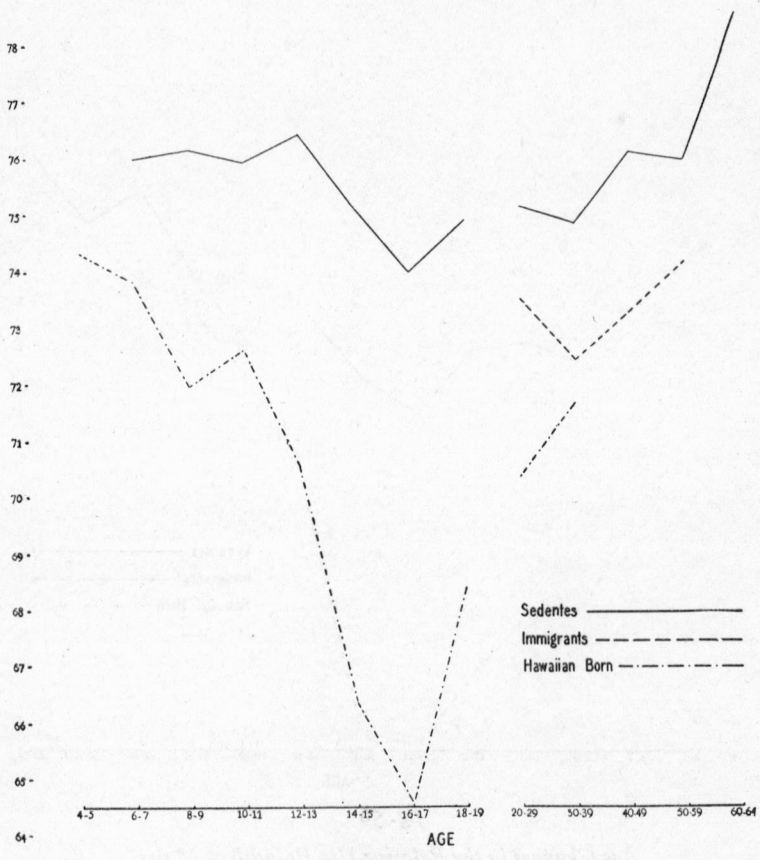

fig. 57

Age Changes in the Shoulder-Hip Index of Males

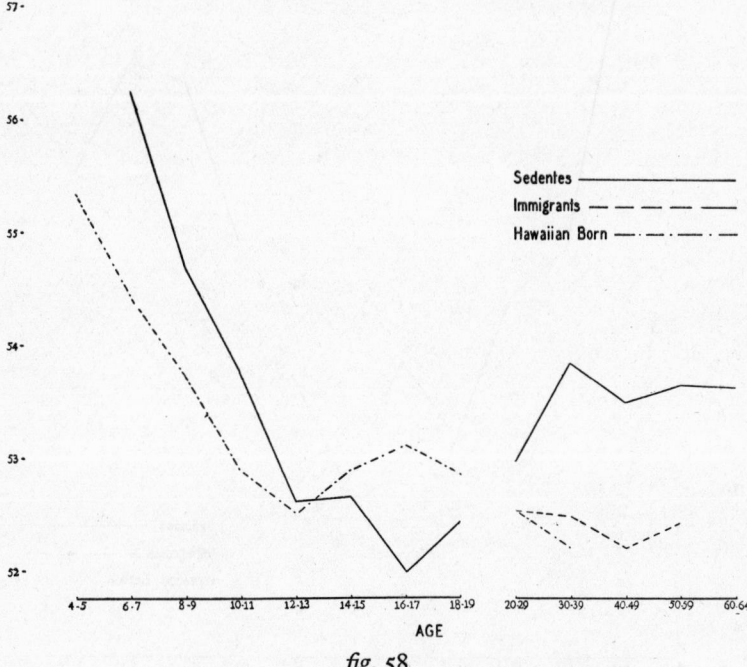

fig. 58

Age Changes in the Relative Sitting Height of Males

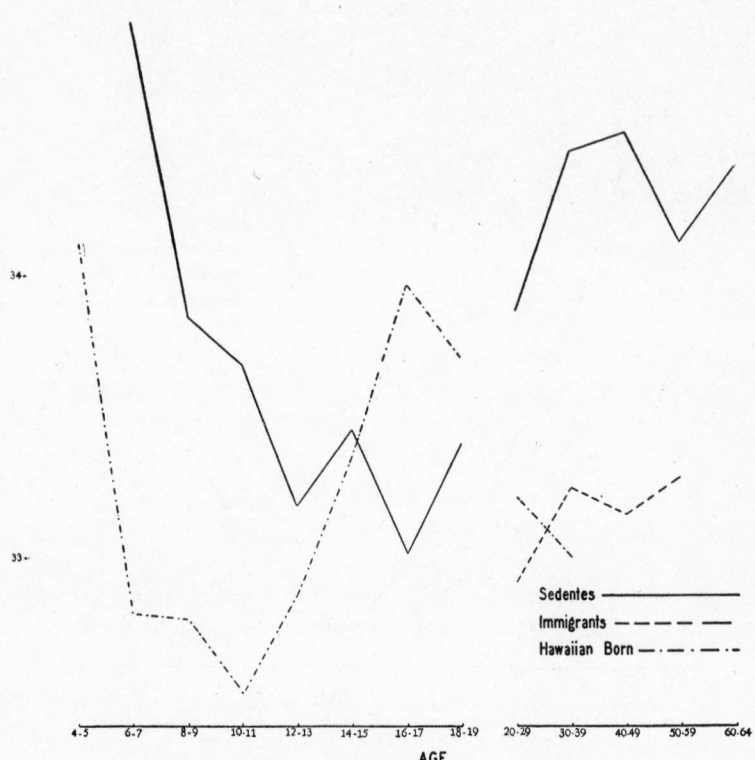

fig. 59

Age Changes in the Relative Trunk Height of Males

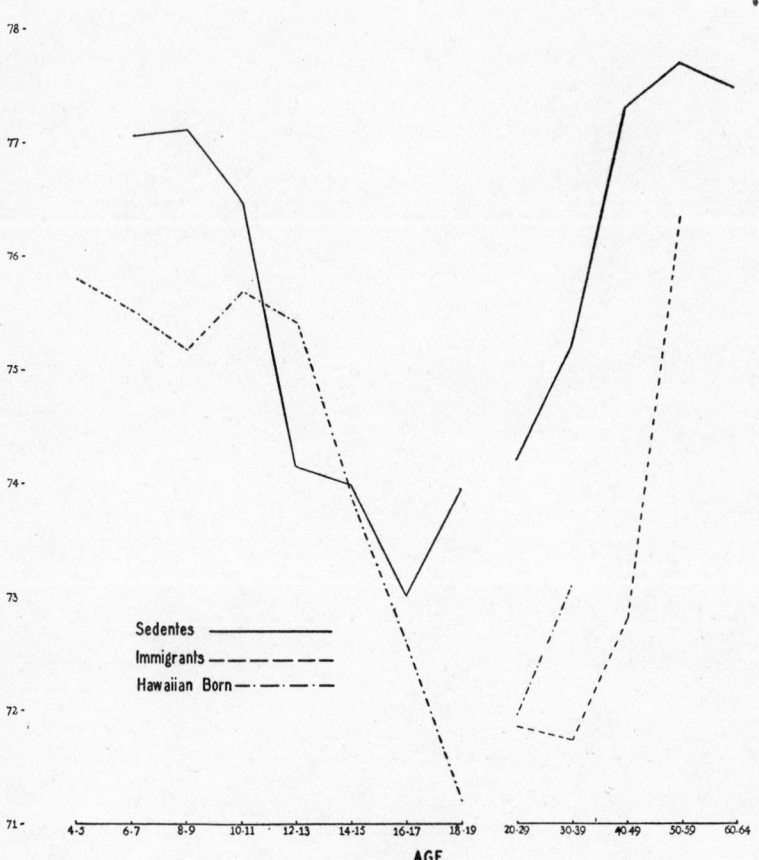

fig. 60

Age Changes in the Thoracic Index of Males

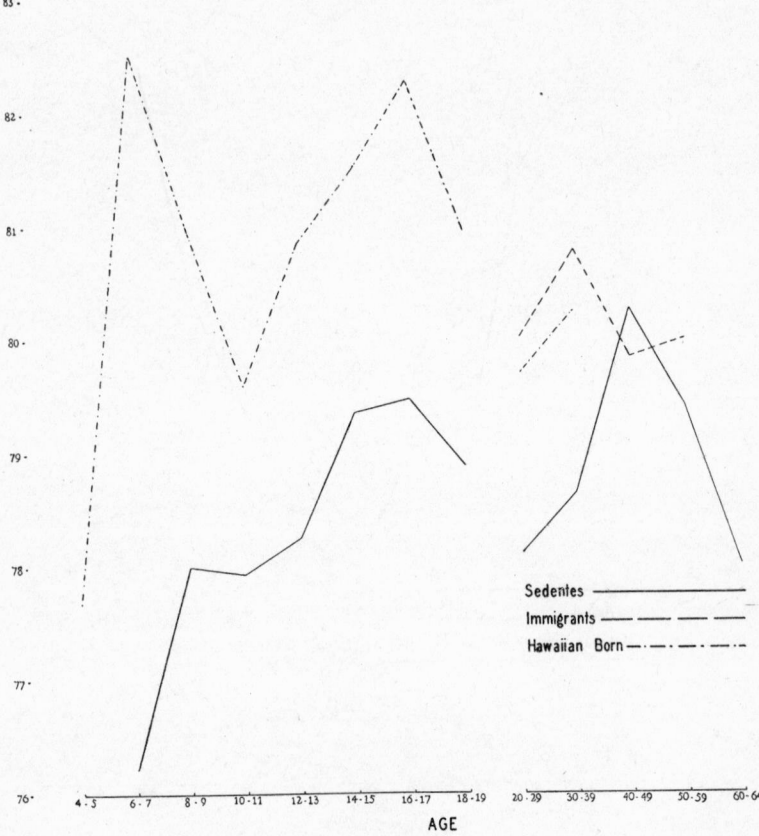

fig. 61

Age Changes in the Brachial Index of Males

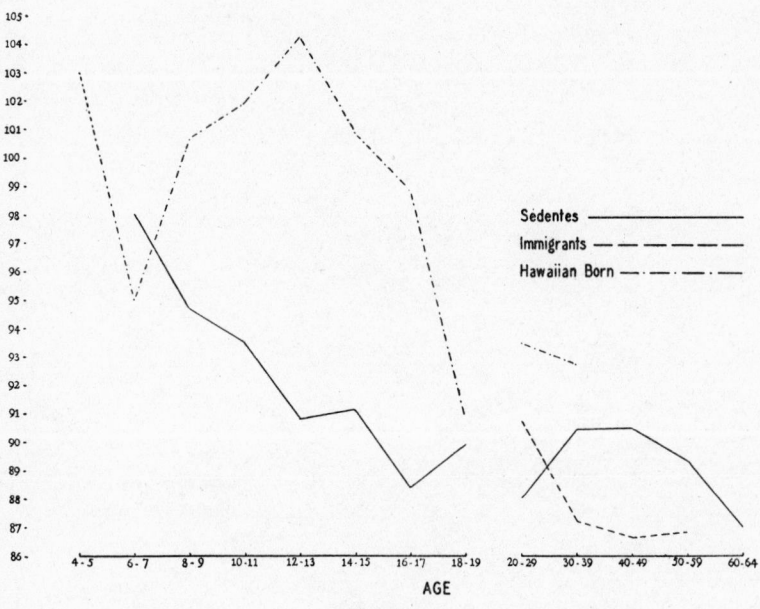

fig. 62

Age Changes in the Tibio-Femoral Index of Males

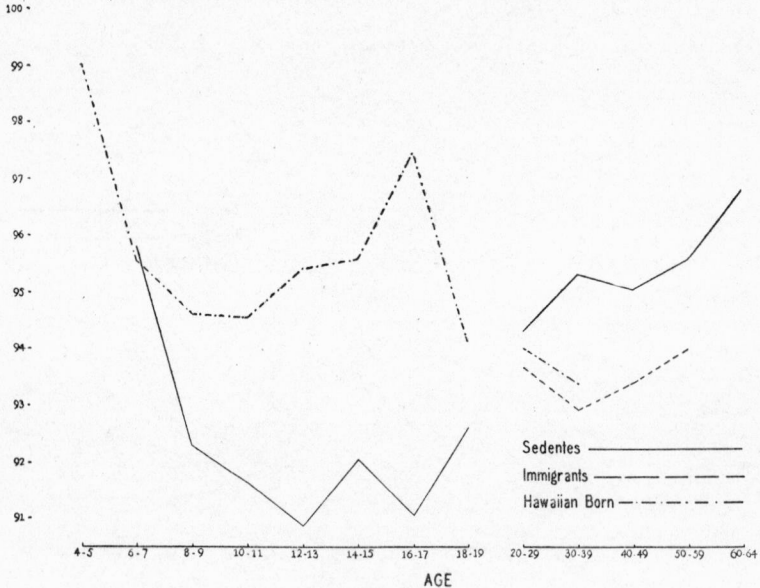

fig. 63

Age Changes in the Inter-Membral Index of Males

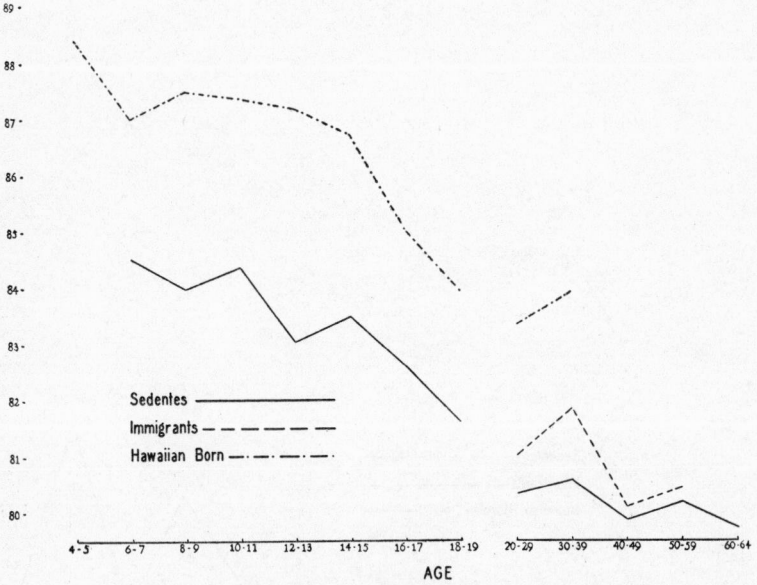

fig. 64

Age Changes in the Cephalic Index of Males

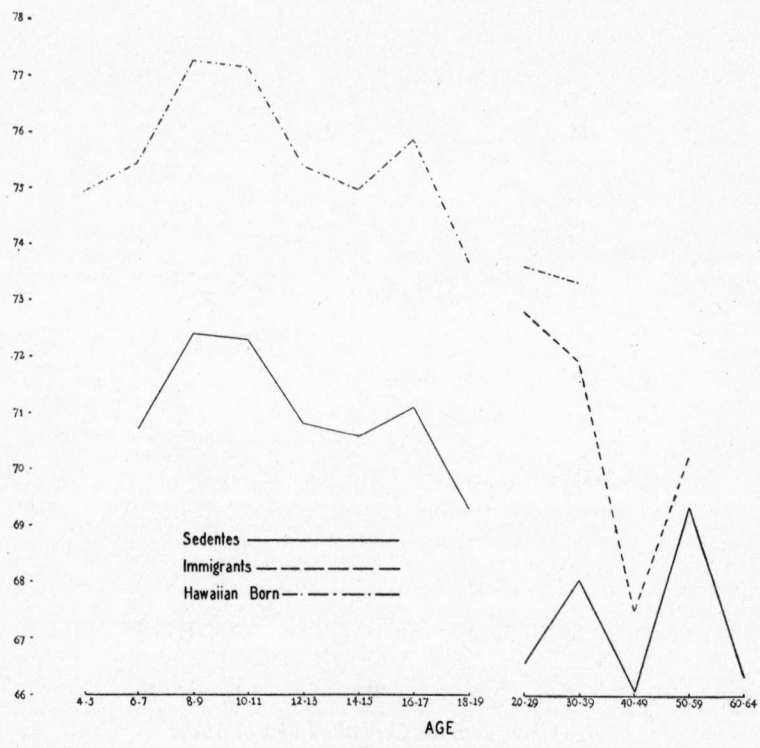

fig. 65

Age Changes in the Length-Height Index of Males

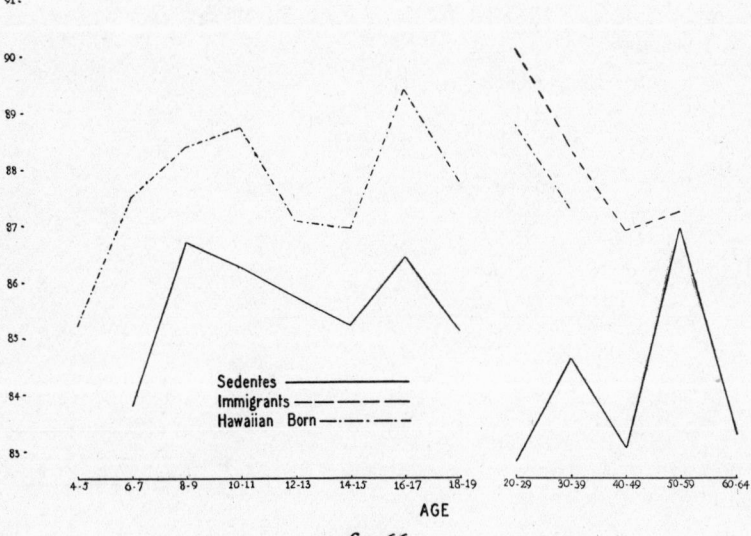

fig. 66

Age Changes in the Breadth-Height Index of Males

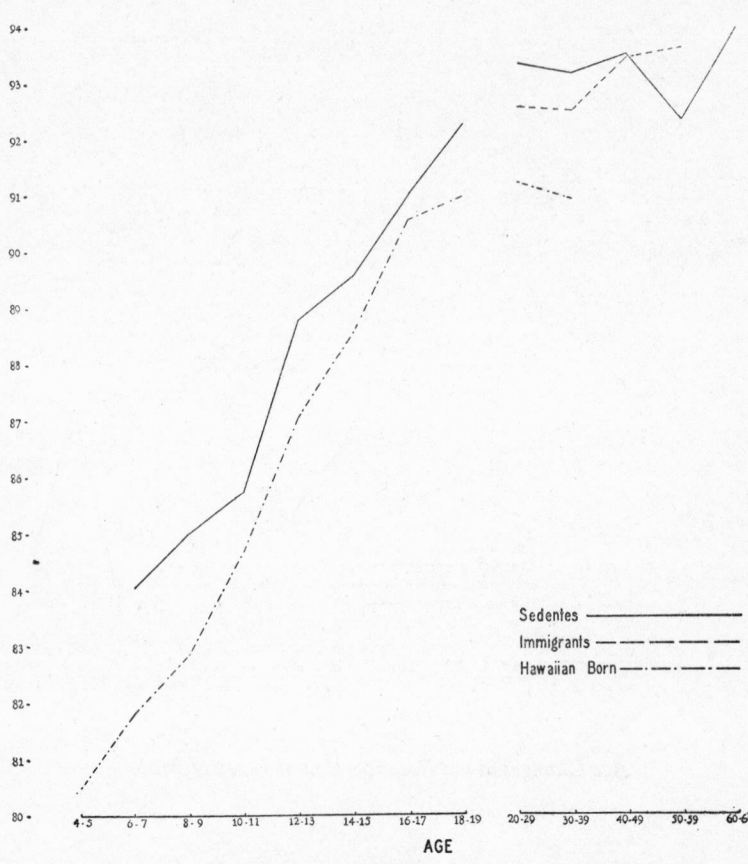

fig. 67

Age Changes in the Cephalo-Facial Index of Males

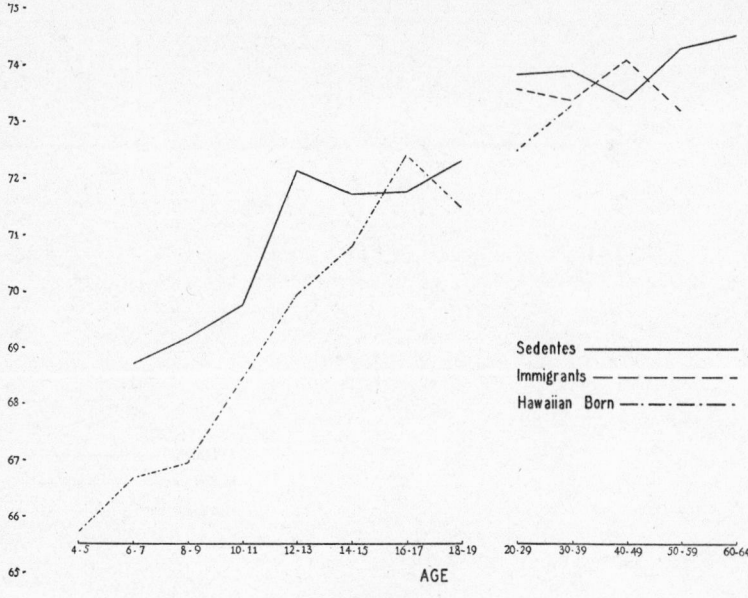

fig. 68

Age Changes in the Fronto-Parietal Index of Males

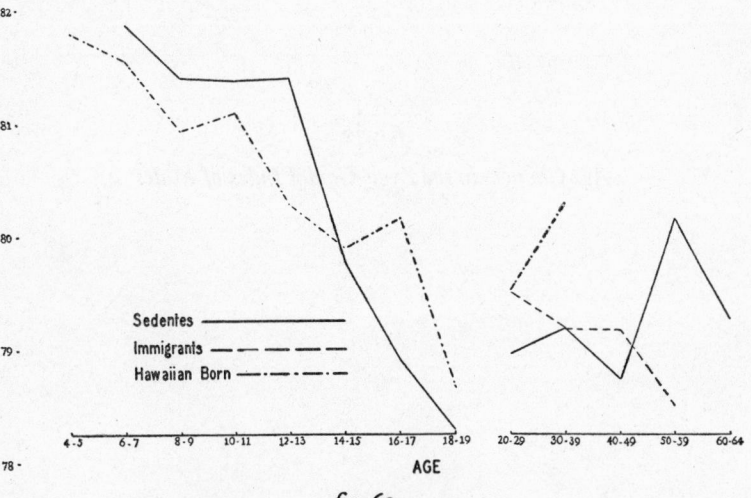

fig. 69

Age Changes in the Zygo-Frontal Index of Males

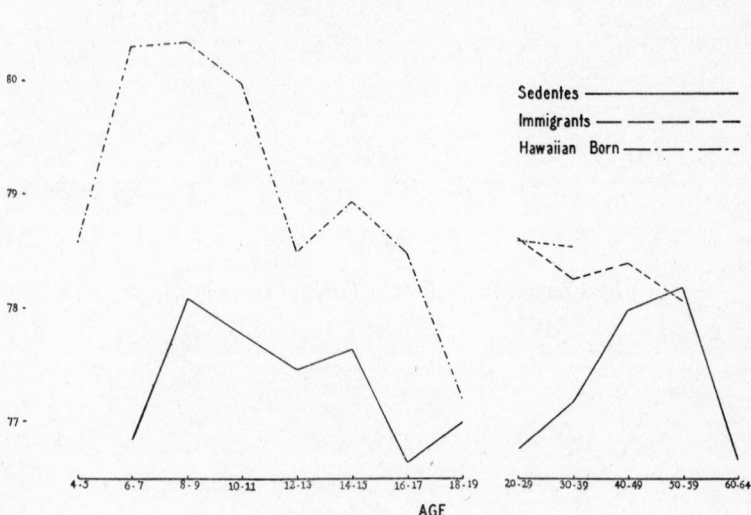

fig. 70

Age Changes in the Zygo-Gonial Index of Males

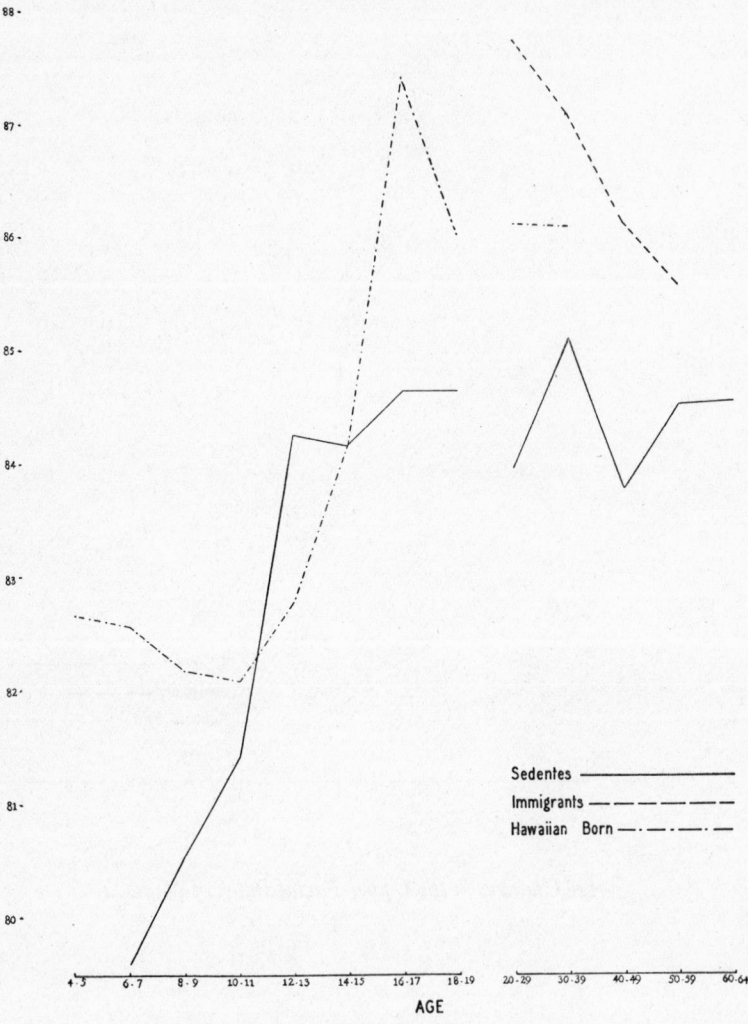

88 -

87 -

86 -

85 -

84 -

83 -

82 -

81 -

80 -

79 -

Sedentes ——————
Immigrants — — — — —
Hawaiian Born —·—·—·—

+·5   6·7   8·9   10·11   12·13   14·15   16·17   18·19   20·29   30·39   40·49   50·59   60·64

AGE

fig. 71

Age Changes in the Facial Index of Males

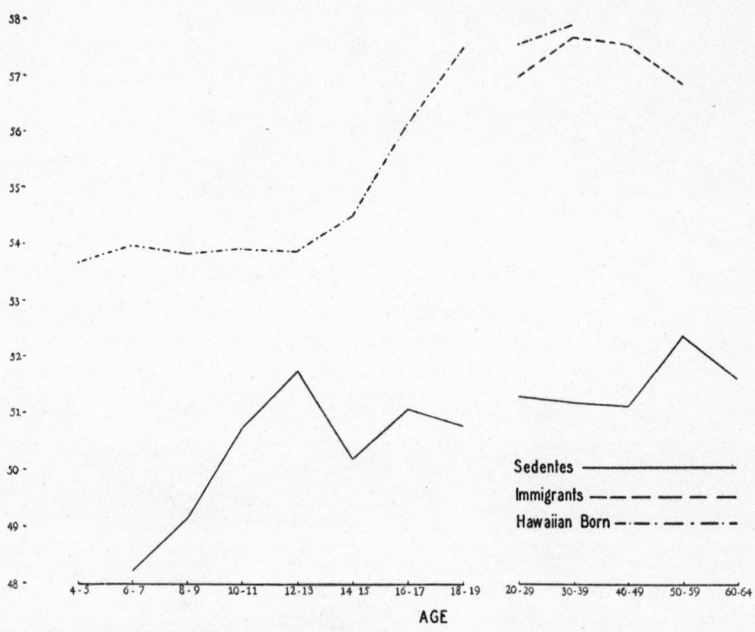

fig. 72

Age Changes in the Upper Facial Index of Males

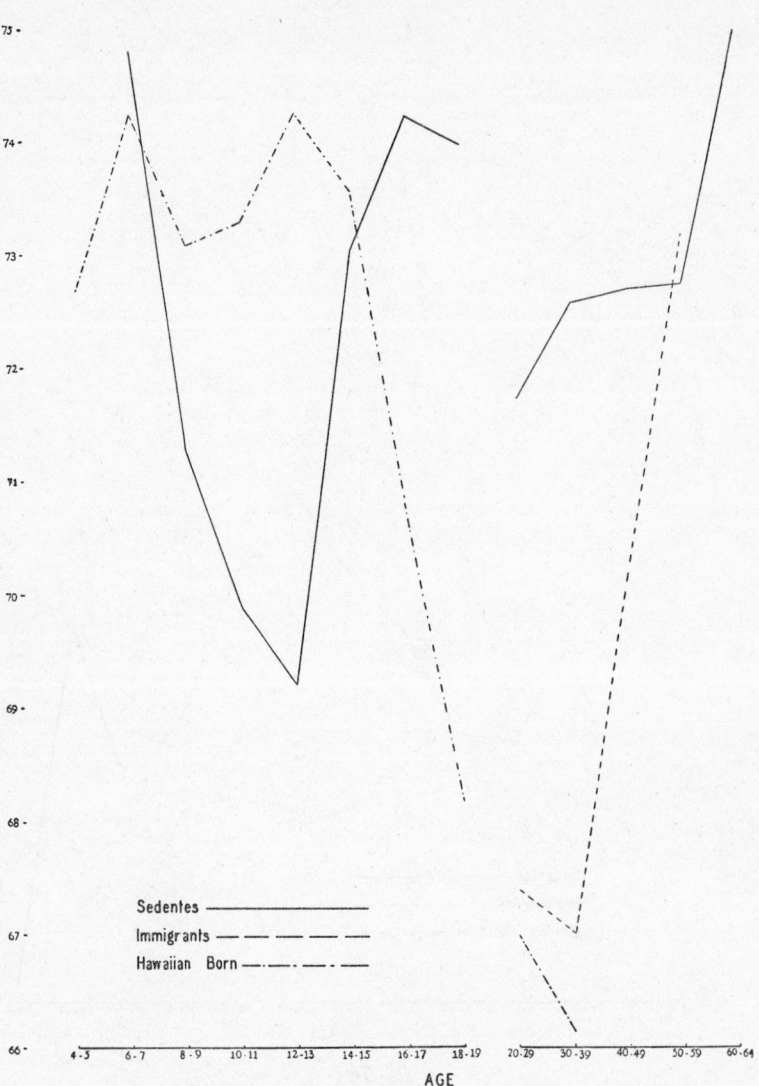

fig. 73

Age Changes in the Nasal Index of Males

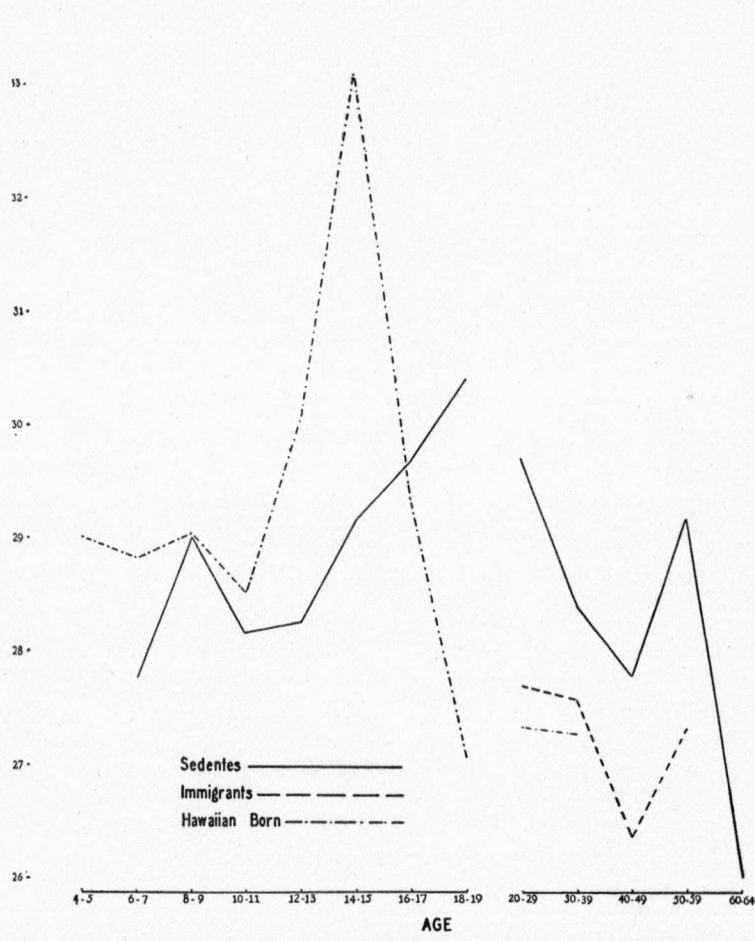

fig. 74

Age Changes in the Nose Salient-Height Index of Males

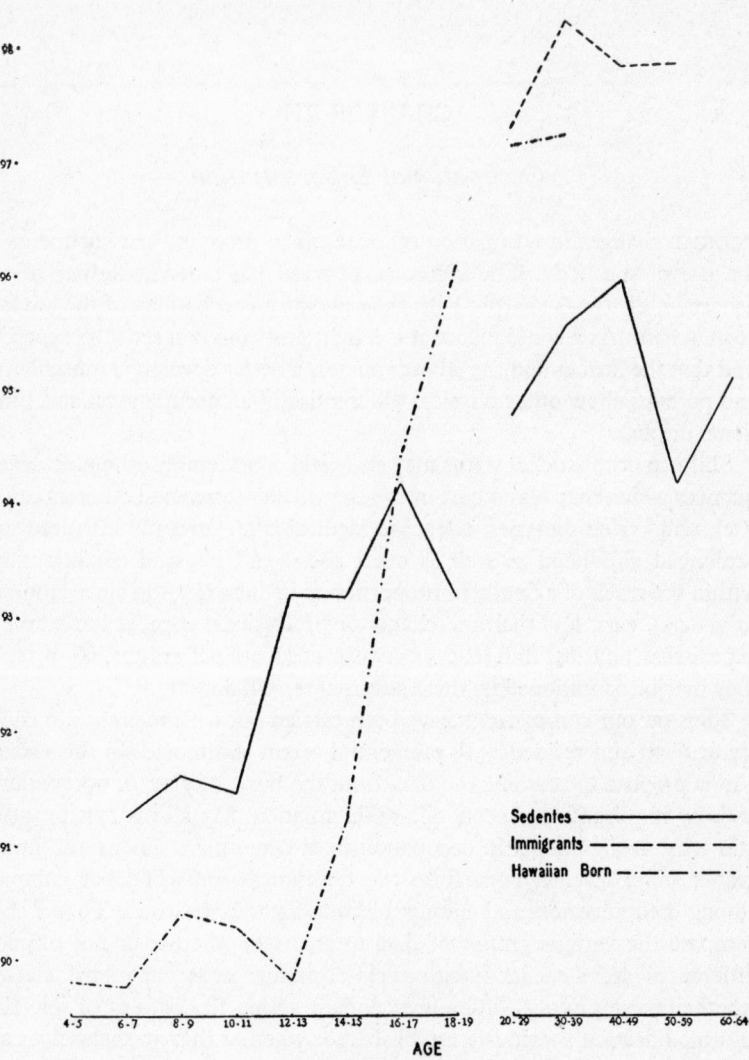

Sedentes ————————
Immigrants – – – – – –
Hawaiian Born –·—·—·—·

AGE

fig. 75

Age Changes in the Nose Length–Height Index of Males

CHAPTER VII

Occupational Differentiation

RADICAL changes in occupation often result in profound readjustments in the use of the body. The vigorous, physical labor of the farmer or the fisherman contrasts sharply with the sedentary occupations of the student or merchant. As a consequence it is a matter of common sense to expect to find that the farmer and the laborer possess a better developed musculature and perhaps show other physical differentiae of an occupational and functional origin.

Shifts in occupational status may also yield considerable economic consequences which may play a part in creating an environmental differentiation. Rich and varied dietaries, adequate medical care, carefully nurtured and prolonged childhood as well as other social and physical conditions are within the reach of a family in proportion to its income. And since laborers, in general, earn less than merchants or professional men, it is natural to expect that physical differences between occupational groups, in so far as they may be conditioned by these advantages, will develop.

Thus far our comparisons have been carried out with reference to country of birth and residence, to prefectural origin and to age. In this section I now propose to examine the data from the point of view of occupational and, by implication, of economic differentiation. My aim is first to ascertain what realignments in occupation have taken place among the immigrants and Hawaiian born from the traditional forms of labor common among their ancestors and among the contemporary sedentes. Then I shall compare the various groups of data to ascertain whether or not physical differences are associated with socio-economic or occupational classes, whether these physical differences remain within the pattern of selection and modification previously established or whether they in themselves are sufficient to account for it.

The following table reveals the degree of occupational change in the three major groups of male Japanese. The classification used here is necessarily rather coarse, in order to obtain sizable groups.

Of the total series of 172 male sedentes information on occupation was secured for only 51, but there is no reason to believe that these are not representative of the total series. Of the sedentes whose occupations are

OCCUPATIONS OF JAPANESE ADULT MALES

	Farmer		Laborer		Fisher-man		All Manual Labor	
	No.	%	No.	%	No.	%	No.	%
Sedentes	34	66.67	1	1.96	3	5.88	38	74.51
Immigrants	2	1.18	52	30.59	5	2.94	59	34.71
Hawaiian Born	10	5.35	32	17.11	3	1.60	45	24.06

	Profes-sional [1]		Student		Other		All Sedentary		Total
	No.	%	No.	%	No.	%	No.	%	
Sedentes	13	25.49	0	0	0	0	13	25.49	51
Immigrants	105	61.76	5	2.94	1 [2]	.59	111	65.29	170
Hawaiian Born	85	45.45	57	30.48	0	0	142	75.93	187

known, 75% are engaged in heavy manual labor. Agriculture alone accounts for two-thirds of the total number. Among the immigrants a shift from manual to sedentary occupations becomes apparent. Only a couple are listed as farmers although 30.59% are classified as laborers, which includes plantation as well as other forms of unskilled labor. Perhaps the most significant change among the immigrants occurs in the notable increase of 'professional' workers who are, however, mainly storekeepers and tradesmen. In the Hawaiian born this trend toward sedentary forms of labor is more pronounced. The percentage of farmers and laborers remains low while the proportion of the combined students and 'professionals' increases. The higher percentage of 'professional' among the immigrants, however, is probably the result of an age factor. Most of the Hawaiian born are in their twenties, and many of them are either still students or not yet established in a business or profession, but the presumption seems justified that most if not all the students are destined to occupy 'professional' positions. Adams [3] has pointed out the marked tendency of the Japanese to abandon plantation labor in preference to business and professional pursuits after their initial period of adjustment in Hawaii. Whereas among the sedentes roughly 75% are manual workers and about 25% follow sedentary pursuits, the Hawaiian born, on the contrary, reverse these percentages with only 24% in manual work and 76% in sedentary occupations. The immigrants are intermediate.

A check on the accuracy of these occupational distributions is provided by the distribution of the occupations of the fathers of our subjects. Un-

1 Includes officials, merchants and tradespeople.
2 Tennis professional.
3 Adams, R.—Interracial Marriage in Hawaii.

fortunately the information on the fathers of the adult sedentes and immigrants is too scanty to be reliable, but 41 of the adult Hawaiian born males were able to give the occupations of their immigrant fathers. Of these 37% were manual workers (farmers, fishermen and laborers) and 63% were in sedentary jobs (tradesmen, merchants and professional). These figures agree with the distributions of immigrants given above. Similarly I have analysed the occupations of the immigrant fathers of Hawaiian born boys and girls. Of 187 immigrant fathers of Hawaiian born girls 54% were manual laborers (farmers, fisherman and unskilled laborers) and 46% were engaged in trade and professional work. Of 332 immigrant fathers of Hawaiian born boys 48.50% held laboring jobs and 51.50% worked in sedentary positions. These distributions lean somewhat more toward the heavy laboring jobs but in general confirm the trend among immigrants toward sedentary occupations.

Recognizing that the Japanese in Hawaii have changed their occupational status and with that have acquired the concomitant advantages which are associated with superior economic ranking, we may now inquire more directly into the possible correlation of these socio-economic factors with the observed modifications in physical characters. There are two obvious ways to pursue this inquiry. We may compare the various occupational groups within each major series for significant differentiation. If occupation should turn out to be closely associated with real differences in physical type, the next step would be to determine whether or not the special characteristics of the occupational groups are responsible for the changes noted among the immigrants and Hawaiian born.

If, on the contrary, each occupational group be studied vertically, that is through the three stages of sedentes, immigrants and Hawaiian born, this would be equivalent to keeping occupation constant. Should changes appear parallel to those already determined for the total series, we might conclude that occupation is not the determining factor in producing the observed differences between the total groups.

In Tables 147–151 I have listed the means of the laborers and of the sedentary workers for each of the major groups of male sedentes, immigrants and Hawaiian born, that is, by country of birth and residence. Accordingly, it is now possible to compare Hawaiian born laborers with Hawaiian born sedentary workers and both with the total Hawaiian born group. Similarly the immigrants and the sedentes divided into occupational categories may be compared with each other and with their total series. All these comparisons have been carried out in Tables 152–160, except for the sedentary workers among the sedentes where a sufficient number were lacking for statistical validity.

Comparing first each occupational group with the total series of which it is part, we find no evidence of any significant differentiation. Each group of manual laborers is statistically identical with its respective total series. The occasional significant differences which do appear in these comparisons are small and with few exceptions do not occur consistently in characters common to all three sets of comparisons. The exceptions are the nasal breadth, thoracic index and nasal index. Each group of laborers tends to have a narrower nasal breadth, a greater thoracic index and a smaller nasal index than the corresponding mean for the total series. The increase in the thoracic index may perhaps be explained on a functional basis, but the decrease in nasal breadth and index has no obvious functional explanation.

Similarly, the sedentary workers display no significant departure from their total groups. (No adequate series of sedentary workers was available for the sedentes.) Moreover, the few significant deviations which these occupational groups show do not agree in specific trait, thereby suggesting chance rather than trend as the reason for their occurrence.

The following table sums up the degree to which these occupational classes depart from their total series. The degree of homogeneity which these figures represent is emphasized if they are compared with the corresponding percentages for the comparisons between the total series (see page 32).

Comparison	Percentage of Significant Differences	
	Measurements	Indices
Manual Laborers, Sedentes and Total Sedentes	13.79	28.57
Manual Laborers, Immigrants and Total Immigrants	.45	9.52
Manual Laborers, Hawaiian Born and Total Hawaiian Born	13.79	23.81
Sedentary Workers, Immigrants and Total Immigrants	0	0
Sedentary Workers, Hawaiian Born and Total Hawaiian Born	0	4.76

Although the percentages of significant differences are relatively low in each of these comparisons, they are not all uniform. The manual laborers of the sedentes group and the manual laborers among the Hawaiian born both show a somewhat greater tendency to deviate than do the manual laborers among the immigrants or the sedentary workers among the immigrants and Hawaiian born. This may be merely the result of chance, but it does suggest another explanation.

Since the sedentary workers in the immigrant series consist largely of former manual laborers who have been enabled in middle life to profit by their greater opportunities in Hawaii, it is reasonable to argue that no essential physical differences are to be expected between these two occupational groups in the immigrant series. This is, in fact, what we find. The occupational distinctions among the sedentes, however, appear to be more profound; the sons of laborers continue in the occupation of their fathers and the sons of sedentary workers follow their sires. To a lesser degree the same situation applies to the Hawaiian born, although here more sons of the laboring classes are able to make the transition. It might, therefore, follow that physical differences associated with occupation would be more apparent among the sedentes and the Hawaiian born than among the immigrants.

This argument, plausible as it may appear, is not supported by the comparisons between manual and sedentary workers of the same series which are discussed in the next paragraphs. The differences between both groups of workers are much the same among immigrants as among Hawaiian born. Unfortunately the absence of a significant series of sedentary workers among the sedentes makes this check incomplete.

Turning now to the comparisons between manual and sedentary workers within each major series, we find as we might expect that the significant differences increase in number, but only slightly in significance. Here we are contrasting two distinct selected groups of a whole series with each other, whereas in the previous comparisons we were setting one part against the whole. The percentage of significant differences still remains low as compared with the percentages of significant differences between the total series themselves. Again most of the differences appear to occur at random, that is to say, no very definite pattern of differences seems apparent. A certain vague indication of conformity to pattern may perhaps be detected in the fact that both the Hawaiian born and the immigrant sedentary workers agree by deviating significantly from the manual workers in the same character at least four times. It is true that part of this agreement in deviation may be accidental, but it is worthy of notice that this similarity occurs in traits in which each group of manual laborers showed common deviations from their total groups. The sedentary workers compared with manual laborers of the same total series have shallower chests and wider noses, and relative to stature, narrower shoulders and hips. They also tend to have reduced thoracic and increased nasal indices. These differences in chest, shoulders and hip proportions between the occupational groups conceivably have a functional basis, but again it is difficult to see any occupational explanation for the differences in nasal width and nasal index.

The manual versus sedentary groups within each of the major series are briefly summarized in the following table of percentages of significant differences.

Comparison [1]	Percentage of Significant Differences	
	Measurements	Indices
Manual Laborers, Immigrants and Sedentary Workers, Immigrants	20.69	28.57
Manual Laborers, Hawaiian Born and Sedentary Workers, Hawaiian Born	20.69	33.33

Thus from these comparisons by occupational groups we discern a minor differentiation between the manual and sedentary workers of each of the three major series. This, however, is not of sufficient proportion to account for the profound deviations which separate the total groups from each other. Moreover, the differentials of the occupational groups are not common to each pair. Only in the chest, shoulder, hip and nasal proportions are any traces of a uniform pattern of deviation detectable.

A quite different and much more significant pattern takes form when similar occupational groups from each of the three master series are compared with each other. Once more we return to the tripartite division of sedentes, immigrants and Hawaiian born, but now classified further according to occupation. The detailed comparisons may be studied in Tables 161–165. In the following table the significant differences have been calculated as percentages of the total number of trait comparisons.

Comparison	Percentage of Significant Differences	
	Measurements	Indices
Manual Laborers, Sedentes and Manual Laborers, Immigrants	20.69	33.33
Manual Laborers, Immigrants and Manual Laborers, Hawaiian Born	48.28	47.62
Manual Laborers, Sedentes and Manual Laborers, Hawaiian Born	41.38	57.14
Sedentary Workers, Immigrants and Sedentary Workers, Hawaiian Born	58.62	38.10

It is clear from these tables that differentiation according to country of birth and country of residence is of far greater significance than the rela-

[1] An adequate series of sedentary workers was lacking for comparison with manual laborers in the series of sedentes.

tively minor occupational distinctions within each total group. In other words we have found that the manual laborers as well as the sedentary workers are primarily differentiated not by the type of labor they perform but rather by the country of birth and nurture and by the selection inherent in migration. The order of differentiation between the two groups of workers of the same total series is of slight proportions; whereas, the same classes of laborers, grouped by country of birth and of residence display much greater differentiation. It is true, however, that the degree of differentiation between similar occupational groups according to their country of birth and residence is not equal to the magnitude of the deviations shown by the total series also analysed by country of birth and residence. This is perhaps to be expected for the total series represent combined sub-groups showing similar trends thereby reducing the probable errors without materially altering the direction of the deviations.

The similarity of deviation between the occupational groups and between the total series may be best illustrated by means of graphs. In Fig. 76 the manual laborers among the sedentes, immigrants and Hawaiian born are compared with each other. The configuration of these graphs is very similar to the analogous graphs for the total series. Unfortunately the absence of a workable series of sedentary workers among the sedentes excludes the graphing of the sedentary workers for comparison, but the Hawaiian born sedentary workers plotted against immigrants of similar occupations fall into a pattern of deviation that closely parallels the graph of Hawaiian born and immigrant manual laborers (Fig. 77). Moreover these graphs of the Hawaiian born manual and sedentary workers conform with the total Hawaiian born similarly plotted against the total immigrants.

It is thus apparent that the occupational groups both statistically and graphically repeat the general patterns formed by the total seriations of sedentes, immigrants and Hawaiian born. Although the summations of the significant differences have served as indexes of the degree of differentiation and the graphs as representations of the general patterns of deviations, we have yet to consider whether the occupational groups divided according to country of birth and of residence are significantly distinguished from each other in the same characters in which the total and age groups are also significantly differentiated. I have, therefore, in the following table listed the characters in which there are significant differences between the occupational groups under consideration. In addition I have indicated with a question mark those changes which do not reach the conventional degree of significance, three times the probable error of the difference, but which are more than twice the probable error. These then are compared with the differences which occur between the total and age series arranged in similar categories of country of origin and of residence.

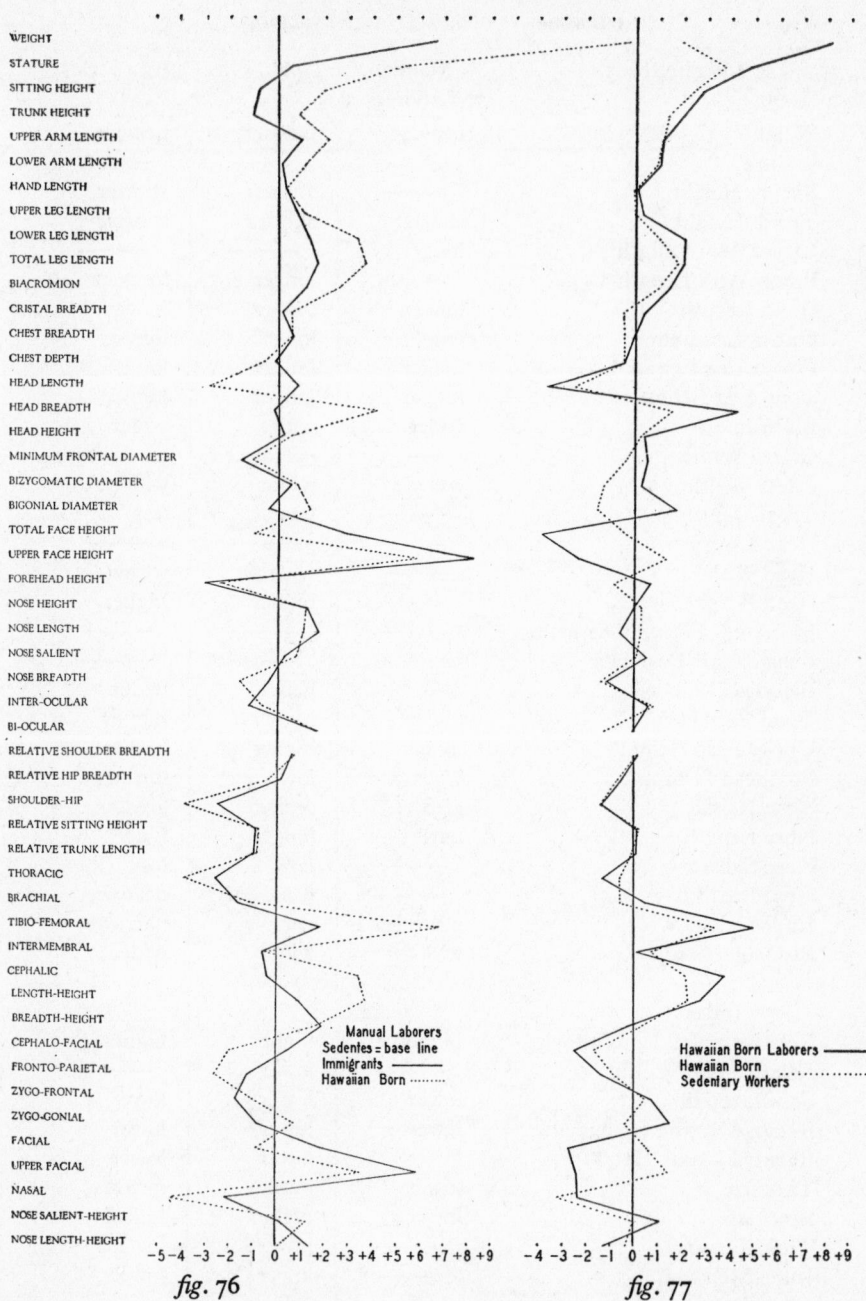

WEIGHT
STATURE
SITTING HEIGHT
TRUNK HEIGHT
UPPER ARM LENGTH
LOWER ARM LENGTH
HAND LENGTH
UPPER LEG LENGTH
LOWER LEG LENGTH
TOTAL LEG LENGTH
BIACROMION
CRISTAL BREADTH
CHEST BREADTH
CHEST DEPTH
HEAD LENGTH
HEAD BREADTH
HEAD HEIGHT
MINIMUM FRONTAL DIAMETER
BIZYGOMATIC DIAMETER
BIGONIAL DIAMETER
TOTAL FACE HEIGHT
UPPER FACE HEIGHT
FOREHEAD HEIGHT
NOSE HEIGHT
NOSE LENGTH
NOSE SALIENT
NOSE BREADTH
INTER-OCULAR
BI-OCULAR
RELATIVE SHOULDER BREADTH
RELATIVE HIP BREADTH
SHOULDER-HIP
RELATIVE SITTING HEIGHT
RELATIVE TRUNK LENGTH
THORACIC
BRACHIAL
TIBIO-FEMORAL
INTERMEMBRAL
CEPHALIC
LENGTH-HEIGHT
BREADTH-HEIGHT
CEPHALO-FACIAL
FRONTO-PARIETAL
ZYGO-FRONTAL
ZYGO-GONIAL
FACIAL
UPPER FACIAL
NASAL
NOSE SALIENT-HEIGHT
NOSE LENGTH-HEIGHT

Manual Laborers
Sedentes = base line
Immigrants ———
Hawaiian Born ·······

Hawaiian Born Laborers ———
Hawaiian Born
Sedentary Workers ···············

−5 −4 −3 −2 −1 0 +1 +2 +3 +4 +5 +6 +7 +8 +9   −4 −3 −2 −1 0 +1 +2 +3 +4 +5 +6 +7 +8 +9

fig. 76   *fig.* 77

Comparison of Male Manual Laborers, Sedentes, Immigrants, and Hawaiian Born

Comparison of Male Hawaiian Born Manual Laborers and Male Hawaiian Born Sedentary Workers by Deviations from Their Corresponding Occupational Group of Immigrants

IMMIGRANTS COMPARED WITH SEDENTES

Measurement	Manual Laborers	Total Series	Age Series
Weight	heavier	heavier	heavier
Stature	——	——	——
Sitting Height	——	shorter	shorter
Trunk Height	shorter ?	shorter	shorter
Upper Arm Length	longer	——	——
Lower Arm Length	——	longer	longer
Hand Length	longer ?	longer	longer
Upper Leg Length	longer ?	longer	longer
Lower Leg Length	longer	longer	longer
Total Leg Length	longer	longer	longer
Biacromion	wider	wider	wider
Cristal Width	——	narrower ?	narrower
Chest Width	wider ?	wider	wider ?
Chest Depth	——	less	less
Head Length	——	——	——
Head Width	——	wider ?	wider ?
Head Height	——	higher	higher
Minimum Frontal Diameter	——	——	——
Bizygomatic Diameter	——	——	——
Bigonial Diameter	——	wider	wider
Total Face Height	higher ?	higher	higher
Upper Face Height	higher	higher	higher
Forehead Height	lower ?	lower ?	lower
Nose Height	greater ?	greater	greater
Nose Length	longer	longer	longer
Nose Salient	——	less	less
Nose Breadth	——	narrower	narrower
Inter-Ocular Width	narrower ?	narrower	narrower ?
Bi-Ocular Width	wider ?	wider	wider
Index			
Relative Shoulder Width	higher	higher	higher
Relative Hip Width	——	lower	——
Shoulder-Hip	lower	lower	lower
Relative Sitting Height	lower	lower	lower
Relative Trunk Height	lower	lower	lower
Thoracic	lower	lower	lower
Brachial	lower ?	higher	higher
Tibio-Femoral	——	lower ?	lower ?
Inter-Membral	——	lower	lower
Cephalic	——	——	——
Length-Height	——	higher	higher

IMMIGRANTS COMPARED WITH SEDENTES—*continued*

Index	Manual Laborers	Total Series	Age Series
Breadth-Height	——	higher	higher
Cephalo-Facial	——	——	——
Fronto-Parietal	lower ?	——	——
Zygo-Frontal	lower	——	——
Zygo-Gonial	——	higher	higher ?
Facial	higher ?	higher	higher
Upper Facial	higher	higher	higher
Nasal	lower ?	lower	lower
Nose Salient-Nose Height	——	lower	lower
Nose Length-Nose Height	higher ?	higher	higher

HAWAIIAN BORN COMPARED WITH IMMIGRANTS

Measurement	Manual Laborers	Sedentary Workers	Total Series	Age Series
Weight	heavier	——	heavier ?	heavier
Stature	taller	taller	taller	taller
Sitting Height	greater	greater	greater	greater
Trunk Height	greater	greater	greater	greater
Upper Arm Length	longer	longer	longer	longer
Lower Arm Length	longer	longer	longer	longer
Hand Length	——	——	——	longer
Upper Leg Length	——	——	——	——
Lower Leg Length	longer	longer	longer	longer
Total Leg Length	longer	longer	longer	longer
Biacromion	wider	wider	wider	wider
Cristal Width	——	narrower	narrower ?	——
Chest Width	——	narrower	narrower	——
Chest Depth	——	less	less	——
Head Length	shorter	shorter	shorter	shorter
Head Width	wider	wider	wider	wider
Head Height	higher ?	——	higher	——
Minimum Frontal Diameter	——	——	——	——
Bizygomatic Diameter	——	narrower	narrower ?	——
Bigonial Diameter	wider ?	narrower	——	——
Total Face Height	shorter	——	shorter	shorter
Upper Face Height	shorter	longer	——	——
Forehead Height	——	——	——	——
Nose Height	——	——	——	greater ?
Nose Length	——	——	——	longer ?
Nose Salient	——	——	——	——
Nose Breadth	narrower	narrower	narrower	——
Inter-Ocular	——	wider ?	wider	——
Bi-Ocular	——	narrower ?	——	——
Index				
Relative Shoulder Width	——	——	——	——
Relative Hip Width	lower	lower	lower	lower ?
Shoulder-Hip	lower ?	lower	lower	lower
Relative Sitting Height	——	——	——	——
Relative Trunk Height	——	——	——	——
Thoracic	——	——	lower ?	——
Brachial	——	——	——	——
Tibio-Femoral	higher	higher	higher	higher
Inter-Membral	——	——	——	——
Cephalic	higher	higher	higher	higher

HAWAIIAN BORN COMPARED WITH IMMIGRANTS—*continued*

Index	Manual Laborers	Sedentary Workers	Total Series	Age Series
Length-Height	higher	higher	higher	higher
Breadth-Height	———	———		
Cephalo-Facial	lower	lower	lower	lower
Fronto-Parietal	lower	lower ?	lower	lower ?
Zygo-Frontal	———	———	higher ?	———
Zygo-Gonial	higher	———	———	———
Facial	lower	———	———	lower
Upper Facial	lower	higher	———	———
Nasal	lower ?	lower	lower	lower ?
Nose Salient-Nose Height	———	———	———	———
Nose Length-Nose Height	lower	———	lower	lower ?

These comparative tables permit us to see to what extent the same traits show similar changes whether in the total, age or occupational seriations. Considering the number of individual traits and the diverse variables involved, something less than identity may well be expected without weakening the thesis suggested. As a matter of fact, the large number of traits in which all the various series behave identically is very impressive. The immigrant manual laborers, the total immigrants and the immigrants corrected for age, each compared with their respective sedentes, agree in 19 out of 29 measurements and disagree in only 9. They are in agreement in 11 out of 21 indices, in disagreement in 7 and are uncertain in 3. The Hawaiian born manual laborers and sedentary workers, the total Hawaiian born and the Hawaiian born corrected for age show similar relationships to their respective immigrant antecedents in 14 (possibly 17) out of 29 measurements, and in 14 (possibly 16) out of 21 indices.

If, however, the results of each intra-occupational comparison are compared separately either with corresponding alignments for the total series or with the total age-corrected series, the number of similarities increases as one would expect where fewer variables are introduced.

The opportunity to compare the behavior of the Hawaiian born manual laborers and sedentary workers with that of the total and age groups not only reveals the extent to which they share a common pattern but also discloses the otherwise obscured effect of occupation on the total seriations. The tendency of the total Hawaiian born to have narrower hips and chests than the total immigrants is revealed to be the contribution of the sedentary workers in the total series. Similarly the total group of Hawaiian born derive their narrower face widths and, in part, their wider inter-ocular widths from the sedentary workers in the series, and from the manual laborers they receive their tendency toward greater weight, shorter total face heights and lower nose length-nose height indices.

CHAPTER VIII

Qualitative Traits

THE principal emphasis in this study has been on those characters which can be measured with more or less accuracy and where variations can be expressed in statistical terms subject to statistical safeguards. But in addition to these quantitative and mensurable characters, there is a class of physical characteristics, often of great significance, which defies exact, impersonal measurement. With improved technical resources many of them will in time receive quantitative expression, but at present we are obliged to distinguish them as qualitative traits. Variations in these qualitative characters must be recorded according to the observer's judgment, experience and standards, with the inevitable consequence that their distributions are often highly subjective and, in the absence of observational errors referable to a common scale, unreliable for comparative purposes. Some workers entertain such profound suspicion of the validity of percentage tables of qualitative characters that they omit them entirely from their studies. I must confess a sympathy with this austere insistence on the most rigorous standards of accuracy. For that reason I include with reservations the following brief discussion of the qualitative characters of the Japanese. My reasons for doing so are two. First, because it is of more than passing interest to determine whether or not the patterns of change characteristic of the size and proportions of immigrant and Hawaiian born Japanese are repeated in their qualitative characters. And second, the fact that all the observations were made by one worker implies a certain degree of homogeneity in the results, which, therefore, offer greater reliability for comparisons within the same body of data.

Tables 166 and 167 set forth the frequency distributions of the various qualitative characters. The data are arranged by total series only.

The immigrant and Hawaiian born males tend to be very slightly darker in the exposed parts of their skin than are the male sedentes. One may attribute this to the more tropical climate of Hawaii, especially since the three groups of Japanese do not differ essentially in the pigmentation of the unexposed skin areas.

The differences between the three male groups in the characteristics of hair are not unequivocal. For example, although all three series have pre-

176

vailingly straight hair, the male immigrants show a slight but consistent trend toward greater waviness which becomes more pronounced in the Hawaiian born. At the same time the texture of the hair becomes less coarse in passing from sedentes to immigrants and finally to Hawaiian born. But it is not beyond the range of probability that the exigencies of fashion play a part in these shifts in frequency. Straight hair is generally admired in Japan and it is conceivable that those with a tendency to wavy hair might seek to disguise it by various hair applications which in turn would render the hair sticky and coarse. In Hawaii, on the contrary, wavy hair is not at a discount.

In hair color the male sedentes and immigrants are practically identical. They both are predominantly black haired with a slight proportion of dark brown hair. The Hawaiian born do show a fairly large decrease in the percentage of black hair with a corresponding increase in dark brown. It should, however, be emphasized that if the sun has a bleaching power on hair then it is altogether to be expected that the young Hawaiian born males show its effect.

The Japanese are not a particularly hairy people; in fact they are rather glabrous than otherwise. In the quantity of facial and head hair no consistent differences appear among the three male groups with which we are concerned.

Similarly all our male groups show like degrees of body hairiness, with the exception of the lower arm and the leg, where the immigrants appear to be rather more glabrous than either sedentes or Hawaiian born.

No noteworthy distinctions can be drawn between the three male series in eye color, in iris structure or in sclera color. With few exceptions all the Japanese regardless of birthplace have brown or 'black' eyes. Grouping the brown eyes, we find that 85.44% of the sedentes fall into this group, 96.06% of the immigrants and 97.88% of the Hawaiian born. The rest have mixed eyes. It is doubtful that the smaller percentage of brown eyes among the sedentes is significant. But this discrepancy of the sedentes may explain the smaller percentage of them with homogeneous irises, since dark brown eyes are apt to be seen with homogeneous iris structure.

Although the epicanthic fold, generally associated with Mongoloid people, is present in a majority of the males of each of our series of Japanese, nevertheless certain differences occur between the sedentes, on the one hand, and the immigrants and Hawaiian born, on the other. The sedentes include an appreciably larger percentage of individuals who completely lacked the epicanthic fold, than the immigrants and Hawaiian born. They also exhibit a lesser degree of epicanthic development than the immigrants and Hawaiian born. In comparing all those showing any evidence of epicanthus, we find the sedentes with 52.59% having only a *slight* degree as against the immigrants and the Hawaiian born, 75.93% and 80.81% of whom have a *medium* degree of epicanthus.

Although the Hawaiian born are considerably younger than the sedentes, age is not entirely accountable for this differentiation in the eye fold. The immigrants who coincide with the Hawaiian born in the development of epicanthus are actually slightly older on the average than the sedentes.

In the axis of the eye the Hawaiian born show a slightly greater tendency than either of the other two groups toward downward slope. The sedentes, on the contrary, have a very slightly greater percentage of upward sloping eyes. A slight difference occurs in the width of the palpebral opening of the eye, the immigrants and Hawaiian born having a somewhat greater percentage with narrow openings.

The eyebrows, both in thickness and in spacing, are similar in all three groups. Minor differences appear but they are of slight significance.

The features of the forehead which were observed included the slope, height, development of brow ridges and development of glabella. Only in the last two do the differences appear to be of major importance. Both the Hawaiian born and the immigrants are distinguished from the sedentes by their greater development of the brow ridge and the glabella. These two traits often show parallel developments.

The two groups resident in Hawaii also are differentiated from the sedentes by their tendency for the temporal hair to encroach onto the forehead.

Seven nasal characteristics were noted. These were nasal profile, height of bridge, height of root, breadth of root, thickness of tip, tilt of tip, axis of nostrils. In all three groups straight nasal profiles were found in at least half of the subjects, with the next commonest form convex. Although moderately high noses were most frequent in each series, the Hawaiian born and the immigrants both display a tendency toward an increase in the height of the bridge. It is consistent, therefore, to find that the Hawaiian born and the immigrants also tend to have fewer depressed nasal roots and more medium and high ones than the sedentes. With this tendency in the immigrants and Hawaiian born toward higher nasal bridges and roots, goes the increased percentage of compressed nasal roots. The nasal tip frequently thickens with age. For that reason it is doubtful that the much higher percentages of sedentes and immigrants, who have thicker nasal tips and are older than the Hawaiian born, are indications of a valid deviation. Suggestive, however, of a slight modification is the fact that the immigrants, although slightly older than the sedentes, have more medium and fewer thick tipped noses. Taken alone these differences might not be significant but allowing for the age difference between immigrants and Hawaiian born they encourage the interpretation that the immigrants and

Hawaiian born have slightly less bulbous nasal tips than the sedentes. The percentages for the tilt of the nasal tip indicate a definite alteration in the Hawaiian born and the immigrants. Whereas the sedentes have 51.16% with depressed tips and only 41.86% with level, the two groups resident in Hawaii have 15.43% and 19.66% with depressed and 73.40% and 73.03% with level tips. Finally the Hawaiian born and the immigrants have slightly higher percentages than the sedentes of antero-posterior nostrils.

From this brief analysis the Hawaiian born and the immigrants appear to agree in certain modifications in the nose. Compared to the sedentes they have higher noses with higher and more compressed roots. It is possible that their nasal tips are less blunt. Their nasal tips tend to be less depressed and the axis of their nostrils are more frequently in an antero-posterior direction. These are all changes which are consistent with each other and which appear to be equally developed in the immigrants and Hawaiian born. It is worthy of comment that the dimensions of the nose and the nasal indices underwent parallel changes.

The decreasing frequency of thick and the increasing percentage of medium lips as one progresses from sedentes to Hawaiian born are large enough to suggest the existence of a real modification. The immigrants are intermediate between the relatively thick lipped sedentes and the relatively thin lipped Hawaiian born.

Judging from the alterations in percentages the Hawaiian born are endowed with much more prominent chins than the sedentes. The immigrants are intermediate. This change harmonizes with the increase among immigrants and Hawaiian born of edge-to-edge and under-bites. It should, however, be pointed out that the percentage distribution of the type of bite among sedentes is based on only 20 cases. The reader will no doubt recall that the two groups resident in Hawaii also revealed profound increases in the total face height, a modification which fits these qualitative changes.

No especial difference occurs in the attachment of the ear lobe. In size the Hawaiian born have distinctly the smallest lobes, but size of the lobe appears to be correlated with age, and this group is definitely the youngest. The roll of the helix remains essentially the same in all three groups.

It is difficult to draw any conclusions from the percentages of the position of upper mesial incisors. No noteworthy difference exists between immigrants and Hawaiian born. The corresponding figures for the sedentes are based on too scanty a representation to be reliable.

Finally in general musculature all three groups agree as closely as their age discrepancy might allow.

Let us now examine the corresponding features of the Japanese women. The three female groups agree fairly well in pigmentation. Considering the variables which affect the degree of exposed skin pigmentation, the slight variations which may be noted are of insignificant proportions.

In hair form, texture and color the percentages in all three groups are quite uniform. In distribution of hair the only noteworthy difference appears among the immigrant women who show an increased tendency to complete glabrosity on lower arm and lower leg. This is interesting since the same peculiarity was observed among the male immigrants.

The eye color is almost exclusively brown, the darker shades predominating. A minor difference occurs in that the female sedentes have rather fewer with dark brown and more with light brown eyes than the two groups resident in Hawaii. The same phenomenon appears in the males and to nearly the same extent. This shift to darker brown eyes among the immigrants and Hawaiian born is confirmed by the proportionate increase among them of homogeneous iris patterns. The sclera undergoes no consistent modification.

Essentially the same frequencies of epicanthus are present in the males and females of each of the three series; consequently the female sedentes agree with the males in having the smallest proportion with epicanthic fold. The immigrants and Hawaiian born, however, are identical; both have about 91% with epicanthus. In a like manner the two sexes agree in the development of the fold. As in the males, the immigrant and Hawaiian born females with epicanthus display a more highly developed degree of it than do the corresponding sedentes.

A slight difference in percentages seems to indicate a tendency for both immigrant and Hawaiian born women to have more downwardly sloping eyes than have the sedentes. A similar discrepancy is observable in the male series. The palpebral opening is with few exceptions narrow or only moderately wide both in male and female Japanese, but among the immigrant and Hawaiian born women there is a slightly greater proportion with narrow palpebral openings. The same trend appears in the percentages of the males but to a lesser extent.

The character of the eyebrows discloses a well defined sex difference. Among the males the eyebrows are much thicker and usually are set closer together. Although the males revealed no appreciable differentiation among the three series, the females appear to fall in a sequence of progressively thicker eyebrow from sedentes to Hawaiian born. In the spacing of the eyebrow, however, no difference is apparent.

The forehead is an area of well defined secondary sex character. In general, the females have straighter and lower foreheads than the males with less marked brow ridges and glabellas. As among the males, the females of all three series are alike in the height and slope of their foreheads. And they also agree with the males in the differentiation of the immigrants and Hawaiian born from the sedentes in the development of the brow ridges and glabella. Both the immigrant and Hawaiian born females have distinctly larger glabellas and heavier brow ridges than the sedentes.

The striking tendency for the temporal hair to encroach further onto the forehead among the Hawaiian born and immigrant males than among the male sedentes is not definite among the females. In fact the sedentes and immigrant females hardly differ at all in this respect, while the Hawaiian born reveal only a slightly increased tendency toward the approximation of the temporal hair and the outer edge of the eyebrow. It may well be that the Hawaiian born females are merely reflecting their paternal inheritance in this characteristic.

In all three groups of Japanese women the commonest type of nasal profile is straight, but whereas the concave profile is next most frequent among the sedentes, it is the convex type which is second in frequency among the immigrant and Hawaiian born women. The change in percentage distribution is only moderate but it is interesting in the absence of a corresponding change in the males. In the nasal bridge height, however, the females follow more specifically the male pattern. In this character the women immigrants and Hawaiian born women have a greater proportion with higher bridges than the sedentes. Similarly, the immigrant and Hawaiian born females unite in having higher and more compressed nasal roots than are found among sedentes.

If allowances for the difference in age were made it is probable that the Hawaiian born women would approach more closely the immigrants in the percentage distribution of the various degrees of nasal tip thickness. In that event both the immigrants and Hawaiian born would display similar differences from the more bulbous nosed sedentes. Likewise the two groups resident in Hawaii have fewer noses with depressed tips than the sedentes. Finally, in the axis of the nostril the immigrant and Hawaiian born women have a higher percentage of antero-posterior than the sedentes.

From this comparison of the nasal characters of the Japanese women it is plain that the women fit into the pattern discernible among the men. Where differences exist the women fall into two groups; one including the immigrants and Hawaiian born, the other consisting of the sedentes. The former have higher bridged noses with higher, more compressed nasal roots and with a tendency to thinner, less depressed nasal tips and more antero-posteriorly directed axes of the nostrils. In one respect only the women resident in Hawaii show a departure from the corresponding males. Among the former we may trace a slight trend toward greater convexity of the nasal profile as compared with the women resident in Japan.

In both the immigrants and Hawaiian born women the proportion of thin lips increases and the proportion of thick lips decreases equally from the distributions characteristic of the sedentes. A similar trend was found among the corresponding males. No significant sex difference is apparent.

The chin frequently characteristic of women in Japan is both receding and set in such a way as to produce an over-bite of the upper jaw. Even the casual observer unaided by statistical support rapidly becomes aware of this distinguishing feature of the Japanese physiognomy. A change, however, occurs among the Japanese of Hawaii. More of them have prominent chins and fewer have receding chins, than their relatives in Japan. This is apparent both in males and females. The immigrant and Hawaiian born women agree very closely in this trend. In the type of bite the immigrant and Hawaiian born women reveal an apparent increase over the sedentes in the frequency of edge-to-edge bite. The reliability of this comparison is somewhat weakened by the fact that the distribution of type of bite among the sedentes is based on only 13 cases. This trend, however, does reflect a similar tendency in the males. Moreover, such a change in type of bite is one that might be anticipated from the associated increase in the prominence of the chin. It was previously mentioned that these alterations of the chins of the Japanese resident in Hawaii are consonant with, and in part explain, their marked increase in face height.

Neither in the attachment of the lobe of the ear nor in its size do any of the three series of women differ appreciably. The smaller size of the lobe of the Hawaiian born women is undoubtedly associated with their younger age. All the groups likewise are quite similar in the roll of the helix. No cases of flat helix were recorded among the women and only two were noted among the males.

It is extremely doubtful that there are any real differences in the position of the upper mesial incisors. The slight deviations of the series of sedentes may be explained more satisfactorily as the result of reduced numbers.

The foregoing traits behave in an exceptionally uniform manner. In some 35 characters the variations of which were observed in both males and females, 18 revealed appreciable changes among immigrants and Hawaiian born from the distributions peculiar to the sedentes. And in 15 or possibly 16 of these 18 the males and females fall into identical patterns. This pattern with few exceptions ranges the immigrants and the Hawaiian born together in contrast to the sedentes. Among females there is a progressive thickening of the eyebrows from sedentes to Hawaiian born; among males, a correspondingly progressive decrease from sedentes to Hawaiian born in the percentage of thick lips. And both male and female immigrants deviate from the sedentes and the Hawaiian born in a greater glabrosity of the arm and leg. In all the other modifications, however, the changes which occur in the immigrants are essentially equivalent to those in the Hawaiian born.

Such a consistent pattern points the conclusion that in the qualitative

characters as well as in the quantitative ones the immigrants are differentiated from the population whence they take their origin. But whereas the
Hawaiian born continue to undergo changes in their size and proportions,
they remain essentially unaltered from the immigrants in their qualitative
aspects.

CHAPTER IX

Recapitulation and Conclusions

ALTHOUGH the individuals of a group vary within fairly wide limits, their average characteristics have commonly been regarded as unchanging over long periods of time. In fact, the vast bulk of comparative racial studies rests on this tacit belief in the stability of the statistical balance of the component variables of a population. This traditional view became so firmly entrenched in practice that it assumed the guise of an article of faith beyond the necessity of examination. In recent years, however, dissatisfaction with this dogma has slowly been gaining headway, without, however, actually attaining sufficient force to affect the established methodology.

I do not mean by this statement to impute to physical anthropologists a reluctance to accept the principle of evolution for human groups. My observation applies only to their assumption that mankind changes so slowly that the change is imperceptible even within relatively long periods of time and becomes consequently negligible when dealing with geologically recent material. As a working hypothesis it permits students to compare contemporary groups living in diametrically opposite environments without regard for the possible effect which these diverse environments might exercise on the very differences they scrutinize. Similarly, it makes conveniently possible the comparison of historic and prehistoric populations as though they were contemporary although the social and physical milieu may have undergone profound alterations.

Were methodology the only consideration at stake, it would still be of great significance to examine the bases of such a belief in the stability of human populations. But other consequences of this dogma likewise come into question. If populations have remained unchanging during millennia of time and through wide fluctuations in environment, it is legitimate to ponder the logical consequences of such an hypothesis on the general theory of human evolution. Such an interpretation would minimize the effect of environmental shifts which we know have on occasion been considerable. It would deny all but the minutest effects to the accumulation of mutations. It would erase from practical consideration the working of differentials in a given population. It would render man static in a world of flux and change. To doubt the accuracy of this representation of man does not thereby impose an acceptance of a state of affairs in which man is a completely unstable organism constantly veering like a weather vane with the winds of environment. It does, however, impose the necessity of re-examining the basis for such a belief by testing it against the reality as we find it in nature.

Although in actuality the methodological approach to the comparative study of human groups and the theoretical discussion of their origins and classification are merely different phases of the same problem, in practice they have been completely severed from each other. The extent of this divorce of theory from practice is illustrated by the fact that proponents have never been lacking to defend the theoretical significance of environment in shaping the organisms of nature, even including man, while on the other hand a critical attitude toward the philosophy underlying comparative methods in racial studies, if it existed at all, escaped exact formulation. In fact, it was not until Professor Boas published his classic investigation of the bodily characteristics of the descendants of immigrants to the United States [1] that most physical anthropologists were even aware that their methodological premises could profitably bear closer scrutiny. This was the first detailed and reliable research into the stability of the bodily characteristics of a migrant population born and bred in one environment and producing children in another. And the data amassed by Boas showed incontrovertibly that in the populations he examined the children born in this country showed slight but definite modifications from their immigrant parents. These modifications, moreover, were greater the longer the residence here of the parents before the birth of the child. Despite the widespread discussion which this work provoked, the criticism of current practices implied in it failed to affect the traditional procedures of racial studies. Even the vistas of research which it opened remained neglected.

There is no doubt that the relationship of physical man to his environment is a problem of the greatest complexity, and that in statistical studies precise weighting for environmental influences is hardly possible at this stage of investigation. Yet the fundamental import of the problem demands continued effort to understand it and to express it in quantitative terms.

The present study is concerned with those gross external features which may be recorded in exact measurement or in proportional distributions among more or less standardized categories. It is an attempt to determine the physical consequences both of migration and of a marked change in environment on a specific population. In this instance the population is Japanese and the migration is from Japan to the Hawaiian Islands, an environmental change of considerable magnitude both physically and socially.

[1] Boas, Franz—Changes in Bodily Form in Descendants of Immigrants.—New York, 1912.

In one sense our data fall into two divisions, based on country of residence: the Japanese living in Hawaii and the Japanese resident in Japan. But since the Japanese in Hawaii actually consist both of a group who were born in Japan but who migrated to Hawaii and of a succeeding generation of Japanese who were born and bred in Hawaii, we have chosen to divide the total data into three distinct groups, based both on country of birth and on country of residence. These three major divisions, therefore, are the following: 1. Hawaiian born Japanese of Japanese immigrant parentage. These are subjects who were born in one of the Hawaiian islands and have continued to live there up to the time of this study. 2. Japanese immigrants now resident in Hawaii but born in Japan. 3. Japanese sedentes. This last group are the relatives of the immigrants and Hawaiian born who have remained in Japan, in the villages from which the immigrants migrated. They represent the stock of which the immigrants were originally a part and they live under conditions similar to those which surrounded the immigrants until their departure for Hawaii. To ensure obtaining strict comparability throughout special efforts were made to include as many relatives as possible in all three groups. In Japan the villages from which the Japanese in Hawaii took their origin were visited and in most instances the living members of the families of our Hawaiian Japanese were measured for inclusion in the series of sedentes. In this manner the sedentes provide a control on the two groups in Hawaii. Although they represent the original population, they are contemporary with the Japanese in Hawaii.

It was necessary to deal with contemporary groups as far as possible since the Japanese appear to be undergoing size changes comparable to those well known in Europe and America. For that reason alone it would have been unwise to attempt to dispose our subjects in successive generations, even assuming that the grandparental generation in Japan had been numerous enough to provide an adequate representation.

After eliminating all subjects who failed to conform to the criteria given above, we obtained the following numbers.

		Males	Females	
Children				
	Hawaiian Born	645	320	
	Sedentes	530	286	
Adults				
	Hawaiian Born	188	91	
	Immigrants	178	93	
	Sedentes	172	91	
Total		1,713	881	2,594

Each subject was measured and his qualitative traits were observed by a single investigator, thereby reducing to a minimum the vexatious element of doubt engendered by personal equations. Whatever bias may exist in these measurements, they are at least consistent and therefore negligible for present purposes. The full field schedule included 43 measurements, 21 indices and 41 observations. Of these 28 measurements, 21 indices and 41 observations were employed in the statistical analysis. The list may be consulted on pages 9–10.

The first step in the analysis was the comparison with each other of the three master series, male and female separately, as outlined above. The comparisons were made in the order of events leading up to the Hawaiian born group. That is, the immigrants, male and female, were compared first with the corresponding series of sedentes, and then with the Hawaiian born.

The Japanese male immigrants now resident in Hawaii entered almost entirely as laborers for sugar and pineapple plantations. They came almost exclusively after 1898, the earlier immigrants having for the most part returned to Japan. Most of them came single, but were joined later by 'picture brides.' Those who successfully established themselves in their new homes remained to rear their families in Hawaii. Obviously, the economically and socially well endowed were not candidates for migration. The vast majority of the male immigrants were laborers, landless or impoverished, who by virtue of economic pressure envisaged an opportunity to better their lot in a new country. Physically, however, no evidence exists of any deliberate selection either by the recruiters or by plantation managers; and, considering the pressing need for labor in Hawaii and the wholesale nature of the movement, none was to be expected. It might be argued that since the immigrants were economically and socially selected, they might have been derived from differentiated elements in the general Japanese population. This reasoning, however, loses its force because the sedentes employed for comparison form part of the same socio-economic level from which the immigrants were secured and genetically belong to the same stock. The sedentes are, in fact, members of the same families to which the immigrants belong. They represent the inheritors of small family holdings and those who for one reason or another preferred to remain at home despite economic pressure.

Some of the female immigrants came to Hawaii together with their husbands, but a very large proportion of them entered as 'picture brides' during the second decade of the present century.

A statistical summary of the 50 characters and indices for which the total series of immigrants and sedentes are compared reveals an astounding degree of significant divergence between the two groups genetically so closely linked. The male immigrants deviate significantly from the sedentes in 72.4% of the measurements and in 76.2% of the indices. Similarly the immigrant females diverge from the sedentes in 67.9% of the measurements and in 45.0% of the indices. With some exceptions both the male and female immigrants tend to deviate in the same characters.

The differentiation of the total immigrants is largely concentrated in disproportionate changes. The distinction is drawn here between proportionate and disproportionate changes. In the former the size is modified but the relationship of the component parts remains constant. Disproportionate changes however imply a disturbance of the ratio of one part to another, with or without a general alteration in size. The total male immigrants, for example, are identical with the sedentes in stature, but they have shorter trunks and longer legs thus reducing their relative trunk and sitting heights. Similarly the immigrant males have absolutely wider shoulders than the sedentes, which in relation to their unchanged stature produces a disproportion from the sedentes in a greater relative shoulder width.

The total immigrant males show significant increases over the sedentes in the following characters.

1. Weight
2. Lower Arm Length
3. Hand Length
4. Upper Leg Length
5. Lower Leg Length
6. Total Leg Length
7. Shoulder Width
8. Chest Width
9. Head Height
10. Bigonial Diameter
11. Total Face Height
12. Upper Face Height
12. Nose Height
14. Nose Length
15. Bi-Ocular Width

In the following they disclose significant decreases.

1. Sitting Height
2. Trunk Height
3. Chest Depth
4. Nose Salient
5. Nose Breadth
6. Inter-Ocular Width

The above significant deviations cause the following disproportionate changes in the bodily and cephalic indices of the immigrants.

1. Higher Relative Shoulder Width
2. Lower Relative Hip Width
3. Lower Shoulder-Hip Index
4. Lower Relative Sitting Height
5. Lower Relative Trunk Height
6. Lower Thoracic Index
7. Higher Brachial Index
8. Lower Inter-Membral Index
9. Higher Length-Height Cephalic Index
10. Higher Breadth-Height Cephalic Index
11. Higher Zygo-Gonial Index
12. Higher Total Facial Index
13. Higher Upper Facial Index
14. Lower Nasal Index
15. Lower Nose Salient-Height Index
16. Higher Nose Length-Height Index

The total immigrant females compared with the total female sedentes show significant increases in the following characters.

1. Weight
2. Stature
3. Upper Arm Length
4. Lower Arm Length
5. Hand Length
6. Lower Leg Length
7. Total Leg Length
8. Shoulder Width
9. Hip Width
10. Head Width
11. Head Height
12. Bizygomatic Width
13. Bigonial Width
14. Total Face Height
15. Upper Face Height
16. Nose Height
17. Nose Length
18. Bi-Ocular Width

In the following they show significant decreases.

1. Trunk Height

In the following indices the female immigrants show significant disproportionate changes.

1. Lower Relative Sitting Height
2. Lower Relative Trunk Height
3. Higher Tibio-Femoral Index
4. Higher Length-Height Index
5. Higher Breadth-Height Index
6. Higher Zygo-Gonial Index
7. Higher Total Facial Index
8. Higher Upper Facial Index
9. Higher Nose Length-Height Index

The Hawaiian born belong without exception to the first generation of
Japanese born in Hawaii. Their parents are direct immigrants from Japan.
The few Japanese who have reached Hawaii via other countries are not
included in this series. Since this generation is only just coming into maturity, there is a fairly large age discrepancy between it and the groups of
immigrants and sedentes. The members of the Hawaiian born series were
unselected, having been secured on various islands of the Hawaiian archi-
pelago and from diverse occupational and economic levels. Compared with
their parents they show a marked shift toward higher occupational pursuits.
The effect of this change will be discussed later.

The comparison of the total male group of Hawaiian born with the immigrants yields significant differences in 55.2% of the measurements and
in 42.9% of the indices. The females similarly contrasted show significant
differences in 46.4% of the measurements and in 45.0% of the indices.
These percentages indicate a degree of differentiation which would be noteworthy between any two groups, but for two groups as intimately associated as these are they denote an arresting modification. That these changes
are projected from the immigrants and not merely reversals to the level of
the sedentes may be tested by comparing the Hawaiian born with the
sedentes. Were the differences between the Hawaiian born and immigrants
the result merely of deviations on the part of the immigrants, then the
Hawaiian born and sedentes should approximate each other. Actually, however the sedentes and Hawaiian born are even more widely separated than
are the sedentes and immigrants, thereby indicating that the Hawaiian born
have undergone additional changes. The Hawaiian born males differ from
the sedentes in 79.3% of the measurements and in 90.5% of the indices.
The Hawaiian born females likewise deviate significantly from the sedentes
in 67.9% of the measurements and in 80.0% of the indices.

To a much greater extent than was true in comparing male immigrants
with sedentes, the Hawaiian born male modifications from the immigrants
are proportionate in the bodily characters, although new disproportions

especially in cephalic indices appear among the Hawaiian born which were not anticipated among the immigrants. Especially notable among the modifications of the Hawaiian born Japanese is the tremendous increase in stature. The males enjoy an increase of 4.11 cm. in stature and the females 1.71 cm. These increases can not be accounted for by the age discrepancy. The Hawaiian born corrected for age remain taller than the immigrants. Such an increase in size might be expected to produce corresponding increments in the various component segments of the body.

The Hawaiian born males show significant increments over the immigrants in the following measurements.

1. Stature
2. Sitting Height
3. Trunk Height
4. Upper Arm Length
5. Lower Arm Length
6. Lower Leg Length
7. Total Leg Length
8. Shoulder Width
9. Head Width
10. Head Height
11. Inter-Ocular Width

They also show significant decreases in the following.

1. Chest Width
2. Chest Depth
3. Head Length
4. Total Face Height
5. Nose Breadth

The following are the significant alterations in proportions among the Hawaiian born males.

1. Lower Relative-Hip Width
2. Lower Shoulder-Hip Index
3. Higher Tibio-Femoral Index
4. Higher Cephalic Index
5. Higher Length-Height Index
6. Lower Cephalo-Facial Index
7. Lower Fronto-Parietal Index
8. Lower Nasal Index
9. Lower Nose Length-Height Index

The Hawaiian born females show significant increases over the immigrants in the following traits.

1. Stature
2. Head Width
3. Inter-Ocular Width

They show significant decreases in the following.

1. Weight
2. Hand Length
3. Shoulder Width
4. Hip Width
5. Chest Width
6. Head Length
7. Bizygomatic Diameter
8. Bigonial Diameter
9. Forehead Height
10. Nose Width

The following are the significant alterations in the proportions of the Hawaiian born females.

1. Lower Relative Shoulder Width
2. Lower Relative Hip Width
3. Lower Shoulder-Hip Index
4. Lower Inter-Membral Index
5. Higher Cephalic Index
6. Higher Length-Height Index
7. Lower Cephalo-Facial Index
8. Lower Fronto-Parietal Index
9. Lower Zygo-Fonial Index

Although the Hawaiian born females fail to follow the Hawaiian born males in the dimensional changes they do agree very well with them in the modification of proportion. This discrepancy seems to be the result of the lesser increment in stature among the Hawaiian born females.

These are the significant changes which occur in the total series. A number of others of almost statistically significant proportions appear which were discussed in the earlier sections.

In analysing the precise geographical origin of the Japanese immigrants and of the Hawaiian born one generation removed from Japan, we found that in the main the stream of migration to Hawaii was fed from four small-ish districts: 1. Yamaguchi, 2. Hiroshima, 3. Kyushu, including Fukuoka and Kumamoto, and 4. Niigata and Fukushima grouped as 'Other Japan.'

Yamaguchi and Hiroshima are contiguous prefectures in the southern tip of the main island of Hondo. Fukuoka and Kumamoto are on the nearby island of Kyushu opposite Yamaguchi and Hiroshima. Separated from these neighboring districts lie Niigata and Fukushima in the central part of Hondo. Since each of the master series varied in their distribution among these prefectures, it was necessary to analyse the data in order to determine whether important geographical differentiations existed and whether the prefectural distributions had affected the differences observed between the total groups.

The comparison of the prefectural groupings reveals a moderate degree of local differentiation among the sedentes. Niigata and Fukushima, comprising the group of 'Other Japan,' are not only the most remote prefectures geographically but the most deviant as well. Among the immigrants, however, and to an even greater extent among the Hawaiian born, the prefectural subdivisions possess a marked homogeneity. This progression from locally differentiated sedentes to homogeneous immigrants strongly suggests that the immigrants constitute a selected group conforming to a definite pattern regardless of prefectural origin. The increase in homogeneity among the Hawaiian born follows from the uniformity of the Hawaiian milieu acting upon a selected group.

An interesting suggestion arises from the comparison of the various prefectural groups of sedentes with the total immigrants. In the first place the resulting differences are expectedly larger than the deviations among the prefectural subdivisions of the sedentes themselves, as they should be to conform with the previous determination of a selected immigrant type. But there also occurs a striking difference in the degree to which the various prefectural groups of sedentes differ from the total immigrants. The sedentes of 'Other Japan' approximate most closely to the immigrants. In fact this percentage of difference is of the same order as the differences between the various prefectural groups of sedentes. This would seem to indicate that the sedentes of 'Other Japan' tend to vary toward the configuration of traits characteristic of the immigrants. Or to state it another way, the immigrant type appears to be more characteristic, or more common, in the prefectures of 'Other Japan' than in the more southern districts. This affinity is reflected in greater detail in the graphs of the various prefectures.

The reality of the immigrant deviations from the population of Japan acquires additional support from the comparison of the immigrants and sedentes originating in the same prefectures. Each of these comparisons repeats the pattern already laid down by the parallel analysis of the total series, with the exceptions anticipated from the inter-play of a large number of variables. The immigrants transcend their prefectural origin to conform to a uniform physical type which apparently occurs in all prefectures but most commonly in 'Other Japan' (Niigata and Fukushima). Moreover, the observed changes among the immigrants receive additional corroboration from a comparison of the pooled prefectures of sedentes and immigrants unweighted for size of the individual series.

Similarly the Hawaiian born and immigrants of each prefectural group were compared and again it was evident that the modifications observed in the total series of Hawaiian born were also encountered among the various subdivisions of them.

The age discrepancy already mentioned which exists between the Hawaiian born, on the one hand, and the immigrants and sedentes, on the other, required analysis in order to determine whether or not differences in age were capable of producing the observed results. Each master series was divided by decades, and the corresponding decades in each of the three series were compared. In addition, the age changes in sedentes and Hawaiian born children were added in order to complete the curves of the adults. In 78% of the comparisons of the male series the results by total series and by age were in complete agreement. Partial agreement occurred in 14%. And only in 8% were partial disagreements apparent. No complete disagreements were evident.

To a large extent the slight discrepancies which appear from these comparisons are the results of differing tempo of age changes in maturity, of reduced numbers in some of the decadal means, and of the abbreviated curve of the Hawaiian born which extends only over two decades of maturity. Most of the discrepancies are very slight; for example, a significant difference being reduced to one just below the conventional margin of significance or the reverse.

Definite emendations as a result of age comparisons become necessary in only 12 out of 150 comparisons. These are as follows.

Immigrants compared with sedentes by age show no change in relative hip width despite the significant reduction in the total series.

Hawaiian born compared with immigrants by age, contrary to the results of the total comparisons, proved to have significantly longer hands, unchanged chest depth and width, unchanged head height, unchanged nose width, unchanged inter-ocular width and lower total facial indices.

Four significant differences which the total series of Hawaiian born yielded on comparison with the total sedentes are rendered uncertain by the age comparisons. The greater sitting height, the narrower hip width, the higher total face and the lower relative hip width of the total Hawaiian born are not completely supported by the age analysis.

Economic status has long been recognized as a probable differentiating factor in a physically homogeneous population. Children from prosperous homes tend not only to be taller and heavier but to vary in other anatomical and even in physiological traits from the norms of the general population. The assumption here, supported by evidences of differences in diet, is that with an increase in the family income the diet as well as other environmental factors improve.

Besides the more passive elements of environment, the more active factors such as the degree of physical labor at various economic levels also assume significance with economic differentiation. For these reasons, therefore, it becomes necessary to re-examine the Japanese from the point-of-view of economic and occupational stratification.

The various subjects of each master series were sub-divided according to occupation since such a classification not only embraced differences in type of labor but also recognized variations in financial rewards. The unskilled plantation laborer works harder physically and, in general, receives far less for his efforts than the sedentary and professional worker. Our classification included the following categories: farmers, unskilled laborers, fishermen, professional workers [1] and students. To obtain more satisfactory statistical results these various sub-divisions were combined into two contrasting groups: the manual laborers, including farmers, unskilled laborers and fishermen, and the sedentary workers. The former engage in heavy manual labor and occupy a low position in the economic scale. The sedentary workers, on the contrary, are relatively better paid and pursue, as the name implies, occupations that require no severe muscular energy. Further division of these occupational groups by age and prefecture was not permitted by the size of the sample. The results of both the age and the prefectural analyses seemed to indicate that the observed changes in the total series were not associated with either of these factors.

An arresting change in type of occupation is noticeable in the progression from sedentes to Hawaiian born. Among the sedentes 75% are manual laborers, mainly farmers. The immigrants, however, show a significant shift from heavy labor to shop-keeping, only 34.71% of them engaging in manual labor and 65.29% in sedentary occupations. As the immigrants have become adjusted to life in Hawaii they have abandoned their original laboring jobs on plantations for mercantile occupations. The Hawaiian born reveal an even greater trend away from the manual occupations, with only 24.06% doing heavy labor and 75.93% as students or sedentary workers. This occupational distribution of the Hawaiian born represents a complete reversal of the percentages for the sedentes.

In order to test the extent to which each master series may be physically sub-divided on the basis of occupation, the two contrasting occupational groups of each series were compared with each other and with the total

1. This group includes government officials, merchants, tradespeople, teachers as well as more strictly professional workers.

series of which they are a part. These comparisons were incomplete because the sedentes lacked an adequate group of sedentary workers. But with this exception all the occupational groups showed a very close agreement with their total series. When the heavy laborers and the sedentary workers of the same total series were compared with each other the number of significant differences continued to remain relatively low but higher than were the preceding comparisons with the total series. The only general pattern of physical difference which appears to be associated with occupation are the following. The sedentary workers, compared with the manual laborers, have absolutely shallower chests and wider noses but relatively narrower shoulder and hip widths. They also tend toward reduced thoracic and increased nasal indices. Although the differences in shoulder, hip and chest may well have an occupational origin, the differences in the absolute and relative nasal width are less readily connected with occupation.

In addition to the comparisons designed to determine the degree of occupational differentiation within each of the three master series, the occupational groups were also aligned vertically. That is to say, the sedentes, immigrants and Hawaiian born were compared with each other by occupation in order to ascertain how closely the pattern established by the total series repeated itself with occupation held constant. Unfortunately the absence of a statistically valid group of sedentary workers among the sedentes prevented a complete comparison along these lines. It was possible, however, to carry the laborers through all three stages and the sedentary workers through two. It appeared both from statistical considerations and from graphic comparisons that each occupational group follows very closely the mutations of the total series thereby confirming the fundamental character of the pattern of immigrant selection and Hawaiian born modification and minimizing the influence of occupation on these changes.

Although occupation does not seem from these circumstances to be the decisive factor in producing the observed changes, nevertheless it does exert a secondary influence which is detectable in certain traits among the Hawaiian born. The trend of the total Hawaiian born toward narrower hips, chests, face widths and toward wider inter-ocular widths than those possessed by the immigrants now appears to be the consequence of correspondingly marked deviations in these very characters among the Hawaiian born sedentary workers. And in their greater weight, shorter total face height and lower nose length-height index the total Hawaiian born are similarly affected by the manual laborers.

In the preceding discussion certain assumptions were made which require further explanation. To satisfy completely the socio-economic implications of an occupational classification it should be based not only on the profession of the subject but on his father's as well, for the environment of the subject in his childhood and youth is controlled by the parental status rather than his own achieved in his maturity. In a traditional and static society the position in life of the son does ordinarily fall close by that of the father, and consequently the occupational status of a subject may be enough to indicate the kind of socio-economic conditions under which he was bred. I have in the above treated the occupational groups as if they were of this nature and strictly exclusive of each other. Actually, of course, this is not true and can hardly be expected in a society of such recent origin and of such rapid economic adjustments as exists in Hawaii. Japanese families in Hawaii barely span two generations. Families covering three—the immigrant and two Hawaiian born generations—are relatively rare. Moreover, the economic equilibrium of the Japanese in the larger Hawaiian economy as well as within their own group is in a state of adjustment. Sons of laborers attend the university and eventually become professional or sedentary workers. Many immigrants have since their arrival shifted their occupations from those involving heavy manual labor to less laborious and more profitable pursuits. Obviously under such conditions occupational classification as an index of socio-economic background is uncertain.

These circumstances, however, afford some comfort indirectly. In general, the occupational trend among the Japanese in Hawaii shows an abandonment of farming and heavy manual labor in favor of skilled labor, trade and professional types of employment. Consequently, we may assume that most of our subjects, whether immigrant or Hawaiian born, who are classified as sedentary workers are sons of laborers and in most cases reared under the economic environment which that implies. Conversely the men listed as laborers are likewise sons of laborers and consequently their classification reflects more truly their socio-economic status during childhood as well as in maturity. It should, however, be pointed out that in the Hawaiian born generations the sons who enjoy the advantages leading to professional or sedentary careers belong usually to families with a rising economic position.

This situation may, indeed, account for the relatively slight occupational differentiation exhibited by our data. It also suggests that occupational differentiation has not yet advanced far enough to allow its effects to be evident. And finally it reveals that essentially the changes with which we have been concerned are largely independent of a socio-economic or occupational origin.

The distinction has previously been drawn between measurable and qualitative characters. The former by virtue of their susceptibility to measurement with consequently greater accuracy of definition ensure greater reliability. For this reason, the discussions have centered largely on these characters. Nevertheless, the qualitative traits, despite their vulnerability to the distortions of personal equation, are often among the most distinctive characteristics of a population. I have, therefore, included a brief analysis of them, but I have confined it only to the three master series, omitting the more refined analysis given the measurable characters. The relatively small groups which further sub-division would have produced seemed to me inadequate to support reliable results from percental comparisons.

The comparison of sedentes, immigrants and Hawaiian born with each other revealed that in 18 out of a total of 35 traits the immigrants diverged distinctly from the sedentes. In practically all the characters in which the immigrants deviate, no additional modification of noteworthy magnitude appeared among the Hawaiian born. Furthermore, the males and females followed practically identical patterns.

These results lead to the conclusion that in both qualitative as well as in measurable characters the immigrants display significant departures from the means and percental distributions of the sedentes. The Hawaiian born, however, fail to show any tendency to develop further modification in their qualitative characters, although in their quantitative traits they undergo considerable modification.

This difference in the behavior of the quantitative measurements from the 'qualitative' observations indicates that the changes observed in the Hawaiian born consist mainly of modifications in size. And conversely, that dimension and size are more sensitive to environmental influence than such qualitative traits as hair form or nasal contour. But the differentiation of the immigrants, being the result of selective factors in migration rather than the response to environmental influences, extends into both categories of traits, quantitative as well as qualitative.

The foregoing analysis has inevitably revealed, to none more forcefully than myself, the necessity of additional data. Moreover, unless betrayed by my own phraseology, I have no wish to imply that the problems actually discussed as well as those suggested find their final solution here. Vastly more work will be required before that will be possible. But the specific dynamic changes observed among the Japanese in Hawaii contain general implications which, despite their speculative nature, can not be altogether passed over in silence. For speculation which is the fruit of research carries the seed of further growth. While I make no apology for the hypothetical character of the following remarks, I do wish, however, to distinguish them from the preceding analysis of the Japanese in Hawaii.

The material herein presented makes it evident that the assumption of stability in man's physical characters is no longer tenable without qualification. Indeed, from the evidence of the Japanese in Hawaii man emerges as a dynamic organism which under certain circumstances is capable of very substantial changes within a single generation. If a Japanese population may thus alter its aggregate characteristics, then the probability certainly exists that other groups in other parts of the world have undergone similar physical changes in the past, since migrations and radical shifts in environment have been not infrequent events in man's history.

Not only may migrant populations undergo modification when transposed to a sufficiently different environment, but physical changes may also occur in fixed populations if their environments alter in the course of time. In fact, abundant evidence is spread in the recent literature demonstrating marked size and associated proportional changes in established European and American populations. The specific environmental factor producing these alterations is not universally agreed upon, but the phenomenon itself is unquestioned. And it bears witness to the dynamic potentiality of the human organism to respond to environmental changes.

This recognition of the dynamic and plastic character of the human organism and, by logical extension, of human populations raises a serious methodological problem. For if populations may be altered by changes in environment then identical populations reared in different milieus may develop physical divergencies. And the simple test of identity or similarity of group means becomes inadequate as the sole criterion of relationship. By such a test, for example, the present data in the absence of their historical setting could not have been satisfactorily appraised.

This suggests that a methodology efficacious in dealing with such possibilities of population change should be designed to grapple with a dynamic system composed of orbits rather than a static universe of fixed points. To devise this, however, we must first determine what particular factors in the environment are effective in eliciting physical responses in the human organism. We need to know the extent and direction of the resultant physical changes. It is, moreover, essential to ascertain whether these adjustments follow definite lines of proportional or differential changes or whether any type of general or selective modification is possible. The available evidence suggests that a given type is characterized by only a limited plasticity, and that the patterns of change are fixed by the nature of its fundamental structure. Consequently we may hardly expect to find that any population may be altered in any direction, or that by some form of transmutation through the agency of environmental alchemy we may transform one stock into the semblance of another. We have no evidence to support such a deduction. Nature, in fact, furnishes abundant evidence to the contrary. But should further investigation corroborate our hypothesis of a dynamic human structure, plastic to environmental influences, but limited in its plasticity both in direction and extent, then our methods of comparison must be adjusted to recognize these possibilities.

The preceding discussion springs mainly from a consideration of the changes undergone by the Japanese born in Hawaii. But our data also indicate that antecedent to this expression of plasticity, some form of selection governed the type of immigrant who ventured to Hawaii. It would appear, therefore, that the difference between the Japanese sedentes in Japan and the Japanese born and bred in Hawaii rests not entirely on environmental factors but is attributable in part to the differentiation which characterized the immigrants. I confess that it is difficult to understand the mechanism which might select such an immigrant type. I have already explained that no physical selection was exercised by recruiters. Economic pressure did, of course, govern the composition of the human stream of laborers who migrated to Hawaii. But that does not explain why the immigrants differ from the sedentes, since the subjects in the control series of sedentes are close relatives of the immigrants and they have both been bred under similar conditions.

Of considerable interest in this connection is the fact that the immigrants coming from 'Other Japan' (Niigata and Fukushima) were more like the sedentes from the same area than were the immigrants and sedentes of the more southerly districts. This taken with the existence of homogeneity between all immigrants from whatever prefecture appears to indicate that the immigrant type is more commonly to be found in the northern districts than in the three southern ones. Whether this has anything to do with the historical movement of Japanese northward, producing thereby a greater concentration of an 'immigrant type' in the north than in the south, I am unable to say. But if the earlier northward movement within Japan were as selective as the present Hawaiian movement appears to be, then here we have an explanation of the greater similarity of immigrants and sedentes in 'Other Japan' than in Hiroshima, Yamaguchi or Kyushu.

If, admitting the inefficacy of a social or economic basis for the selection of an immigrant type, we turn to a psychological explanation then we are faced with other difficulties. It becomes necessary to assume that the immigrants are differentiated not only physically but psychologically as well, and that physical differences are associated with innate psychological ones. While innate psychological drives no doubt exist, it is extremely doubtful that they are genetically linked with special physical variations within a mixed population. Moreover, it also becomes necessary to explain the similar selection found among the immigrant women. Although they are not as definitely differentiated from the sedentes as are the immigrant males, nevertheless they do parallel the male pattern. The immigrant women either accompanied their husbands or were sent to Hawaii as 'picture brides'. In neither case does individual choice appear to have been especially open to the women. Consequently, the psychology of the immigrant does not appear to have determined their migration.

Still another explanation of the immigrant differentiation suggests itself. It may be argued that the divergence of the immigrants from the sedentes is not so much an original difference as it is the result of a modification induced by the Hawaiian environment. But this is unsatisfactory for corollary reasons. In the first place, the immigrants with few exceptions were adult on their arrival in Hawaii. And secondly, changes of the degree shown by the immigrants are contrary to our knowledge of the plasticity of adults. It is true men and women show some alteration in their dimensions during the period of maturity and senility but these changes are usually relatively slight in comparison to the numerous significant differences which distinguish immigrants from the sedentes. It would, for example, be highly improbable to expect that the marked drop in the absolute and relative trunk height among the immigrants be achieved in maturity and as a consequence of an environmental change. Furthermore, it is perhaps significant that whereas the Hawaiian born reflect environmental changes only in their quantitative or size characters, the immigrants, on the other hand, show definite evidence of differentiation in their qualitative traits as well.

We are thus reduced to the position of suspended judgment. Although the phenomenon of immigrant differentiation emerges clearly enough in this instance, further investigation is obviously necessary in order to test its occurrence in other circumstances and to determine the factors which govern its action.

The data of this study also suggest another line of speculation, which unfortunately our evidence was not designed to elucidate. It has undoubtedly occurred to the reader to ponder whether the immigrants represent a phenotypically or a genotypically selected population. This is a question which has considerable theoretical importance. It can only be solved by a study of the returned immigrants and their children born in Japan or reared in Japan. Such a population exists but its investigation was an impractical extension of our research.

Although this discussion is not intended to be an exhaustive exploration of the speculative consequences of the present data, I can not close these concluding remarks without at least mention of the possible significance which the physical history of the Japanese in Hawaii may possess for the understanding of human evolution and differentiation. If migratory groups represent selected strains of a population which may later undergo additional modification through environmental influences, then a mechanism is provided here to explain some of the variation which is encountered among related populations. I do not suggest that selective migration and environmental modification are the only or even the major forces in evolution or in producing group variations, but they do offer contributory factors to the complex process of differentiation and evolution. I see no reason why evolution and variation need necessarily be confined to a single mechanism. It seems to me that a truer picture would include the combined inter-action of a large number of factors and circumstances.

In conclusion I should like to restate the immediate results of this investigation in the hope that I may forestall any misunderstanding. The evidence which this study brings forward leads me to believe that two factors are responsible for the differences which distinguish the Japanese born and bred in Hawaii from their relatives born and bred in Japan: selection and modification by environment. The Japanese immigrants to Hawaii constitute a distinct sub-group of the population from which they were derived. That this is a universal phenomenon appearing wherever migration occurs I doubt. Migrations are often the result of complicated sociological and psychological circumstances. The forces which are resolved by migration in one instance may be quite different in another. But it must also be remembered that if selective migration, associated with physical differentiation, occurs once, it may occur again.

The second factor influencing the Hawaiian born Japanese is the environment in which they were bred.

This expression of plasticity appears to be a response which I regard as common to all organisms. So little, however, is known of its nature that I can not venture to predict how much change in milieu is necessary to produce physical alteration, nor to single out which of the many elements composing the environment are especially effective. I do, however, believe that these changes when they occur, move in accordance with the fundamental structure of the organism and only to a limited degree. I emphatically do not believe that the Japanese will ever become identical with Hawaiians as a result of enjoying an identical environment and I do not expect to find that the Japanese in Hawaii will eventually lose all similarity to the stock from which they came.

Tables

TABLE I

MEANS OF TOTAL MALE SEDENTES

Measurement		No.	Range	Mean	S.D.	V.
Age		172	20– 64	35.55 ± .64	12.45 ± .45	35.02 ± 1.27
Weight	(lb.)	143	81–160	119.80 ± .77	13.60 ± .54	11.35 ± .45
Stature	(cm.)	171	145–174	158.39 ± .28	5.37 ± .20	3.39 ± .12
Sitting Height	(cm.)	171	74– 95	84.50 ± .20	3.80 ± .14	4.50 ± .16
Trunk Height	(cm.)	170	44– 65	54.16 ± .17	3.38 ± .12	6.24 ± .23
Upper Arm Length	(cm.)	172	23– 34	29.40 ± .09	1.82 ± .07	6.19 ± .23
Lower Arm Length	(cm.)	172	19– 27	23.15 ± .07	1.39 ± .05	6.00 ± .22
Hand Length	(cm.)	172	15– 20	17.47 ± .04	.87 ± .03	4.98 ± .18
Upper Leg Length	(cm.)	170	27– 46	35.78 ± .17	3.34 ± .12	9.33 ± .34
Lower Leg Length	(cm.)	171	27– 37	31.71 ± .10	1.98 ± .07	6.24 ± .23
Total Leg Length	(cm.)	171	63– 84	73.76 ± .20	3.94 ± .14	5.34 ± .19
Biacromion	(cm.)	171	35– 44	39.53 ± .10	1.85 ± .07	4.68 ± .17
Cristal Breadth	(cm.)	171	25– 33	29.85 ± .09	1.73 ± .06	5.80 ± .21
Chest Breadth	(cm.)	172	22– 30	27.27 ± .08	1.57 ± .06	5.76 ± .21
Chest Depth	(cm.)	169	17– 26	20.62 ± .07	1.32 ± .05	6.40 ± .23
Head Length	(mm.)	172	166–213	189.70 ± .35	6.78 ± .25	3.57 ± .13
Head Breadth	(mm.)	172	131–164	151.90 ± .26	5.02 ± .18	3.30 ± .12
Head Height	(cm.)	172	10– 16	12.73 ± .06	1.10 ± .04	8.64 ± .31
Minimum Frontal Diameter	(mm.)	171	94–129	112.10 ± .29	5.55 ± .20	4.95 ± .18
Bizygomatic Diameter	(mm.)	172	128–157	141.75 ± .24	4.74 ± .17	3.34 ± .12
Bigonial Diameter	(mm.)	172	97–123	109.43 ± .27	5.22 ± .19	4.77 ± .17
Total Face Height	(mm.)	172	103–141	119.66 ± .35	6.78 ± .25	5.67 ± .21
Upper Face Height	(mm.)	172	63– 88	72.66 ± .23	4.42 ± .16	6.08 ± .22
Forehead Height	(mm.)	158	38– 77	60.86 ± .42	7.76 ± .29	12.75 ± .48
Nose Height	(mm.)	172	40– 63	50.54 ± .17	3.38 ± .12	6.69 ± .24

		N	Range	Mean	S.D.	C.V.
Nose Length	(mm.)	172	32– 61	47.88 ± .19	3.78 ± .14	7.89 ± .29
Nose Salient	(mm.)	172	9– 22	14.63 ± .11	2.22 ± .08	15.17 ± .55
Nose Breadth	(mm.)	172	28– 43	36.50 ± .14	2.82 ± .10	7.73 ± .28
Inter-Ocular	(mm.)	172	24– 44	31.62 ± .15	2.97 ± .11	9.39 ± .34
Bi-Ocular	(mm.)	172	86–111	99.56 ± .26	4.96 ± .18	4.98 ± .18
Index						
Relative Shoulder Breadth		170	21– 28	24.92 ± .07	1.26 ± .05	5.06 ± .18
Relative Hip Breadth		171	16– 21	18.94 ± .06	1.16 ± .04	6.12 ± .22
Shoulder-Hip		171	62– 88	75.60 ± .23	4.38 ± .16	5.79 ± .21
Relative Sitting Height		171	48– 58	53.37 ± .09	1.78 ± .06	3.34 ± .12
Relative Trunk Height		170	29– 39	34.17 ± .10	1.86 ± .07	5.44 ± .20
Thoracic		169	62– 93	75.64 ± .27	5.28 ± .19	6.98 ± .26
Brachial		171	67– 90	78.78 ± .24	4.64 ± .17	5.89 ± .21
Tibio-Femoral		170	60–114	89.05 ± .52	10.10 ± .37	11.34 ± .41
Inter-Membral		171	78–109	94.98 ± .25	4.94 ± .18	5.20 ± .19
Cephalic		172	68– 97	80.22 ± .19	3.68 ± .13	4.59 ± .17
Length-Height		171	54– 81	67.06 ± .29	5.64 ± .21	8.41 ± .31
Breadth-Height		171	66–105	83.72 ± .37	7.18 ± .26	8.58 ± .31
Cephalo-Facial		172	85–108	93.26 ± .16	3.18 ± .12	3.41 ± .12
Fronto-Parietal		171	64– 83	73.84 ± .18	3.50 ± .13	4.74 ± .17
Zygo-Frontal		171	68– 87	79.14 ± .18	3.44 ± .13	4.35 ± .16
Zygo-Gonial		172	64– 89	77.24 ± .18	3.46 ± .13	4.48 ± .16
Facial		172	72– 98	84.25 ± .27	5.19 ± .19	6.16 ± .22
Upper Facial		172	37– 63	51.41 ± .18	3.51 ± .13	6.83 ± .25
Nasal		172	54– 99	72.44 ± .40	7.78 ± .28	10.74 ± .39
Nose Salient-Height		172	19– 42	28.94 ± .22	4.32 ± .16	14.93 ± .54
Nose Length-Height		172	76–103	95.14 ± .18	3.54 ± .13	3.72 ± .14

TABLE 2

MEANS OF TOTAL MALE IMMIGRANTS

Measurement		No.	Range	Mean	S.D.	V.
Age		178	20– 64	40.60 ± .55	10.80 ± .39	26.60 ± .95
Weight	(lb.)	174	81–180	124.00 ± .84	16.50 ± .60	13.31 ± .48
Stature	(cm.)	178	145–174	158.72 ± .26	5.19 ± .19	3.27 ± .12
Sitting Height	(cm.)	178	76– 99	83.10 ± .19	3.70 ± .13	4.45 ± .16
Trunk Height	(cm.)	178	44– 61	52.62 ± .16	3.20 ± .11	6.08 ± .22
Upper Arm Length	(cm.)	178	25– 34	29.37 ± .09	1.71 ± .06	5.82 ± .21
Lower Arm Length	(cm.)	178	20– 30	23.48 ± .08	1.56 ± .06	6.64 ± .24
Hand Length	(cm.)	178	15– 20	17.80 ± .04	.82 ± .03	4.61 ± .16
Upper Leg Length	(cm.)	177	29– 46	37.52 ± .15	3.04 ± .11	8.10 ± .29
Lower Leg Length	(cm.)	178	28– 38	32.65 ± .10	1.95 ± .07	5.97 ± .21
Total Leg Length	(cm.)	177	67– 88	75.56 ± .20	3.96 ± .14	5.24 ± .19
Biacromion	(cm.)	178	35– 46	40.28 ± .09	1.84 ± .07	4.57 ± .16
Cristal Breadth	(cm.)	178	25– 36	29.54 ± .10	1.98 ± .07	6.70 ± .24
Chest Breadth	(cm.)	178	24– 33	27.67 ± .09	1.71 ± .06	6.18 ± .22
Chest Depth	(cm.)	178	15– 27	20.29 ± .09	1.85 ± .07	9.12 ± .33
Head Length	(mm.)	178	172–205	189.38 ± .32	6.36 ± .23	3.36 ± .12
Head Breadth	(mm.)	178	143–170	152.72 ± .27	5.34 ± .19	3.50 ± .13
Head Height	(cm.)	176	10– 16	13.41 ± .06	1.19 ± .04	8.87 ± .32
Minimum Frontal Diameter	(mm.)	178	97–126	112.64 ± .28	5.46 ± .20	4.85 ± .17
Bizygomatic Diameter	(mm.)	177	125–154	142.35 ± .24	4.83 ± .17	3.39 ± .12
Bigonial Diameter	(mm.)	178	97–129	111.68 ± .32	6.30 ± .23	5.64 ± .20
Total Face Height	(mm.)	177	106–141	123.23 ± .30	5.97 ± .21	4.84 ± .17
Upper Face Height	(mm.)	178	67– 96	81.40 ± .25	4.96 ± .18	6.09 ± .22
Forehead Height	(mm.)	176	38– 81	59.38 ± .41	8.00 ± .29	13.47 ± .48
Nose Height	(mm.)	176	42– 63	51.66 ± .18	3.50 ± .13	6.78 ± .24

	N	Range			
Nose Length (mm.)	176	40– 63	50.24 ± .20	3.84 ± .14	7.64 ± .27
Nose Salient (mm.)	175	9– 19	13.93 ± .11	2.16 ± .08	15.51 ± .56
Nose Breadth (mm.)	176	26– 43	35.80 ± .15	2.98 ± .11	8.32 ± .30
Inter-Ocular (mm.)	178	21– 42	30.54 ± .18	3.52 ± .13	11.53 ± .41
Bi-Ocular (mm.)	178	82–119	100.82 ± .30	5.94 ± .21	5.89 ± .21
Index					
Relative Shoulder Breadth	178	23– 30	25.30 ± .07	1.32 ± .05	5.22 ± .19
Relative Hip Breadth	178	14– 23	18.60 ± .07	1.42 ± .05	7.63 ± .27
Shoulder-Hip	178	59– 97	73.41 ± .24	4.80 ± .17	6.54 ± .23
Relative Sitting Height	178	47– 61	52.37 ± .09	1.82 ± .06	3.48 ± .12
Relative Trunk Height	178	28– 38	33.14 ± .09	1.69 ± .06	5.10 ± .18
Thoracic	178	58– 89	73.24 ± .28	5.58 ± .20	7.62 ± .27
Brachial	178	63– 92	80.18 ± .26	5.18 ± .19	6.46 ± .23
Tibio-Femoral	177	65–119	87.50 ± .43	8.55 ± .31	9.77 ± .35
Inter-Membral	177	84–117	93.54 ± .23	4.60 ± .16	4.92 ± .18
Cephalic	178	72– 95	80.72 ± .20	3.96 ± .14	4.91 ± .18
Length-Height	176	56– 89	70.82 ± .34	6.74 ± .24	9.52 ± .34
Breadth-Height	176	68–111	87.90 ± .40	7.92 ± .28	9.01 ± .32
Cephalo-Facial	177	83–102	93.12 ± .17	3.30 ± .12	3.54 ± .13
Fronto-Parietal	178	62– 81	73.62 ± .18	3.54 ± .13	4.81 ± .17
Zygo-Frontal	177	62– 89	79.06 ± .17	3.28 ± .12	4.15 ± .15
Zygo-Gonial	177	70– 89	78.38 ± .18	3.54 ± .13	4.52 ± .16
Facial	176	72–101	86.53 ± .25	4.98 ± .18	5.76 ± .21
Upper Facial	177	46– 69	57.35 ± .20	3.99 ± .14	6.96 ± .25
Nasal	176	50– 95	69.64 ± .36	7.16 ± .26	10.28 ± .37
Nose Salient-Height	176	16– 39	26.93 ± .20	3.96 ± .14	14.70 ± .53
Nose Length-Height	176	86–105	97.82 ± .16	3.16 ± .11	3.23 ± .12

TABLE 3

DIFFERENCES OF TOTAL MALE IMMIGRANTS FROM TOTAL MALE SEDENTES

Measurement	Difference	x p.e.
Age	5.05 ± .84	6.01
Weight	4.20 ± 1.14	3.68
Stature	.33 ± .38	.87
Sitting Height	−1.40 ± .28	5.00
Trunk Height	−1.54 ± .23	6.70
Upper Arm Length	− .03 ± .13	.23
Lower Arm Length	.33 ± .11	3.00
Hand Length	.33 ± .06	5.50
Upper Leg Length	1.74 ± .23	7.57
Lower Leg Length	.94 ± .14	6.71
Total Leg Length	1.80 ± .28	6.43
Biacromion	.75 ± .13	5.77
Cristal Breadth	− .31 ± .13	2.38
Chest Breadth	.40 ± .12	3.33
Chest Depth	− .33 ± .11	3.00
Head Length	− .32 ± .47	.68
Head Breadth	.82 ± .37	2.22
Head Height	.68 ± .08	8.50
Minimum Frontal Diameter	.54 ± .40	1.35
Bizygomatic Diameter	.60 ± .34	1.76
Bigonial Diameter	2.25 ± .42	5.36
Total Face Height	3.57 ± .46	7.76
Upper Face Height	8.74 ± .34	25.71
Forehead Height	−1.48 ± .59	2.51
Nose Height	1.12 ± .25	4.48
Nose Length	2.36 ± .28	8.43
Nose Salient	− .70 ± .16	4.38
Nose Breadth	− .70 ± .21	3.33
Inter-Ocular	−1.08 ± .23	4.70
Bi-Ocular	1.26 ± .40	3.15
Index		
Relative Shoulder Breadth	.38 ± .10	3.80
Relative Hip Breadth	− .34 ± .09	3.78
Shoulder-Hip	−2.19 ± .33	6.64
Relative Sitting Height	−1.00 ± .13	7.69
Relative Trunk Height	−1.03 ± .13	7.92
Thoracic	−2.40 ± .39	6.15
Brachial	1.40 ± .35	4.00
Tibio-Femoral	−1.55 ± .67	2.31
Inter-Membral	−1.44 ± .34	4.24
Cephalic	.50 ± .28	1.79

[TABLE 3—*continued*]

DIFFERENCES OF TOTAL MALE IMMIGRANTS FROM TOTAL MALE SEDENTES

Index	Difference	x p.e.
Length-Height	3.76 ± .45	8.36
Breadth-Height	4.18 ± .54	7.74
Cephalo-Facial	− .14 ± .23	.61
Fronto-Parietal	− .22 ± .25	.88
Zygo-Frontal	− .08 ± .25	.32
Zygo-Gonial	1.14 ± .25	4.56
Facial	2.28 ± .37	6.16
Upper Facial	5.94 ± .27	22.00
Nasal	−2.80 ± .54	5.19
Nose Salient-Height	−2.01 ± .30	6.70
Nose Length-Height	2.68 ± .24	11.17

DISTRIBUTION OF THE X P.E.'S OF THE DIFFERENCES BETWEEN
TOTAL MALE IMMIGRANTS AND TOTAL MALE SEDENTES

	0–.99	1.00–1.99	2.00–2.99	3.00–3.99
Measurements	3	2	3	6
Indices	3	1	1	2

	4.00–4.99	5.00–5.99	6.00–X
Measurements	3	4	8
Indices	3	1	10

TABLE 4

MEANS OF TOTAL FEMALE SEDENTES

Measurement		No.	Range	Mean	S.D.	V.
Age		91	20– 64	38.60 ± .88	12.45 ± .62	32.25 ± 1.61
Weight	(lb.)	71	69–176	104.38 ± 1.16	14.52 ± .82	13.91 ± .79
Stature	(cm.)	91	136–159	146.00 ± .32	4.50 ± .22	3.08 ± .15
Sitting Height	(cm.)	91	72– 85	78.86 ± .23	3.32 ± .17	4.21 ± .21
Trunk Height	(cm.)	91	44– 57	50.96 ± .20	2.84 ± .14	5.57 ± .28
Upper Arm Length	(cm.)	91	23– 30	26.88 ± .11	1.55 ± .08	5.77 ± .29
Lower Arm Length	(cm.)	91	18– 24	21.01 ± .09	1.23 ± .06	5.85 ± .29
Hand Length	(cm.)	91	14– 18	16.10 ± .05	.69 ± .03	4.29 ± .21
Upper Leg Length	(cm.)	91	25– 40	32.68 ± .23	3.30 ± .16	10.10 ± .50
Lower Leg Length	(cm.)	91	24– 34	29.09 ± .12	1.68 ± .08	5.78 ± .29
Total Leg Length	(cm.)	91	59– 74	67.08 ± .23	3.32 ± .17	4.95 ± .25
Biacromion	(cm.)	91	32– 41	36.05 ± .11	1.59 ± .08	4.41 ± .22
Cristal Breadth	(cm.)	90	26– 34	29.10 ± .12	1.73 ± .09	5.94 ± .30
Chest Breadth	(cm.)	91	22– 31	25.85 ± .13	1.89 ± .09	7.31 ± .37
Head Length	(mm.)	82	168–199	182.40 ± .46	6.14 ± .32	3.37 ± .18
Head Breadth	(mm.)	91	133–156	145.24 ± .33	4.70 ± .24	3.24 ± .16
Head Height	(cm.)	91	9– 16	12.21 ± .10	1.36 ± .07	11.14 ± .56
Minimum Frontal Diameter	(mm.)	91	97–120	108.95 ± .30	4.23 ± .21	3.88 ± .19
Bizygomatic Diameter	(mm.)	91	122–145	134.22 ± .28	3.99 ± .20	2.97 ± .15
Bigonial Diameter	(mm.)	91	88–114	102.41 ± .35	4.92 ± .25	4.80 ± .24
Total Face Height	(mm.)	91	97–129	111.92 ± .45	6.33 ± .32	5.66 ± .28
Upper Face Height	(mm.)	91	57– 82	69.58 ± .32	4.50 ± .22	6.47 ± .32
Forehead Height	(mm.)	90	42– 77	58.58 ± .50	7.00 ± .35	11.95 ± .60
Nose Height	(mm.)	91	40– 57	47.80 ± .24	3.38 ± .17	7.07 ± .35
Nose Length	(mm.)	91	34– 53	44.70 ± .27	3.78 ± .19	8.46 ± .42

		N	Range						
Nose Salient	(mm.)	91	10– 18	13.25 ±	.12	1.65 ±	.08	12.45 ±	.62
Nose Breadth	(mm.)	91	26– 39	33.18 ±	.17	2.40 ±	.12	7.23 ±	.36
Inter-Ocular	(mm.)	90	24– 38	31.07 ±	.20	2.79 ±	.14	8.98 ±	.45
Bi-Ocular	(mm.)	90	86–107	96.50 ±	.31	4.40 ±	.22	4.56 ±	.23
Index									
Relative Shoulder Breadth		91	21– 28	24.80 ±	.09	1.28 ±	.06	5.16 ±	.26
Relative Hip Breadth		90	18– 23	19.94 ±	.09	1.26 ±	.06	6.32 ±	.32
Shoulder-Hip		90	71– 91	80.82 ±	.32	4.47 ±	.22	5.53 ±	.28
Relative Sitting Height		91	50– 58	54.05 ±	.12	1.76 ±	.09	3.26 ±	.16
Relative Trunk Height		91	30– 40	34.93 ±	.13	1.79 ±	.09	5.12 ±	.26
Brachial		91	69– 92	78.62 ±	.34	4.74 ±	.24	6.03 ±	.30
Tibio-Femoral		91	65–124	90.25 ±	.82	11.60 ±	.58	12.85 ±	.64
Inter-Membral		91	84–107	95.54 ±	.33	4.64 ±	.23	4.86 ±	.24
Cephalic		82	70– 91	79.72 ±	.28	3.82 ±	.20	4.79 ±	.25
Length-Height		82	46– 85	67.14 ±	.57	7.70 ±	.41	11.47 ±	.60
Breadth-Height		91	64–111	84.08 ±	.67	9.42 ±	.47	11.20 ±	.56
Cephalo-Facial		91	85–102	92.44 ±	.21	3.04 ±	.15	3.29 ±	.16
Fronto-Parietal		91	66– 87	75.20 ±	.26	3.62 ±	.18	4.81 ±	.24
Zygo-Frontal		91	72– 89	81.14 ±	.24	3.46 ±	.17	4.26 ±	.21
Zygo-Gonial		91	62– 85	76.28 ±	.26	3.74 ±	.19	4.90 ±	.24
Facial		91	72– 98	83.35 ±	.34	4.77 ±	.24	5.72 ±	.29
Upper Facial		91	43– 60	52.04 ±	.25	3.60 ±	.18	6.92 ±	.35
Nasal		91	54– 85	69.76 ±	.47	6.68 ±	.33	9.58 ±	.48
Nose Salient-Height		91	19– 36	27.62 ±	.24	3.42 ±	.17	12.38 ±	.62
Nose Length-Height		91	82–103	93.92 ±	.26	3.70 ±	.18	3.94 ±	.20

TABLE 5

MEANS OF TOTAL FEMALE IMMIGRANTS

Measurement		No.	Range	Mean	S.D.	V.
Age		89	20– 64	38.50 ± .72	10.05 ± .51	26.10 ± 1.32
Weight	(lb.)	78	69–176	113.02 ± 1.48	19.32 ± 1.04	17.09 ± .92
Stature	(cm.)	93	136–162	148.52 ± .31	4.47 ± .22	3.01 ± .15
Sitting Height	(cm.)	93	72– 89	78.84 ± .24	3.46 ± .17	4.39 ± .22
Trunk Height	(cm.)	93	42– 61	49.56 ± .23	3.28 ± .16	6.62 ± .33
Upper Arm Length	(cm.)	93	24– 32	27.82 ± .12	1.78 ± .09	6.40 ± .32
Lower Arm Length	(cm.)	93	19– 25	21.74 ± .09	1.29 ± .06	5.93 ± .29
Hand Length	(cm.)	93	15– 19	16.60 ± .06	.82 ± .04	4.94 ± .24
Upper Leg Length	(cm.)	91	23– 44	33.72 ± .29	4.08 ± .20	12.10 ± .60
Lower Leg Length	(cm.)	92	27– 38	31.49 ± .14	1.99 ± .10	6.32 ± .31
Total Leg Length	(cm.)	93	61– 82	70.22 ± .27	3.90 ± .19	5.55 ± .27
Biacromion	(cm.)	93	33– 43	37.00 ± .14	1.93 ± .10	5.22 ± .26
Cristal Breadth	(cm.)	85	25– 36	29.98 ± .17	2.30 ± .12	7.67 ± .40
Chest Breadth	(cm.)	84	22– 33	26.08 ± .18	2.39 ± .12	9.16 ± .48
Head Length	(mm.)	74	168–201	182.82 ± .52	6.68 ± .37	3.65 ± .20
Head Breadth	(mm.)	93	137–158	146.98 ± .38	5.48 ± .27	3.73 ± .18
Head Height	(cm.)	92	10– 15	12.82 ± .08	1.14 ± .06	8.89 ± .44
Minimum Frontal Diameter	(mm.)	93	97–120	110.24 ± .37	5.25 ± .26	4.76 ± .24
Bizygomatic Diameter	(mm.)	92	119–160	136.20 ± .46	6.54 ± .32	4.80 ± .24
Bigonial Diameter	(mm.)	93	94–129	109.07 ± .43	6.21 ± .31	5.69 ± .28
Total Face Height	(mm.)	93	97–138	115.46 ± .45	6.42 ± .32	5.56 ± .28
Upper Face Height	(mm.)	93	55– 90	75.20 ± .45	6.40 ± .32	8.51 ± .42
Forehead Height	(mm.)	93	42– 77	58.38 ± .51	7.28 ± .36	12.47 ± .62
Nose Height	(mm.)	93	40– 57	49.00 ± .26	3.78 ± .19	7.71 ± .38
Nose Length	(mm.)	93	30– 55	46.58 ± .31	4.48 ± .22	9.62 ± .48

		N	Range			
Nose Salient	(mm.)	92	7– 21	12.85 ± .17	2.46 ± .12	19.14 ± .95
Nose Breadth	(mm.)	93	26– 39	33.22 ± .19	2.68 ± .13	8.07 ± .40
Inter-Ocular	(mm.)	93	23– 38	30.23 ± .22	3.13 ± .16	10.35 ± .51
Bi-Ocular	(mm.)	93	82–109	99.14 ± .35	5.06 ± .25	5.10 ± .25
Index						
Relative Shoulder Breadth		93	23– 30	24.82 ± .09	1.32 ± .06	5.32 ± .26
Relative Hip Breadth		85	16– 25	20.00 ± .13	1.74 ± .09	8.70 ± .45
Shoulder-Hip		85	68– 94	80.73 ± .37	5.10 ± .26	6.32 ± .33
Relative Sitting Height		93	47– 57	52.78 ± .13	1.88 ± .09	3.56 ± .18
Relative Trunk Height		93	28– 39	33.27 ± .14	2.00 ± .10	6.01 ± .30
Brachial		93	67– 92	78.30 ± .34	4.86 ± .24	6.21 ± .31
Tibio-Femoral		90	70–139	94.90 ± 1.00	14.05 ± .71	14.80 ± .74
Inter-Membral		93	80–113	94.46 ± .39	5.64 ± .28	5.97 ± .30
Cephalic		74	72– 93	80.56 ± .32	4.12 ± .23	5.11 ± .28
Length-Height		73	58– 87	70.52 ± .52	6.52 ± .36	9.25 ± .52
Breadth-Height		92	70–109	87.18 ± .55	7.88 ± .39	9.04 ± .45
Cephalo-Facial		92	81–104	92.38 ± .25	3.52 ± .18	3.81 ± .19
Fronto-Parietal		93	66– 83	74.94 ± .23	3.32 ± .16	4.43 ± .22
Zygo-Frontal		92	72– 91	80.94 ± .25	3.50 ± .17	4.32 ± .22
Zygo-Gonial		92	72– 89	80.16 ± .26	3.70 ± .18	4.62 ± .23
Facial		92	69–101	85.15 ± .39	5.58 ± .28	6.55 ± .33
Upper Facial		92	43– 69	56.15 ± .37	5.25 ± .26	9.35 ± .46
Nasal		93	54– 89	68.56 ± .56	8.06 ± .40	11.76 ± .58
Nose Salient-Height		92	13– 42	26.39 ± .38	5.40 ± .27	20.46 ± 1.02
Nose Length-Height		93	76–103	95.44 ± .30	4.32 ± .21	4.53 ± .22

TABLE 6

DIFFERENCES OF TOTAL FEMALE IMMIGRANTS FROM TOTAL FEMALE SEDENTES

Measurement	Difference	x p.e.
Age	− .10 ± 1.14	.09
Weight	8.64 ± 1.88	4.60
Stature	2.52 ± .45	5.60
Sitting Height	− .02 ± .33	.06
Trunk Height	−1.40 ± .30	4.67
Upper Arm Length	.94 ± .16	5.88
Lower Arm Length	.73 ± .13	5.62
Hand Length	.50 ± .08	6.25
Upper Leg Length	1.04 ± .37	2.81
Lower Leg Length	2.40 ± .18	13.33
Total Leg Length	3.14 ± .36	8.72
Biacromion	.95 ± .18	5.28
Cristal Breadth	.88 ± .21	4.19
Chest Breadth	.23 ± .22	1.05
Head Length	.42 ± .69	.61
Head Breadth	1.74 ± .50	3.48
Head Height (cm.)	.61 ± .13	4.69
Minimum Frontal Diameter	1.29 ± .48	2.69
Bizygomatic Diameter	1.98 ± .54	3.67
Bigonial Diameter	6.66 ± .55	12.11
Total Face Height	3.54 ± .64	5.53
Upper Face Height	5.62 ± .55	10.22
Forehead Height	− .20 ± .71	.28
Nose Height	1.20 ± .35	3.43
Nose Length	1.88 ± .41	4.59
Nose Salient	− .40 ± .21	1.90
Nose Breadth	.04 ± .25	.16
Inter-Ocular	− .84 ± .30	2.80
Bi-Ocular	2.64 ± .47	5.62

Index		
Relative Shoulder Breadth	.02 ± .13	.15
Relative Hip Breadth	.06 ± .16	.38
Shoulder-Hip	− .09 ± .49	.18
Relative Sitting Height	−1.27 ± .18	7.06
Relative Trunk Height	−1.66 ± .17	9.76
Brachial	− .32 ± .48	.67
Tibio-Femoral	4.65 ± 1.29	3.60
Inter-Membral	−1.08 ± .51	2.12
Cephalic	.84 ± .43	1.95
Length Height	3.38 ± .77	4.39
Breadth Height	3.10 ± .87	3.56

[TABLE 6—*continued*]

DIFFERENCES OF TOTAL FEMALE IMMIGRANTS FROM TOTAL FEMALE SEDENTES

Index	Difference	x p.e.
Cephalo-Facial	$- .06 \pm .33$	.18
Fronto-Parietal	$- .26 \pm .35$	.74
Zygo-Frontal	$- .20 \pm .35$	.57
Zygo-Gonial	$3.88 \pm .37$	10.49
Facial	$1.80 \pm .52$	3.46
Upper Facial	$4.11 \pm .45$	9.13
Nasal	$-1.20 \pm .73$	1.64
Nose Salient-Height	$-1.23 \pm .45$	2.73
Nose Length-Height	$1.52 \pm .40$	3.80

DISTRIBUTION OF THE X P.E.'S OF THE DIFFERENCES BETWEEN THE TOTAL
FEMALE IMMIGRANTS AND THE TOTAL FEMALE SEDENTES

	0–.99	1.00–1.99	2.00–2.99	3.00–3.99
Measurements	4	2	3	3
Indices	7	2	2	4

	4.00–4.99	5.00–5.99	6.00–X
Measurements	5	6	5
Indices	1	0	4

TABLE 7

DIFFERENCES OF TOTAL FEMALE SEDENTES FROM TOTAL FEMALE IMMIGRANTS,
CORRECTED TO STATURE OF SEDENTES

Measurement	Difference		x p.e.
Stature	0		0
Weight	5.05 lb.	± 1.88	2.69
Sitting Height	−1.17 cm.	± .33	3.55
Trunk Height	−2.21 "	± .30	7.37
Upper Arm Length	.46 "	± .16	2.88
Lower Arm Length	.41 "	± .13	3.15
Hand Length	.32 "	± .08	4.00
Upper Leg Length	− .02 "	± .37	.05
Lower Leg Length	1.94 "	± .18	10.78
Total Leg Length	1.82 "	± .36	5.06
Biacromion	.50 "	± .18	2.78
Cristal Breadth	.88 "	± .21	4.19
Chest Breadth	− .15 "	± .22	.68
Head Length	− .97 mm.	± .69	1.41
Head Width	1.15 "	± .50	2.30
Head Height	.43 cm.	± .13	3.31
Minimum Frontal Diameter	1.29 mm.	± .48	2.69
Bizygomatic Diameter	1.13 "	± .54	2.09
Bigonial Diameter	5.47 "	± .55	9.95
Total Face Height	2.82 "	± .64	4.41
Upper Face Height	5.62 "	± .55	10.22
Forehead Height	− .20 "	± .71	.28
Nose Height	1.20 "	± .35	3.43
Nose Length	1.88 "	± .41	4.59
Nose Salient	− .83 "	± .21	3.95
Nose Breadth	.04 "	± .25	.16
Inter-Ocular	−1.25 "	± .30	4.17
Bi-Ocular	2.64 "	± .47	5.62
Index			
Relative Shoulder Breadth	.02 "	± .13	.15
Relative Hip Width	.29 "	± .16	1.81
Shoulder-Hip	− .09 "	± .49	.18
Relative Sitting Height	−1.27 "	± .18	7.06
Relative Trunk Height	−1.66 "	± .17	9.76
Brachial	− .32 "	± .48	.67
Tibio-Femoral	6.31 "	± 1.29	4.89
Inter-Membral	−1.08 "	± .51	2.12
Cephalic	.84 "	± .43	1.95
Length-Height	3.38 "	± .77	4.39
Breadth-Height	2.26 "	± .87	2.60

[TABLE 7—*continued*]

DIFFERENCES OF TOTAL FEMALE SEDENTES FROM TOTAL FEMALE IMMIGRANTS,
CORRECTED TO STATURE OF SEDENTES

Index	Difference	x p.e.
Cephalo-Facial	— .06 mm. ± .33	.18
Fronto-Parietal	— .26 " ± .35	.74
Zygo-Frontal	— .20 " ± .35	.57
Zygo-Gonial	3.88 " ± .37	10.49
Facial	1.80 " ± .52	3.46
Upper Facial	4.11 " ± .45	9.13
Nasal	—1.20 " ± .73	1.64
Nose Salient-Height	—1.96 " ± .45	4.36
Nose Length-Height	1.52 " ± .40	3.80

TABLE 8

COMPARISON OF THE DIVERGENCE OF THE IMMIGRANT MALES AND IMMIGRANT
FEMALES FROM THEIR RESPECTIVE SEDENTES

Measurement	Male	Female	Female (corrected for stature)
	x p.e.	x p.e.	x p.e.
Weight	3.68	4.60	2.69
Stature	.87	5.60	
Sitting Height	− 5.00	− .06	3.55
Trunk Height	− 6.70	− 4.67	7.37
Upper Arm Length	− .23	5.88	2.88
Lower Arm Length	3.00	5.62	3.15
Hand Length	5.50	6.25	4.00
Upper Leg Length	7.57	2.81	.05
Lower Leg Length	6.71	13.33	10.78
Total Leg Length	6.43	8.72	5.06
Biacromion	5.77	5.28	2.78
Cristal Breadth	− 2.38	4.19	4.19
Chest Breadth	3.33	1.05	.68
Chest Depth	− 3.00		
Head Length	− .68	.61	1.41
Head Width	2.22	3.48	2.30
Head Height	8.50	4.69	3.31
Minimum Frontal Diameter	1.35	2.69	2.69
Bizygomatic Diameter	1.76	3.67	2.09
Bigonial Diameter	5.36	12.11	9.95
Total Face Height	7.76	5.53	4.41
Upper Face Height	25.71	10.22	10.22
Forehead Height	− 2.51	− .28	.28
Nose Height	4.48	3.43	3.43
Nose Length	8.43	4.59	4.59
Nose Salient	− 4.38	− 1.90	3.95
Nose Breadth	− 3.33	.16	.16
Inter-Ocular	− 4.70	− 2.80	4.17
Bi-Ocular	3.15	5.62	5.62
Index			
Relative Shoulder Breadth	3.80	.15	.15
Relative Hip Width	− 3.78	.38	1.81
Shoulder-Hip	− 6.64	− .18	.18
Relative Sitting Height	− 7.69	− 7.06	7.06
Relative Trunk Height	− 7.92	− 9.76	9.76
Thoracic	− 6.15		
Brachial	4.00	− .67	.67

[TABLE 8—*continued*]

COMPARISON OF THE DIVERGENCE OF THE IMMIGRANT MALES AND IMMIGRANT
FEMALES FROM THEIR RESPECTIVE SEDENTES

Index	Male	Female	Female (corrected for stature)
	x p.e.	x p.e.	x p.e.
Tibio-Femoral	− 2.31	3.60	4.89
Inter-Membral	− 4.24	− 2.12	2.12
Cephalic	1.79	1.95	1.95
Length-Height	8.36	4.39	4.39
Breadth-Height	7.74	3.56	2.60
Cephalo-Facial	− .61	− .18	.18
Fronto-Parietal	− .88	− .74	.74
Zygo-Frontal	− .32	− .57	.57
Zygo-Gonial	4.56	10.49	10.49
Facial	6.16	3.46	3.46
Upper Facial	22.00	9.13	9.13
Nasal	− 5.19	− 1.64	1.64
Nose Salient-Height	− 6.70	− 2.73	4.36
Nose Length-Height	11.17	3.80	3.80

TABLE 9

MEANS OF TOTAL MALE HAWAIIAN BORN

Measurement		No.	Range	Mean	S.D.	V.
Age		188	20– 49	26.15 ± .26	5.35 ± .19	20.46 ± .71
Weight	(lb.)	185	91–230	127.40 ± .93	18.70 ± .66	14.68 ± .52
Stature	(cm.)	188	148–177	162.83 ± .26	5.28 ± .18	3.24 ± .11
Sitting Height	(cm.)	187	76– 95	85.48 ± .18	3.72 ± .13	4.35 ± .15
Trunk Height	(cm.)	187	46– 63	54.12 ± .16	3.32 ± .12	6.14 ± .21
Upper Arm Length	(cm.)	186	26– 35	30.52 ± .09	1.76 ± .06	5.77 ± .20
Lower Arm Length	(cm.)	187	20– 28	24.31 ± .08	1.55 ± .05	6.38 ± .22
Hand Length	(cm.)	188	15– 20	17.81 ± .04	.88 ± .03	4.94 ± .17
Upper Leg Length	(cm.)	186	29– 46	37.72 ± .16	3.16 ± .11	8.38 ± .29
Lower Leg Length	(cm.)	188	29– 42	33.93 ± .10	2.11 ± .07	6.22 ± .22
Total Leg Length	(cm.)	187	65– 90	77.44 ± .20	4.08 ± .14	5.27 ± .18
Biacromion	(cm.)	187	37– 47	41.35 ± .09	1.78 ± .06	4.30 ± .15
Cristal Breadth	(cm.)	188	25– 36	29.23 ± .10	1.99 ± .07	6.81 ± .24
Chest Breadth	(cm.)	188	23– 39	27.28 ± .10	2.04 ± .07	7.48 ± .26
Chest Depth	(cm.)	187	16– 27	19.65 ± .09	1.79 ± .06	9.11 ± .32
Head Length	(mm.)	188	168–205	186.54 ± .32	6.56 ± .23	3.52 ± .12
Head Breadth	(mm.)	188	139–174	155.08 ± .28	5.78 ± .20	3.73 ± .13
Head Height	(cm.)	183	11– 16	13.68 ± .05	1.09 ± .04	7.97 ± .28
Minimum Frontal Diameter	(mm.)	188	97–126	112.46 ± .24	4.95 ± .17	4.40 ± .15
Bizygomatic Diameter	(mm.)	187	125–160	141.36 ± .26	5.31 ± .18	3.76 ± .13
Bigonial Diameter	(mm.)	188	88–126	110.93 ± .28	5.76 ± .20	5.19 ± .18
Total Face Height	(mm.)	186	106–138	121.76 ± .28	5.70 ± .20	4.68 ± .16
Upper Face Height	(mm.)	187	67– 94	81.62 ± .25	5.00 ± .17	6.13 ± .21
Forehead Height	(mm.)	187	38– 81	59.10 ± .37	7.44 ± .26	12.59 ± .44
Nose Height	(mm.)	188	42– 61	51.82 ± .16	3.36 ± .12	6.48 ± .22

Nose Length	(mm.)	188	40– 59	50.22 ± .18	3.58 ± .12	7.13 ± .25
Nose Salient	(mm.)	188	9– 21	14.12 ± .12	2.36 ± .08	16.71 ± .58
Nose Breadth	(mm.)	188	28– 43	34.56 ± .14	2.80 ± .10	8.10 ± .28
Inter-Ocular	(mm.)	188	23– 41	31.33 ± .17	3.49 ± .12	11.14 ± .39
Bi-Ocular	(mm.)	187	84–113	100.14 ± .25	5.10 ± .18	5.09 ± .18
Index						
Relative Shoulder Breadth		187	23– 28	25.38 ± .06	1.14 ± .04	4.49 ± .16
Relative Hip Breadth		188	14– 21	17.88 ± .06	1.24 ± .04	6.94 ± .24
Shoulder-Hip		187	62– 85	70.62 ± .22	4.38 ± .15	6.20 ± .22
Relative Sitting Height		187	47– 58	52.46 ± .09	1.79 ± .06	3.41 ± .12
Relative Trunk Height		187	29– 38	33.18 ± .09	1.78 ± .06	5.36 ± .19
Thoracic		187	54– 85	72.06 ± .28	5.68 ± .20	7.88 ± .27
Brachial		186	69– 90	79.82 ± .22	4.48 ± .16	5.61 ± .20
Tibio-Femoral		186	70–124	90.95 ± .42	8.50 ± .30	9.35 ± .33
Inter-Membral		185	82–107	93.90 ± .20	4.10 ± .14	4.37 ± .15
Cephalic		188	74– 93	83.32 ± .20	4.06 ± .14	4.87 ± .17
Length-Height		183	56– 91	73.36 ± .31	6.16 ± .22	8.40 ± .30
Breadth-Height		183	68–107	88.32 ± .36	7.16 ± .25	8.11 ± .29
Cephalo-Facial		187	83–102	91.14 ± .15	2.96 ± .10	3.25 ± .11
Fronto-Parietal		188	62– 83	72.58 ± .16	3.36 ± .12	4.63 ± .16
Zygo-Frontal		187	72– 87	79.66 ± .14	2.88 ± .10	3.62 ± .13
Zygo-Gonial		187	68– 89	78.60 ± .15	3.04 ± .11	3.87 ± .14
Facial		185	72– 98	86.14 ± .23	4.59 ± .16	5.33 ± .19
Upper Facial		186	46– 69	57.74 ± .19	3.93 ± .14	6.81 ± .24
Nasal		188	50– 83	66.82 ± .30	6.10 ± .21	9.13 ± .32
Nose Salient-Height		188	16– 45	27.32 ± .23	4.59 ± .16	16.80 ± .58
Nose Length-Height		188	86–103	97.16 ± .15	2.96 ± .10	3.05 ± .11

TABLE 10

DIFFERENCES OF TOTAL MALE HAWAIIAN BORN FROM
TOTAL MALE IMMIGRANTS

Measurement	Difference	x p.e.
Age	−14.45 ± .61	23.69
Weight	3.40 ± 1.25	2.72
Stature	4.11 ± .37	11.11
Sitting Height	2.38 ± .26	9.15
Trunk Height	1.50 ± .23	6.52
Upper Arm Length	1.15 ± .13	8.85
Lower Arm Length	.83 ± .11	7.55
Hand Length	.01 ± .06	.17
Upper Leg Length	.20 ± .22	.91
Lower Leg Length	1.28 ± .14	9.14
Total Leg Length	1.88 ± .28	6.71
Biacromion	1.07 ± .13	8.23
Cristal Breadth	− .31 ± .14	2.21
Chest Breadth	− .39 ± .13	3.00
Chest Depth	− .64 ± .13	4.92
Head Length	− 2.84 ± .45	6.31
Head Breadth	2.36 ± .39	6.05
Head Height	.27 ± .08	3.38
Minimum Frontal Diameter	− .18 ± .37	.49
Bizygomatic Diameter	− .99 ± .35	2.83
Bigonial Diameter	− .75 ± .42	1.79
Total Face Height	− 1.47 ± .41	3.59
Upper Face Height	.22 ± .35	.63
Forehead Height	− .28 ± .55	.51
Nose Height	.16 ± .24	.67
Nose Length	− .02 ± .27	.07
Nose Salient	.19 ± .16	1.19
Nose Breadth	− 1.24 ± .21	5.90
Inter-Ocular	.79 ± .25	3.16
Bi-Ocular	− .68 ± .39	1.74
Index		
Relative Shoulder Breadth	.08 ± .09	.89
Relative Hip Breadth	− .72 ± .09	8.00
Shoulder-Hip	− 2.79 ± .33	8.45
Relative Sitting Height	.09 ± .13	.69
Relative Trunk Height	.04 ± .13	.31
Thoracic	− 1.18 ± .40	2.95
Brachial	− .36 ± .34	1.06
Tibio-Femoral	3.45 ± .60	5.75
Inter-Membral	.36 ± .30	1.20

[TABLE 10—*continued*]

DIFFERENCE OF TOTAL MALE HAWAIIAN BORN FROM
TOTAL MALE IMMIGRANTS

Index	Difference	x p.e.
Cephalic	2.60 ± .28	9.29
Length-Height	2.54 ± .46	5.52
Breadth-Height	.42 ± .54	.78
Cephalo-Facial	−1.98 ± .23	8.61
Fronto-Parietal	−1.04 ± .24	4.33
Zygo-Frontal	.60 ± .22	2.73
Zygo-Gonial	.22 ± .23	.96
Facial	− .39 ± .34	1.15
Upper Facial	.39 ± .28	1.39
Nasal	−2.82 ± .47	6.00
Nose Salient-Height	.39 ± .30	1.30
Nose Length-Height	− .66 ± .22	3.00

DISTRIBUTION OF THE X P.E.'S OF THE DIFFERENCES BETWEEN THE TOTAL MALE
HAWAIIAN BORN AND THE TOTAL MALE IMMIGRANTS

	0–.99	1.00–1.99	2.00–2.99	3.00–3.99
Measurements	7	3	3	4
Indices	5	5	2	1

	4.00–4.99	5.00–5.99	6.00–X
Measurements	1	1	10
Indices	1	2	5

TABLE 11

DIFFERENCES OF TOTAL MALE HAWAIIAN BORN FROM TOTAL MALE SEDENTES

Measurement	Difference	x p.e.
Age	—9.40	13.62
Weight	7.60	6.28
Stature	4.44	11.38
Sitting Height	.98	3.63
Trunk Height	— .04	.17
Upper Arm Length	1.12	8.62
Lower Arm Length	1.16	10.55
Hand Length	.34	5.67
Upper Leg Length	1.94	8.43
Lower Leg Length	2.22	15.86
Total Leg Length	3.68	13.14
Biacromion	1.82	14.00
Cristal Breadth	— .62	4.77
Chest Breadth	.01	.04
Chest Depth	— .97	8.82
Head Length	—3.16	6.72
Head Breadth	3.18	8.37
Head Height	.95	11.88
Minimum Frontal Diameter	.36	.95
Bizygomatic Diameter	— .39	1.11
Bigonial Diameter	1.50	3.85
Total Face Height	2.10	4.67
Upper Face Height	8.96	26.35
Forehead Height	—1.76	3.14
Nose Height	1.28	5.57
Nose Length	2.34	9.00
Nose Salient	— .51	3.19
Nose Breadth	—1.94	9.70
Inter-Ocular	— .29	1.26
Bi-Ocular	.58	1.61
Index		
Relative Shoulder Breadth	.46	5.11
Relative Hip Breadth	—1.06	13.25
Shoulder-Hip	—4.98	15.56
Relative Sitting Height	— .91	7.00
Relative Trunk Height	— .99	7.62
Thoracic	—3.58	9.18
Brachial	1.04	3.15
Tibio-Femoral	1.90	2.84
Inter-Membral	—1.08	3.38
Cephalic	3.10	11.07

[TABLE 11—*continued*]

DIFFERENCES OF TOTAL MALE HAWAIIAN BORN FROM TOTAL MALE SEDENTES

Index	Difference	x p.e.
Length-Height	6.30	15.00
Breadth-Height	4.60	8.85
Cephalo-Facial	−2.12	9.64
Fronto-Parietal	−1.26	5.25
Zygo-Frontal	.52	2.26
Zygo-Gonial	1.36	5.91
Facial	1.89	5.40
Upper Facial	6.33	24.35
Nasal	−5.62	11.24
Nose Salient-Height	−1.62	5.06
Nose Length-Height	2.02	8.78

DISTRIBUTION OF THE X P.E.'S OF THE DIFFERENCES BETWEEN THE TOTAL MALE HAWAIIAN BORN AND THE TOTAL MALE SEDENTES

	0–.99	1.00–1.99	2.00–2.99	3.00–3.99
Measurements	3	3	0	4
Indices	0	0	2	2

	4.00–4.99	5.00–5.99	6.00–X
Measurements	2	2	15
Indices	0	5	12

TABLE 12

MEANS OF TOTAL FEMALE HAWAIIAN BORN

Measurement		No.	Range	Mean	S.D.	V.
Age		90	20– 49	24.55 ± .33	4.60 ± .23	18.74 ± .94
Weight	(lb.)	86	81–164	103.30 ± 1.03	14.16 ± .73	13.71 ± .70
Stature	(cm.)	91	139–165	150.23 ± .34	4.83 ± .24	3.22 ± .16
Sitting Height	(cm.)	91	72– 87	78.88 ± .15	3.06 ± .15	3.88 ± .19
Trunk Height	(cm.)	91	40– 63	49.58 ± .24	3.46 ± .17	6.98 ± .35
Upper Arm Length	(cm.)	91	24– 32	28.01 ± .12	1.68 ± .08	6.00 ± .30
Lower Arm Length	(cm.)	90	19– 25	21.61 ± .09	1.31 ± .07	6.06 ± .30
Hand Length	(cm.)	91	14– 18	16.21 ± .06	.81 ± .04	5.00 ± .25
Upper Leg Length	(cm.)	91	25– 42	34.76 ± .24	3.36 ± .17	9.67 ± .48
Lower Leg Length	(cm.)	91	26– 36	31.97 ± .14	1.91 ± .10	5.97 ± .30
Total Leg Length	(cm.)	91	61– 80	71.30 ± .25	3.58 ± .18	5.02 ± .25
Biacromion	(cm.)	91	32– 42	36.13 ± .12	1.75 ± .09	4.84 ± .24
Cristal Breadth	(cm.)	90	23– 34	28.11 ± .16	2.25 ± .11	8.00 ± .40
Chest Breadth	(cm.)	90	21– 31	24.23 ± .14	1.92 ± .10	7.92 ± .40
Head Length	(mm.)	85	164–199	178.08 ± .44	6.02 ± .31	3.38 ± .18
Head Breadth	(mm.)	91	133–164	149.00 ± .40	5.58 ± .28	3.74 ± .19
Head Height	(cm.)	91	11– 16	13.10 ± .08	1.18 ± .06	9.01 ± .45
Minimum Frontal Diameter	(mm.)	91	100–123	109.01 ± .30	4.29 ± .21	3.94 ± .20
Bizygomatic Diameter	(mm.)	91	122–157	134.07 ± .41	5.76 ± .29	4.30 ± .22
Bigonial Diameter	(mm.)	91	91–120	105.26 ± .40	5.67 ± .28	5.39 ± .27
Total Face Height	(mm.)	91	100–129	113.72 ± .43	6.03 ± .30	5.30 ± .26
Upper Face Height	(mm.)	91	59– 86	76.26 ± .34	4.78 ± .24	6.27 ± .31
Forehead Height	(mm.)	91	38– 81	55.78 ± .52	7.28 ± .36	13.05 ± .65
Nose Height	(mm.)	90	38– 59	48.36 ± .23	3.28 ± .16	6.78 ± .34
Nose Length	(mm.)	88	34– 55	46.18 ± .24	3.38 ± .17	7.32 ± .37

Nose Salient	(mm.)	90	9– 18	12.62 ± .13	1.84 ± .09	14.58 ± .73
Nose Breadth	(mm.)	90	26– 39	31.96 ± .17	2.36 ± .12	7.38 ± .37
Inter-Ocular	(mm.)	90	25– 40	31.68 ± .22	3.02 ± .15	9.53 ± .48
Bi-Ocular	(mm.)	90	90–109	99.32 ± .31	4.42 ± .22	4.45 ± .22
Index						
Relative Shoulder Breadth		91	21– 28	24.10 ± .09	1.24 ± .06	5.14 ± .26
Relative Hip Breadth		90	14– 23	18.76 ± .11	1.50 ± .08	8.00 ± .40
Shoulder-Hip		90	62– 88	77.76 ± .34	4.83 ± .24	6.21 ± .31
Relative Sitting Height		91	48– 56	52.50 ± .12	1.69 ± .08	3.22 ± .16
Relative Trunk Height		91	26– 42	32.98 ± .15	2.18 ± .11	6.61 ± .33
Brachial		90	67– 88	77.42 ± .32	4.48 ± .22	5.79 ± .29
Tibio-Femoral		91	70–124	92.75 ± .74	10.50 ± .52	11.32 ± .57
Inter-Membral		90	82–103	92.44 ± .33	4.58 ± .23	4.95 ± .25
Cephalic		85	74– 93	83.80 ± .26	3.58 ± .18	4.27 ± .22
Length-Height		85	60– 91	73.58 ± .50	6.84 ± .35	9.30 ± .48
Breadth-Height		91	70–105	87.90 ± .56	7.92 ± .40	9.01 ± .45
Cephalo-Facial		91	79–106	90.12 ± .25	3.56 ± .18	3.95 ± .20
Fronto-Parietal		91	66– 81	73.24 ± .23	3.22 ± .16	4.40 ± .22
Zygo-Frontal		91	64– 91	81.20 ± .25	3.52 ± .18	4.34 ± .22
Zygo-Gonial		91	68– 87	78.48 ± .26	3.60 ± .18	4.59 ± .23
Facial		91	66– 98	84.70 ± .38	5.37 ± .27	6.34 ± .32
Upper Facial		91	37– 66	56.90 ± .28	3.96 ± .20	6.95 ± .35
Nasal		90	52– 89	66.46 ± .46	6.50 ± .33	9.78 ± .49
Nose Salient-Height		90	19– 42	26.24 ± .28	3.96 ± .20	15.09 ± .76
Nose Length-Height		88	86–101	95.62 ± .21	2.94 ± .15	3.07 ± .16

TABLE 13

DIFFERENCES OF TOTAL FEMALE HAWAIIAN BORN FROM
TOTAL FEMALE IMMIGRANTS

Measurement	Difference	x p.e.
Age	−13.95 ± .79	17.66
Weight	− 9.72 ± 1.80	5.45
Stature	1.71 ± .46	3.72
Sitting Height	.04 ± .33	.12
Trunk Height	.02 ± .33	.06
Upper Arm Length	.19 ± .17	1.12
Lower Arm Length	− .13 ± .13	1.00
Hand Length	− .39 ± .08	4.88
Upper Leg Length	1.04 ± .38	2.74
Lower Leg Length	.48 ± .20	2.40
Total Leg Length	1.08 ± .37	2.92
Biacromion	− .87 ± .18	4.83
Cristal Breadth	− 1.87 ± .23	8.13
Chest Breadth	− 1.85 ± .23	8.04
Head Length	− 4.74 ± .68	6.97
Head Breadth	2.02 ± .55	3.67
Head Height (cm.)	.28 ± .11	2.55
Minimum Frontal Diameter	− 1.23 ± .48	2.56
Bizygomatic Diameter	− 2.13 ± .62	3.44
Bigonial Diameter	− 5.81 ± .59	9.85
Total Face Height	− 1.74 ± .62	2.81
Upper Face Height	1.06 ± .57	1.86
Forehead Height	− 2.60 ± .73	3.56
Nose Height	− .64 ± .35	1.83
Nose Length	− .40 ± .39	1.03
Nose Salient	− .23 ± .21	1.10
Nose Breadth	− 1.26 ± .25	5.04
Inter-Ocular	1.45 ± .31	4.68
Bi-Ocular	.18 ± .47	.38
Index		
Relative Shoulder Breadth	− .72 ± .13	5.54
Relative Hip Breadth	− 1.24 ± .17	7.29
Shoulder-Hip	− 2.97 ± .50	5.94
Relative Sitting Height	− .28 ± .18	1.56
Relative Trunk Height	− .29 ± .21	1.38
Brachial	− .88 ± .47	1.87
Tibio-Femoral	− 2.15 ± 1.24	1.73
Inter-Membral	− 2.02 ± .51	3.96
Cephalic	3.24 ± .41	7.90
Length-Height	3.06 ± .72	4.25

[TABLE 13—*continued*]

DIFFERENCES OF TOTAL FEMALE HAWAIIAN BORN FROM TOTAL FEMALE IMMIGRANTS

Index	Difference	x p.e.
Breadth-Height	.72 ± .79	.91
Cephalo-Facial	− 2.26 ± .35	6.46
Fronto-Parietal	− 1.70 ± .33	5.15
Zygo-Frontal	.26 ± .35	.74
Zygo-Gonial	− 1.68 ± .37	4.54
Facial	− .45 ± .55	.82
Upper Facial	.75 ± .46	1.63
Nasal	− 2.10 ± .73	2.88
Nose Salient-Height	− .15 ± .47	.32
Nose Length-Height	.18 ± .37	.49

DISTRIBUTION OF THE X P.E.'S OF THE DIFFERENCES BETWEEN THE TOTAL FEMALE HAWAIIAN BORN AND THE TOTAL FEMALE IMMIGRANTS

	0–.99	1.00–1.99	2.00–2.99	3.00–3.99
Measurements	3	6	6	4
Indices	5	5	1	1

	4.00–4.99	5.00–5.99	6.00–X
Measurements	3	2	4
Indices	2	3	3

TABLE 14

DIFFERENCES OF TOTAL FEMALE HAWAIIAN BORN FROM
TOTAL FEMALE SEDENTES

Measurement	Difference	x p.e.
Age	−14.05 ± .94	14.95
Weight	− 1.08 ± 1.55	.70
Stature	4.23 ± .47	9.00
Sitting Height	.02 ± .32	.06
Trunk Height	− 1.38 ± .31	4.45
Upper Arm Length	1.13 ± .16	7.06
Lower Arm Length	.60 ± .13	4.62
Hand Length	.11 ± .07	1.57
Upper Leg Length	2.08 ± .33	6.30
Lower Leg Length	2.88 ± .18	16.00
Total Leg Length	4.22 ± .34	12.41
Biacromion	.08 ± .16	.50
Cristal Breadth	− .99 ± .20	4.95
Chest Breadth	− 1.62 ± .19	8.53
Head Length	− 4.32 ± .64	6.75
Head Breadth	3.76 ± .52	7.23
Head Height (cm.)	.89 ± .13	6.85
Minimum Frontal Diameter	.06 ± .42	.14
Bizygomatic Diameter	− .15 ± .50	.30
Bigonial Diameter	2.85 ± .53	5.38
Total Face Height	1.80 ± .62	2.90
Upper Face Height	6.68 ± .47	14.22
Forehead Height	− 2.80 ± .72	3.89
Nose Height	.56 ± .33	1.70
Nose Length	1.48 ± .36	4.11
Nose Salient	− .63 ± .18	3.50
Nose Breadth	− 1.22 ± .24	5.08
Inter-Ocular	.61 ± .30	2.03
Bi-Ocular	2.82 ± .44	6.41
Index		
Relative Shoulder Breadth	− .70 ± .13	5.38
Relative Hip Breadth	− 1.18 ± .14	8.43
Shoulder-Hip	− 3.06 ± .47	6.51
Relative Sitting Height	− 1.55 ± .17	9.12
Relative Trunk Height	− 1.95 ± .20	9.75
Brachial	− 1.20 ± .47	2.55
Tibio-Femoral	2.50 ± 1.10	2.27
Inter-Membral	− 3.10 ± .47	6.60
Cephalic	4.08 ± .38	10.74
Length-Height	6.44 ± .76	8.47

[TABLE 14—*continued*]

DIFFERENCES OF TOTAL FEMALE HAWAIIAN BORN FROM
TOTAL FEMALE SEDENTES

Index	Difference	x p.e.
Breadth-Height	3.82 ± .87	4.39
Cephalo-Facial	− 2.32 ± .33	7.03
Fronto-Parietal	− 1.96 ± .35	5.60
Zygo-Frontal	.06 ± .35	.17
Zygo-Gonial	2.20 ± .37	5.95
Facial	1.35 ± .51	2.65
Upper Facial	4.86 ± .38	12.58
Nasal	− 3.30 ± .66	5.00
Nose Salient-Height	− 1.38 ± .37	3.73
Nose Length-Height	1.70 ± .33	5.15

DISTRIBUTION OF THE X P.E.'S OF THE DIFFERENCES BETWEEN THE TOTAL
FEMALE HAWAIIAN BORN AND THE TOTAL FEMALE SEDENTES

	0–.99	1.00–1.99	2.00–2.99	3.00–3.99
Measurements	5	2	2	2
Indices	1	0	3	1

	4.00–4.99	5.00–5.99	6.00–X
Measurements	4	2	11
Indices	1	5	9

TABLE 15

MEANS OF HIROSHIMA SEDENTES—MALES

Measurement		No.	Range	Mean	S.D.	V.
Age		68	20– 64	34.80 ± 1.01	12.35 ± .71	35.49 ± 2.05
Weight	(lb.)	63	81–140	117.70 ± 1.09	12.80 ± .77	10.88 ± .65
Stature	(cm.)	68	145–171	158.18 ± .44	5.40 ± .31	3.41 ± .20
Sitting Height	(cm.)	68	74– 93	84.14 ± .33	4.02 ± .23	4.78 ± .28
Trunk Height	(cm.)	67	44– 61	53.54 ± .28	3.40 ± .20	6.35 ± .37
Upper Arm Length	(cm.)	68	23– 33	29.18 ± .14	1.74 ± .10	5.96 ± .34
Lower Arm Length	(cm.)	68	20– 27	23.16 ± .11	1.38 ± .08	5.96 ± .34
Hand Length	(cm.)	68	16– 20	17.32 ± .08	.93 ± .05	5.37 ± .31
Upper Leg Length	(cm.)	67	29– 44	36.24 ± .28	3.38 ± .20	9.33 ± .54
Lower Leg Length	(cm.)	68	27– 36	31.25 ± .16	1.96 ± .11	6.27 ± .36
Total Leg Length	(cm.)	68	63– 84	73.68 ± .35	4.30 ± .25	5.84 ± .34
Biacromion	(cm.)	67	35– 43	39.39 ± .14	1.75 ± .10	4.44 ± .26
Cristal Breadth	(cm.)	67	26– 33	29.43 ± .13	1.52 ± .09	5.16 ± .30
Chest Breadth	(cm.)	68	22– 30	26.63 ± .12	1.50 ± .09	5.63 ± .33
Chest Depth	(cm.)	68	18– 23	20.46 ± .10	1.18 ± .07	5.77 ± .33
Head Length	(mm.)	68	174–207	188.94 ± .50	6.06 ± .35	3.21 ± .19
Head Breadth	(mm.)	68	141–164	151.24 ± .41	4.98 ± .29	3.29 ± .19
Head Height	(cm.)	68	11– 15	12.60 ± .08	1.00 ± .06	7.94 ± .46
Minimum Frontal Diameter	(mm.)	68	100–123	112.37 ± .42	5.10 ± .29	4.54 ± .26
Bizygomatic Diameter	(mm.)	68	128–154	141.03 ± .41	5.04 ± .29	3.57 ± .21
Bigonial Diameter	(mm.)	68	97–123	109.97 ± .39	4.74 ± .27	4.31 ± .25
Total Face Height	(mm.)	68	103–141	119.87 ± .55	6.78 ± .39	5.66 ± .33
Upper Face Height	(mm.)	68	63– 88	72.44 ± .38	4.70 ± .27	6.49 ± .38
Forehead Height	(mm.)	63	38– 77	59.82 ± .63	7.44 ± .45	12.44 ± .75
Nose Height	(mm.)	68	40– 63	50.88 ± .33	3.98 ± .23	7.82 ± .45

Index		N	Range			
Nose Length	(mm.)	68	38– 61	48.20 ± .34	4.18 ± .24	8.67 ± .50
Nose Salient	(mm.)	68	9– 22	14.50 ± .19	2.32 ± .13	16.00 ± .93
Nose Breadth	(mm.)	68	28– 41	36.12 ± .24	2.90 ± .17	8.03 ± .46
Inter-Ocular	(mm.)	68	24– 38	31.10 ± .25	3.02 ± .17	9.71 ± .56
Bi-Ocular	(mm.)	68	86–111	99.48 ± .42	5.18 ± .30	5.21 ± .30
Index						
Relative Shoulder Breadth		67	21– 28	24.84 ± .10	1.26 ± .07	5.07 ± .30
Relative Hip Breadth		68	16– 21	18.74 ± .08	1.00 ± .06	5.34 ± .31
Shoulder-Hip		67	65– 88	75.00 ± .37	4.50 ± .26	6.00 ± .35
Relative Sitting Height		68	49– 58	53.31 ± .16	2.01 ± .12	3.77 ± .22
Relative Trunk Height		67	29– 38	33.88 ± .16	1.99 ± .12	5.87 ± .34
Thoracic		68	66– 91	76.82 ± .38	4.64 ± .27	6.04 ± .35
Brachial		67	71– 90	79.30 ± .19	2.36 ± .14	2.98 ± .17
Tibio-Femoral		67	60–109	86.40 ± .16	1.97 ± .11	2.28 ± .13
Inter-Membral		68	82–109	94.38 ± .46	5.60 ± .32	5.93 ± .34
Cephalic		68	74– 87	80.18 ± .24	2.98 ± .17	3.72 ± .22
Length-Height		68	56– 81	66.88 ± .44	5.36 ± .31	8.01 ± .46
Breadth-Height		68	70–105	83.44 ± .58	7.06 ± .41	8.46 ± .49
Cephalo-Facial		68	85– 98	92.24 ± .21	2.58 ± .15	2.80 ± .16
Fronto-Parietal		68	66– 81	74.36 ± .26	3.20 ± .19	4.30 ± .25
Zygo-Frontal		68	70– 87	80.26 ± .29	3.56 ± .21	4.44 ± .26
Zygo-Gonial		68	64– 89	77.88 ± .28	3.42 ± .20	4.39 ± .25
Facial		68	72– 98	84.79 ± .43	5.25 ± .30	6.19 ± .36
Upper Facial		68	43– 60	51.38 ± .29	3.57 ± .21	6.95 ± .40
Nasal		68	54– 93	71.12 ± .67	8.20 ± .47	11.53 ± .66
Nose Salient-Height		68	19– 42	28.52 ± .36	4.44 ± .26	15.57 ± .90
Nose Length-Height		68	88–103	95.08 ± .28	3.48 ± .20	3.66 ± .21

TABLE 16

MEANS OF YAMAGUCHI SEDENTES—MALES

Measurement		No.	Range	Mean	S.D.	V.
Age		36	20– 64	37.30 ± 1.44	12.85 ± 1.02	34.45 ± 2.74
Weight	(lb.)	26	91–160	119.00 ± 1.80	13.60 ± 1.27	11.43 ± 1.07
Stature	(cm.)	35	145–168	158.33 ± .60	5.22 ± .42	3.30 ± .27
Sitting Height	(cm.)	35	74– 91	85.30 ± .38	3.36 ± .27	3.94 ± .32
Trunk Height	(cm.)	35	46– 61	54.96 ± .34	3.00 ± .24	5.46 ± .44
Upper Arm Length	(cm.)	36	25– 33	29.50 ± .20	1.75 ± .14	5.93 ± .47
Lower Arm Length	(cm.)	36	19– 26	23.03 ± .18	1.56 ± .12	6.77 ± .54
Hand Length	(cm.)	36	15– 19	17.58 ± .12	1.06 ± .08	6.03 ± .48
Upper Leg Length	(cm.)	35	27– 46	34.88 ± .42	3.66 ± .30	10.49 ± .85
Lower Leg Length	(cm.)	35	28– 35	31.94 ± .21	1.81 ± .15	5.67 ± .46
Total Leg Length	(cm.)	35	63– 80	72.98 ± .41	3.62 ± .29	4.96 ± .40
Biacromion	(cm.)	36	36– 44	39.58 ± .18	1.60 ± .13	4.04 ± .32
Cristal Breadth	(cm.)	36	26– 33	30.47 ± .16	1.44 ± .11	4.73 ± .38
Chest Breadth	(cm.)	36	25– 30	27.31 ± .14	1.22 ± .10	4.47 ± .36
Chest Depth	(cm.)	34	17– 26	20.44 ± .18	1.58 ± .13	7.73 ± .63
Head Length	(mm.)	36	176–207	189.34 ± .69	6.12 ± .49	3.23 ± .26
Head Breadth	(mm.)	36	143–162	153.34 ± .48	4.30 ± .34	2.80 ± .22
Head Height	(cm.)	35	10– 14	12.49 ± .12	1.05 ± .08	8.41 ± .68
Minimum Frontal Diameter	(mm.)	35	103–123	110.87 ± .51	4.50 ± .36	4.06 ± .33
Bizygomatic Diameter	(mm.)	36	134–154	142.26 ± .46	4.08 ± .32	2.87 ± .23
Bigonial Diameter	(mm.)	36	97–120	108.26 ± .59	5.25 ± .42	4.85 ± .39
Total Face Height	(mm.)	36	103–132	119.75 ± .75	6.66 ± .53	5.56 ± .44
Upper Face Height	(mm.)	36	67– 84	72.94 ± .44	3.94 ± .31	5.40 ± .43
Forehead Height	(mm.)	33	46– 77	62.30 ± .80	6.84 ± .57	10.98 ± .91
Nose Height	(mm.)	36	44– 57	50.34 ± .29	2.60 ± .21	5.16 ± .41

		N	Range	Mean ±	±	±
Nose Length	(mm.)	36	40– 53	47.34 ± .35	3.10 ± .25	6.55 ± .52
Nose Salient	(mm.)	36	11– 21	15.19 ± .25	2.24 ± .18	14.75 ± 1.17
Nose Breadth	(mm.)	36	32– 43	37.56 ± .29	2.56 ± .20	6.82 ± .54
Inter-Ocular	(mm.)	36	26– 36	31.47 ± .25	2.19 ± .17	6.96 ± .55
Bi-Ocular	(mm.)	36	86–109	99.88 ± .57	5.08 ± .40	5.09 ± .40
Index						
Relative Shoulder Breadth		35	23– 28	24.92 ± .12	1.02 ± .08	4.09 ± .33
Relative Hip Breadth		35	18– 21	19.36 ± .11	1.00 ± .08	5.17 ± .42
Shoulder-Hip		36	68– 82	76.74 ± .38	3.42 ± .27	4.46 ± .35
Relative Sitting Height		35	48– 57	53.83 ± .18	1.56 ± .13	2.90 ± .23
Relative Trunk Height		35	30– 38	34.80 ± .17	1.53 ± .12	4.40 ± .35
Thoracic		34	62– 93	74.80 ± .70	6.02 ± .49	8.05 ± .66
Brachial		36	69– 90	78.12 ± .53	4.72 ± .38	6.04 ± .48
Tibio-Femoral		35	60–114	92.30 ± 1.24	10.90 ± .88	11.81 ± .95
Inter-Membral		35	80–107	95.92 ± .50	4.42 ± .36	4.61 ± .37
Cephalic		36	74– 97	81.28 ± .49	4.38 ± .35	5.39 ± .43
Length-Height		35	56– 79	65.88 ± .61	5.36 ± .43	8.14 ± .66
Breadth-Height		35	66– 93	81.42 ± .78	6.86 ± .55	8.43 ± .68
Cephalo-Facial		36	85– 98	92.66 ± .31	2.72 ± .22	2.94 ± .23
Fronto-Parietal		35	68– 83	72.68 ± .37	3.22 ± .26	4.43 ± .36
Zygo-Frontal		35	72– 83	78.16 ± .26	2.32 ± .19	2.97 ± .24
Zygo-Gonial		36	66– 83	76.28 ± .26	2.32 ± .18	3.04 ± .24
Facial		36	72– 95	84.01 ± .59	5.25 ± .42	6.25 ± .50
Upper Facial		36	37– 63	51.83 ± .47	4.14 ± .33	7.99 ± .64
Nasal		36	62– 99	74.72 ± .74	6.56 ± .52	8.78 ± .70
Nose Salient-Height		36	22– 42	29.84 ± .43	3.84 ± .31	12.87 ± 1.02
Nose Length-Height		36	90–101	94.62 ± .33	2.98 ± .24	3.15 ± .25

TABLE 17

MEANS OF KYUSHU SEDENTES—MALES

Measurement		No.	Range	Mean	S.D.	V.
Age		22	20– 64	29.75 ± 1.62	11.25 ± 1.14	37.82 ± 3.85
Weight	(lb.)	15	101–150	126.80 ± 2.09	12.00 ± 1.48	9.46 ± 1.16
Stature	(cm.)	22	151–174	161.00 ± .77	5.34 ± .54	3.32 ± .34
Sitting Height	(cm.)	22	80– 95	86.14 ± .49	3.40 ± .35	3.95 ± .40
Trunk Height	(cm.)	22	50– 63	55.40 ± .39	2.74 ± .28	4.95 ± .50
Upper Arm Length	(cm.)	22	28– 34	30.55 ± .24	1.70 ± .17	5.56 ± .57
Lower Arm Length	(cm.)	22	21– 25	23.23 ± .16	1.09 ± .11	4.69 ± .48
Hand Length	(cm.)	22	16– 19	17.41 ± .09	.65 ± .07	3.73 ± .38
Upper Leg Length	(cm.)	22	31– 40	35.40 ± .41	2.86 ± .29	8.08 ± .82
Lower Leg Length	(cm.)	22	30– 37	32.91 ± .27	1.85 ± .19	5.62 ± .57
Total Leg Length	(cm.)	22	67– 84	74.86 ± .54	3.78 ± .38	5.05 ± .51
Biacromion	(cm.)	22	37– 43	40.00 ± .21	1.48 ± .15	3.70 ± .38
Cristal Breadth	(cm.)	22	29– 33	31.18 ± .18	1.23 ± .12	3.94 ± .40
Chest Breadth	(cm.)	22	27– 30	28.64 ± .14	.98 ± .10	3.42 ± .35
Chest Depth	(cm.)	21	19– 23	20.71 ± .16	1.12 ± .12	5.41 ± .56
Head Length	(mm.)	22	166–213	187.78 ± 1.33	9.22 ± .94	4.91 ± .50
Head Breadth	(mm.)	22	141–158	150.96 ± .52	3.62 ± .37	2.40 ± .24
Head Height	(cm.)	22	11– 15	12.95 ± .13	.93 ± .09	7.18 ± .73
Minimum Frontal Diameter	(mm.)	22	94–117	107.96 ± .75	5.22 ± .53	4.84 ± .49
Bizygomatic Diameter	(mm.)	22	131–148	141.54 ± .69	4.77 ± .48	3.37 ± .34
Bigonial Diameter	(mm.)	22	97–120	108.35 ± .51	3.55 ± .36	3.28 ± .33
Total Face Height	(mm.)	22	103–132	119.00 ± .79	5.49 ± .56	4.61 ± .47
Upper Face Height	(mm.)	22	67– 86	71.86 ± .55	3.84 ± .39	5.34 ± .54
Forehead Height	(mm.)	22	42– 73	58.78 ± 1.23	8.52 ± .87	14.49 ± 1.47
Nose Height	(mm.)	22	46– 57	50.78 ± .35	2.44 ± .25	4.80 ± .49

Nose Length	(mm.)	22	44– 53	48.14 ± .36	2.52 ± .26	5.23 ± .53
Nose Salient	(mm.)	22	13– 18	15.59 ± .22	1.56 ± .16	10.01 ± 1.02
Nose Breadth	(mm.)	22	32– 43	36.78 ± .33	2.28 ± .23	6.20 ± .63
Inter-Ocular	(mm.)	22	27– 39	32.50 ± .46	3.19 ± .32	9.82 ± 1.00
Bi-Ocular	(mm.)	22	90–109	98.78 ± .63	4.40 ± .45	4.45 ± .45
Index						
Relative Shoulder Breadth		22	23– 26	26.22 ± .14	.96 ± .10	3.66 ± .37
Relative Hip Breadth		22	16– 21	19.50 ± .17	1.16 ± .12	5.95 ± .60
Shoulder-Hip		22	71– 88	76.85 ± .63	4.38 ± .45	5.70 ± .58
Relative Sitting Height		22	51– 56	53.45 ± .21	1.47 ± .15	2.75 ± .28
Relative Trunk Height		22	31– 37	34.36 ± .23	1.61 ± .16	4.69 ± .48
Thoracic		21	66– 81	72.12 ± .57	3.84 ± .40	5.32 ± .55
Brachial		22	67– 86	76.04 ± .60	4.18 ± .43	5.50 ± .56
Tibio-Femoral		22	80–114	94.05 ± 1.37	9.50 ± .97	10.10 ± 1.03
Inter-Membral		22	90–101	95.68 ± .35	2.46 ± .25	2.57 ± .26
Cephalic		22	70– 87	80.22 ± .51	3.58 ± .36	4.46 ± .45
Length-Height		22	58– 77	68.60 ± .75	5.24 ± .53	7.64 ± .78
Breadth-Height		22	74– 99	85.60 ± .84	5.84 ± .59	6.82 ± .69
Cephalo-Facial		22	87–100	93.68 ± .51	3.56 ± .36	3.80 ± .39
Fronto-Parietal		22	64– 79	71.50 ± .49	3.40 ± .35	4.76 ± .48
Zygo-Frontal		22	68– 85	76.32 ± .49	3.40 ± .35	4.45 ± .45
Zygo-Gonial		22	68– 83	76.40 ± .49	3.38 ± .34	4.42 ± .45
Facial		22	75– 92	84.19 ± .56	3.87 ± .39	4.60 ± .47
Upper Facial		22	46– 60	50.96 ± .35	2.46 ± .25	4.83 ± .49
Nasal		22	54– 83	72.22 ± .91	6.32 ± .64	8.75 ± .89
Nose Salient-Height		22	22– 39	30.65 ± .53	3.72 ± .38	12.14 ± 1.23
Nose Length-Height		22	90–101	95.68 ± .37	2.60 ± .26	2.72 ± .28

TABLE 18

MEANS OF 'OTHER JAPAN' SEDENTES—MALES

Measurement		No.	Range	Mean	S.D.	V.
Age		26	20– 64	41.80 ± 1.65	12.50 ± 1.17	29.90 ± 2.80
Weight	(lb.)	21	91–150	119.80 ± 2.06	14.00 ± 1.46	11.69 ± 1.22
Stature	(cm.)	26	148–168	157.19 ± .65	4.89 ± .46	3.11 ± .29
Sitting Height	(cm.)	26	74– 91	83.12 ± .41	3.08 ± .29	3.71 ± .35
Trunk Height	(cm.)	26	44– 61	53.42 ± .47	3.56 ± .33	6.66 ± .62
Upper Arm Length	(cm.)	26	25– 32	29.00 ± .23	1.77 ± .17	6.10 ± .57
Lower Arm Length	(cm.)	26	22– 26	23.31 ± .15	1.13 ± .11	4.85 ± .45
Hand Length	(cm.)	26	17– 19	17.85 ± .08	.60 ± .06	3.36 ± .31
Upper Leg Length	(cm.)	26	29– 46	36.66 ± .45	3.38 ± .32	9.22 ± .86
Lower Leg Length	(cm.)	26	28– 37	31.69 ± .28	2.14 ± .20	6.75 ± .63
Total Leg Length	(cm.)	26	67– 84	74.12 ± .51	3.88 ± .36	5.23 ± .49
Biacromion	(cm.)	26	35– 44	39.58 ± .30	2.27 ± .21	5.74 ± .54
Cristal Breadth	(cm.)	26	25– 33	29.08 ± .29	2.16 ± .20	7.43 ± .69
Chest Breadth	(cm.)	26	25– 30	27.77 ± .21	1.55 ± .14	5.58 ± .52
Chest Depth	(cm.)	26	19– 25	20.88 ± .18	1.34 ± .13	6.42 ± .60
Head Length	(mm.)	26	184–209	193.20 ± .67	5.08 ± .48	2.63 ± .25
Head Breadth	(mm.)	26	143–164	153.42 ± .69	5.22 ± .49	3.40 ± .32
Head Height	(cm.)	26	11– 15	13.15 ± .17	1.29 ± .12	9.81 ± .92
Minimum Frontal Diameter	(mm.)	26	109–129	117.38 ± .56	4.26 ± .40	3.63 ± .34
Bizygomatic Diameter	(mm.)	26	134–157	144.45 ± .62	4.68 ± .44	3.24 ± .30
Bigonial Diameter	(mm.)	26	106–123	112.76 ± .50	3.81 ± .36	3.38 ± .32
Total Face Height	(mm.)	26	106–138	121.19 ± .98	7.41 ± .69	6.11 ± .57
Upper Face Height	(mm.)	26	65– 82	73.88 ± .61	4.60 ± .43	6.23 ± .58
Forehead Height	(mm.)	23	42– 77	63.34 ± 1.34	9.56 ± .95	15.09 ± 1.50
Nose Height	(mm.)	26	44– 57	50.34 ± .39	2.98 ± .28	5.92 ± .55

		N	Range	Mean		
Nose Length	(mm.)	26	42– 55	48.58 ± .37	2.80 ± .26	5.76 ± .54
Nose Salient	(mm.)	26	11– 18	14.08 ± .27	2.02 ± .19	14.35 ± 1.34
Nose Breadth	(mm.)	26	30– 41	35.66 ± .34	2.54 ± .24	7.12 ± .67
Inter-Ocular	(mm.)	26	27– 44	32.54 ± .46	3.47 ± .32	10.66 ± 1.00
Bi-Ocular	(mm.)	26	90–109	101.50 ± .33	2.52 ± .24	2.48 ± .23
Index						
Relative Shoulder Breadth		26	21– 28	25.12 ± .22	1.66 ± .16	6.61 ± .62
Relative Hip Breadth		26	16– 21	18.50 ± .19	1.46 ± .14	7.89 ± .74
Shoulder-Hip		26	62– 85	73.86 ± .68	5.13 ± .48	6.95 ± .65
Relative Sitting Height		26	50– 57	52.85 ± .23	1.73 ± .16	3.27 ± .31
Relative Trunk Height		26	30– 39	33.85 ± .25	1.92 ± .18	5.67 ± .53
Thoracic		26	68– 89	75.20 ± .61	4.64 ± .43	6.17 ± .58
Brachial		26	71– 88	80.66 ± .54	4.12 ± .39	5.11 ± .48
Tibio-Femoral		26	70–114	87.40 ± 1.22	9.20 ± .86	10.53 ± .98
Inter-Membral		26	78–105	95.12 ± .62	4.72 ± .44	4.96 ± .46
Cephalic		26	74– 89	79.50 ± .44	3.34 ± .31	4.20 ± .39
Length-Height		26	56– 79	68.20 ± .84	6.32 ± .59	9.27 ± .87
Breadth-Height		26	68–101	85.74 ± 1.10	8.30 ± .78	9.68 ± .91
Cephalo-Facial		26	87–100	94.20 ± .48	3.64 ± .34	3.86 ± .36
Fronto-Parietal		26	70– 83	76.34 ± .45	3.42 ± .32	4.48 ± .42
Zygo-Frontal		26	72– 87	80.96 ± .42	3.16 ± .30	3.90 ± .36
Zygo-Gonial		26	70– 85	78.20 ± .42	3.20 ± .30	4.25 ± .40
Facial		26	72– 95	86.38 ± .75	5.67 ± .53	6.78 ± .63
Upper Facial		26	43– 60	51.14 ± .48	3.66 ± .34	7.16 ± .67
Nasal		26	56– 85	71.04 ± .91	6.88 ± .64	9.68 ± .91
Nose Salient-Height		26	19– 39	27.95 ± .55	4.17 ± .39	14.92 ± 1.40
Nose Length-Height		26	92–101	96.66 ± .34	2.54 ± .24	2.63 ± .25

TABLE 19

DIFFERENCES OF HIROSHIMA SEDENTES AND TOTAL SEDENTES—MALES

Measurement	Difference	x p.e.
Age	− .75 ± 1.02	.74
Weight	−2.10 ± 1.16	1.81
Stature	− .21 ± .44	.48
Sitting Height	− .36 ± .31	1.16
Trunk Height	− .62 ± .28	2.21
Upper Arm Length	− .22 ± .15	1.47
Lower Arm Length	.01 ± .11	.09
Hand Length	− .15 ± .07	2.14
Upper Leg Length	.46 ± .28	1.64
Lower Leg Length	− .46 ± .16	2.88
Total Leg Length	− .08 ± .32	.25
Biacromion	− .14 ± .15	.93
Cristal Breadth	− .42 ± .14	3.00
Chest Breadth	− .64 ± .13	4.92
Chest Depth	− .16 ± .11	1.45
Head Length	− .76 ± .55	1.38
Head Breadth	− .66 ± .41	1.61
Head Height	− .13 ± .09	1.44
Minimum Frontal Diameter	.27 ± .45	.60
Bizygomatic Diameter	− .72 ± .39	1.85
Bigonial Diameter	.54 ± .43	1.26
Total Face Height	.21 ± .55	.38
Upper Face Height	− .22 ± .36	.61
Forehead Height	−1.04 ± .66	1.58
Nose Height	.34 ± .28	1.21
Nose Length	.32 ± .31	1.03
Nose Salient	− .13 ± .18	.72
Nose Breadth	− .38 ± .23	1.65
Inter-Ocular	− .52 ± .24	2.17
Bi-Ocular	− .08 ± .41	.20
Index		
Relative Shoulder Breadth	− .08 ± .10	.80
Relative Hip Breadth	− .20 ± .09	2.22
Shoulder-Hip	− .60 ± .36	1.67
Relative Sitting Height	− .06 ± .15	.40
Relative Trunk Height	− .29 ± .15	1.93
Thoracic	1.18 ± .43	2.74
Brachial	.52 ± .38	1.37
Tibio-Femoral	−2.65 ± .83	3.19
Inter-Membral	− .60 ± .40	1.50
Cephalic	− .04 ± .30	.13

[TABLE 19—*continued*]

DIFFERENCES OF HIROSHIMA SEDENTES AND TOTAL SEDENTES—MALES

Index	Difference	x p.e.
Length-Height	− .18 ± .46	.39
Breadth-Height	− .28 ± .59	.47
Cephalo-Facial	−1.02 ± .26	3.92
Fronto-Parietal	.52 ± .29	1.79
Zygo-Frontal	1.12 ± .28	4.00
Zygo-Gonial	.64 ± .28	2.29
Facial	.54 ± .42	1.29
Upper Facial	− .03 ± .29	.10
Nasal	−1.32 ± .64	2.06
Nose Salient-Height	− .42 ± .35	1.20
Nose Length-Height	− .06 ± .29	.21

TABLE 20

DIFFERENCES OF YAMAGUCHI SEDENTES AND TOTAL SEDENTES—MALES

Measurement	Difference	x p.e.
Age	1.75 ± 1.40	1.25
Weight	− .80 ± 1.80	.44
Stature	− .60 ± .61	.10
Sitting Height	.80 ± .43	1.86
Trunk Height	.80 ± .39	2.05
Upper Arm Length	.10 ± .20	.50
Lower Arm Length	− .12 ± .16	.75
Hand Length	.11 ± .10	1.10
Upper Leg Length	− .90 ± .38	2.37
Lower Leg Length	.23 ± .23	1.00
Total Leg Length	− .78 ± .45	1.73
Biacromion	.05 ± .21	.24
Cristal Breadth	.62 ± .19	3.26
Chest Breadth	.04 ± .18	.22
Chest Depth	− .18 ± .15	1.20
Head Length	− .36 ± .76	.47
Head Breadth	1.44 ± .56	2.57
Head Height	− .24 ± .13	1.85
Minimum Frontal Diameter	−1.23 ± .63	1.95
Bizygomatic Diameter	.51 ± .53	.96
Bigonial Diameter	−1.17 ± .59	1.98
Total Face Height	.09 ± .76	.12
Upper Face Height	.28 ± .50	.56
Forehead Height	1.44 ± .91	1.58
Nose Height	− .20 ± .38	.53
Nose Length	− .54 ± .42	1.29
Nose Salient	.56 ± .25	2.24
Nose Breadth	1.06 ± .32	3.31
Inter-Ocular	− .15 ± .33	.45
Bi-Ocular	.32 ± .56	.57
Index		
Relative Shoulder Breadth	.0 ± .14	.00
Relative Hip Breadth	.42 ± .13	3.23
Shoulder-Hip	1.14 ± .49	2.33
Relative Sitting Height	.46 ± .20	2.30
Relative Trunk Height	.63 ± .21	3.00
Thoracic	− .84 ± .61	1.38
Brachial	− .66 ± .52	1.27
Tibio-Femoral	3.25 ± 1.15	2.83
Inter-Membral	.94 ± .56	1.68
Cephalic	1.06 ± .41	2.59

[TABLE 20—*continued*]

DIFFERENCES OF YAMAGUCHI SEDENTES AND TOTAL SEDENTES—MALES

Index	Difference	x p.e.
Length-Height	−1.18 ± .64	1.84
Breadth-Height	−2.30 ± .82	2.80
Cephalo-Facial	− .60 ± .36	1.67
Fronto-Parietal	−1.16 ± .40	2.90
Zygo-Frontal	− .98 ± .39	2.51
Zygo-Gonial	− .96 ± .39	2.46
Facial	− .24 ± .58	.41
Upper Facial	.42 ± .39	1.08
Nasal	2.28 ± .87	2.62
Nose Salient-Height	.90 ± .49	1.84
Nose Length-Height	− .52 ± .40	1.30

TABLE 21

DIFFERENCES OF KYUSHU SEDENTES AND TOTAL SEDENTES—MALES

Measurement	Difference	x p.e.
Age	−5.80 ± 1.79	3.24
Weight	7.00 ± 2.37	2.95
Stature	2.61 ± .77	3.39
Sitting Height	1.64 ± .55	2.98
Trunk Height	1.24 ± .49	2.53
Upper Arm Length	1.15 ± .26	4.42
Lower Arm Length	.08 ± .20	.40
Hand Length	− .06 ± .13	.46
Upper Leg Length	− .38 ± .48	.79
Lower Leg Length	1.20 ± .28	4.29
Total Leg Length	1.10 ± .57	1.93
Biacromion	.47 ± .27	1.74
Cristal Breadth	1.33 ± .25	5.32
Chest Breadth	1.37 ± .23	5.96
Chest Depth	.09 ± .19	.47
Head Length	−1.92 ± .97	1.98
Head Breadth	− .94 ± .72	1.31
Head Height	.22 ± .16	1.38
Minimum Frontal Diameter	−4.14 ± .80	5.18
Bizygomatic Diameter	− .21 ± .68	.31
Bigonial Diameter	−1.08 ± .75	1.44
Total Face Height	− .66 ± .97	.68
Upper Face Height	− .80 ± .64	1.25
Forehead Height	−2.08 ± 1.12	1.86
Nose Height	.24 ± .49	.49
Nose Length	.26 ± .54	.48
Nose Salient	.96 ± .32	3.00
Nose Breadth	.28 ± .41	.68
Inter-Ocular	.88 ± .43	2.05
Bi-Ocular	− .78 ± .71	1.10
Index		
Relative Shoulder Breadth	1.30 ± .18	7.22
Relative Hip Breadth	.56 ± .17	3.29
Shoulder-Hip	1.25 ± .63	1.98
Relative Sitting Height	.08 ± .26	.31
Relative Trunk Height	.19 ± .27	.70
Thoracic	−3.52 ± .78	4.51
Brachial	−2.74 ± .67	4.09
Tibio-Femoral	5.00 ± 1.45	3.45
Inter-Membral	.70 ± .71	.99
Cephalic	.00 ± .53	.00

[TABLE 21—*continued*]

DIFFERENCES OF KYUSHU SEDENTES AND TOTAL SEDENTES—MALES

Index	Difference	x p.e.
Length-Height	1.54 ± .81	1.90
Breadth-Height	1.88 ± 1.03	1.83
Cephalo-Facial	.42 ± .46	.91
Fronto-Parietal	−2.34 ± .50	4.68
Zygo-Frontal	−2.82 ± .49	5.76
Zygo-Gonial	− .84 ± .50	1.68
Facial	− .06 ± .75	.08
Upper Facial	− .45 ± .50	.90
Nasal	− .22 ± 1.12	.20
Nose Salient-Height	1.71 ± .62	2.76
Nose Length-Height	.54 ± .51	1.06

TABLE 22

DIFFERENCES OF 'OTHER JAPAN' SEDENTES AND TOTAL SEDENTES—MALES

Measurement	Difference	x p.e.
Age	6.25 ± 1.65	3.79
Weight	.00 ± 2.00	.00
Stature	−1.20 ± .71	1.69
Sitting Height	−1.38 ± .50	2.76
Trunk Height	− .74 ± .45	1.64
Upper Arm Length	− .40 ± .24	1.67
Lower Arm Length	.16 ± .18	.89
Hand Length	.38 ± .12	3.17
Upper Leg Length	.88 ± .44	2.00
Lower Leg Length	− .02 ± .26	.08
Total Leg Length	.36 ± .52	.69
Biacromion	.05 ± .24	.21
Cristal Breadth	− .77 ± .23	3.35
Chest Breadth	.50 ± .21	2.38
Chest Depth	.26 ± .17	1.53
Head Length	3.50 ± .90	3.89
Head Breadth	1.52 ± .66	2.30
Head Height	.42 ± .15	2.80
Minimum Frontal Diameter	5.28 ± .73	7.23
Bizygomatic Diameter	2.70 ± .63	4.29
Bigonial Diameter	3.33 ± .69	4.83
Total Face Height	1.53 ± .90	1.70
Upper Face Height	1.22 ± .58	2.10
Forehead Height	2.48 ± 1.09	2.28
Nose Height	− .20 ± .45	.44
Nose Length	.70 ± .50	1.40
Nose Salient	− .55 ± .29	1.90
Nose Breadth	− .84 ± .37	2.27
Inter-Ocular	.92 ± .39	2.36
Bi-Ocular	1.94 ± .66	2.94
Index		
Relative Shoulder Breadth	.20 ± .17	1.18
Relative Hip Breadth	− .44 ± .15	2.93
Shoulder-Hip	−1.74 ± .58	3.00
Relative Sitting Height	− .52 ± .24	2.17
Relative Trunk Height	− .32 ± .25	1.28
Thoracic	− .44 ± .70	.63
Brachial	1.88 ± .61	3.08
Tibio-Femoral	−1.65 ± 1.34	1.23
Inter-Membral	.14 ± .65	.22
Cephalic	− .72 ± .49	1.47

[TABLE 22—*continued*]

DIFFERENCES OF 'OTHER JAPAN' SEDENTES AND TOTAL SEDENTES—MALES

Index	Difference	x p.e.
Length-Height	1.14 ± .75	1.52
Breadth-Height	2.02 ± .95	2.13
Cephalo-Facial	.94 ± .42	2.24
Fronto-Parietal	2.50 ± .46	5.43
Zygo-Frontal	1.82 ± .46	3.96
Zygo-Gonial	.96 ± .46	2.09
Facial	2.13 ± .69	3.09
Upper Facial	— .27 ± .46	.59
Nasal	—1.40 ± 1.03	1.36
Nose Salient-Height	— .99 ± .57	1.74
Nose Length-Height	1.52 ± .47	3.23

TABLE 23

DISTRIBUTION OF THE X P.E.'S OF THE DIFFERENCES BETWEEN THE PREFECTURAL GROUPS OF MALE SEDENTES AND THE TOTAL MALE SEDENTES

		0–.99	1.00–1.99	2.00–2.99	3.00–3.99	4.00–4.99	5.00–5.99	6.00–X
Hiroshima Sedentes	Measurements	9	14	4	1	1	0	0
Total Sedentes	Indices	7	7	4	2	1	0	0
Yamaguchi Sedentes	Measurements	13	10	4	2	0	0	0
Total Sedentes	Indices	2	8	9	2	0	0	0
Kyushu Sedentes	Measurements	9	9	4	2	2	3	0
Total Sedentes	Indices	8	5	1	2	3	1	1
'Other Japan' Sedentes	Measurements	6	7	10	3	2	0	1
Total Sedentes	Indices	3	7	5	5	0	1	0

TABLE 24

Hiroshima
Yamaguchi

Measurement	Difference	x p.e.
Age	2.50 ± 1.76	1.42
Weight	1.30 ± 2.10	.62
Stature	.15 ± .74	.20
Sitting Height	1.16 ± .50	2.32
Trunk Height	1.42 ± .44	3.23
Upper Arm Length	.32 ± .24	1.33
Lower Arm Length	− .13 ± .21	.62
Hand Length	.26 ± .14	1.86
Upper Leg Length	−1.36 ± .50	2.72
Lower Leg Length	.69 ± .26	2.65
Total Leg Length	− .70 ± .54	1.30
Biacromion	.19 ± .23	.83
Cristal Breadth	1.04 ± .21	4.95
Chest Breadth	.68 ± .18	3.78
Chest Depth	− .02 ± .21	.10
Head Length	.40 ± .85	.47
Head Breadth	2.10 ± .63	3.33
Head Height	− .11 ± .14	.79
Minimum Frontal Diameter	−1.50 ± .66	2.27
Bizygomatic Diameter	1.23 ± .48	2.56
Bigonial Diameter	−1.71 ± .71	2.41
Total Face Height	− .12 ± .93	.13
Upper Face Height	.50 ± .58	.86
Forehead Height	2.48 ± 1.02	2.43
Nose Height	− .54 ± .44	1.23
Nose Length	− .86 ± .49	1.76
Nose Salient	.69 ± .31	2.23
Nose Breadth	1.44 ± .38	3.79
Inter-Ocular	.37 ± .35	1.06
Bi-Ocular	.40 ± .71	.56

Index		
Relative Shoulder Breadth	.08 ± .16	.50
Relative Hip Breadth	.62 ± .14	4.43
Shoulder-Hip	1.74 ± .53	3.28
Relative Sitting Height	.52 ± .24	2.17
Relative Trunk Height	.92 ± .23	4.00
Thoracic	−2.02 ± .80	2.52
Brachial	−1.18 ± .56	2.11

[Continued]

[TABLE 24—*continued*]

DIFFERENCES OF MEANS OF MALE SEDENTES BY PREFECTURE

Hiroshima
Yamaguchi

Index	Difference	x p.e.
Tibio-Femoral	5.90 ± 1.25	4.72
Inter-Membral	1.54 ± .68	2.26
Cephalic	1.10 ± .55	2.00
Length-Height	−1.00 ± .75	1.33
Breadth-Height	−2.02 ± .97	2.08
Cephalo-Facial	.42 ± .37	1.14
Fronto-Parietal	−1.68 ± .45	3.73
Zygo-Frontal	−2.10 ± .39	5.38
Zygo-Gonial	−1.60 ± .38	4.21
Facial	− .78 ± .73	1.07
Upper Facial	.45 ± .55	.82
Nasal	3.60 ± 1.00	3.60
Nose Salient-Height	1.32 ± .56	2.36
Nose Length-Height	− .46 ± .43	1.07

TABLE 25

DIFFERENCES OF MEANS OF MALE SEDENTES BY PREFECTURE

<u>Hiroshima</u>
Kyushu

Measurement	Difference	x p.e.
Age	5.05 ± 1.91	2.64
Weight	−9.10 ± 2.36	3.86
Stature	−2.82 ± .89	3.17
Sitting Height	−2.00 ± .59	3.39
Trunk Height	−1.86 ± .48	3.88
Upper Arm Length	−1.37 ± .28	4.89
Lower Arm Length	− .07 ± .19	.37
Hand Length	− .09 ± .12	.75
Upper Leg Length	.84 ± .50	1.68
Lower Leg Length	−1.66 ± .31	5.35
Total Leg Length	−1.18 ± .64	1.84
Biacromion	− .61 ± .25	2.44
Cristal Breadth	−1.75 ± .22	7.95
Chest Breadth	−2.01 ± .18	11.17
Chest Depth	− .25 ± .19	1.32
Head Length	1.16 ± 1.42	.82
Head Breadth	.28 ± .66	.42
Head Height	− .35 ± .15	2.33
Minimum Frontal Diameter	4.41 ± .86	5.13
Bizygomatic Diameter	− .51 ± .70	.73
Bigonial Diameter	1.62 ± .64	2.53
Total Face Height	.87 ± .96	.91
Upper Face Height	.58 ± .67	.87
Forehead Height	1.04 ± 1.38	.75
Nose Height	.10 ± .48	.21
Nose Length	.06 ± .50	.12
Nose Salient	−1.09 ± .29	3.76
Nose Breadth	− .66 ± .41	1.61
Inter-Ocular	−1.40 ± .52	2.69
Bi-Ocular	.70 ± .76	.92
Index		
Relative Shoulder Breadth	−1.38 ± .17	8.12
Relative Hip Breadth	− .76 ± .19	4.00
Shoulder-Hip	−1.85 ± .73	2.53
Relative Sitting Height	− .14 ± .26	.54
Relative Trunk Height	− .48 ± .28	1.71
Thoracic	4.70 ± .68	6.91
Brachial	3.26 ± .63	5.17

[*Continued*]

[TABLE 25—*continued*]

DIFFERENCES OF MEANS OF MALE SEDENTES BY PREFECTURE

Hiroshima
Kyushu

Index	Difference	x p.e.
Tibio-Femoral	−7.65 ± 1.38	5.54
Inter-Membral	−1.30 ± .58	2.24
Cephalic	− .04 ± .56	.07
Length-Height	−1.72 ± .87	1.98
Breadth-Height	−2.16 ± 1.02	2.12
Cephalo-Facial	−1.44 ± .55	2.62
Fronto-Parietal	2.86 ± .55	5.20
Zygo-Frontal	3.94 ± .57	6.91
Zygo-Gonial	1.48 ± .56	2.64
Facial	.60 ± .71	.84
Upper Facial	.42 ± .45	.93
Nasal	−1.10 ± 1.13	.97
Nose Salient-Height	−2.13 ± .64	3.33
Nose Length-Height	− .60 ± .46	1.30

TABLE 26

DIFFERENCES OF MEANS OF MALE SEDENTES BY PREFECTURE

Hiroshima
'Other Japan'

Measurement	Difference	x p.e.
Age	−7.00 ± 1.93	3.63
Weight	−2.10 ± 2.33	.90
Stature	.99 ± .78	1.27
Sitting Height	1.02 ± .53	1.92
Trunk Height	.12 ± .55	.22
Upper Arm Length	.18 ± .27	.67
Lower Arm Length	− .15 ± .19	.79
Hand Length	− .53 ± .11	4.82
Upper Leg Length	− .42 ± .53	.79
Lower Leg Length	− .44 ± .32	1.38
Total Leg Length	− .44 ± .62	.71
Biacromion	− .19 ± .33	.58
Cristal Breadth	.35 ± .32	1.09
Chest Breadth	−1.14 ± .24	4.75
Chest Depth	− .42 ± .21	2.00
Head Length	−4.26 ± .60	7.10
Head Breadth	−2.18 ± .80	2.72
Head Height	− .55 ± .19	2.89
Minimum Frontal Diameter	−5.01 ± .70	7.16
Bizygomatic Diameter	−3.42 ± .64	5.34
Bigonial Diameter	−2.79 ± .63	4.43
Total Face Height	−1.32 ± 1.12	1.18
Upper Face Height	−1.44 ± .72	2.00
Forehead Height	−3.52 ± 1.48	2.38
Nose Height	.54 ± .51	1.06
Nose Length	− .38 ± .50	.76
Nose Salient	.42 ± .33	1.27
Nose Breadth	.46 ± .42	1.10
Inter-Ocular	−1.44 ± .52	2.77
Bi-Ocular	−2.02 ± .53	3.81
Index		
Relative Shoulder Breadth	− .28 ± .24	1.17
Relative Hip Breadth	.24 ± .21	1.14
Shoulder-Hip	1.14 ± .77	1.48
Relative Sitting Height	.46 ± .28	1.64
Relative Trunk Height	.03 ± .30	.10
Thoracic	1.62 ± .72	2.25
Brachial	−1.36 ± .57	2.39

[Continued]

[TABLE 26—*continued*]

DIFFERENCES OF MEANS OF MALE SEDENTES BY PREFECTURE

Hiroshima
'Other Japan'

Index	Difference	x p.e.
Tibio-Femoral	−1.00 ± 1.23	.81
Inter-Membral	− .74 ± .77	.96
Cephalic	.68 ± .50	1.36
Length-Height	−1.32 ± .95	1.39
Breadth-Height	−2.30 ± 1.24	1.85
Cephalo-Facial	−1.96 ± .52	3.77
Fronto-Parietal	−1.98 ± .52	3.81
Zygo-Frontal	− .70 ± .51	1.37
Zygo-Gonial	− .32 ± .50	.64
Facial	−1.59 ± .86	1.85
Upper Facial	.24 ± .56	.43
Nasal	.08 ± 1.13	.07
Nose Salient-Height	.57 ± .66	.86
Nose Length-Height	−1.58 ± .44	3.59

TABLE 27

DIFFERENCES OF MEANS OF MALE SEDENTES BY PREFECTURE

Yamaguchi
Kyushu

Measurement	Difference	x p.e.
Age	7.55 ± 2.17	3.48
Weight	−7.80 ± 2.76	2.83
Stature	−2.67 ± .98	2.72
Sitting Height	− .84 ± .62	1.35
Trunk Height	− .44 ± .52	.85
Upper Arm Length	−1.05 ± .31	3.39
Lower Arm Length	− .20 ± .24	.83
Hand Length	.17 ± .15	1.13
Upper Leg Length	− .52 ± .59	.88
Lower Leg Length	− .97 ± .34	2.85
Total Leg Length	−1.88 ± .68	2.76
Biacromion	− .42 ± .28	1.50
Cristal Breadth	− .71 ± .24	2.96
Chest Breadth	−1.33 ± .20	6.65
Chest Depth	− .27 ± .24	1.12
Head Length	1.56 ± 1.50	1.04
Head Breadth	2.38 ± .71	3.35
Head Height	− .46 ± .18	2.56
Minimum Frontal Diameter	2.91 ± .91	3.20
Bizygomatic Diameter	.72 ± .83	.87
Bigonial Diameter	− .09 ± .78	.12
Total Face Height	.75 ± 1.09	.69
Upper Face Height	1.08 ± .70	1.54
Forehead Height	3.52 ± 1.47	2.39
Nose Height	− .44 ± .45	.98
Nose Length	− .80 ± .50	1.60
Nose Salient	− .40 ± .33	1.21
Nose Breadth	.78 ± .44	1.77
Inter-Ocular	−1.03 ± .52	1.98
Bi-Ocular	1.10 ± .85	1.29

Index		
Relative Shoulder Breadth	−1.30 ± .18	7.22
Relative Hip Breadth	− .14 ± .20	.70
Shoulder-Hip Breadth	− .11 ± .74	.15
Relative Sitting Height	.38 ± .28	1.36
Relative Trunk Height	.44 ± .29	1.52
Thoracic	2.68 ± .90	2.98
Brachial	2.08 ± .80	2.60

[Continued]

[TABLE 27—*continued*]

DIFFERENCES OF MEANS OF MALE SEDENTES BY PREFECTURE

Yamaguchi
Kyushu

Index	Difference	x p.e.
Tibio-Femoral	-1.75 ± 1.85	.95
Inter-Membral	$.24 \pm .61$	.39
Cephalic	$1.06 \pm .71$	1.49
Length-Height	$-2.72 \pm .97$	2.80
Breadth-Height	-4.18 ± 1.14	3.67
Cephalo-Facial	$-1.02 \pm .60$	1.70
Fronto-Parietal	$1.18 \pm .61$	1.93
Zygo-Frontal	$1.84 \pm .55$	3.35
Zygo-Gonial	$-.12 \pm .55$	.22
Facial	$-.18 \pm .81$	.22
Upper Facial	$.87 \pm .59$	1.47
Nasal	2.50 ± 1.17	2.14
Nose Salient-Height	$-.81 \pm .68$	1.19
Nose Length-Height	$-1.06 \pm .50$	2.12

TABLE 28

DIFFERENCES OF MEANS OF MALE SEDENTES BY PREFECTURE

Yamaguchi
'Other Japan'

Measurement	Difference	x p.e.
Age	−4.50 ± 2.19	2.05
Weight	− .80 ± 2.73	.29
Stature	1.14 ± .88	1.30
Sitting Height	2.18 ± .56	3.89
Trunk Height	1.54 ± .58	2.66
Upper Arm Length	.50 ± .30	1.67
Lower Arm Length	− .28 ± .23	1.22
Hand Length	− .27 ± .14	1.93
Upper Leg Length	−1.78 ± .62	2.87
Lower Leg Length	.25 ± .35	.71
Total Leg Length	−1.14 ± .65	1.75
Biacromion	.00 ± .35	.00
Cristal Breadth	1.39 ± .33	4.21
Chest Breadth	− .46 ± .25	1.84
Chest Depth	− .44 ± .25	1.76
Head Length	−3.86 ± .77	5.01
Head Breadth	− .08 ± .84	.10
Head Height	− .66 ± .21	3.14
Minimum Frontal Diameter	−6.51 ± .76	8.57
Bizygomatic Diameter	−2.19 ± .77	2.84
Bigonial Diameter	−4.50 ± .77	5.84
Total Face Height	−1.44 ± 1.23	1.17
Upper Face Height	− .94 ± .75	1.25
Forehead Height	−1.04 ± 1.56	.67
Nose Height	.00 ± .49	.00
Nose Length	−1.24 ± .51	2.43
Nose Salient	1.11 ± .39	2.85
Nose Breadth	1.90 ± .45	4.22
Inter-Ocular	−1.07 ± .52	2.06
Bi-Ocular	−1.62 ± .66	2.45
Index		
Relative Shoulder Breadth	− .20 ± .25	.80
Relative Hip Breadth	.86 ± .22	3.91
Shoulder-Hip	2.88 ± .78	3.69
Relative Sitting Height	.98 ± .29	3.38
Relative Trunk Height	.95 ± .30	3.17
Thoracic	− .40 ± .93	.43
Brachial	−2.54 ± .76	3.34

[Continued]

[TABLE 28—*continued*]

DIFFERENCES OF MEANS OF MALE SEDENTES BY PREFECTURE

Yamaguchi
'Other Japan'

Index	Difference	x p.e.
Tibio-Femoral	4.90 ± 1.74	2.82
Inter-Membral	.80 ± .80	1.00
Cephalic	1.78 ± .66	2.70
Length-Height	−2.32 ± 1.04	2.23
Breadth-Height	−4.32 ± 1.35	3.20
Cephalo-Facial	−1.54 ± .57	2.70
Fronto-Parietal	−3.66 ± .58	6.31
Zygo-Frontal	−2.80 ± .49	5.71
Zygo-Gonial	−1.92 ± .49	3.92
Facial	−2.37 ± .95	2.49
Upper Facial	.69 ± .67	1.03
Nasal	3.68 ± 1.17	3.15
Nose Salient-Height	1.89 ± .70	2.70
Nose Length-Height	−2.04 ± .47	4.34

TABLE 29

DIFFERENCES OF MEANS OF MALE SEDENTES BY PREFECTURE

Kyushu
'Other Japan'

Measurement	Difference	x p.e.
Age	-12.05 ± 2.31	5.22
Weight	7.00 ± 2.93	2.39
Stature	3.81 ± 1.01	3.77
Sitting Height	$3.02 \pm .64$	4.72
Trunk Height	$1.98 \pm .61$	3.25
Upper Arm Length	$1.55 \pm .33$	4.70
Lower Arm Length	$- .08 \pm .22$	.36
Hand Length	$- .44 \pm .12$	3.67
Upper Leg Length	$- 1.26 \pm .61$	2.07
Lower Leg Length	$1.22 \pm .39$	3.13
Total Leg Length	$.74 \pm .74$	1.00
Biacromion	$.42 \pm .37$	1.14
Cristal Breadth	$2.10 \pm .34$	6.18
Chest Breadth	$.87 \pm .25$	3.48
Chest Depth	$- .17 \pm .24$	.71
Head Length	$- 5.42 \pm 1.37$	3.96
Head Breadth	$- 2.46 \pm .86$	2.86
Head Height	$- .20 \pm .21$	.95
Minimum Frontal Diameter	$- 9.42 \pm .94$	10.02
Bizygomatic Diameter	$- 2.91 \pm .93$	3.13
Bigonial Diameter	$- 4.41 \pm .71$	6.21
Total Face Height	$- 2.19 \pm 1.26$	1.74
Upper Face Height	$- 2.02 \pm .82$	2.46
Forehead Height	$- 4.56 \pm 1.82$	2.51
Nose Height	$.44 \pm .52$	.85
Nose Length	$- .44 \pm .52$	.85
Nose Salient	$1.51 \pm .35$	4.31
Nose Breadth	$1.12 \pm .47$	2.38
Inter-Ocular	$- .04 \pm .65$	.06
Bi-Ocular	$- 2.72 \pm .71$	3.83
Index		
Relative Shoulder Breadth	$1.10 \pm .26$	4.23
Relative Hip Breadth	$1.00 \pm .25$	4.00
Shoulder-Hip	$2.99 \pm .93$	3.22
Relative Sitting Height	$.60 \pm .31$	1.94
Relative Trunk Height	$.51 \pm .34$	1.50
Thoracic	$- 3.08 \pm .83$	3.71
Brachial	$- 4.62 \pm .81$	5.70

[Continued]

[TABLE 29—*continued*]

DIFFERENCES OF MEANS OF MALE SEDENTES BY PREFECTURE

Kyushu
'Other Japan'

Index	Difference	x p.e.
Tibio-Femoral	6.65 ± 1.84	3.61
Inter-Membral	.56 ± .71	.79
Cephalic	.72 ± .67	1.07
Length-Height	.40 ± 1.13	.35
Breadth-Height	— .14 ± 1.39	.10
Cephalo-Facial	— .52 ± .70	.74
Fronto-Parietal	— 4.84 ± .67	7.22
Zygo-Frontal	— 4.64 ± .65	7.14
Zygo-Gonial	— 1.80 ± .65	2.77
Facial	— 2.19 ± .94	2.33
Upper Facial	— .18 ± .59	.30
Nasal	1.18 ± 1.29	.91
Nose Salient-Height	2.70 ± .76	3.55
Nose Length-Height	— .98 ± .50	1.96

TABLE 30

DISTRIBUTION OF THE X P.E.'S OF THE DIFFERENCES BETWEEN THE VARIOUS PREFECTURAL GROUPS OF MALE SEDENTES

		0-.99	1.00-1.99	2.00-2.99	3.00-3.99	4.00-4.99	5.00-5.99	6.00-X
Hiroshima / Yamaguchi	Measurements	10	6	8	4	1	0	0
	Indices	2	4	7	3	4	1	0
Hiroshima / Kyushu	Measurements	11	4	4	5	1	2	2
	Indices	5	3	5	1	1	3	3
Hiroshima / 'Other Japan'	Measurements	8	8	6	1	3	1	2
	Indices	7	9	2	3	0	0	0
Yamaguchi / Kyushu	Measurements	7	11	7	3	0	0	1
	Indices	6	7	5	2	0	0	1
Yamaguchi / 'Other Japan'	Measurements	6	9	7	2	2	2	1
	Indices	2	2	6	8	1	1	1
Kyushu / 'Other Japan'	Measurements	6	3	6	8	3	0	3
	Indices	6	4	2	4	2	1	2

TABLE 31

MEANS OF HIROSHIMA IMMIGRANTS—MALES

Measurement		No.	Range	Mean ±	S.D. ±	V. ±
Age		48	25– 64	43.15 ± .94	9.70 ± .67	22.48 ± 1.55
Weight	(lb.)	47	81–170	122.30 ± 1.61	16.40 ± 1.14	13.41 ± .93
Stature	(cm.)	48	145–171	157.94 ± .53	5.46 ± .38	3.46 ± .24
Sitting Height	(cm.)	48	76– 91	82.08 ± .31	3.16 ± .22	3.85 ± .26
Trunk Height	(cm.)	48	46– 59	51.92 ± .27	2.78 ± .19	5.35 ± .37
Upper Arm Length	(cm.)	48	26– 34	29.25 ± .18	1.85 ± .13	6.32 ± .44
Lower Arm Length	(cm.)	48	20– 27	23.71 ± .15	1.54 ± .11	6.50 ± .45
Hand Length	(cm.)	48	16– 19	17.79 ± .07	.71 ± .05	3.99 ± .27
Upper Leg Length	(cm.)	48	33– 46	38.00 ± .31	3.16 ± .22	8.32 ± .57
Lower Leg Length	(cm.)	48	28– 36	32.50 ± .18	1.80 ± .12	5.54 ± .38
Total Leg Length	(cm.)	48	69– 88	75.70 ± .42	4.32 ± .30	5.71 ± .39
Biacromion	(cm.)	48	36– 44	40.06 ± .17	1.70 ± .12	4.24 ± .29
Cristal Breadth	(cm.)	48	25– 33	29.75 ± .17	1.79 ± .12	6.02 ± .41
Chest Breadth	(cm.)	48	24– 33	27.52 ± .16	1.67 ± .11	6.07 ± .42
Chest Depth	(cm.)	48	15– 24	20.56 ± .18	1.87 ± .13	9.10 ± .63
Head Length	(mm.)	48	176–205	188.38 ± .59	6.04 ± .42	3.21 ± .22
Head Breadth	(mm.)	48	143–160	152.70 ± .45	4.62 ± .32	3.03 ± .21
Head Height	(cm.)	48	11– 16	13.33 ± .10	1.03 ± .07	7.73 ± .53
Minimum Frontal Diameter	(mm.)	48	97–126	112.43 ± .58	5.97 ± .41	5.31 ± .37
Bizygomatic Diameter	(mm.)	48	131–154	143.13 ± .51	5.22 ± .36	3.65 ± .25
Bigonial Diameter	(mm.)	48	103–129	112.31 ± .62	6.42 ± .44	5.72 ± .39
Total Face Height	(mm.)	48	106–138	122.24 ± .58	5.94 ± .41	4.86 ± .33
Upper Face Height	(mm.)	48	67– 96	80.70 ± .50	5.10 ± .35	6.32 ± .44
Forehead Height	(mm.)	47	42– 81	59.26 ± .79	8.00 ± .56	13.50 ± .94
Nose Height	(mm.)	47	42– 61	51.14 ± .37	3.78 ± .26	7.39 ± .51

Nose Length (mm.)	47	40– 57	49.56 ± .43	4.34 ± .30	8.76 ± .61
Nose Salient (mm.)	47	10– 19	13.85 ± .20	1.99 ± .14	14.37 ± 1.00
Nose Breadth (mm.)	47	30– 43	35.90 ± .30	3.06 ± .21	8.52 ± .59
Inter-Ocular (mm.)	48	23– 38	30.25 ± .32	3.26 ± .22	10.78 ± .74
Bi-Ocular (mm.)	48	88–119	101.92 ± .62	6.36 ± .44	6.24 ± .43
Index					
Relative Shoulder Breadth	48	23– 30	25.34 ± .11	1.14 ± .08	4.50 ± .31
Relative Hip Breadth	48	14– 23	18.80 ± .13	1.36 ± .09	7.23 ± .50
Shoulder-Hip	48	59– 82	73.69 ± .45	4.59 ± .32	6.23 ± .43
Relative Sitting Height	48	47– 55	52.04 ± .16	1.67 ± .11	3.21 ± .22
Relative Trunk Height	48	29– 36	32.92 ± .16	1.66 ± .11	5.04 ± .35
Thoracic	48	60– 87	74.66 ± .53	5.44 ± .37	7.29 ± .50
Brachial	48	63– 90	81.26 ± .54	5.52 ± .38	6.79 ± .47
Tibio-Femoral	48	70–119	85.65 ± .67	6.90 ± .47	8.06 ± .55
Inter-Membral	48	84–103	93.38 ± .36	3.74 ± .26	4.01 ± .28
Cephalic	48	76– 89	81.20 ± .30	3.04 ± .21	3.74 ± .26
Length-Height	48	58– 85	70.84 ± .54	5.56 ± .38	7.85 ± .54
Breadth-Height	48	70–111	87.38 ± .74	7.62 ± .52	8.72 ± .60
Cephalo-Facial	48	87–102	93.66 ± .29	3.02 ± .21	3.22 ± .22
Fronto-Parietal	48	64– 81	73.58 ± .34	3.54 ± .24	4.81 ± .33
Zygo-Frontal	48	70– 85	78.70 ± .33	3.34 ± .23	4.24 ± .29
Zygo-Gonial	48	72– 89	78.46 ± .35	3.62 ± .25	4.61 ± .32
Facial	48	72–101	85.51 ± .52	5.34 ± .37	6.24 ± .43
Upper Facial	48	46– 69	56.63 ± .40	4.11 ± .28	7.26 ± .50
Nasal	47	52– 89	70.46 ± .60	6.14 ± .43	8.71 ± .61
Nose Salient-Height	47	19– 39	27.20 ± .35	3.54 ± .25	13.01 ± .91
Nose Length-Height	47	90–105	99.60 ± .34	3.50 ± .24	3.51 ± .24

TABLE 32

MEANS OF YAMAGUCHI IMMIGRANTS—MALES

Measurement		No.	Range	Mean	S.D.	V.
Age		35	20– 64	43.85 ± 1.23	10.75 ± .87	24.91 ± 2.01
Weight	(lb.)	35	81–150	116.90 ± 1.64	14.40 ± 1.16	12.32 ± .99
Stature	(cm.)	35	145–171	158.87 ± .57	5.04 ± .41	3.17 ± .26
Sitting Height	(cm.)	35	76– 99	83.92 ± .52	4.56 ± .37	5.43 ± .44
Trunk Height	(cm.)	35	44– 61	53.24 ± .40	3.54 ± .29	6.65 ± .54
Upper Arm Length	(cm.)	35	25– 33	29.37 ± .22	1.93 ± .16	6.57 ± .53
Lower Arm Length	(cm.)	35	21– 26	23.14 ± .14	1.24 ± .10	5.36 ± .43
Hand Length	(cm.)	35	17– 19	17.86 ± .07	.59 ± .05	3.30 ± .27
Upper Leg Length	(cm.)	34	31– 44	37.62 ± .36	3.14 ± .26	8.35 ± .68
Lower Leg Length	(cm.)	35	29– 38	32.77 ± .22	1.94 ± .16	5.92 ± .48
Total Leg Length	(cm.)	34	67– 86	75.32 ± .50	4.32 ± .35	5.74 ± .47
Biacromion	(cm.)	35	35– 44	39.89 ± .22	1.92 ± .15	4.81 ± .39
Cristal Breadth	(cm.)	35	26– 32	28.57 ± .15	1.34 ± .11	4.69 ± .38
Chest Breadth	(cm.)	35	25– 30	27.23 ± .16	1.37 ± .11	5.03 ± .41
Chest Depth	(cm.)	35	16– 23	19.46 ± .19	1.68 ± .14	8.63 ± .70
Head Length	(mm.)	35	172–203	186.90 ± .70	6.18 ± .50	3.31 ± .27
Head Breadth	(mm.)	35	143–168	153.94 ± .66	5.82 ± .47	3.78 ± .30
Head Height	(cm.)	34	12– 16	13.79 ± .15	1.30 ± .11	9.43 ± .77
Minimum Frontal Diameter	(mm.)	35	100–123	112.49 ± .64	5.58 ± .45	4.96 ± .40
Bizygomatic Diameter	(mm.)	34	128–154	141.18 ± .58	4.98 ± .41	3.53 ± .29
Bigonial Diameter	(mm.)	35	97–123	111.47 ± .68	5.94 ± .48	5.33 ± .43
Total Face Height	(mm.)	35	109–138	123.98 ± .66	5.79 ± .47	4.67 ± .38
Upper Face Height	(mm.)	35	71– 94	82.76 ± .55	4.86 ± .39	5.87 ± .47
Forehead Height	(mm.)	35	46– 77	60.18 ± .89	7.80 ± .63	12.96 ± 1.04
Nose Height	(mm.)	34	46– 57	51.74 ± .28	2.42 ± .20	4.68 ± .38

Nose Length	(mm.)	34	40– 57	50.50 ± .38	3.26 ± .27	6.46 ± .53
Nose Salient	(mm.)	34	9– 17	13.91 ± .26	2.22 ± .18	15.96 ± 1.31
Nose Breadth	(mm.)	34	30– 43	35.98 ± .28	2.44 ± .20	6.78 ± .55
Inter-Ocular	(mm.)	35	21– 42	29.83 ± .46	4.02 ± .32	13.48 ± 1.09
Bi-Ocular	(mm.)	35	86–119	101.08 ± .70	6.16 ± .50	6.09 ± .49
Index						
Relative Shoulder Breadth		35	23– 28	24.98 ± .15	1.30 ± .10	5.20 ± .42
Relative Hip Breadth		35	16– 21	18.04 ± .13	1.18 ± .10	6.54 ± .53
Shoulder-Hip		35	62– 79	71.49 ± .40	3.48 ± .28	4.87 ± .39
Relative Sitting Height		35	48– 61	52.69 ± .28	2.46 ± .20	4.67 ± .38
Relative Trunk Height		35	29– 38	33.40 ± .21	1.84 ± .15	5.51 ± .44
Thoracic		35	58– 85	71.30 ± .67	5.84 ± .47	8.19 ± .66
Brachial		35	69– 88	79.38 ± .51	4.46 ± .36	5.62 ± .45
Tibio-Femoral		34	70–109	87.45 ± .88	7.60 ± .62	8.69 ± .71
Inter-Membral		34	84–105	93.20 ± .55	4.78 ± .39	5.13 ± .42
Cephalic		35	74– 95	82.28 ± .49	4.28 ± .34	5.20 ± .42
Length-Height		34	58– 89	73.32 ± .90	7.78 ± .64	10.61 ± .87
Breadth-Height		34	74–107	89.92 ± .92	7.94 ± .65	8.83 ± .72
Cephalo-Facial		34	85– 98	91.68 ± .34	2.92 ± .24	3.18 ± .26
Fronto-Parietal		35	68– 79	73.12 ± .36	3.12 ± .25	4.27 ± .34
Zygo-Frontal		34	72– 89	79.56 ± .39	3.34 ± .27	4.20 ± .34
Zygo-Gonial		34	70– 85	78.62 ± .37	3.18 ± .26	4.04 ± .33
Facial		34	75– 98	87.73 ± .60	5.22 ± .43	5.95 ± .49
Upper Facial		34	49– 66	58.82 ± .44	3.78 ± .31	6.43 ± .53
Nasal		34	54– 83	69.92 ± .68	5.92 ± .48	8.47 ± .69
Nose Salient-Height		34	16– 33	26.87 ± .46	3.96 ± .32	14.74 ± 1.21
Nose Length-Height		34	86–105	97.92 ± .37	3.20 ± .26	3.27 ± .27

TABLE 33

MEANS OF KYUSHU IMMIGRANTS—MALES

Measurement		No.	Range	Mean	S.D.	V.
Age		41	20–64	40.40 ± 1.02	9.70 ± .72	24.01 ± 1.79
Weight	(lb.)	41	101–180	127.90 ± 1.80	17.10 ± 1.27	13.37 ± 1.00
Stature	(cm.)	41	148–171	158.87 ± .47	4.50 ± .34	2.83 ± .21
Sitting Height	(cm.)	41	78–93	83.14 ± .34	3.24 ± .24	3.90 ± .29
Trunk Height	(cm.)	41	48–59	52.36 ± .30	2.88 ± .21	5.50 ± .41
Upper Arm Length	(cm.)	41	25–33	29.44 ± .20	1.86 ± .14	6.32 ± .47
Lower Arm Length	(cm.)	41	20–28	23.34 ± .17	1.60 ± .12	6.86 ± .51
Hand Length	(cm.)	41	16–20	17.93 ± .09	.89 ± .07	4.96 ± .37
Upper Leg Length	(cm.)	41	31–42	37.20 ± .26	2.44 ± .18	6.56 ± .49
Lower Leg Length	(cm.)	41	28–37	32.95 ± .21	2.04 ± .15	6.19 ± .46
Total Leg Length	(cm.)	41	69–82	75.64 ± .33	3.14 ± .23	4.15 ± .31
Biacromion	(cm.)	41	37–44	40.56 ± .19	1.78 ± .13	4.39 ± .33
Cristal Breadth	(cm.)	41	25–36	29.61 ± .27	2.52 ± .19	8.51 ± .63
Chest Breadth	(cm.)	41	25–32	27.93 ± .19	1.77 ± .13	6.34 ± .47
Chest Depth	(cm.)	41	17–24	20.51 ± .17	1.64 ± .12	8.00 ± .60
Head Length	(mm.)	41	174–205	191.86 ± .65	6.18 ± .46	3.22 ± .24
Head Breadth	(mm.)	41	143–166	151.80 ± .51	4.82 ± .36	3.18 ± .24
Head Height	(cm.)	40	12–16	13.30 ± .22	2.08 ± .16	1.71 ± .13
Minimum Frontal Diameter	(mm.)	41	100–123	113.06 ± .51	4.86 ± .36	4.30 ± .32
Bizygomatic Diameter	(mm.)	41	134–151	142.89 ± .39	3.72 ± .28	2.60 ± .19
Bigonial Diameter	(mm.)	41	97–125	111.32 ± .64	6.03 ± .45	5.49 ± .41
Total Face Height	(mm.)	41	109–141	123.47 ± .59	5.58 ± .42	4.52 ± .34
Upper Face Height	(mm.)	41	71–92	81.94 ± .44	4.18 ± .31	5.10 ± .38
Forehead Height	(mm.)	41	38–77	59.78 ± .83	7.84 ± .58	13.11 ± .98
Nose Height	(mm.)	41	44–59	51.82 ± .32	3.04 ± .23	5.87 ± .44

		Range	N	M ±	±	±
Nose Length	(mm.)	44– 57	41	50.46 ± .31	2.92 ± .22	5.79 ± .43
Nose Salient	(mm.)	10– 17	40	13.68 ± .20	1.85 ± .14	13.52 ± 1.02
Nose Breadth	(mm.)	30– 41	41	35.92 ± .30	2.88 ± .21	8.02 ± .60
Inter-Ocular	(mm.)	23– 36	41	31.20 ± .28	2.62 ± .20	8.40 ± .63
Bi-Ocular	(mm.)	86–111	41	99.42 ± .52	4.98 ± .37	5.01 ± .37
Index						
Relative Shoulder Breadth		23– 30	41	25.40 ± .15	1.46 ± .11	5.75 ± .43
Relative Hip Breadth		16– 23	41	18.70 ± .18	1.70 ± .13	9.09 ± .68
Shoulder-Hip		62– 88	41	72.81 ± .53	5.04 ± .38	6.92 ± .52
Relative Sitting Height		49– 55	41	52.34 ± .15	1.39 ± .10	2.66 ± .20
Relative Trunk Height		30– 36	41	33.02 ± .16	1.49 ± .11	4.51 ± .34
Thoracic		64– 89	41	73.76 ± .59	5.56 ± .41	7.54 ± .56
Brachial		67– 88	41	79.54 ± .53	5.06 ± .38	6.36 ± .47
Tibio-Femoral		70–119	41	88.70 ± .59	5.64 ± .42	6.36 ± .47
Inter-Membral		86–107	41	93.58 ± .44	4.14 ± .31	4.42 ± .33
Cephalic		72– 91	41	79.18 ± .43	4.04 ± .30	5.10 ± .38
Length-Height		60– 85	40	68.60 ± .59	5.54 ± .42	8.08 ± .61
Breadth-Height		76–107	40	86.66 ± .79	7.40 ± .56	8.54 ± .64
Cephalo-Facial		87–102	41	94.24 ± .33	3.18 ± .24	3.37 ± .25
Fronto-Parietal		62– 81	41	73.96 ± .40	3.80 ± .28	5.14 ± .38
Zygo-Frontal		62– 87	41	78.60 ± .39	3.70 ± .28	4.71 ± .35
Zygo-Gonial		70– 87	41	77.92 ± .40	3.76 ± .28	4.83 ± .36
Facial		75– 98	41	86.02 ± .43	4.11 ± .31	4.78 ± .36
Upper Facial		46– 66	41	57.47 ± .40	3.75 ± .28	6.53 ± .49
Nasal		56– 81	41	69.38 ± .71	6.72 ± .50	9.69 ± .72
Nose Salient-Height		19– 36	40	26.54 ± .37	3.48 ± .26	13.11 ± .99
Nose Length-Height		90–105	41	97.96 ± .33	3.18 ± .24	3.25 ± .24

TABLE 34

MEANS OF 'OTHER JAPAN' IMMIGRANTS—MALES

Measurement		No.	Range	Mean	S.D.	V.
Age		36	20– 64	37.30 ± 1.33	11.85 ± .94	31.77 ± 2.53
Weight	(lb.)	33	91–160	125.50 ± 1.50	12.80 ± 1.06	10.20 ± .85
Stature	(cm.)	36	148–174	159.74 ± .64	5.70 ± .45	3.57 ± .28
Sitting Height	(cm.)	36	76– 93	83.38 ± .46	4.12 ± .33	4.94 ± .39
Trunk Height	(cm.)	36	44– 61	52.88 ± .42	3.74 ± .30	7.07 ± .56
Upper Arm Length	(cm.)	36	27– 32	29.61 ± .13	1.14 ± .09	3.85 ± .31
Lower Arm Length	(cm.)	36	20– 26	23.81 ± .14	1.22 ± .10	5.12 ± .41
Hand Length	(cm.)	36	16– 20	17.72 ± .11	.96 ± .08	5.42 ± .43
Upper Leg Length	(cm.)	36	29– 46	37.62 ± .37	3.30 ± .26	8.77 ± .70
Lower Leg Length	(cm.)	36	28– 38	32.61 ± .20	1.80 ± .14	5.52 ± .44
Total Leg Length	(cm.)	36	67– 84	76.12 ± .45	4.04 ± .32	5.31 ± .42
Biacromion	(cm.)	36	34– 46	40.31 ± .21	1.89 ± .15	4.69 ± .37
Cristal Breadth	(cm.)	36	25– 34	30.03 ± .19	1.71 ± .14	5.69 ± .45
Chest Breadth	(cm.)	36	25– 32	27.92 ± .17	1.53 ± .12	5.48 ± .44
Chest Depth	(cm.)	36	17– 24	20.36 ± .18	1.58 ± .13	7.76 ± .62
Head Length	(mm.)	36	174–205	190.50 ± .65	5.76 ± .46	3.02 ± .24
Head Breadth	(mm.)	36	143–162	151.78 ± .54	4.84 ± .38	3.19 ± .25
Head Height	(cm.)	36	11– 16	13.64 ± .15	1.34 ± .11	9.82 ± .78
Minimum Frontal Diameter	(mm.)	36	103–123	112.07 ± .53	4.68 ± .37	4.18 ± .33
Bizygomatic Diameter	(mm.)	36	134–151	141.84 ± .45	3.96 ± .31	2.79 ± .22
Bigonial Diameter	(mm.)	36	97–129	110.66 ± .70	6.21 ± .49	5.61 ± .45
Total Face Height	(mm.)	36	106–135	122.66 ± .78	6.93 ± .55	5.65 ± .45
Upper Face Height	(mm.)	36	71– 94	80.56 ± .61	5.44 ± .43	6.75 ± .54
Forehead Height	(mm.)	35	42– 73	57.78 ± .83	7.24 ± .58	12.53 ± 1.01
Nose Height	(mm.)	36	44– 63	51.16 ± .45	4.00 ± .32	7.82 ± .62

		N	Range	M ±	S.D. ±	C.V. ±
Nose Length	(mm.)	36	42– 63	50.38 ± .48	4.24 ± .34	8.42 ± .67
Nose Salient	(mm.)	36	9– 19	13.97 ± .28	2.50 ± .20	17.90 ± 1.42
Nose Breadth	(mm.)	36	30– 43	35.66 ± .33	2.92 ± .23	8.19 ± .65
Inter-Ocular	(mm.)	36	22– 40	31.08 ± .44	3.88 ± .31	12.48 ± .99
Bi-Ocular	(mm.)	36	88–115	100.56 ± .60	5.34 ± .42	5.31 ± .42
Index						
Relative Shoulder Breadth		36	23– 28	25.16 ± .14	1.28 ± .10	5.09 ± .40
Relative Hip Breadth		36	16– 23	18.72 ± .14	1.24 ± .10	6.62 ± .53
Shoulder-Hip		36	65– 97	75.24 ± .58	5.16 ± .41	6.86 ± .55
Relative Sitting Height		36	48– 56	52.28 ± .21	1.85 ± .15	3.54 ± .28
Relative Trunk Height		36	28– 37	33.11 ± .21	1.88 ± .15	5.68 ± .45
Thoracic		36	62– 81	72.78 ± .53	4.70 ± .37	6.46 ± .51
Brachial		36	71– 90	80.38 ± .49	4.38 ± .35	5.45 ± .43
Tibio-Femoral		36	70–109	88.40 ± .99	8.80 ± .70	9.95 ± .79
Inter-Membral		36	88–105	93.72 ± .52	4.60 ± .37	4.91 ± .39
Cephalic		36	72– 87	79.78 ± .37	3.30 ± .26	4.14 ± .33
Length-Height		36	56– 87	71.66 ± .85	7.54 ± .60	10.52 ± .84
Breadth-Height		36	68–103	90.34 ± .94	8.34 ± .66	9.23 ± .73
Cephalo-Facial		36	87– 98	93.06 ± .28	2.46 ± .20	2.64 ± .21
Fronto-Parietal		36	66– 81	73.78 ± .37	3.28 ± .26	4.45 ± .35
Zygo-Frontal		36	72– 85	79.22 ± .30	2.64 ± .21	3.33 ± .26
Zygo-Gonial		36	70– 87	78.00 ± .40	3.54 ± .28	4.54 ± .36
Facial		36	72– 98	86.74 ± .57	5.10 ± .41	5.88 ± .47
Upper Facial		36	52– 63	56.84 ± .38	3.36 ± .27	5.91 ± .47
Nasal		36	50– 95	69.56 ± .94	8.40 ± .67	12.08 ± .96
Nose Salient-Height		36	16– 36	26.84 ± .51	4.56 ± .36	16.99 ± 1.35
Nose Length-Height		36	92–105	98.22 ± .32	2.84 ± .23	2.89 ± .23

TABLE 35

DIFFERENCES OF HIROSHIMA IMMIGRANTS FROM TOTAL IMMIGRANTS—MALES

Measurement	Difference	x p.e.
Age	2.55 ± 1.05	2.43
Weight	−1.70 ± 1.62	1.05
Stature	− .78 ± .51	1.53
Sitting Height	−1.02 ± .36	2.83
Trunk Height	− .70 ± .31	2.26
Upper Arm Length	− .12 ± .17	.71
Lower Arm Length	.23 ± .15	1.53
Hand Length	− .01 ± .08	.12
Upper Leg Length	.48 ± .30	1.60
Lower Leg Length	− .15 ± .19	.79
Total Leg Length	.14 ± .39	.36
Biacromion	− .22 ± .18	1.22
Cristal Breadth	.21 ± .19	1.11
Chest Breadth	− .15 ± .17	.88
Chest Depth	.27 ± .18	1.50
Head Length	−1.00 ± .62	1.61
Head Breadth	− .02 ± .52	.04
Head Height	− .08 ± .12	.67
Minimum Frontal Diameter	− .21 ± .53	.40
Bizygomatic Diameter	.78 ± .47	1.66
Bigonial Diameter	.63 ± .61	1.03
Total Face Height	− .99 ± .58	1.71
Upper Face Height	− .70 ± .48	1.46
Forehead Height	− .12 ± .79	.15
Nose Height	− .52 ± .34	1.53
Nose Length	− .68 ± .38	1.79
Nose Salient	− .08 ± .21	.38
Nose Breadth	.10 ± .29	.34
Inter-Ocular	− .29 ± .34	.85
Bi-Ocular	1.10 ± .58	1.90
Index		
Relative Shoulder Breadth	.04 ± .13	.31
Relative Hip Breadth	.20 ± .14	1.43
Shoulder-Hip	.28 ± .47	.60
Relative Sitting Height	− .33 ± .18	1.83
Relative Trunk Height	− .22 ± .16	1.38
Thoracic	1.42 ± .54	2.63
Brachial	1.08 ± .50	2.16
Tibio-Femoral	−1.85 ± .83	2.23
Inter-Membral	− .16 ± .45	.36
Cephalic	.48 ± .39	1.23

[TABLE 35—*continued*]

DIFFERENCES OF HIROSHIMA IMMIGRANTS FROM TOTAL IMMIGRANTS—MALES

Index	Difference	x p.e.
Length-Height	.02 ± .66	.03
Breadth-Height	− .52 ± .77	.68
Cephalo-Facial	.54 ± .32	1.69
Fronto-Parietal	− .04 ± .34	.12
Zygo-Frontal	− .36 ± .32	1.12
Zygo-Gonial	.08 ± .34	.24
Facial	−1.02 ± .48	2.12
Upper Facial	− .72 ± .39	1.85
Nasal	.82 ± .70	1.17
Nose Salient-Height	.27 ± .39	.69
Nose Length-Height	1.78 ± .31	5.74

TABLE 36

DIFFERENCES OF YAMAGUCHI IMMIGRANTS FROM TOTAL IMMIGRANTS—MALES

Measurement	Difference	x p.e.
Age	3.25 ± 1.23	2.64
Weight	−7.10 ± 1.88	3.78
Stature	.15 ± .59	.25
Sitting Height	.82 ± .42	1.95
Trunk Height	.62 ± .36	1.72
Upper Arm Length	.00 ± .19	.00
Lower Arm Length	− .34 ± .18	1.89
Hand Length	.06 ± .09	.67
Upper Leg Length	.10 ± .35	.29
Lower Leg Length	.12 ± .22	.55
Total Leg Length	− .24 ± .46	.52
Biacromion	− .39 ± .21	1.86
Cristal Breadth	− .97 ± .23	4.22
Chest Breadth	− .44 ± .19	2.32
Chest Depth	− .83 ± .21	3.95
Head Length	−2.48 ± .73	3.40
Head Breadth	1.22 ± .61	2.00
Head Height	.38 ± .14	2.71
Minimum Frontal Diameter	− .15 ± .62	.24
Bizygomatic Diameter	−1.17 ± .56	2.09
Bigonial Diameter	− .21 ± .72	.29
Total Face Height	.75 ± .68	1.10
Upper Face Height	1.36 ± .57	2.39
Forehead Height	.80 ± .91	.88
Nose Height	.08 ± .40	.20
Nose Length	.26 ± .44	.59
Nose Salient	− .02 ± .25	.08
Nose Breadth	.18 ± .34	.53
Inter-Ocular	− .71 ± .40	1.78
Bi-Ocular	.26 ± .68	.38
Index		
Relative Shoulder Breadth	− .32 ± .15	2.13
Relative Hip Breadth	− .56 ± .16	3.50
Shoulder-Hip	−1.92 ± .55	3.49
Relative Sitting Height	.32 ± .21	1.52
Relative Trunk Height	.26 ± .19	1.37
Thoracic	−1.94 ± .64	3.03
Brachial	− .80 ± .59	1.36
Tibio-Femoral	− .05 ± .99	.05
Inter-Membral	− .34 ± .53	.64
Cephalic	1.56 ± .45	3.47

[TABLE 36—*continued*]

DIFFERENCES OF YAMAGUCHI IMMIGRANTS FROM TOTAL IMMIGRANTS—MALES

Index	Difference	x p.e.
Length-Height	2.50 ± .78	3.21
Breadth-Height	2.02 ± .92	2.20
Cephalo-Facial	−1.44 ± .38	3.79
Fronto-Parietal	− .50 ± .40	1.25
Zygo-Frontal	.50 ± .38	1.32
Zygo-Gonial	.24 ± .41	.59
Facial	1.20 ± .58	2.07
Upper Facial	1.47 ± .46	3.20
Nasal	.28 ± .83	.34
Nose Salient-Height	− .06 ± .46	.13
Nose Length-Height	.10 ± .37	.27

TABLE 37

DIFFERENCES OF KYUSHU IMMIGRANTS FROM TOTAL IMMIGRANTS—MALES

Measurement	Difference	x p.e.
Age	− .20 ± 1.14	.18
Weight	3.90 ± 1.74	2.24
Stature	.15 ± .55	.27
Sitting Height	.04 ± .39	.10
Trunk Height	− .26 ± .34	.76
Upper Arm Length	.07 ± .18	.39
Lower Arm Length	− .14 ± .16	.88
Hand Length	.13 ± .09	1.44
Upper Leg Length	− .32 ± .32	1.00
Lower Leg Length	.30 ± .21	1.43
Total Leg Length	.08 ± .42	.19
Biacromion	.28 ± .19	1.47
Cristal Breadth	.07 ± .21	.33
Chest Breadth	.26 ± .18	1.44
Chest Depth	.22 ± .19	1.16
Head Length	2.48 ± .67	3.70
Head Breadth	− .92 ± .56	1.64
Head Height	− .11 ± .13	.85
Minimum Frontal Diameter	.42 ± .58	.72
Bizygomatic Diameter	.54 ± .51	1.06
Bigonial Diameter	− .36 ± .66	.55
Total Face Height	.24 ± .63	.38
Upper Face Height	.54 ± .52	1.04
Forehead Height	.40 ± .84	.48
Nose Height	.16 ± .37	.43
Nose Length	.22 ± .40	.55
Nose Salient	− .25 ± .23	1.09
Nose Breadth	.12 ± .31	.39
Inter-Ocular	.66 ± .37	1.78
Bi-Ocular	−1.40 ± .63	2.22
Index		
Relative Shoulder Breadth	.10 ± .14	.71
Relative Hip Breadth	.10 ± .15	.67
Shoulder-Hip	− .60 ± .51	1.18
Relative Sitting Height	− .03 ± .19	.16
Relative Trunk Height	− .12 ± .18	.67
Thoracic	.52 ± .59	.88
Brachial	− .64 ± .55	1.16
Tibio-Femoral	1.20 ± .90	1.33
Inter-Membral	.04 ± .48	.08
Cephalic	−1.54 ± .42	3.67

[TABLE 37—*continued*]

DIFFERENCES OF KYUSHU IMMIGRANTS FROM TOTAL IMMIGRANTS—MALES

Index	Difference	x p.e.
Length-Height	$-2.22 \pm .72$	3.08
Breadth-Height	$-1.24 \pm .84$	1.48
Cephalo-Facial	$1.12 \pm .35$	3.20
Fronto-Parietal	$.34 \pm .37$	.92
Zygo-Frontal	$-.46 \pm .35$	1.31
Zygo-Gonial	$-.46 \pm .37$	1.24
Facial	$-.51 \pm .52$	.98
Upper Facial	$.12 \pm .42$	.29
Nasal	$-.26 \pm .75$	.35
Nose Salient-Height	$-.39 \pm .42$	.93
Nose Length-Height	$.14 \pm .33$	.42

TABLE 38

DIFFERENCES OF 'OTHER JAPAN' IMMIGRANTS FROM TOTAL IMMIGRANTS—MALES

Measurement	Difference	x p.e.
Age	−3.30 ± 1.21	2.73
Weight	1.50 ± 1.94	.77
Stature	1.02 ± .58	1.76
Sitting Height	.28 ± .42	.67
Trunk Height	.26 ± .36	.72
Upper Arm Length	.24 ± .19	1.26
Lower Arm Length	.33 ± .18	1.83
Hand Length	− .08 ± .09	.89
Upper Leg Length	.10 ± .34	.29
Lower Leg Length	− .04 ± .22	.18
Total Leg Length	.56 ± .45	1.24
Biacromion	.03 ± .21	.14
Cristal Breadth	.49 ± .22	2.23
Chest Breadth	.25 ± .19	1.32
Chest Depth	.07 ± .21	.33
Head Length	1.12 ± .71	1.58
Head Breadth	− .94 ± .60	1.57
Head Height	.23 ± .13	1.77
Minimum Frontal Diameter	− .57 ± .61	.93
Bizygomatic Diameter	− .51 ± .54	.94
Bigonial Diameter	−1.02 ± .71	1.44
Total Face Height	− .57 ± .67	.85
Upper Face Height	− .84 ± .56	1.50
Forehead Height	−1.60 ± .91	1.76
Nose Height	− .50 ± .39	1.28
Nose Length	.14 ± .43	.33
Nose Salient	.04 ± .24	.17
Nose Breadth	− .14 ± .33	.42
Inter-Ocular	.54 ± .40	1.35
Bi-Ocular	− .26 ± .67	.39
Index		
Relative Shoulder Breadth	− .14 ± .15	.93
Relative Hip Breadth	.12 ± .16	.75
Shoulder-Hip	1.83 ± .54	3.39
Relative Sitting Height	− .09 ± .20	.45
Relative Trunk Height	− .03 ± .19	.16
Thoracic	− .46 ± .63	.73
Brachial	.20 ± .58	.34
Tibio-Femoral	.90 ± .96	.94
Inter-Membral	.18 ± .52	.35
Cephalic	− .94 ± .45	2.09

[TABLE 38—*continued*]

DIFFERENCES OF 'OTHER JAPAN' IMMIGRANTS FROM TOTAL IMMIGRANTS—MALES

Index	Difference	x p.e.
Length-Height	.84 ± .76	1.11
Breadth-Height	2.44 ± .89	2.74
Cephalo-Facial	− .06 ± .37	.16
Fronto-Parietal	.16 ± .40	.40
Zygo-Frontal	.16 ± .37	.43
Zygo-Gonial	− .38 ± .40	.95
Facial	.21 ± .56	.38
Upper Facial	− .51 ± .45	1.13
Nasal	− .08 ± .80	.10
Nose Salient-Height	− .09 ± .45	.20
Nose Length-Height	.40 ± .36	1.11

TABLE 39

DISTRIBUTION OF THE X P.E.'S OF THE DIFFERENCES BETWEEN THE PREFECTURAL GROUPS OF MALE IMMIGRANTS AND THE TOTAL MALE IMMIGRANTS

		0–99	1.00–1.99	2.00–2.99	3.00–3.99	4.00–4.99	5.00–5.99	6.00–X
Hiroshima Immigrants / Total Immigrants	{ Measurements	12	15	2	0	0	0	0
	{ Indices	8	8	4	0	0	1	0
Yamaguchi Immigrants / Total Immigrants	{ Measurements	14	6	5	3	1	0	0
	{ Indices	6	5	3	7	0	0	0
Kyushu Immigrants / Total Immigrants	{ Measurements	15	11	2	1	0	0	0
	{ Indices	12	6	0	3	0	0	0
'Other Japan' Immigrants / Total Immigrants	{ Measurements	15	13	1	0	0	0	0
	{ Indices	15	3	2	1	0	0	0

TABLE 40

DIFFERENCES OF MEANS OF MALE IMMIGRANTS BY PREFECTURE

Hiroshima
——————
Yamaguchi

Measurement	Difference	x p.e.
Age	.70 ± 1.55	.45
Weight	−5.40 ± 2.30	2.35
Stature	.93 ± .78	1.19
Sitting Height	1.84 ± .61	3.02
Trunk Height	1.32 ± .48	2.75
Upper Arm Length	.12 ± .28	.43
Lower Arm Length	− .57 ± .21	2.71
Hand Length	.07 ± .10	.70
Upper Leg Length	− .38 ± .48	.79
Lower Leg Length	.27 ± .28	.96
Total Leg Length	− .38 ± .65	.58
Biacromion	− .17 ± .28	.61
Cristal Breadth	−1.18 ± .23	5.13
Chest Breadth	− .29 ± .23	1.26
Chest Depth	−1.10 ± .26	4.23
Head Length	−1.48 ± .92	1.61
Head Breadth	1.24 ± .80	1.55
Head Height	.46 ± .18	2.56
Minimum Frontal Diameter	.06 ± .86	.07
Bizygomatic Diameter	−1.95 ± .77	2.53
Bigonial Diameter	− .84 ± .92	.91
Total Face Height	1.74 ± .88	1.98
Upper Face Height	2.06 ± .74	2.78
Forehead Height	.92 ± 1.19	.77
Nose Height	.60 ± .46	1.30
Nose Length	.94 ± .57	1.65
Nose Salient	.06 ± .33	.18
Nose Breadth	.08 ± .41	.20
Inter-Ocular	− .42 ± .56	.75
Bi-Ocular	− .84 ± .94	.89
Index		
Relative Shoulder Breadth	− .36 ± .19	1.89
Relative Hip Breadth	− .76 ± .18	4.22
Shoulder-Hip	−2.20 ± .60	3.67
Relative Sitting Height	.65 ± .32	2.03
Relative Trunk Height	.48 ± .26	1.85
Thoracic	−3.36 ± .85	3.95
Brachial	−1.88 ± .74	2.54

[*Continued*]

[TABLE 40—*continued*]

DIFFERENCES OF MEANS OF MALE IMMIGRANTS BY PREFECTURE

Hiroshima
Yamaguchi

Index	Difference	x p.e.
Tibio-Femoral	1.80 ± 1.10	1.64
Inter-Membral	− .18 ± .66	.27
Cephalic	1.08 ± .57	1.89
Length-Height	2.48 ± 1.05	2.36
Breadth-Height	2.54 ± 1.18	2.15
Cephalo-Facial	−1.98 ± .45	4.40
Fronto-Parietal	− .46 ± .50	.92
Zygo-Frontal	.86 ± .51	1.69
Zygo-Gonial	.16 ± .51	.31
Facial	2.22 ± .79	2.81
Upper Facial	2.19 ± .59	3.71
Nasal	− .54 ± .91	.59
Nose Salient-Height	− .33 ± .58	.57
Nose Length-Height	−1.68 ± .50	3.36

TABLE 41

DIFFERENCES OF MEANS OF MALE IMMIGRANTS BY PREFECTURE

Hiroshima
Kyushu

Measurement	Difference	x p.e.
Age	2.75 ± 1.39	1.98
Weight	−5.60 ± 2.41	2.32
Stature	− .93 ± .71	1.31
Sitting Height	−1.06 ± .46	2.30
Trunk Height	− .44 ± .40	1.10
Upper Arm Length	− .19 ± .27	.70
Lower Arm Length	.37 ± .23	1.61
Hand Length	− .14 ± .11	1.27
Upper Leg Length	.80 ± .40	2.00
Lower Leg Length	− .45 ± .28	1.61
Total Leg Length	.06 ± .53	.11
Biacromion	− .50 ± .25	2.00
Cristal Breadth	.14 ± .32	.44
Chest Breadth	− .41 ± .25	1.64
Chest Depth	.05 ± .25	.20
Head Length	−3.48 ± .88	3.95
Head Breadth	.90 ± .68	1.32
Head Height	.03 ± .24	.12
Minimum Frontal Diameter	− .63 ± .77	.82
Bizygomatic Diameter	.24 ± .64	.38
Bigonial Diameter	.99 ± .89	1.11
Total Face Height	−1.23 ± .83	1.48
Upper Face Height	−1.24 ± .67	1.85
Forehead Height	− .52 ± 1.14	.46
Nose Height	− .68 ± .49	1.39
Nose Length	− .90 ± .53	1.70
Nose Salient	.17 ± .28	.61
Nose Breadth	− .02 ± .42	.05
Inter-Ocular	− .95 ± .43	2.21
Bi-Ocular	2.50 ± .81	3.09
Index		
Relative Shoulder Breadth	− .06 ± .19	.32
Relative Hip Breadth	.10 ± .22	.45
Shoulder-Hip	.88 ± .70	1.26
Relative Sitting Height	− .30 ± .22	1.36
Relative Trunk Height	− .10 ± .23	.43
Thoracic	.90 ± .79	1.14
Brachial	1.72 ± .76	2.26

[Continued]

[TABLE 41—*continued*]

DIFFERENCES OF MEANS OF MALE IMMIGRANTS BY PREFECTURE

Hiroshima
―――――――――
Kyushu

Index	Difference	x p.e.
Tibio-Femoral	$-3.05 \pm .89$	3.43
Inter-Membral	$- .20 \pm .57$	.35
Cephalic	$2.02 \pm .52$	3.88
Length-Height	$2.24 \pm .80$	2.80
Breadth-Height	$.72 \pm 1.08$	.67
Cephalo-Facial	$- .58 \pm .44$	1.32
Fronto-Parietal	$- .38 \pm .52$	.73
Zygo-Frontal	$.10 \pm .51$	.20
Zygo-Gonial	$.54 \pm .53$	1.02
Facial	$- .51 \pm .67$	.76
Upper Facial	$- .84 \pm .57$	1.47
Nasal	$1.08 \pm .93$	1.16
Nose Salient-Height	$.66 \pm .51$	1.29
Nose Length-Height	$1.64 \pm .47$	3.49

TABLE 42

DIFFERENCES OF MEANS OF MALE IMMIGRANTS BY PREFECTURE

Hiroshima

'Other Japan'

Measurement	Difference	x p.e.
Age	5.85 ± 1.63	3.59
Weight	−3.20 ± 2.20	1.45
Stature	−1.80 ± .83	2.17
Sitting Height	−1.30 ± .55	2.36
Trunk Height	− .96 ± .50	1.92
Upper Arm Length	− .36 ± .22	1.64
Lower Arm Length	− .10 ± .21	.48
Hand Length	.07 ± .13	.54
Upper Leg Length	.38 ± .48	.79
Lower Leg Length	− .11 ± .27	.41
Total Leg Length	− .42 ± .62	.68
Biacromion	− .25 ± .27	.93
Cristal Breadth	− .28 ± .25	1.12
Chest Breadth	− .40 ± .23	1.74
Chest Depth	.20 ± .25	.80
Head Length	−2.12 ± .88	2.41
Head Breadth	.92 ± .70	1.31
Head Height	− .31 ± .18	1.72
Minimum Frontal Diameter	.36 ± .79	.46
Bizygomatic Diameter	1.29 ± .68	1.90
Bigonial Diameter	1.65 ± .94	1.76
Total Face Height	− .42 ± .97	.43
Upper Face Height	.14 ± .79	.18
Forehead Height	1.48 ± 1.14	1.30
Nose Height	− .02 ± .58	.03
Nose Length	− .82 ± .64	1.28
Nose Salient	− .12 ± .34	.35
Nose Breadth	.24 ± .45	.53
Inter-Ocular	− .83 ± .54	1.54
Bi-Ocular	1.36 ± .86	1.58
Index		
Relative Shoulder Breadth	.18 ± .18	1.00
Relative Hip Breadth	.08 ± .19	.42
Shoulder-Hip	−1.55 ± .73	2.12
Relative Sitting Height	− .24 ± .26	.92
Relative Trunk Height	− .19 ± .26	.73
Thoracic	1.88 ± .75	2.51
Brachial	.88 ± .73	1.21

[Continued]

[TABLE 42—*continued*]

DIFFERENCES OF MEANS OF MALE IMMIGRANTS BY PREFECTURE

Hiroshima
'Other Japan'

Index	Difference	x p.e.
Tibio-Femoral	−2.75 ± 1.20	2.29
Inter-Membral	− .34 ± .63	.54
Cephalic	1.42 ± .48	2.96
Length-Height	− .82 ± 1.00	.82
Breadth-Height	−2.96 ± 1.20	2.47
Cephalo-Facial	.60 ± .40	1.50
Fronto-Parietal	− .20 ± .50	.40
Zygo-Frontal	− .52 ± .45	1.16
Zygo-Gonial	.46 ± .53	.87
Facial	−1.23 ± .77	1.60
Upper Facial	− .21 ± .55	.38
Nasal	.90 ± 1.11	.81
Nose Salient-Height	.36 ± .62	.58
Nose Length-Height	1.38 ± .47	2.94

TABLE 43

DIFFERENCES OF MEANS OF MALE IMMIGRANTS BY PREFECTURE

Yamaguchi
Kyushu

Measurement	Difference	x p.e.
Age	3.45 ± 1.60	2.16
Weight	—11.00 ± 2.44	4.51
Stature	.00 ± .74	.00
Sitting Height	.78 ± .62	1.26
Trunk Height	.88 ± .50	1.76
Upper Arm Length	— .07 ± .30	.23
Lower Arm Length	— .20 ± .22	.91
Hand Length	— .07 ± .11	.64
Upper Leg Length	.42 ± .44	.95
Lower Leg Length	— .18 ± .30	.60
Total Leg Length	— .32 ± .60	.53
Biacromion	— .67 ± .29	2.31
Cristal Breadth	— 1.04 ± .31	3.35
Chest Breadth	— .70 ± .25	2.80
Chest Depth	— 1.05 ± .25	4.20
Head Length	— 4.96 ± .96	5.17
Head Breadth	2.14 ± .83	2.58
Head Height	.49 ± .27	1.81
Minimum Frontal Diameter	— .57 ± .82	.70
Bizygomatic Diameter	— 1.71 ± .70	2.44
Bigonial Diameter	.15 ± .93	.16
Total Face Height	.51 ± .89	.57
Upper Face Height	.82 ± .70	1.17
Forehead Height	.40 ± 1.22	.33
Nose Height	— .08 ± .43	.19
Nose Length	.04 ± .49	.08
Nose Salient	.23 ± .33	.70
Nose Breadth	.06 ± .41	.15
Inter-Ocular	— 1.37 ± .54	2.54
Bi-Ocular	1.66 ± .87	1.91

Index		
Relative Shoulder Breadth	— .42 ± .21	2.00
Relative Hip Breadth	— .66 ± .22	3.00
Shoulder-Hip	— 1.32 ± .66	2.00
Relative Sitting Height	.35 ± .32	1.09
Relative Trunk Height	.38 ± .26	1.46
Thoracic	— 2.46 ± .89	2.76
Brachial	— .16 ± .74	.22

[*Continued*]

[TABLE 43—*continued*]

DIFFERENCES OF MEANS OF MALE IMMIGRANTS BY PREFECTURE

Yamaguchi
_____
Kyushu

Index	Difference	x p.e.
Tibio-Femoral	− 1.25 ± 1.06	1.18
Inter-Membral	− .38 ± .70	.54
Cephalic	3.10 ± .65	4.77
Length-Height	4.72 ± 1.08	4.37
Breadth-Height	3.26 ± 1.21	2.69
Cephalo-Facial	− 2.56 ± .47	5.45
Fronto-Parietal	− .84 ± .54	1.56
Zygo-Frontal	.96 ± .55	1.75
Zygo-Gonial	.70 ± .54	1.30
Facial	1.71 ± .74	2.31
Upper Facial	1.35 ± .59	2.29
Nasal	.54 ± .98	.55
Nose Salient-Height	.33 ± .59	.56
Nose Length-Height	− .04 ± .50	.08

TABLE 44

DIFFERENCES OF MEANS OF MALE IMMIGRANTS BY PREFECTURE

Yamaguchi
'Other Japan'

Measurement	Difference	x p.e.
Age	6.55 ± 1.81	3.62
Weight	−8.60 ± 2.22	3.87
Stature	− .87 ± .86	1.01
Sitting Height	.54 ± .69	.78
Trunk Height	.36 ± .58	.62
Upper Arm Length	− .24 ± .26	.92
Lower Arm Length	− .67 ± .20	3.35
Hand Length	.14 ± .13	1.08
Upper Leg Length	.00 ± .52	.00
Lower Leg Length	.16 ± .30	.53
Total Leg Length	− .80 ± .67	1.19
Biacromion	− .42 ± .30	1.40
Cristal Breadth	−1.46 ± .24	6.08
Chest Breadth	− .69 ± .23	3.00
Chest Depth	− .90 ± .26	3.46
Head Length	−3.60 ± .96	3.75
Head Breadth	2.16 ± .85	2.54
Head Height	.15 ± .21	.71
Minimum Frontal Diameter	.42 ± .83	.51
Bizygomatic Diameter	− .66 ± .73	.90
Bigonial Diameter	.81 ± .98	.83
Total Face Height	1.32 ± 1.02	1.29
Upper Face Height	2.20 ± .82	2.68
Forehead Height	2.40 ± 1.22	1.97
Nose Height	.58 ± .53	1.09
Nose Length	.12 ± .61	.20
Nose Salient	− .06 ± .38	.16
Nose Breadth	.32 ± .43	.74
Inter-Ocular	−1.25 ± .64	1.95
Bi-Ocular	.52 ± .92	.57

Index		
Relative Shoulder Breadth	− .18 ± .21	.86
Relative Hip Breadth	− .68 ± .19	3.58
Shoulder-Hip	−3.75 ± .70	5.36
Relative Sitting Height	.41 ± .35	1.17
Relative Trunk Height	.29 ± .30	.97
Thoracic	−1.48 ± .85	1.74
Brachial	−1.00 ± .71	1.41

[*Continued*]

[TABLE 44—*continued*]

DIFFERENCES OF MEANS OF MALE IMMIGRANTS BY PREFECTURE

Yamaguchi
'Other Japan'

Index	Difference	x p.e.
Tibio-Femoral	− .95 ± 1.32	.72
Inter-Membral	− .52 ± .76	.68
Cephalic	2.50 ± .61	4.10
Length-Height	1.66 ± 1.24	1.34
Breadth-Height	− .42 ± 1.32	.32
Cephalo-Facial	−1.38 ± .44	3.14
Fronto-Parietal	− .66 ± .52	1.27
Zygo-Frontal	.34 ± .49	.69
Zygo-Gonial	.62 ± .54	1.15
Facial	.99 ± .83	1.19
Upper Facial	1.98 ± .58	3.41
Nasal	.36 ± 1.16	.31
Nose Salient-Height	.03 ± .69	.04
Nose Length-Height	− .30 ± .49	.61

TABLE 45

DIFFERENCES OF MEANS OF MALE IMMIGRANTS BY PREFECTURE

Kyushu
'Other Japan'

Measurement	Difference	x p.e.
Age	3.10 ± 1.68	1.85
Weight	2.40 ± 2.34	1.03
Stature	− .87 ± .79	1.10
Sitting Height	− .24 ± .57	.42
Trunk Height	− .52 ± .52	1.00
Upper Arm Length	− .17 ± .24	.71
Lower Arm Length	− .47 ± .22	2.14
Hand Length	.21 ± .14	1.40
Upper Leg Length	− .42 ± .45	.93
Lower Leg Length	.34 ± .29	1.17
Total Leg Length	− .48 ± .56	.86
Biacromion	.25 ± .28	.89
Cristal Breadth	− .42 ± .33	1.27
Chest Breadth	.01 ± .25	.04
Chest Depth	.15 ± .25	.60
Head Length	1.36 ± .92	1.48
Head Breadth	.02 ± .74	.03
Head Height	− .34 ± .27	1.26
Minimum Frontal Diameter	.99 ± .74	1.34
Bizygomatic Diameter	1.05 ± .60	1.75
Bigonial Diameter	.66 ± .95	.69
Total Face Height	.81 ± .98	.83
Upper Face Height	1.38 ± .75	1.84
Forehead Height	2.00 ± 1.17	1.71
Nose Height	.66 ± .55	1.20
Nose Length	.08 ± .57	.14
Nose Salient	− .29 ± .34	.85
Nose Breadth	.26 ± .45	.58
Inter-Ocular	.12 ± .52	.23
Bi-Ocular	−1.14 ± .79	1.44

Index

Relative Shoulder Breadth	.24 ± .21	1.14
Relative Hip Breadth	− .02 ± .23	.09
Shoulder-Hip	−2.43 ± .79	3.06
Relative Sitting Height	.06 ± .26	.23
Relative Trunk Height	− .09 ± .26	.35
Thoracic	.98 ± .79	1.24
Brachial	− .84 ± .72	1.17

[*Continued*]

[TABLE 45—*continued*]

DIFFERENCES OF MEANS OF MALE IMMIGRANTS BY PREFECTURE

Kyushu
'Other Japan'

Index	Difference	x p.e.
Tibio-Femoral	.30 ± 1.15	.26
Inter-Membral	− .14 ± .68	.21
Cephalic	− .60 ± .57	1.05
Length-Height	−3.06 ± 1.03	2.97
Breadth-Height	−3.68 ± 1.23	2.99
Cephalo-Facial	1.18 ± .43	2.74
Fronto-Parietal	.18 ± .54	.33
Zygo-Frontal	− .62 ± .49	1.27
Zygo-Gonial	− .08 ± .57	.14
Facial	− .72 ± .71	1.01
Upper Facial	.63 ± .55	1.15
Nasal	− .18 ± 1.18	.15
Nose Salient-Height	− .30 ± .63	.48
Nose Length-Height	− .26 ± .46	.57

TABLE 46

DISTRIBUTION OF THE X P.E.'S OF THE DIFFERENCES BETWEEN THE VARIOUS PREFECTURAL GROUPS OF MALE IMMIGRANTS

		0–.99	1.00–1.99	2.00–2.99	3.00–3.99	4.00–4.99	5.00–5.99	6.00–X
Hiroshima / Yamaguchi	Measurements	13	7	6	1	1	1	0
	Indices	5	5	5	4	2	0	0
Hiroshima / Kyushu	Measurements	10	12	5	2	0	0	0
	Indices	8	8	2	3	0	0	0
Hiroshima / 'Other Japan'	Measurements	13	13	3	0	0	0	0
	Indices	10	5	6	0	0	0	0
Yamaguchi / Kyushu	Measurements	15	5	5	1	2	1	0
	Indices	5	6	6	1	2	1	0
Yamaguchi / 'Other Japan'	Measurements	13	8	2	5	0	0	1
	Indices	9	7	0	3	1	1	0
Kyushu / 'Other Japan'	Measurements	14	14	1	0	0	0	0
	Indices	10	7	3	1	0	0	0

TABLE 47

MEANS OF HIROSHIMA HAWAIIAN BORN—MALES

Measurement		No.	Range	Mean	S.D.	V.
Age		36	20– 39	25.20 ± .53	4.75 ± .38	18.85 ± 1.50
Weight	(lb.)	34	91–200	125.50 ± 1.97	17.00 ± 1.39	13.55 ± 1.11
Stature	(cm.)	36	148–171	162.08 ± .58	5.19 ± .41	3.20 ± .25
Sitting Height	(cm.)	36	76– 91	85.16 ± .40	3.52 ± .28	4.13 ± .33
Trunk Height	(cm.)	36	46– 61	53.84 ± .37	3.26 ± .26	6.05 ± .48
Upper Arm Length	(cm.)	36	28– 35	30.86 ± .18	1.57 ± .12	5.09 ± .40
Lower Arm Length	(cm.)	36	22– 27	24.53 ± .13	1.17 ± .09	4.77 ± .38
Hand Length	(cm.)	36	16– 20	17.81 ± .10	.91 ± .07	5.11 ± .41
Upper Leg Length	(cm.)	36	29– 46	36.88 ± .40	3.58 ± .28	9.71 ± .77
Lower Leg Length	(cm.)	36	29– 38	33.97 ± .24	2.11 ± .17	6.21 ± .49
Total Leg Length	(cm.)	36	65– 84	76.50 ± .46	4.12 ± .33	5.39 ± .43
Biacromion	(cm.)	35	38– 44	40.91 ± .17	1.52 ± .12	3.72 ± .30
Cristal Breadth	(cm.)	36	25– 33	28.89 ± .21	1.91 ± .15	6.61 ± .53
Chest Breadth	(cm.)	36	24– 34	27.28 ± .20	1.79 ± .14	6.56 ± .52
Chest Depth	(cm.)	35	16– 27	19.69 ± .24	2.07 ± .17	10.51 ± .85
Head Length	(mm.)	36	174–201	184.28 ± .65	5.82 ± .46	3.16 ± .25
Head Breadth	(mm.)	36	145–168	155.28 ± .57	5.08 ± .40	3.27 ± .26
Head Height	(cm.)	34	12– 16	13.62 ± .14	1.22 ± .10	8.96 ± .73
Minimum Frontal Diameter	(mm.)	36	100–123	112.49 ± .56	4.98 ± .40	4.43 ± .35
Bizygomatic Diameter	(mm.)	35	128–157	141.27 ± .56	4.92 ± .40	3.48 ± .28
Bigonial Diameter	(mm.)	36	88–120	109.91 ± .68	6.09 ± .48	5.54 ± .44
Total Face Height	(mm.)	36	109–135	122.18 ± .63	5.61 ± .45	4.59 ± .36
Upper Face Height	(mm.)	36	69– 92	82.44 ± .52	4.66 ± .37	5.65 ± .45
Forehead Height	(mm.)	36	46– 77	61.26 ± .77	6.84 ± .54	11.17 ± .89
Nose Height	(mm.)	36	46– 61	52.00 ± .40	3.60 ± .29	6.92 ± .55

		N	Range	Mean	S.D.	V
Nose Length	(mm.)	36	46– 59	50.34 ± .38	3.42 ± .27	6.79 ± .54
Nose Salient	(mm.)	36	10– 19	13.86 ± .25	2.25 ± .18	16.23 ± 1.29
Nose Breadth	(mm.)	36	28– 41	34.84 ± .35	3.14 ± .25	9.01 ± .72
Inter-Ocular	(mm.)	36	26– 40	32.31 ± .43	3.86 ± .31	11.95 ± .95
Bi-Ocular	(mm.)	35	92–113	99.82 ± .56	4.88 ± .39	4.89 ± .39
Index						
Relative Shoulder Breadth		35	23– 28	25.32 ± .11	1.00 ± .08	3.95 ± .32
Relative Hip Breadth		36	16– 21	17.78 ± .14	1.26 ± .10	7.09 ± .56
Shoulder-Hip		35	62– 82	70.62 ± .50	4.38 ± .35	6.20 ± .50
Relative Sitting Height		36	50– 58	52.75 ± .19	1.66 ± .13	3.15 ± .25
Relative Trunk Height		36	30– 38	33.25 ± .21	1.85 ± .15	5.56 ± .44
Thoracic		35	58– 83	72.10 ± .61	5.38 ± .43	7.46 ± .60
Brachial		36	69– 86	79.72 ± .49	4.36 ± .35	5.47 ± .43
Tibio-Femoral		36	75–114	93.25 ± 1.04	9.25 ± .74	9.92 ± .79
Inter-Membral		36	88–107	96.06 ± .41	3.68 ± .29	3.83 ± .30
Cephalic		36	76– 91	84.22 ± .42	3.72 ± .30	4.42 ± .35
Length-Height		34	62– 87	73.92 ± .72	6.22 ± .51	8.41 ± .69
Breadth-Height		34	76–101	87.74 ± .85	7.34 ± .60	8.37 ± .68
Cephalo-Facial		35	87–100	90.98 ± .30	2.64 ± .21	2.90 ± .23
Fronto-Parietal		36	66– 83	72.50 ± .38	3.34 ± .27	4.61 ± .37
Zygo-Frontal		35	72– 87	79.64 ± .34	2.96 ± .24	3.72 ± .30
Zygo-Gonial		35	68– 83	77.88 ± .38	3.34 ± .27	4.29 ± .35
Facial		35	75– 95	86.20 ± .47	4.14 ± .33	4.80 ± .39
Upper Facial		35	49– 66	58.31 ± .39	3.45 ± .28	5.92 ± .48
Nasal		36	50– 79	67.22 ± .70	6.26 ± .50	9.31 ± .74
Nose Salient-Height		36	16– 36	26.66 ± .53	4.71 ± .37	17.67 ± 1.40
Nose Length-Height		36	92–101	96.94 ± .27	2.36 ± .19	2.43 ± .19

TABLE 48

MEANS OF YAMAGUCHI HAWAIIAN BORN—MALES

Measurement		No.	Range	Mean	S.D.	V.
Age		53	20– 49	25.50 ± .51	5.55 ± .51	21.76 ± 1.43
Weight	(lb.)	52	91–180	127.40 ± 1.62	17.30 ± 1.14	13.58 ± .90
Stature	(cm.)	53	151–177	163.37 ± .47	5.04 ± .33	3.08 ± .20
Sitting Height	(cm.)	53	78– 95	85.64 ± .32	3.44 ± .23	4.02 ± .26
Trunk Height	(cm.)	53	48– 63	54.04 ± .28	3.06 ± .20	5.66 ± .37
Upper Arm Length	(cm.)	52	27– 33	30.52 ± .13	1.44 ± .10	4.72 ± .31
Lower Arm Length	(cm.)	53	21– 28	24.32 ± .13	1.45 ± .09	5.96 ± .39
Hand Length	(cm.)	53	16– 19	17.77 ± .08	.84 ± .06	4.73 ± .31
Upper Leg Length	(cm.)	52	31– 44	38.34 ± .26	2.78 ± .18	7.25 ± .48
Lower Leg Length	(cm.)	53	29– 42	33.77 ± .21	2.24 ± .15	6.63 ± .43
Total Leg Length	(cm.)	53	69– 86	78.02 ± .33	3.56 ± .23	4.56 ± .30
Biacromion	(cm.)	53	37– 45	41.42 ± .16	1.76 ± .12	4.25 ± .28
Cristal Breadth	(cm.)	53	25– 33	28.74 ± .17	1.82 ± .12	6.33 ± .41
Chest Breadth	(cm.)	53	24– 31	27.06 ± .14	1.49 ± .10	5.51 ± .36
Chest Depth	(cm.)	53	16– 24	19.58 ± .16	1.76 ± .12	8.99 ± .59
Head Length	(mm.)	53	176–201	187.36 ± .52	5.64 ± .37	3.01 ± .20
Head Breadth	(mm.)	53	143–168	154.74 ± .47	5.08 ± .33	3.28 ± .21
Head Height	(cm.)	53	12– 16	13.87 ± .10	1.13 ± .07	8.15 ± .53
Minimum Frontal Diameter	(mm.)	53	97–123	112.16 ± .51	5.49 ± .36	4.89 ± .32
Bizygomatic Diameter	(mm.)	53	131–154	141.75 ± .44	4.71 ± .31	3.32 ± .22
Bigonial Diameter	(mm.)	53	94–125	111.08 ± .55	5.91 ± .39	5.32 ± .35
Total Face Height	(mm.)	52	109–132	121.82 ± .47	5.01 ± .33	4.11 ± .27
Upper Face Height	(mm.)	52	71– 94	81.76 ± .45	4.80 ± .32	5.87 ± .39
Forehead Height	(mm.)	52	42– 77	59.82 ± .66	7.02 ± .46	11.74 ± .78
Nose Height	(mm.)	53	42– 61	51.64 ± .30	3.20 ± .21	6.20 ± .41

		N	Range	Mean		
Nose Length	(mm.)	53	40– 59	49.74 ± .34	3.66 ± .24	7.36 ± .48
Nose Salient	(mm.)	53	10– 19	14.47 ± .20	2.21 ± .14	15.27 ± 1.00
Nose Breadth	(mm.)	53	28– 43	35.00 ± .28	3.04 ± .20	8.69 ± .57
Inter-Ocular	(mm.)	53	24– 41	31.02 ± .27	2.96 ± .19	9.54 ± .62
Bi-Ocular	(mm.)	53	90–109	101.14 ± .42	4.58 ± .30	4.53 ± .30
Index						
Relative Shoulder Breadth		53	23– 28	25.20 ± .11	1.20 ± .08	4.76 ± .31
Relative Hip Breadth		53	14– 21	17.60 ± .12	1.26 ± .08	7.16 ± .47
Shoulder-Hip		53	62– 82	69.27 ± .39	4.17 ± .27	6.02 ± .39
Relative Sitting Height		53	50– 56	52.34 ± .14	1.53 ± .10	2.92 ± .19
Relative Trunk Height		53	30– 37	33.00 ± .14	1.56 ± .10	4.73 ± .31
Thoracic		53	54– 85	72.42 ± .53	5.70 ± .37	7.87 ± .52
Brachial		52	69– 90	79.66 ± .43	4.60 ± .30	5.77 ± .38
Tibio-Femoral		52	70–124	89.00 ± .82	8.75 ± .58	9.83 ± .65
Inter-Membral		52	82–101	93.30 ± .33	3.48 ± .23	3.73 ± .25
Cephalic		53	74– 93	82.68 ± .33	3.60 ± .24	4.35 ± .28
Length-Height		53	62– 91	74.12 ± .57	6.14 ± .40	8.28 ± .54
Breadth-Height		53	76–107	89.64 ± .69	7.46 ± .49	8.32 ± .54
Cephalo-Facial		53	85–100	91.54 ± .28	3.00 ± .20	3.28 ± .21
Fronto-Parietal		53	62– 83	72.50 ± .36	3.90 ± .26	5.38 ± .35
Zygo-Frontal		53	72– 87	79.22 ± .29	3.10 ± .20	3.91 ± .26
Zygo-Gonial		53	70– 85	78.76 ± .28	3.06 ± .20	3.89 ± .25
Facial		52	75– 98	86.11 ± .40	4.26 ± .28	4.95 ± .33
Upper Facial		52	49– 69	57.86 ± .34	3.66 ± .24	6.33 ± .42
Nasal		53	58– 83	67.86 ± .62	6.68 ± .44	9.84 ± .64
Nose Salient-Height		53	19– 45	28.10 ± .41	4.47 ± .29	15.91 ± 1.04
Nose Length-Height		53	90–103	96.76 ± .31	3.30 ± .22	3.41 ± .22

TABLE 49

MEANS OF KYUSHU HAWAIIAN BORN—MALES

Measurement		No.	Range	Mean	S.D.	V.
Age		32	20– 44	25.60 ± .60	5.00 ± .42	19.53 ± 1.65
Weight	(lb.)	32	91–180	128.90 ± 2.37	19.90 ± 1.68	15.44 ± 1.30
Stature	(cm.)	32	151–174	163.25 ± .72	6.03 ± .51	3.69 ± .31
Sitting Height	(cm.)	32	78– 93	85.32 ± .50	4.18 ± .35	4.90 ± .41
Trunk Height	(cm.)	32	46– 61	53.68 ± .47	3.96 ± .33	7.38 ± .62
Upper Arm Length	(cm.)	31	26– 35	30.68 ± .27	2.24 ± .19	7.30 ± .63
Lower Arm Length	(cm.)	31	20– 28	24.45 ± .23	1.92 ± .16	7.85 ± .67
Hand Length	(cm.)	32	15– 19	17.59 ± .11	.89 ± .08	5.06 ± .43
Upper Leg Length	(cm.)	32	31– 46	37.88 ± .39	3.26 ± .27	8.61 ± .73
Lower Leg Length	(cm.)	32	29– 38	33.88 ± .24	2.03 ± .17	5.99 ± .50
Total Leg Length	(cm.)	32	69– 88	78.00 ± .50	4.16 ± .35	5.33 ± .45
Biacromion	(cm.)	32	38– 45	41.50 ± .23	1.92 ± .16	4.63 ± .39
Cristal Breadth	(cm.)	32	25– 33	29.47 ± .25	2.11 ± .18	7.16 ± .60
Chest Breadth	(cm.)	32	24– 39	27.56 ± .36	3.05 ± .26	11.07 ± .93
Chest Depth	(cm.)	32	17– 25	19.75 ± .22	1.87 ± .16	9.47 ± .80
Head Length	(mm.)	32	168–205	187.56 ± .94	7.92 ± .67	4.22 ± .36
Head Breadth	(mm.)	32	145–164	154.50 ± .67	5.66 ± .48	3.66 ± .31
Head Height	(cm.)	30	12– 15	13.67 ± .10	.83 ± .07	6.07 ± .53
Minimum Frontal Diameter	(mm.)	32	103–120	111.50 ± .42	3.51 ± .30	3.15 ± .27
Bizygomatic Diameter	(mm.)	32	131–148	140.64 ± .56	4.68 ± .39	3.33 ± .28
Bigonial Diameter	(mm.)	32	100–120	111.14 ± .49	4.08 ± .34	3.67 ± .31
Total Face Height	(mm.)	32	106–135	121.16 ± .62	5.19 ± .44	4.28 ± .36
Upper Face Height	(mm.)	32	67– 90	81.38 ± .59	4.92 ± .41	6.05 ± .51
Forehead Height	(mm.)	32	38– 77	57.62 ± .93	7.76 ± .65	13.47 ± 1.14
Nose Height	(mm.)	32	44– 61	51.68 ± .37	3.12 ± .26	6.04 ± .51

Nose Length	(mm.)	32	44– 59	50.26 ± .39	3.24 ± .27	6.45 ± .54
Nose Salient	(mm.)	32	10– 19	14.47 ± .28	2.36 ± .20	16.31 ± 1.38
Nose Breadth	(mm.)	32	30– 39	34.00 ± .29	2.40 ± .20	7.06 ± .60
Inter-Ocular	(mm.)	32	25– 39	31.06 ± .42	3.52 ± .30	11.33 ± .96
Bi-Ocular	(mm.)	32	92–109	100.44 ± .56	4.66 ± .39	4.64 ± .39
Index						
Relative Shoulder Breadth		32	23– 28	25.32 ± .12	1.04 ± .09	4.11 ± .35
Relative Hip Breadth		32	16– 21	17.82 ± .15	1.28 ± .11	7.18 ± .61
Shoulder-Hip		32	65– 79	70.98 ± .46	3.87 ± .33	5.45 ± .46
Relative Sitting Height		32	49– 56	52.19 ± .22	1.84 ± .16	3.53 ± .30
Relative Trunk Height		32	29– 37	32.84 ± .24	2.01 ± .17	6.12 ± .52
Thoracic		32	56– 85	71.88 ± .71	5.98 ± .50	8.32 ± .70
Brachial		31	71– 90	79.96 ± .55	4.50 ± .39	5.63 ± .48
Tibio-Femoral		32	75–104	90.45 ± .83	7.00 ± .59	7.74 ± .65
Inter-Membral		31	82–103	92.56 ± .59	4.88 ± .42	5.27 ± .45
Cephalic		32	74– 91	82.68 ± .52	4.34 ± .37	5.25 ± .44
Length-Height		30	64– 87	73.36 ± .61	4.98 ± .43	6.79 ± .59
Breadth-Height		30	76–103	88.56 ± .75	6.12 ± .53	6.91 ± .60
Cephalo-Facial		32	85– 98	91.06 ± .28	2.34 ± .20	2.57 ± .22
Fronto-Parietal		32	66– 79	72.32 ± .33	2.80 ± .24	3.87 ± .33
Zygo-Frontal		32	72– 85	79.50 ± .34	2.82 ± .24	3.55 ± .30
Zygo-Gonial		32	74– 85	79.00 ± .27	2.30 ± .19	2.91 ± .25
Facial		32	78– 95	86.23 ± .54	4.50 ± .38	5.22 ± .44
Upper Facial		32	49– 69	57.68 ± .48	4.05 ± .34	7.02 ± .59
Nasal		32	54– 77	65.62 ± .74	6.24 ± .53	9.51 ± .80
Nose Salient-Height		32	16– 36	27.02 ± .50	4.20 ± .35	15.54 ± 1.31
Nose Length-Height		32	88–101	97.12 ± .33	2.80 ± .24	2.88 ± .24

TABLE 50

MEANS OF 'OTHER JAPAN' HAWAIIAN BORN—MALES

Measurement	No.	Range	Mean
Age	6	20– 29	22.85
Weight	6	101–160	127.20
Stature	6	160–171	166.01
Sitting Height	6	88– 95	90.16
Trunk Height	6	54– 61	57.84
Upper Arm Length	6	28– 31	30.17
Lower Arm Length	6	24– 25	24.50
Hand Length	6	18– 19	18.33
Upper Leg Length	6	33– 40	36.50
Lower Leg Length	6	32– 35	33.50
Total Leg Length	6	71– 80	76.16
Biacromion	6	39– 44	41.67
Cristal Breadth	6	26– 32	28.33
Chest Breadth	6	26– 29	27.67
Chest Depth	6	17– 21	19.83
Head Length	6	176–195	187.84
Head Breadth	6	145–162	155.16
Head Height (cm.)	5	11– 14	13.00
Minimum Frontal Diameter	6	106–117	112.49
Bizygomatic Diameter	6	134–154	143.49
Bigonial Diameter	6	106–123	112.01
Total Face Height	6	115–138	125.51
Upper Face Height	6	81– 90	85.84
Forehead Height	6	61– 81	67.49
Nose Height	6	50– 59	54.16
Nose Length	6	48– 57	51.84
Nose Salient	6	14– 18	15.67
Nose Breadth	6	30– 37	34.84
Inter-Ocular	6	28– 36	32.00
Bi-Ocular	6	96–107	101.50
Index			
Relative Shoulder Breadth	6	23– 26	25.16
Relative Hip Breadth	6	16– 19	16.84
Shoulder-Hip	6	62– 76	67.50
Relative Sitting Height	6	53– 56	54.17
Relative Trunk Height	6	34– 36	34.83
Thoracic	6	64– 79	71.50
Brachial	6	79– 86	82.16
Tibio-Femoral	6	85– 99	91.15
Inter-Membral	6	88–101	95.84
Cephalic	6	76– 87	83.16

[TABLE 5—*continued*]

MEANS OF 'OTHER JAPAN' HAWAIIAN BORN—MALES

Index	No.	Range	Mean
Length-Height	5	56– 79	68.90
Breadth-Height	5	68– 93	84.50
Cephalo-Facial	6	89– 96	92.16
Fronto-Parietal	6	70– 75	72.84
Zygo-Frontal	6	76– 85	79.16
Zygo-Gonial	6	70– 83	78.50
Facial	6	84– 92	87.49
Upper Facial	6	58– 63	61.01
Nasal	6	62– 75	65.16
Nose Salient-Height	6	25– 33	29.00
Nose Length-Height	6	94– 99	96.16

TABLE 51

DIFFERENCES OF HIROSHIMA HAWAIIAN BORN FROM TOTAL
HAWAIIAN BORN—MALES

Measurement	Difference	x p.e.
Age	− .95 ± .60	1.58
Weight	−1.90 ± 2.16	.88
Stature	− .75 ± .59	1.27
Sitting Height	− .32 ± .42	.76
Trunk Height	− .28 ± .37	.76
Upper Arm Length	.34 ± .20	1.70
Lower Arm Length	.22 ± .17	1.29
Hand Length	.00 ± .10	.00
Upper Leg Length	− .84 ± .36	2.33
Lower Leg Length	.04 ± .24	.17
Total Leg Length	− .94 ± .46	2.04
Biacromion	− .44 ± .20	2.20
Cristal Breadth	− .34 ± .22	1.55
Chest Breadth	.00 ± .23	.00
Chest Depth	.04 ± .20	.20
Head Length	−2.26 ± .74	3.05
Head Breadth	.20 ± .65	.31
Head Height	− .06 ± .13	.46
Minimum Frontal Diameter	.03 ± .56	.05
Bizygomatic Diameter	− .09 ± .61	.15
Bigonial Diameter	−1.02 ± .65	1.57
Total Face Height	.42 ± .64	.66
Upper Face Height	.82 ± .56	1.46
Forehead Height	2.16 ± .84	2.57
Nose Height	.18 ± .38	.47
Nose Length	.12 ± .40	.30
Nose Salient	− .26 ± .27	.96
Nose Breadth	.28 ± .31	.90
Inter-Ocular	.98 ± .39	2.51
Bi-Ocular	− .32 ± .58	.55
Index		
Relative Shoulder Breadth	− .06 ± .13	.46
Relative Hip Breadth	− .10 ± .14	.71
Shoulder-Hip	.00 ± .50	.00
Relative Sitting Height	.29 ± .20	1.45
Relative Trunk Height	.07 ± .20	.35
Thoracic	.04 ± .65	.06
Brachial	− .10 ± .50	.20
Tibio-Femoral	2.30 ± .96	2.40
Inter-Membral	2.16 ± .46	4.70

[TABLE 51—*continued*]

DIFFERENCES OF HIROSHIMA HAWAIIAN BORN FROM TOTAL
HAWAIIAN BORN—MALES

Index	Difference	x p.e.
Cephalic	.90 ± .46	1.96
Length-Height	.56 ± .71	.79
Breadth-Height	− .58 ± .83	.70
Cephalo-Facial	− .16 ± .34	.47
Fronto-Parietal	− .08 ± .38	.21
Zygo-Frontal	− .02 ± .33	.06
Zygo-Gonial	− .72 ± .35	2.06
Facial	.06 ± .52	.12
Upper Facial	.57 ± .45	1.27
Nasal	.40 ± .69	.58
Nose Salient-Height	− .66 ± .52	1.27
Nose Length-Height	− .22 ± .33	.67

TABLE 52

DIFFERENCES OF YAMAGUCHI HAWAIIAN BORN FROM TOTAL
HAWAIIAN BORN—MALES

Measurement	Difference	x p.e.
Age	− .65 ± .50	1.30
Weight	.00 ± 1.75	.00
Stature	.54 ± .49	1.10
Sitting Height	.16 ± .34	.47
Trunk Height	− .08 ± .31	.26
Upper Arm Length	.00 ± .16	.00
Lower Arm Length	.01 ± .14	.07
Hand Length	− .04 ± .08	.50
Upper Leg Length	.62 ± .30	2.07
Lower Leg Length	− .16 ± .20	.80
Total Leg Length	.58 ± .38	1.53
Biacromion	.07 ± .16	.44
Cristal Breadth	− .49 ± .18	2.72
Chest Breadth	− .22 ± .19	1.16
Chest Depth	− .07 ± .17	.41
Head Length	.82 ± .61	1.34
Head Breadth	− .34 ± .54	.63
Head Height	.19 ± .10	1.90
Minimum Frontal Diameter	− .30 ± .46	.65
Bizygomatic Diameter	.39 ± .49	.80
Bigonial Diameter	.15 ± .53	.28
Total Face Height	.06 ± .53	.11
Upper Face Height	.14 ± .47	.30
Forehead Height	.72 ± .70	1.03
Nose Height	− .18 ± .31	.58
Nose Length	− .48 ± .33	1.45
Nose Salient	.35 ± .22	1.59
Nose Breadth	.44 ± .26	1.69
Inter-Ocular	− .31 ± .32	.97
Bi-Ocular	1.00 ± .47	2.13
Index		
Relative Shoulder Breadth	− .18 ± .11	1.64
Relative Hip Breadth	− .28 ± .11	2.55
Shoulder-Hip	−1.35 ± .41	3.29
Relative Sitting Height	− .12 ± .17	.71
Relative Trunk Height	− .18 ± .16	1.12
Thoracic	.36 ± .53	.68
Brachial	− .16 ± .42	.38
Tibio-Femoral	−1.95 ± .80	2.44
Inter-Membral	− .60 ± .38	1.58

[TABLE 52—*continued*]

DIFFERENCES OF YAMAGUCHI HAWAIIAN BORN FROM TOTAL
HAWAIIAN BORN—MALES

Index	Difference	x p.e.
Cephalic	$-$ .64 $\pm$ .38	1.68
Length-Height	.76 $\pm$ .57	1.33
Breadth-Height	1.32 $\pm$ .66	2.00
Cephalo-Facial	.40 $\pm$ .27	1.48
Fronto-Parietal	$-$ .08 $\pm$ .31	.26
Zygo-Frontal	$-$ .44 $\pm$ .27	1.63
Zygo-Gonial	.16 $\pm$ .28	.57
Facial	$-$ .03 $\pm$ .43	.07
Upper Facial	.12 $\pm$ .37	.32
Nasal	1.04 $\pm$ .57	1.82
Nose Salient-Height	.78 $\pm$ .43	1.81
Nose Length-Height	$-$ .40 $\pm$ .27	1.48

TABLE 53

DIFFERENCES OF KYUSHU HAWAIIAN BORN FROM TOTAL HAWAIIAN
BORN—MALES

Measurement	Difference	x p.e.
Age	− .55 ± .64	.86
Weight	1.50 ± 2.23	.67
Stature	.42 ± .63	.67
Sitting Height	− .16 ± .44	.36
Trunk Height	− .44 ± .40	1.10
Upper Arm Length	.16 ± .21	.76
Lower Arm Length	− .14 ± .19	.74
Hand Length	− .22 ± .10	2.20
Upper Leg Length	.16 ± .38	.42
Lower Leg Length	− .05 ± .25	.20
Total Leg Length	.56 ± .49	1.14
Biacromion	.15 ± .21	.71
Cristal Breadth	.24 ± .24	1.00
Chest Breadth	.28 ± .24	1.17
Chest Depth	.10 ± .21	.48
Head Length	1.02 ± .78	1.31
Head Breadth	− .58 ± .69	.84
Head Height	− .01 ± .13	.80
Minimum Frontal Diameter	− .96 ± .59	1.63
Bizygomatic Diameter	− .72 ± .63	1.14
Bigonial Diameter	.21 ± .69	.30
Total Face Height	− .60 ± .68	.88
Upper Face Height	− .24 ± .60	.40
Forehead Height	−1.48 ± .89	1.66
Nose Height	− .14 ± .40	.35
Nose Length	.04 ± .43	.09
Nose Salient	.35 ± .28	1.25
Nose Breadth	− .56 ± .33	1.70
Inter-Ocular	− .27 ± .42	.64
Bi-Ocular	.30 ± .61	.49
Index		
Relative Shoulder Breadth	− .06 ± .14	.43
Relative Hip Breadth	− .06 ± .15	.40
Shoulder-Hip	.36 ± .52	.69
Relative Sitting Height	− .27 ± .21	1.29
Relative Trunk Height	− .34 ± .21	1.62
Thoracic	− .18 ± .68	.26
Brachial	.14 ± .54	.26
Tibio-Femoral	− .50 ± 1.01	.50
Inter-Membral	−1.34 ± .50	2.68

[TABLE 53—*continued*]

DIFFERENCES OF KYUSHU HAWAIIAN BORN FROM TOTAL HAWAIIAN
BORN—MALES

Index	Difference	x p.e.
Cephalic	— .64 ± .48	1.33
Length-Height	.00 ± .76	.00
Breadth-Height	.24 ± .88	.27
Cephalo-Facial	— .08 ± .35	.23
Fronto-Parietal	— .26 ± .40	.65
Zygo-Frontal	— .16 ± .34	.47
Zygo-Gonial	.40 ± .36	1.11
Facial	.09 ± .55	.16
Upper Facial	— .06 ± .47	.13
Nasal	—1.20 ± .73	1.64
Nose Salient-Height	— .30 ± .55	.55
Nose Length-Height	— .04 ± .35	.11

TABLE 54

DISTRIBUTION OF THE X P.E.'S OF THE DIFFERENCES BETWEEN THE PREFECTURAL GROUPS OF HAWAIIAN BORN MALES AND THE TOTAL MALE HAWAIIAN BORN

		0–.99	1.00–1.99	2.00–2.99	3.00–3.99	4.00–4.99	5.00–5.99	6.00–X
Hiroshima Hawaiian Born / Total Hawaiian born	Measurements	17	6	5	1	0	0	0
	Indices	14	4	2	0	1	0	0
Yamaguchi Hawaiian Born / Total Hawaiian Born	Measurements	17	9	3	0	0	0	0
	Indices	7	10	3	1	0	0	0
Kyushu Hawaiian Born / Total Hawaiian Born	Measurements	18	10	1	0	0	0	0
	Indices	15	5	1	0	0	0	0

TABLE 55

DIFFERENCES OF MEANS OF HAWAIIAN BORN MALES BY PREFECTURE

Hiroshima
Yamaguchi

Measurement	Difference	x p.e.
Age	.30 ± .74	.41
Weight	1.90 ± 2.55	.74
Stature	1.29 ± .75	1.72
Sitting Height	.48 ± .51	.94
Trunk Height	.20 ± .46	.43
Upper Arm Length	− .34 ± .22	1.55
Lower Arm Length	− .21 ± .18	1.17
Hand Length	− .04 ± .13	.31
Upper Leg Length	1.46 ± .48	3.04
Lower Leg Length	− .20 ± .32	.62
Total Leg Length	1.52 ± .57	2.67
Biacromion	.51 ± .23	2.22
Cristal Breadth	− .15 ± .27	.56
Chest Breadth	− .22 ± .24	.92
Chest Depth	− .11 ± .29	.38
Head Length	3.08 ± .83	3.71
Head Breadth	− .54 ± .74	.73
Head Height	.25 ± .17	1.47
Minimum Frontal Diameter	− .33 ± .76	.43
Bizygomatic Diameter	.48 ± .71	.68
Bigonial Diameter	1.17 ± .87	1.34
Total Face Height	− .36 ± .79	.46
Upper Face Height	− .68 ± .69	.99
Forehead Height	−1.44 ± 1.01	1.43
Nose Height	− .36 ± .50	.72
Nose Length	− .60 ± .51	1.18
Nose Salient	.61 ± .32	1.91
Nose Breadth	.16 ± .45	.36
Inter-Ocular	−1.29 ± .51	2.53
Bi-Ocular	1.32 ± .70	1.89

Index		
Relative Shoulder Breadth	− .12 ± .16	.75
Relative Hip Breadth	− .18 ± .18	1.00
Shoulder-Hip	−1.35 ± .63	2.14
Relative Sitting Height	− .41 ± .24	1.71
Relative Trunk Height	− .25 ± .25	1.00
Thoracic	.32 ± .81	.40
Brachial	− .06 ± .65	.09

[*Continued*]

[TABLE 55—*continued*]

DIFFERENCES OF MEANS OF HAWAIIAN BORN MALES BY PREFECTURE

Hiroshima
Yamaguchi

Index	Difference	x p.e.
Tibio-Femoral	−4.25 ± 1.32	3.22
Inter-Membral	−2.76 ± .53	5.21
Cephalic	−1.54 ± .53	2.91
Length-Height	.20 ± .92	.22
Breadth-Height	1.90 ± 1.10	1.73
Cephalo-Facial	.56 ± .41	1.37
Fronto-Parietal	.00 ± .52	.00
Zygo-Frontal	− .42 ± .45	.93
Zygo-Gonial	.88 ± .47	1.87
Facial	− .09 ± .62	.15
Upper Facial	− .45 ± .52	.87
Nasal	.64 ± .94	.68
Nose Salient-Height	1.44 ± .67	2.15
Nose Length-Height	− .18 ± .41	.44

TABLE 56

DIFFERENCES OF MEANS OF HAWAIIAN BORN MALES BY PREFECTURE

Hiroshima
Kyushu

Measurement	Difference	x p.e.
Age	− .40 ± .80	.50
Weight	−3.40 ± 3.08	1.10
Stature	−1.17 ± .92	1.27
Sitting Height	− .16 ± .64	.25
Trunk Height	.16 ± .60	.27
Upper Arm Length	.18 ± .32	.56
Lower Arm Length	.08 ± .26	.31
Hand Length	.22 ± .15	1.47
Upper Leg Length	−1.00 ± .56	1.79
Lower Leg Length	.09 ± .34	.26
Total Leg Length	−1.50 ± .68	2.21
Biacromion	− .59 ± .29	2.03
Cristal Breadth	− .58 ± .33	1.76
Chest Breadth	− .28 ± .41	.68
Chest Depth	− .06 ± .33	.18
Head Length	−3.28 ± 1.14	2.88
Head Breadth	.78 ± .88	.89
Head Height	− .05 ± .17	.29
Minimum Frontal Diameter	.99 ± .70	1.41
Bizygomatic Diameter	.63 ± .79	.80
Bigonial Diameter	−1.23 ± .84	1.46
Total Face Height	1.02 ± .88	1.16
Upper Face Height	1.06 ± .79	1.34
Forehead Height	3.64 ± 1.21	3.01
Nose Height	.32 ± .54	.59
Nose Length	.08 ± .54	.15
Nose Salient	− .61 ± .38	1.61
Nose Breadth	.84 ± .45	1.87
Inter-Ocular	1.25 ± .60	2.08
Bi-Ocular	− .62 ± .79	.78
Index		
Relative Shoulder Breadth	.00 ± .16	.00
Relative Hip Breadth	− .04 ± .21	.19
Shoulder-Hip	− .36 ± .68	.53
Relative Sitting Height	.56 ± .29	1.93
Relative Trunk Height	.41 ± .32	1.28
Thoracic	.22 ± .94	.23
Brachial	− .24 ± .74	.32

[Continued]

[TABLE 56—*continued*]

DIFFERENCES OF MEANS OF HAWAIIAN BORN MALES BY PREFECTURE

<u>Hiroshima</u>
Kyushu

Index	Difference	x p.e.
Tibio-Femoral	2.80 ± 1.33	2.11
Inter-Membral	3.50 ± .72	4.86
Cephalic	1.54 ± .67	2.30
Length-Height	.56 ± .94	.60
Breadth-Height	− .82 ± 1.13	.73
Cephalo-Facial	− .08 ± .41	.20
Fronto-Parietal	.18 ± .50	.36
Zygo-Frontal	.14 ± .48	.29
Zygo-Gonial	−1.12 ± .47	2.38
Facial	− .03 ± .72	.04
Upper Facial	.63 ± .62	1.02
Nasal	1.60 ± 1.02	1.57
Nose Salient-Height	− .36 ± .73	.49
Nose Length-Height	− .18 ± .43	.42

TABLE 57

DIFFERENCES OF MEANS OF HAWAIIAN BORN MALES BY PREFECTURE

Yamaguchi
Kyushu

Measurement	Difference	x p.e.
Age	− .10 ± .79	.13
Weight	−1.50 ± 2.87	.52
Stature	.12 ± .86	.14
Sitting Height	.32 ± .59	.54
Trunk Height	.36 ± .55	.65
Upper Arm Length	− .16 ± .30	.53
Lower Arm Length	− .13 ± .26	.50
Hand Length	.18 ± .14	1.29
Upper Leg Length	.46 ± .47	.98
Lower Leg Length	− .11 ± .32	.34
Total Leg Length	.02 ± .60	.03
Biacromion	− .08 ± .28	.29
Cristal Breadth	− .73 ± .30	2.43
Chest Breadth	− .50 ± .39	1.28
Chest Depth	− .17 ± .27	.63
Head Length	− .20 ± 1.07	.19
Head Breadth	.24 ± .82	.29
Head Height	.20 ± .14	1.43
Minimum Frontal Diameter	.66 ± .66	1.00
Bizygomatic Diameter	1.11 ± .71	1.56
Bigonial Diameter	− .06 ± .74	.08
Total Face Height	.66 ± .78	.85
Upper Face Height	.38 ± .74	.51
Forehead Height	2.20 ± 1.14	1.93
Nose Height	− .04 ± .48	.08
Nose Length	− .52 ± .52	1.00
Nose Salient	.00 ± .34	.00
Nose Breadth	1.00 ± .40	2.50
Inter-Ocular	− .04 ± .50	.08
Bi-Ocular	.70 ± .70	1.00
Index		
Relative Shoulder Breadth	− .12 ± .16	.75
Relative Hip Breadth	− .22 ± .19	1.16
Shoulder-Hip	−1.71 ± .60	2.85
Relative Sitting Height	.15 ± .26	.58
Relative Trunk Height	.16 ± .28	.57
Thoracic	.54 ± .89	.61
Brachial	− .30 ± .70	.43

[*Continued*]

[TABLE 57—*continued*]

DIFFERENCES OF MEANS OF HAWAIIAN BORN MALES BY PREFECTURE

Yamaguchi
—————
Kyushu

Index	Difference	x p.e.
Tibio-Femoral	−1.45 ± 1.17	1.24
Inter-Membral	.74 ± .68	1.09
Cephalic	.00 ± .62	.00
Length-Height	.76 ± .83	.92
Breadth-Height	1.08 ± 1.02	1.06
Cephalo-Facial	.48 ± .40	1.20
Fronto-Parietal	.18 ± .49	.37
Zygo-Frontal	− .28 ± .45	.62
Zygo-Gonial	− .24 ± .39	.62
Facial	− .12 ± .67	.18
Upper Facial	.18 ± .59	.30
Nasal	2.24 ± .97	2.31
Nose Salient-Height	1.08 ± .65	1.66
Nose Length-Height	− .36 ± .45	.80

TABLE 58

DISTRIBUTION OF THE X P.E.'S OF THE DIFFERENCES BETWEEN THE VARIOUS PREFECTURAL GROUPS OF HAWAIIAN BORN MALES

		0–99	1.00–1.99	2.00–2.99	3.00–3.99	4.00–4.99	5.00–5.99	6.00–X
Hiroshima	Measurements	15	9	3	2	0	0	0
Yamaguchi	Indices	10	6	3	1	0	1	0
Hiroshima	Measurements	13	11	4	1	0	0	0
Kyushu	Indices	13	4	3	0	1	0	0
Yamaguchi	Measurements	19	8	2	0	0	0	0
Kyushu	Indices	13	6	2	0	0	0	0

TABLE 59

MEANS OF HIROSHIMA SEDENTES—FEMALES

Measurement		No.	Range	Mean	S.D.	V.
Age		27	20– 64	39.60 ± 1.75	13.45 ± 1.23	33.96 ± 3.12
Weight	(lb.)	26	69–116	99.94 ± 1.48	11.16 ± 1.04	11.17 ± 1.04
Stature	(cm.)	27	139–159	146.00 ± .57	4.41 ± .40	3.02 ± .28
Sitting Height	(cm.)	27	74– 85	78.58 ± .42	3.24 ± .30	4.12 ± .38
Trunk Height	(cm.)	27	44– 57	50.72 ± .33	2.58 ± .24	5.09 ± .47
Upper Arm Length	(cm.)	27	24– 30	26.96 ± .19	1.45 ± .13	5.38 ± .49
Lower Arm Length	(cm.)	27	20– 24	21.19 ± .14	1.09 ± .10	5.14 ± .47
Hand Length	(cm.)	27	15– 18	16.11 ± .10	.74 ± .07	4.59 ± .42
Upper Leg Length	(cm.)	27	27– 40	33.42 ± .37	2.86 ± .26	8.56 ± .79
Lower Leg Length	(cm.)	27	24– 34	28.70 ± .24	1.86 ± .17	6.48 ± .59
Total Leg Length	(cm.)	27	63– 74	67.42 ± .40	3.10 ± .28	4.60 ± .42
Biacromion	(cm.)	27	32– 38	35.19 ± .16	1.24 ± .11	3.52 ± .32
Cristal Breadth	(cm.)	26	26– 30	28.35 ± .18	1.36 ± .13	4.80 ± .45
Chest Breadth	(cm.)	27	23– 28	25.22 ± .20	1.55 ± .14	6.15 ± .56
Head Length	(mm.)	23	172–191	183.02 ± .70	4.98 ± .50	2.72 ± .27
Head Breadth	(mm.)	27	135–156	145.06 ± .64	4.90 ± .45	3.38 ± .31
Head Height	(cm.)	27	10– 16	12.30 ± .17	1.30 ± .12	10.57 ± .97
Minimum Frontal Diameter	(mm.)	27	103–120	110.90 ± .49	3.81 ± .35	3.44 ± .32
Bizygomatic Diameter	(mm.)	27	125–145	135.33 ± .55	4.20 ± .39	3.10 ± .28
Bigonial Diameter	(mm.)	27	88–114	103.67 ± .70	5.43 ± .50	5.24 ± .48
Total Face Height	(mm.)	27	100–129	112.55 ± .91	7.02 ± .64	6.24 ± .57
Upper Face Height	(mm.)	27	65– 82	70.68 ± .53	4.08 ± .37	5.77 ± .53
Forehead Height	(mm.)	26	42– 73	57.02 ± .87	6.60 ± .62	11.57 ± 1.08
Nose Height	(mm.)	27	42– 55	48.64 ± .40	3.08 ± .28	6.33 ± .58
Nose Length	(mm.)	27	38– 51	45.38 ± .43	3.32 ± .30	7.32 ± .67

Index		N	Range	Mean ±	S.D. ±	C.V. ±
Nose Salient	(mm.)	27	10– 17	13.26 ± .24	1.84 ± .17	13.88 ± 1.27
Nose Breadth	(mm.)	27	28– 39	33.62 ± .33	2.56 ± .23	7.61 ± .70
Inter-Ocular	(mm.)	26	28– 38	31.88 ± .35	2.62 ± .24	8.22 ± .77
Bi-Ocular	(mm.)	26	88–105	97.26 ± .65	4.88 ± .46	5.02 ± .47
Index						
Relative Shoulder Breadth		27	21– 26	24.02 ± .15	1.16 ± .11	4.83 ± .44
Relative Hip Breadth		26	18– 21	19.42 ± .13	1.00 ± .09	5.15 ± .48
Shoulder-Hip		26	74– 88	80.76 ± .56	4.23 ± .40	5.24 ± .49
Relative Sitting Height		27	50– 57	53.81 ± .22	1.72 ± .16	3.20 ± .29
Relative Trunk Height		27	30– 38	34.67 ± .22	1.66 ± .15	4.79 ± .44
Brachial		27	69– 88	79.28 ± .59	4.56 ± .42	5.75 ± .53
Tibio-Femoral		27	70–124	87.95 ± 1.55	11.95 ± 1.10	13.59 ± 1.25
Inter-Membral		27	84–103	95.38 ± .61	4.70 ± .43	4.93 ± .45
Cephalic		23	72– 87	79.54 ± .48	3.42 ± .34	4.30 ± .43
Length-Height		23	56– 85	67.64 ± 1.00	7.10 ± .71	10.50 ± 1.04
Breadth-Height		27	68–111	84.88 ± 1.27	9.76 ± .90	11.50 ± 1.06
Cephalo-Facial		27	87–100	93.42 ± .39	3.00 ± .28	3.21 ± .29
Fronto-Parietal		27	70– 87	76.58 ± .47	3.64 ± .33	4.75 ± .44
Zygo-Frontal		27	74– 87	81.84 ± .46	3.56 ± .33	4.35 ± .40
Zygo-Gonial		27	68– 83	76.50 ± .46	3.52 ± .32	4.60 ± .42
Facial		27	75– 98	83.44 ± .70	5.37 ± .49	6.44 ± .59
Upper Facial		27	43– 60	52.10 ± .42	3.27 ± .30	6.28 ± .58
Nasal		27	54– 83	68.94 ± .86	6.66 ± .61	9.66 ± .89
Nose Salient-Height		27	19– 36	26.99 ± .46	3.54 ± .32	13.12 ± 1.20
Nose Length-Height		27	84–103	94.06 ± .48	3.66 ± .34	3.89 ± .36

TABLE 60

MEANS OF YAMAGUCHI SEDENTES—FEMALES

Measurement		No.	Range	Mean	S.D.	V.
Age		16	20– 59	40.10 ± 1.84	10.90 ± 1.30	27.18 ± 3.24
Weight	(lb.)	11	93–176	110.50 ± 4.17	20.52 ± 2.95	18.57 ± 2.67
Stature	(cm.)	16	139–153	147.32 ± .64	3.81 ± .45	2.59 ± .31
Sitting Height	(cm.)	16	76– 85	80.12 ± .41	2.46 ± .29	3.07 ± .37
Trunk Height	(cm.)	16	44– 57	51.62 ± .43	2.56 ± .31	4.96 ± .59
Upper Arm Length	(cm.)	16	25– 30	27.06 ± .21	1.25 ± .15	4.62 ± .55
Lower Arm Length	(cm.)	16	18– 24	21.00 ± .26	1.54 ± .18	7.33 ± .87
Hand Length	(cm.)	16	15– 17	16.25 ± .11	.66 ± .08	4.06 ± .48
Upper Leg Length	(cm.)	16	25– 40	32.50 ± .66	3.94 ± .47	12.12 ± 1.44
Lower Leg Length	(cm.)	16	26– 32	28.69 ± .24	1.40 ± .17	4.88 ± .58
Total Leg Length	(cm.)	16	61– 74	67.38 ± .59	3.50 ± .30	5.19 ± .62
Biacromion	(cm.)	16	34– 41	36.44 ± .32	1.87 ± .22	5.13 ± .61
Cristal Breadth	(cm.)	16	27– 33	29.94 ± .26	1.52 ± .18	5.08 ± .61
Chest Breadth	(cm.)	16	23– 31	25.69 ± .30	1.79 ± .21	6.97 ± .83
Head Length	(mm.)	15	172–189	179.56 ± .78	4.50 ± .55	2.51 ± .31
Head Breadth	(mm.)	16	141–152	147.26 ± .48	2.82 ± .34	1.91 ± .23
Head Height	(cm.)	16	10– 15	11.88 ± .24	1.45 ± .17	12.21 ± 1.46
Minimum Frontal Diameter	(mm.)	16	97–114	106.43 ± .76	4.53 ± .54	4.26 ± .51
Bizygomatic Diameter	(mm.)	16	128–139	134.64 ± .44	2.58 ± .31	1.92 ± .23
Bigonial Diameter	(mm.)	16	88–108	101.57 ± .80	4.77 ± .57	4.70 ± .56
Total Face Height	(mm.)	16	100–120	111.14 ± 1.01	5.97 ± .71	5.37 ± .64
Upper Face Height	(mm.)	16	57– 76	66.88 ± .82	4.88 ± .58	7.30 ± .87
Forehead Height	(mm.)	16	46– 73	58.50 ± 1.25	7.40 ± .88	12.65 ± 1.51
Nose Height	(mm.)	16	40– 53	46.74 ± .55	3.24 ± .39	6.93 ± .83
Nose Length	(mm.)	16	34– 49	43.26 ± .61	3.60 ± .43	8.32 ± .99

Nose Salient (mm.)	16	12– 16	13.75 ± .22	1.30 ± .15	9.45 ± 1.13
Nose Breadth (mm.)	16	32– 35	33.26 ± .17	.98 ± .12	2.95 ± .35
Inter-Ocular (mm.)	16	28– 34	30.81 ± .39	2.30 ± .27	7.47 ± .89
Bi-Ocular (mm.)	16	88–105	96.62 ± .69	4.10 ± .49	4.24 ± .51
Index					
Relative Shoulder Breadth	16	23– 28	24.88 ± .20	1.16 ± .14	4.66 ± .56
Relative Hip Breadth	16	18– 23	20.38 ± .22	1.32 ± .16	6.48 ± .77
Shoulder-Hip	16	74– 91	81.93 ± .77	4.59 ± .55	5.60 ± .67
Relative Sitting Height	16	51– 58	54.38 ± .30	1.80 ± .21	3.31 ± .39
Relative Trunk Height	16	30– 40	35.12 ± .36	2.12 ± .25	6.04 ± .72
Brachial	16	69– 86	77.62 ± .72	4.28 ± .51	5.51 ± .66
Tibio-Femoral	16	65–109	88.55 ± 1.95	11.55 ± 1.38	13.04 ± 1.55
Inter-Membral	16	86–103	95.88 ± .72	4.28 ± .51	4.46 ± .53
Cephalic	15	76– 85	82.10 ± .41	2.34 ± .29	2.85 ± .35
Length-Height	15	54– 83	65.96 ± 1.41	8.08 ± .99	12.25 ± 1.51
Breadth-Height	16	66–103	80.74 ± 1.68	9.94 ± 1.19	12.31 ± 1.47
Cephalo-Facial	15	87– 94	90.96 ± .30	1.70 ± .21	1.87 ± .23
Fronto-Parietal	16	66– 77	72.12 ± .50	2.94 ± .35	4.08 ± .49
Zygo-Frontal	16	72– 85	79.00 ± .60	3.58 ± .43	4.53 ± .54
Zygo-Gonial	16	62– 81	75.12 ± .74	4.40 ± .52	5.86 ± .70
Facial	16	75– 89	82.00 ± .64	3.81 ± .45	4.65 ± .55
Upper Facial	16	43– 57	49.82 ± .58	3.42 ± .41	6.86 ± .82
Nasal	16	62– 85	71.38 ± .88	5.24 ± .62	7.34 ± .88
Nose Salient-Height	16	25– 36	29.18 ± .42	2.49 ± .30	8.53 ± 1.02
Nose Length-Height	16	88–101	92.26 ± .65	3.86 ± .46	4.18 ± .50

TABLE 61

MEANS OF KYUSHU SEDENTES—FEMALES

Measurement		No.	Range	Mean	S.D.	V.
Age		18	20– 59	36.60 ± 2.07	13.05 ± 1.47	35.56 ± 4.00
Weight	(lb.)	12	69–140	106.54 ± 2.92	15.00 ± 2.07	14.08 ± 1.94
Stature	(cm.)	18	136–156	146.84 ± .81	5.07 ± .57	3.45 ± .39
Sitting Height	(cm.)	18	74– 85	79.94 ± .51	3.18 ± .36	3.98 ± .45
Trunk Height	(cm.)	18	46– 57	52.06 ± .40	2.54 ± .29	4.88 ± .55
Upper Arm Length	(cm.)	18	26– 30	27.83 ± .18	1.12 ± .13	4.02 ± .45
Lower Arm Length	(cm.)	18	20– 23	21.06 ± .14	.85 ± .10	4.04 ± .45
Hand Length	(cm.)	18	14– 17	15.83 ± .12	.76 ± .09	4.80 ± .54
Upper Leg Length	(cm.)	18	27– 38	32.06 ± .44	2.74 ± .31	8.55 ± .96
Lower Leg Length	(cm.)	18	27– 31	29.61 ± .18	1.16 ± .13	3.92 ± .44
Total Leg Length	(cm.)	18	59– 72	66.94 ± .59	3.70 ± .42	5.53 ± .62
Biacromion	(cm.)	18	35– 39	37.17 ± .17	1.07 ± .12	2.88 ± .32
Cristal Breadth	(cm.)	18	26– 34	29.89 ± .28	1.76 ± .20	5.89 ± .66
Chest Breadth	(cm.)	18	23– 31	27.56 ± .31	1.92 ± .22	6.97 ± .78
Head Length	(mm.)	17	170–199	182.98 ± 1.09	6.66 ± .77	3.64 ± .42
Head Breadth	(mm.)	18	137–154	143.84 ± .77	4.82 ± .54	3.35 ± .38
Head Height	(cm.)	18	11– 13	12.06 ± .14	.91 ± .10	7.55 ± .85
Minimum Frontal Diameter	(mm.)	18	103–114	107.51 ± .45	2.85 ± .32	2.65 ± .30
Bizygomatic Diameter	(mm.)	18	122–142	133.68 ± .64	4.05 ± .46	3.03 ± .34
Bigonial Diameter	(mm.)	18	91–108	101.99 ± .71	4.47 ± .50	4.38 ± .49
Total Face Height	(mm.)	18	100–126	111.50 ± .87	5.49 ± .62	4.92 ± .55
Upper Face Height	(mm.)	18	63– 78	69.62 ± .54	3.42 ± .38	4.91 ± .55
Forehead Height	(mm.)	18	46– 77	58.18 ± 1.18	7.40 ± .83	12.72 ± 1.43
Nose Height	(mm.)	18	40– 53	46.84 ± .45	2.84 ± .32	6.06 ± .68
Nose Length	(mm.)	18	36– 49	43.94 ± .57	3.58 ± .40	8.15 ± .92

Nose Salient	(mm.)	18	11– 16	13.17 ± .19	1.17 ± .13	8.88 ± 1.00
Nose Breadth	(mm.)	18	28– 37	33.72 ± .30	1.90 ± .21	5.63 ± .63
Inter-Ocular	(mm.)	18	24– 35	31.17 ± .47	2.98 ± .33	9.56 ± 1.07
Bi-Ocular	(mm.)	18	86–105	97.38 ± .66	4.18 ± .47	4.29 ± .48
Index						
Relative Shoulder Breadth		18	23– 28	25.50 ± .15	.94 ± .11	3.69 ± .41
Relative Hip Breadth		18	18– 23	20.38 ± .20	1.24 ± .14	6.08 ± .68
Shoulder-Hip		18	71– 91	80.34 ± .70	4.41 ± .50	5.49 ± .62
Relative Sitting Height		18	52– 58	54.39 ± .24	1.50 ± .17	2.76 ± .31
Relative Trunk Height		18	34– 39	35.61 ± .21	1.34 ± .15	3.76 ± .42
Brachial		18	71– 82	75.84 ± .45	2.84 ± .32	3.74 ± .42
Tibio-Femoral		18	75–124	93.65 ± 1.54	9.70 ± 1.09	10.36 ± 1.16
Inter-Membral		18	90–107	96.72 ± .76	4.80 ± .54	4.96 ± .56
Cephalic		17	70– 85	78.38 ± .61	3.72 ± .43	4.75 ± .55
Length-Height		17	56– 75	66.50 ± .88	5.40 ± .62	8.12 ± .94
Breadth-Height		18	72– 93	84.62 ± .96	6.06 ± .68	7.16 ± .80
Cephalo-Facial		18	87–102	93.16 ± .59	3.74 ± .42	4.01 ± .45
Fronto-Parietal		18	68– 83	75.06 ± .54	3.38 ± .38	4.50 ± .51
Zygo-Frontal		18	74– 85	80.16 ± .41	2.60 ± .29	3.24 ± .36
Zygo-Gonial		18	68– 81	76.38 ± .48	3.02 ± .34	3.95 ± .44
Facial		18	75– 95	83.68 ± .75	4.71 ± .53	5.63 ± .63
Upper Facial		18	46– 60	52.01 ± .48	3.00 ± .34	5.77 ± .65
Nasal		18	60– 83	72.28 ± .92	5.76 ± .65	7.97 ± .90
Nose Salient-Height		18	22– 36	28.16 ± .41	2.61 ± .29	9.27 ± 1.04
Nose Length-Height		18	82–101	94.28 ± .67	4.20 ± .47	4.45 ± .50

TABLE 62

MEANS OF 'OTHER JAPAN' SEDENTES—FEMALES

Measurement		No.	Range	Mean	S.D.	V.
Age		16	20– 64	41.05 ± 1.84	10.90 ± 1.30	26.55 ± 3.17
Weight	(lb.)	13	81–128	107.74 ± 2.18	11.64 ± 1.54	10.80 ± 1.43
Stature	(cm.)	16	136–156	145.07 ± .73	4.35 ± .52	3.00 ± .36
Sitting Height	(cm.)	16	72– 81	76.12 ± .51	3.02 ± .36	3.97 ± .47
Trunk Height	(cm.)	16	44– 53	48.88 ± .48	2.84 ± .34	5.81 ± .69
Upper Arm Length	(cm.)	16	23– 30	27.00 ± .34	2.03 ± .24	7.52 ± .90
Lower Arm Length	(cm.)	16	19– 23	20.94 ± .23	1.35 ± .16	6.45 ± .77
Hand Length	(cm.)	16	16– 18	16.31 ± .10	.58 ± .07	3.56 ± .42
Upper Leg Length	(cm.)	16	27– 40	33.88 ± .50	2.94 ± .35	8.68 ± 1.03
Lower Leg Length	(cm.)	16	25– 33	29.69 ± .37	2.20 ± .26	7.41 ± .88
Total Leg Length	(cm.)	16	59– 74	67.88 ± .54	3.18 ± .38	4.68 ± .56
Biacromion	(cm.)	16	32– 39	35.94 ± .28	1.68 ± .20	4.67 ± .56
Cristal Breadth	(cm.)	16	26– 32	28.56 ± .29	1.73 ± .21	6.06 ± .72
Chest Breadth	(cm.)	16	23– 28	25.38 ± .24	1.45 ± .17	5.71 ± .68
Head Length	(mm.)	15	168–199	183.56 ± 1.42	8.16 ± 1.00	4.45 ± .55
Head Breadth	(mm.)	16	137–154	145.88 ± .82	4.86 ± .58	3.33 ± .40
Head Height	(cm.)	16	9– 15	12.94 ± .26	1.56 ± .19	12.06 ± 1.44
Minimum Frontal Diameter	(mm.)	16	103–120	110.57 ± .70	4.14 ± .49	3.74 ± .45
Bizygomatic Diameter	(mm.)	16	125–139	132.75 ± .63	3.75 ± .45	2.82 ± .34
Bigonial Diameter	(mm.)	16	94–114	101.36 ± .85	5.07 ± .60	5.00 ± .60
Total Face Height	(mm.)	16	106–126	113.75 ± 1.02	6.03 ± .72	5.30 ± .63
Upper Face Height	(mm.)	16	63– 78	72.00 ± .61	3.64 ± .43	5.06 ± .60
Forehead Height	(mm.)	16	46– 77	60.74 ± 1.25	7.44 ± .89	12.25 ± 1.46
Nose Height	(mm.)	16	42– 57	49.26 ± .65	3.86 ± .46	7.84 ± .93
Nose Length	(mm.)	16	40– 53	46.62 ± .57	3.36 ± .40	7.21 ± .86

Nose Salient	(mm.)	16	10–15	12.50 ± .27	1.58 ± .19	12.64 ± 1.51
Nose Breadth	(mm.)	16	26–37	32.00 ± .46	2.70 ± .32	8.44 ± 1.01
Inter-Ocular	(mm.)	16	24–33	29.56 ± .43	2.57 ± .31	8.69 ± 1.04
Bi-Ocular	(mm.)	16	88–103	97.00 ± .54	3.20 ± .38	3.30 ± .39
Index						
Relative Shoulder Breadth		16	21–28	25.12 ± .24	1.44 ± .17	5.73 ± .68
Relative Hip Breadth		16	18–23	19.88 ± .23	1.36 ± .16	6.84 ± .82
Shoulder-Hip		16	71–85	79.32 ± .64	3.81 ± .45	4.80 ± .57
Relative Sitting Height		16	50–57	52.81 ± .27	1.59 ± .19	3.01 ± .36
Relative Trunk Height		16	30–37	33.81 ± .31	1.81 ± .22	5.35 ± .64
Brachial		16	69–92	81.26 ± .89	5.28 ± .63	6.50 ± .77
Tibio-Femoral		16	70–114	88.55 ± 1.70	10.10 ± 1.20	11.41 ± 1.36
Inter-Membral		16	86–103	93.12 ± .81	4.78 ± .57	5.13 ± .61
Cephalic		15	72–91	79.70 ± .93	5.36 ± .66	6.73 ± .83
Length-Height		15	46–83	70.24 ± 1.66	9.52 ± 1.17	13.55 ± 1.67
Breadth-Height		16	64–105	88.12 ± 1.74	10.30 ± 1.23	11.69 ± 1.39
Cephalo-Facial		16	85–96	91.00 ± .39	2.30 ± .27	2.53 ± .30
Fronto-Parietal		16	72–81	75.88 ± .41	2.42 ± .29	3.19 ± .38
Zygo-Frontal		16	78–89	83.26 ± .45	2.64 ± .31	3.17 ± .38
Zygo-Gonial		16	68–85	76.50 ± .75	4.42 ± .53	5.78 ± .69
Facial		16	78–92	85.36 ± .71	4.23 ± .50	4.96 ± .59
Upper Facial		16	46–60	54.32 ± .51	3.00 ± .36	5.52 ± .66
Nasal		16	54–79	65.74 ± 1.20	7.10 ± .85	10.80 ± 1.29
Nose Salient-Height		16	19–33	25.43 ± .57	3.39 ± .40	13.33 ± 1.59
Nose Length-Height		16	92–101	95.62 ± .32	1.88 ± .22	1.97 ± .23

TABLE 63

DIFFERENCES OF HIROSHIMA SEDENTES AND TOTAL SEDENTES—FEMALES

Measurement	Difference	x p.e.
Age	1.00 ± 1.62	.62
Weight	−4.44 ± 1.92	2.31
Stature	.00 ± .58	.00
Sitting Height	− .28 ± .43	.65
Trunk Height	− .24 ± .37	.65
Upper Arm Length	.08 ± .20	.40
Lower Arm Length	.18 ± .16	1.12
Hand Length	.01 ± .09	.11
Upper Leg Length	.74 ± .43	1.72
Lower Leg Length	− .39 ± .22	1.77
Total Leg Length	.34 ± .43	.79
Biacromion	− .86 ± .21	4.10
Cristal Breadth	− .75 ± .23	3.26
Chest Breadth	− .63 ± .25	2.52
Head Length	.62 ± .86	.72
Head Breadth	− .18 ± .61	.30
Head Height (cm.)	.09 ± .18	.50
Minimum Frontal Diameter	1.95 ± .55	3.55
Bizygomatic Diameter	1.11 ± .52	2.13
Bigonial Diameter	1.26 ± .64	1.97
Total Face Height	.63 ± .82	.77
Upper Face Height	1.10 ± .58	1.90
Forehead Height	−1.56 ± .93	1.68
Nose Height	.84 ± .44	1.91
Nose Length	.68 ± .49	1.39
Nose Salient	.01 ± .21	.05
Nose Breadth	.44 ± .31	1.42
Inter-Ocular	.81 ± .37	2.19
Bi-Ocular	.76 ± .58	1.31
Index		
Relative Shoulder Breadth	− .78 ± .17	4.59
Relative Hip Breadth	− .52 ± .17	3.06
Shoulder-Hip	− .06 ± .59	.10
Relative Sitting Height	− .24 ± .23	1.04
Relative Trunk Height	− .26 ± .23	1.13
Brachial	.66 ± .62	1.06
Tibio-Femoral	−2.30 ± 1.51	1.52
Inter-Membral	− .16 ± .60	.27
Cephalic	− .18 ± .54	.33
Length-Height	.50 ± 1.08	.46
Breadth-Height	.80 ± 1.22	.66

[TABLE 63—*continued*]

DIFFERENCES OF HIROSHIMA SEDENTES AND TOTAL SEDENTES—FEMALES

Index	Difference	x p.e.
Cephalo-Facial	.98 ± .39	2.51
Fronto-Parietal	1.38 ± .47	2.94
Zygo-Frontal	.70 ± .45	1.56
Zygo-Gonial	.22 ± .49	.45
Facial	.09 ± .62	.15
Upper Facial	.06 ± .47	.13
Nasal	− .82 ± .87	.94
Nose Salient-Height	− .63 ± .44	1.43
Nose Length-Height	.14 ± .48	.29

TABLE 64

DIFFERENCES OF YAMAGUCHI SEDENTES AND TOTAL SEDENTES—FEMALES

Measurement	Difference	x p.e.
Age	1.50 ± 2.10	.71
Weight	6.12 ± 2.95	2.07
Stature	1.32 ± .76	1.74
Sitting Height	1.26 ± .56	2.25
Trunk Height	.66 ± .48	1.38
Upper Arm Length	.18 ± .26	.69
Lower Arm Length	− .01 ± .21	.05
Hand Length	.15 ± .12	1.25
Upper Leg Length	− .18 ± .56	.32
Lower Leg Length	− .40 ± .28	1.43
Total Leg Length	.30 ± .56	.54
Biacromion	.39 ± .27	1.44
Cristal Breadth	.84 ± .29	2.90
Chest Breadth	− .16 ± .32	.50
Head Length	−2.84 ± 1.07	2.65
Head Breadth	2.02 ± .79	2.56
Head Height (cm.)	− .33 ± .23	1.43
Minimum Frontal Diameter	−2.52 ± .71	3.55
Bizygomatic Diameter	.42 ± .67	.63
Bigonial Diameter	− .84 ± .83	1.01
Total Face Height	− .78 ± 1.07	.73
Upper Face Height	−2.70 ± .76	3.55
Forehead Height	− .08 ± 1.18	.07
Nose Height	−1.06 ± .57	1.86
Nose Length	−1.44 ± .64	2.25
Nose Salient	.50 ± .28	1.79
Nose Breadth	.08 ± .40	.20
Inter-Ocular	− .26 ± .47	.55
Bi-Ocular	.12 ± .74	.16
Index		
Relative Shoulder Breadth	.08 ± .22	.36
Relative Hip Breadth	.44 ± .21	2.10
Shoulder-Hip	1.11 ± .75	1.48
Relative Sitting Height	.33 ± .30	1.10
Relative Trunk Height	.19 ± .30	.63
Brachial	−1.00 ± .80	1.25
Tibio-Femoral	−1.70 ± 1.96	.87
Inter-Membral	.34 ± .78	.44
Cephalic	2.38 ± .67	3.55
Length-Height	−1.18 ± 1.34	.88
Breadth-Height	−3.34 ± 1.59	2.10

[TABLE 64—*continued*]

DIFFERENCES OF YAMAGUCHI SEDENTES AND TOTAL SEDENTES—FEMALES

Index	Difference	x p.e.
Cephalo-Facial	$-1.48 \pm .53$	2.79
Fronto-Parietal	$-3.08 \pm .61$	5.05
Zygo-Frontal	$-2.14 \pm .58$	3.69
Zygo-Gonial	$-1.16 \pm .63$	1.84
Facial	$-1.35 \pm .80$	1.69
Upper Facial	$-2.22 \pm .61$	3.64
Nasal	1.62 ± 1.13	1.43
Nose Salient-Height	$1.56 \pm .58$	2.69
Nose Length-Height	$-1.66 \pm .62$	2.68

TABLE 65

DIFFERENCES OF KYUSHU SEDENTES AND TOTAL SEDENTES—FEMALES

Measurement	Difference	x p.e.
Age	−2.00 ± 1.98	1.01
Weight	2.16 ± 2.83	.76
Stature	.84 ± .72	1.17
Sitting Height	1.08 ± .53	2.04
Trunk Height	1.10 ± .45	2.44
Upper Arm Length	.95 ± .25	3.80
Lower Arm Length	.05 ± .20	.25
Hand Length	− .27 ± .11	2.45
Upper Leg Length	− .62 ± .52	1.19
Lower Leg Length	.52 ± .27	1.93
Total Leg Length	− .14 ± .53	.26
Biacromion	1.12 ± .25	4.48
Cristal Breadth	.79 ± .28	2.82
Chest Breadth	1.71 ± .30	5.70
Head Length	.58 ± 1.00	.58
Head Breadth	−1.40 ± .75	1.87
Head Height (cm.)	− .15 ± .22	.68
Minimum Frontal Diameter	−1.44 ± .67	2.15
Bizygomatic Diameter	− .54 ± .63	.86
Bigonial Diameter	− .42 ± .78	.54
Total Face Height	− .42 ± 1.01	.42
Upper Face Height	.04 ± .72	.06
Forehead Height	− .40 ± 1.11	.36
Nose Height	− .96 ± .54	1.78
Nose Length	− .76 ± .60	1.27
Nose Salient	− .08 ± .26	.31
Nose Breadth	.54 ± .38	1.42
Inter-Ocular	.10 ± .44	.23
Bi-Ocular	.88 ± .70	1.26
Index		
Relative Shoulder Breadth	.70 ± .20	3.50
Relative Hip Breadth	.44 ± .20	2.20
Shoulder-Hip	− .48 ± .71	.68
Relative Sitting Height	.34 ± .28	1.21
Relative Trunk Height	.68 ± .28	2.43
Brachial	−2.78 ± .75	3.71
Tibio-Femoral	3.40 ± 1.84	1.85
Inter-Membral	1.18 ± .74	1.59
Cephalic	−1.34 ± .62	2.16
Length-Height	− .64 ± 1.26	.51
Breadth-Height	.54 ± 1.50	.36

[TABLE 65—*continued*]

DIFFERENCES OF KYUSHU SEDENTES AND TOTAL SEDENTES—FEMALES

Index	Difference	x p.e.
Cephalo-Facial	.72 ± .48	1.50
Fronto-Parietal	— .14 ± .58	.24
Zygo-Frontal	— .98 ± .55	1.78
Zygo-Gonial	.10 ± .59	.17
Facial	.33 ± .76	.43
Upper Facial	— .03 ± .57	.05
Nasal	2.52 ± 1.06	2.38
Nose Salient-Height	.54 ± .54	1.00
Nose Length-Height	.36 ± .59	.61

TABLE 66

DIFFERENCES OF 'OTHER JAPAN' SEDENTES AND TOTAL SEDENTES—FEMALES

Measurement	Difference	x p.e.
Age	2.45 ± 2.10	1.17
Weight	3.36 ± 2.45	1.37
Stature	− .93 ± .76	1.22
Sitting Height	−2.74 ± .56	4.89
Trunk Height	−2.08 ± .48	4.33
Upper Arm Length	.12 ± .26	.46
Lower Arm Length	− .07 ± .21	.33
Hand Length	.21 ± .12	1.75
Upper Leg Length	1.20 ± .56	2.14
Lower Leg Length	.60 ± .28	2.14
Total Leg Length	.80 ± .56	1.43
Biacromion	− .11 ± .27	.41
Cristal Breadth	− .54 ± .29	1.86
Chest Breadth	− .47 ± .32	1.47
Head Length	1.16 ± 1.07	1.08
Head Breadth	.64 ± .79	.81
Head Height (cm.)	.73 ± .23	3.17
Minimum Frontal Diameter	1.62 ± .71	2.28
Bizygomatic Diameter	−1.47 ± .67	2.19
Bigonial Diameter	−1.05 ± .83	1.26
Total Face Height	1.83 ± 1.07	1.71
Upper Face Height	2.42 ± .76	3.18
Forehead Height	2.16 ± 1.18	1.83
Nose Height	1.46 ± .57	2.56
Nose Length	1.92 ± .64	3.00
Nose Salient	− .75 ± .28	2.68
Nose Breadth	−1.18 ± .40	2.95
Inter-Ocular	−1.51 ± .47	3.21
Bi-Ocular	.50 ± .74	.68

Index		
Relative Shoulder Breadth	.32 ± .22	1.45
Relative Hip Breadth	− .06 ± .21	.29
Shoulder-Hip	−1.50 ± .75	2.00
Relative Sitting Height	−1.24 ± .30	4.13
Relative Trunk Height	−1.12 ± .30	3.73
Brachial	2.64 ± .80	3.30
Tibio-Femoral	−1.70 ± 1.96	.87
Inter-Membral	−2.42 ± .78	3.10
Cephalic	− .02 ± .67	.03
Length-Height	3.10 ± 1.34	2.31
Breadth-Height	4.04 ± 1.59	2.54

[TABLE 66—*continued*]

Index	Difference	x p.e.
Cephalo-Facial	$-1.44 \pm .51$	2.82
Fronto-Parietal	$.68 \pm .61$	1.11
Zygo-Frontal	$2.12 \pm .58$	3.66
Zygo-Gonial	$.22 \pm .63$	.35
Facial	$2.01 \pm .80$	2.51
Upper Facial	$2.28 \pm .61$	3.74
Nasal	-4.02 ± 1.13	3.56
Nose Salient-Height	$-2.19 \pm .58$	3.78
Nose Length-Height	$1.70 \pm .62$	2.74

TABLE 67

DISTRIBUTION OF THE x P.E.'s OF THE DIFFERENCES BETWEEN THE PREFECTURAL GROUPS OF FEMALE SEDENTES AND THE TOTAL FEMALE SEDENTES

		0–99	1.00–1.99	2.00–2.99	3.00–3.99	4.00–4.99	5.00–5.99	6.00–X
Hiroshima Sedentes / Total Sedentes	Measurements	11	10	4	2	1	0	0
	Indices	10	6	2	1	1	0	0
Yamaguchi Sedentes / Total Sedentes	Measurements	11	9	6	2	0	0	0
	Indices	5	6	5	3	0	1	0
Kyushu Sedentes / Total Sedentes	Measurements	12	8	5	1	1	1	0
	Indices	8	6	4	2	0	0	0
'Other Japan' Sedentes / Total Sedentes	Measurements	5	10	7	4	2	0	0
	Indices	4	2	6	7	1	0	0

TABLE 68

DIFFERENCES OF MEANS OF FEMALE SEDENTES BY PREFECTURE

Hiroshima
Yamaguchi

Measurement	Difference	x p.e.
Age	.50 ± 2.54	.20
Weight	10.56 ± 4.42	2.39
Stature	1.32 ± .86	1.53
Sitting Height	1.54 ± .59	2.61
Trunk Height	.90 ± .54	1.67
Upper Arm Length	.10 ± .28	.36
Lower Arm Length	— .19 ± .30	.63
Hand Length	.14 ± .15	.93
Upper Leg Length	— .92 ± .76	1.21
Lower Leg Length	— .01 ± .34	.03
Total Leg Length	— .04 ± .71	.06
Biacromion	1.25 ± .36	3.47
Cristal Breadth	1.59 ± .32	4.97
Chest Breadth	.47 ± .36	1.31
Head Length	— 3.46 ± 1.05	3.30
Head Breadth	2.20 ± .80	2.75
Head Height	— .42 ± .29	1.45
Minimum Frontal Diameter	— 4.47 ± .90	4.97
Bizygomatic Diameter	— .69 ± .70	.99
Bigonial Diameter	— 2.10 ± 1.06	1.98
Total Face Height	— 1.41 ± 1.36	1.04
Upper Face Height	— 3.80 ± .98	3.88
Forehead Height	1.48 ± 1.52	.97
Nose Height	— 1.90 ± .68	2.79
Nose Length	— 2.12 ± .75	2.83
Nose Salient	.49 ± .33	1.48
Nose Breadth	— .36 ± .37	.97
Inter-Ocular	— 1.07 ± .52	2.06
Bi-Ocular	— .64 ± .95	.67
Index		
Relative Shoulder Breadth	.86 ± .25	3.44
Relative Hip Breadth	.96 ± .26	3.69
Shoulder-Hip	1.17 ± .95	1.23
Relative Sitting Height	.57 ± .37	1.54
Relative Trunk Height	.45 ± .42	1.07
Brachial	— 1.66 ± .93	1.78
Tibio-Femoral	.60 ± 2.49	.24
Inter-Membral	.50 ± .94	.53

[*Continued*]

[TABLE 68—*continued*]

DIFFERENCES OF MEANS OF FEMALE SEDENTES BY PREFECTURE

Hiroshima
Yamaguchi

Index	Difference	x p.e.
Cephalic	2.56 ± .63	4.06
Length-Height	— 1.68 ± 1.73	.97
Breadth-Height	— 4.14 ± 2.11	1.96
Cephalo-Facial	— 2.46 ± .49	5.02
Fronto-Parietal	— 4.46 ± .69	6.46
Zygo-Frontal	— 2.84 ± .76	3.74
Zygo-Gonial	— 1.38 ± .87	1.59
Facial	— 1.44 ± .95	1.52
Upper Facial	— 2.28 ± .72	3.17
Nasal	2.44 ± 1.23	1.98
Nose Salient-Height	2.19 ± .62	3.53
Nose Length-Height	— 1.80 ± .81	2.22

TABLE 69

DIFFERENCES OF MEANS OF FEMALE SEDENTES BY PREFECTURE

Hiroshima
Kyushu

Measurement	Difference	x p.e.
Age	3.00 ± 2.71	1.11
Weight	−6.60 ± 3.27	2.02
Stature	− .84 ± .99	.85
Sitting Height	−1.36 ± .66	2.06
Trunk Height	−1.34 ± .52	2.58
Upper Arm Length	− .87 ± .26	3.35
Lower Arm Length	.13 ± .20	.65
Hand Length	.28 ± .16	1.75
Upper Leg Length	1.36 ± .57	2.39
Lower Leg Length	− .91 ± .30	3.03
Total Leg Length	.48 ± .71	.68
Biacromion	−1.98 ± .23	8.61
Cristal Breadth	−1.54 ± .33	4.67
Chest Breadth	−2.34 ± .37	6.32
Head Length	.04 ± 1.30	.03
Head Breadth	1.22 ± 1.00	1.22
Head Height	.24 ± .22	1.09
Minimum Frontal Diameter	3.39 ± .67	5.06
Bizygomatic Diameter	1.65 ± .84	1.96
Bigonial Diameter	1.68 ± 1.00	1.68
Total Face Height	1.05 ± 1.26	.83
Upper Face Height	1.06 ± .76	1.39
Forehead Height	−1.16 ± 1.47	.79
Nose Height	1.80 ± .60	3.00
Nose Length	1.44 ± .71	2.03
Nose Salient	.09 ± .31	.29
Nose Breadth	− .10 ± .45	.22
Inter-Ocular	.71 ± .59	1.20
Bi-Ocular	− .12 ± .93	.13
Index		
Relative Shoulder Breadth	−1.48 ± .21	7.05
Relative Hip Breadth	− .96 ± .24	4.00
Shoulder-Hip	.42 ± .90	.47
Relative Sitting Height	− .58 ± .33	1.76
Relative Trunk Height	− .94 ± .30	3.13
Brachial	3.44 ± .74	4.65
Tibio-Femoral	−5.70 ± 2.18	2.61
Inter-Membral	−1.34 ± .97	1.38

[*Continued*]

[TABLE 69—*continued*]

DIFFERENCES OF MEANS OF FEMALE SEDENTES BY PREFECTURE

Hiroshima
———————
Kyushu

Index	Difference	x p.e.
Cephalic	1.16 ± .78	1.49
Length-Height	1.14 ± 1.33	.86
Breadth-Height	.26 ± 1.59	.16
Cephalo-Facial	.26 ± .71	.37
Fronto-Parietal	1.52 ± .72	2.11
Zygo-Frontal	1.68 ± .62	2.71
Zygo-Gonial	.12 ± .66	.18
Facial	− .24 ± 1.02	.24
Upper Facial	.09 ± .64	.14
Nasal	−3.34 ± 1.26	2.65
Nose Salient-Height	−1.17 ± .62	1.89
Nose Length-Height	− .22 ± .82	.27

TABLE 70

DIFFERENCES OF MEANS OF FEMALE SEDENTES BY PREFECTURE

Hiroshima
——————
'Other Japan'

Measurement	Difference	x p.e.
Age	-1.45 ± 2.54	.57
Weight	-7.80 ± 2.63	2.97
Stature	$.93 \pm .93$	1.00
Sitting Height	$2.46 \pm .66$	3.73
Trunk Height	$1.84 \pm .58$	3.17
Upper Arm Length	$- .04 \pm .39$	.10
Lower Arm Length	$.25 \pm .27$	.93
Hand Length	$- .20 \pm .14$	1.43
Upper Leg Length	$- .46 \pm .62$	.74
Lower Leg Length	$- .99 \pm .44$	2.25
Total Leg Length	$- .46 \pm .67$	.69
Biacromion	$- .75 \pm .32$	2.34
Cristal Breadth	$- .21 \pm .34$	.62
Chest Breadth	$- .16 \pm .31$	.52
Head Length	$- .54 \pm 1.58$	.34
Head Breadth	$- .82 \pm 1.04$	.79
Head Height	$- .64 \pm .31$	2.06
Minimum Frontal Diameter	$.33 \pm .85$	.39
Bizygomatic Diameter	$2.58 \pm .84$	3.07
Bigonial Diameter	2.31 ± 1.10	2.10
Total Face Height	-1.20 ± 1.37	.88
Upper Face Height	$-1.32 \pm .81$	1.63
Forehead Height	-3.72 ± 1.52	2.45
Nose Height	$- .62 \pm .76$	.82
Nose Length	$-1.24 \pm .71$	1.75
Nose Salient	$.76 \pm .36$	2.11
Nose Breadth	$1.62 \pm .57$	2.84
Inter-Ocular	$2.32 \pm .55$	4.22
Bi-Ocular	$.26 \pm .84$	.31

Index		
Relative Shoulder Breadth	$-1.10 \pm .28$	3.93
Relative Hip Breadth	$- .46 \pm .26$	1.77
Shoulder-Hip	$1.44 \pm .85$	1.69
Relative Sitting Height	$1.00 \pm .35$	2.86
Relative Trunk Height	$.86 \pm .38$	2.26
Brachial	-1.98 ± 1.07	1.85
Tibio-Femoral	$- .60 \pm 2.30$	.26
Inter-Membral	2.26 ± 1.01	2.24

[Continued]

[TABLE 70—*continued*]

DIFFERENCES OF MEANS OF FEMALE SEDENTES BY PREFECTURE

<u>Hiroshima</u>

'Other Japan'

Index	Difference	x p.e.
Cephalic	− .16 ± 1.05	.15
Length-Height	−2.60 ± 1.94	1.34
Breadth-Height	−3.24 ± 2.15	1.51
Cephalo-Facial	2.42 ± .55	4.40
Fronto-Parietal	.70 ± .62	1.13
Zygo-Frontal	−1.42 ± .64	2.22
Zygo-Gonial	.00 ± .88	.00
Facial	−1.92 ± 1.00	1.92
Upper Facial	−2.22 ± .66	3.36
Nasal	3.20 ± 1.48	2.16
Nose Salient-Height	1.56 ± .73	2.14
Nose Length-Height	−1.56 ± .58	2.69

TABLE 71

DIFFERENCES OF MEANS OF FEMALE SEDENTES BY PREFECTURE

Yamaguchi
Kyushu

Measurement	Difference	x p.e.
Age	3.50 ± 2.77	1.26
Weight	3.96 ± 5.09	.78
Stature	.48 ± 1.03	.47
Sitting Height	.18 ± .65	.28
Trunk Height	— .44 ± .59	.75
Upper Arm Length	— .77 ± .28	2.75
Lower Arm Length	— .06 ± .30	.20
Hand Length	.42 ± .16	2.62
Upper Leg Length	.44 ± .79	.56
Lower Leg Length	— .92 ± .30	3.07
Total Leg Length	.44 ± .83	.53
Biacromion	— .73 ± .36	2.03
Cristal Breadth	.05 ± .38	.13
Chest Breadth	—1.87 ± .43	4.35
Head Length	—3.42 ± 1.34	2.55
Head Breadth	3.42 ± .91	3.76
Head Height	— .18 ± .28	.64
Minimum Frontal Diameter	—1.08 ± .88	1.23
Bizygomatic Diameter	.96 ± .78	1.23
Bigonial Diameter	— .42 ± 1.07	.39
Total Face Height	— .36 ± 1.33	.27
Upper Face Height	—2.74 ± .98	2.80
Forehead Height	.32 ± 1.72	.19
Nose Height	— .10 ± .71	.14
Nose Length	— .68 ± .83	.82
Nose Salient	.58 ± .29	2.00
Nose Breadth	— .46 ± .34	1.35
Inter-Ocular	— .36 ± .61	.59
Bi-Ocular	— .76 ± .95	.80
Index		
Relative Shoulder Breadth	— .62 ± .25	2.48
Relative Hip Breadth	.00 ± .30	.00
Shoulder-Hip	1.59 ± 1.04	1.53
Relative Sitting Height	— .01 ± .38	.03
Relative Trunk Height	— .49 ± .42	1.17
Brachial	1.78 ± .85	2.09
Tibio-Femoral	—5.10 ± 2.48	2.06
Inter-Membral	— .84 ± 1.05	.80

[Continued]

[TABLE 71—*continued*]

DIFFERENCES OF MEANS OF FEMALE SEDENTES BY PREFECTURE

Yamaguchi
—————
Kyushu

Index	Difference	x p.e.
Cephalic	3.72 ± .73	5.10
Length-Height	− .54 ± 1.66	.33
Breadth-Height	−3.88 ± 1.93	2.01
Cephalo-Facial	−2.20 ± .66	3.33
Fronto-Parietal	−2.94 ± .74	3.97
Zygo-Frontal	−1.16 ± .73	1.59
Zygo-Gonial	−1.26 ± .88	1.43
Facial	−1.68 ± .99	1.70
Upper Facial	−2.19 ± .75	2.92
Nasal	− .90 ± 1.27	.71
Nose Salient-Height	1.02 ± .59	1.73
Nose Length-Height	−2.02 ± .93	2.17

TABLE 72

DIFFERENCES OF MEANS OF FEMALE SEDENTES BY PREFECTURE

Yamaguchi
'Other Japan'

Measurement	Difference	x p.e.
Age	− .95 ± 2.60	.37
Weight	2.76 ± 4.71	.59
Stature	2.25 ± .97	2.32
Sitting Height	4.00 ± .65	6.15
Trunk Height	2.74 ± .64	4.28
Upper Arm Length	.06 ± .40	.15
Lower Arm Length	.06 ± .35	.17
Hand Length	− .06 ± .15	.40
Upper Leg Length	−1.38 ± .83	1.66
Lower Leg Length	−1.00 ± .44	2.27
Total Leg Length	− .50 ± .80	.62
Biacromion	.50 ± .43	1.16
Cristal Breadth	1.38 ± .39	3.54
Chest Breadth	.31 ± .38	.82
Head Length	−4.00 ± 1.62	2.47
Head Breadth	1.38 ± .95	1.45
Head Height	−1.06 ± .35	3.03
Minimum Frontal Diameter	−4.14 ± 1.03	4.02
Bizygomatic Diameter	1.89 ± .77	2.45
Bigonial Diameter	.21 ± 1.17	.18
Total Face Height	−2.61 ± 1.44	1.81
Upper Face Height	−5.12 ± 1.02	5.02
Forehead Height	−2.24 ± 1.77	1.27
Nose Height	−2.52 ± .85	2.96
Nose Length	−3.36 ± .83	4.05
Nose Salient	1.25 ± .35	3.57
Nose Breadth	1.26 ± .49	2.57
Inter-Ocular	1.25 ± .58	2.16
Bi-Ocular	− .38 ± .88	.43
Index		
Relative Shoulder Breadth	− .24 ± .31	.77
Relative Hip Breadth	.50 ± .32	1.56
Shoulder-Hip	2.61 ± 1.00	2.61
Relative Sitting Height	1.57 ± .40	3.92
Relative Trunk Height	1.31 ± .48	2.73
Brachial	−3.64 ± 1.14	3.19
Tibio-Femoral	.00 ± 2.59	.00
Inter-Membral	2.76 ± 1.08	2.56

[Continued]

[TABLE 72—*continued*]

DIFFERENCES OF MEANS OF FEMALE SEDENTES BY PREFECTURE

Yamaguchi
'Other Japan'

Index	Difference	x p.e.
Cephalic	2.40 ± 1.01	2.38
Length-Height	−4.28 ± 2.18	1.96
Breadth-Height	−7.38 ± 2.42	3.05
Cephalo-Facial	− .04 ± .49	.08
Fronto-Parietal	−3.76 ± .65	5.78
Zygo-Frontal	−4.26 ± .75	5.68
Zygo-Gonial	−1.38 ± 1.05	1.31
Facial	−3.36 ± .96	3.50
Upper Facial	−4.50 ± .77	5.84
Nasal	5.64 ± 1.49	3.79
Nose Salient-Height	3.75 ± .71	5.28
Nose Length-Height	−3.36 ± .72	4.67

TABLE 73

DIFFERENCES OF MEANS OF FEMALE SEDENTES BY PREFECTURE

Kyushu

'Other Japan'

Measurement	Difference	x p.e.
Age	−4.45 ± 2.77	1.61
Weight	−1.20 ± 3.64	.33
Stature	1.77 ± 1.09	1.62
Sitting Height	3.82 ± .72	5.31
Trunk Height	3.18 ± .62	5.13
Upper Arm Length	.83 ± .38	2.18
Lower Arm Length	.12 ± .27	.44
Hand Length	− .48 ± .16	3.00
Upper Leg Length	−1.82 ± .67	2.72
Lower Leg Length	− .08 ± .41	.20
Total Leg Length	− .94 ± .80	1.18
Biacromion	1.23 ± .33	3.73
Cristal Breadth	1.33 ± .40	3.32
Chest Breadth	2.18 ± .39	5.59
Head Length	− .58 ± 1.79	.32
Head Breadth	−2.04 ± 1.13	1.81
Head Height	− .88 ± .30	2.93
Minimum Frontal Diameter	−3.06 ± .83	3.69
Bizygomatic Diameter	.93 ± .90	1.03
Bigonial Diameter	.63 ± 1.11	.57
Total Face Height	−2.25 ± 1.34	1.68
Upper Face Height	−2.38 ± .81	2.94
Forehead Height	−2.56 ± 1.72	1.49
Nose Height	−2.42 ± .79	3.06
Nose Length	−2.68 ± .81	3.31
Nose Salient	.67 ± .33	2.03
Nose Breadth	1.72 ± .55	3.13
Inter-Ocular	1.61 ± .64	2.52
Bi-Ocular	.38 ± .85	.45
Index		
Relative Shoulder Breadth	.38 ± .28	1.36
Relative Hip Breadth	.50 ± .30	1.67
Shoulder-Hip	1.02 ± .95	1.07
Relative Sitting Height	1.58 ± .36	4.39
Relative Trunk Height	1.80 ± .37	4.86
Brachial	−5.42 ± 1.00	5.42
Tibio-Femoral	5.10 ± 2.29	2.23
Inter-Membral	3.60 ± 1.11	3.24

[Continued]

[TABLE 73—*continued*]

DIFFERENCES OF MEANS OF FEMALE SEDENTES BY PREFECTURE

Kyushu
'Other Japan'

Index	Difference	x p.e.
Cephalic	−1.32 ± 1.11	1.19
Length-Height	−3.74 ± 1.88	1.99
Breadth-Height	−3.50 ± 1.99	1.76
Cephalo-Facial	2.16 ± .71	3.04
Fronto-Parietal	− .82 ± .68	1.21
Zygo-Frontal	−3.10 ± .61	5.08
Zygo-Gonial	− .12 ± .89	.13
Facial	−1.68 ± 1.03	1.63
Upper Facial	−2.31 ± .70	3.30
Nasal	6.54 ± 1.51	4.33
Nose Salient-Height	2.73 ± .70	3.90
Nose Length-Height	−1.34 ± .74	1.81

TABLE 74

DISTRIBUTION OF THE X P.E.'S OF THE DIFFERENCES BETWEEN THE VARIOUS PREFECTURAL GROUPS OF FEMALE SEDENTES

		0–.99	1.00–1.99	2.00–2.99	3.00–3.99	4.00–4.99	5.00–5.99	6.00–X
Hiroshima / Yamaguchi	Measurements	9	8	6	3	2	0	0
	Indices	3	8	1	5	1	1	1
Hiroshima / Kyushu	Measurements	9	7	5	3	1	1	2
	Indices	8	4	4	1	2	0	1
Hiroshima / 'Other Japan'	Measurements	12	4	8	3	1	0	0
	Indices	3	7	7	2	1	0	0
Yamaguchi / Kyushu	Measurements	16	3	6	2	1	0	0
	Indices	5	6	6	2	0	1	0
Yamaguchi / 'Other Japan'	Measurements	8	5	7	3	3	1	1
	Indices	3	3	4	5	1	4	0
Kyushu / 'Other Japan'	Measurements	6	6	6	7	0	3	0
	Indices	1	9	1	4	3	2	0

TABLE 75

MEANS OF HIROSHIMA IMMIGRANTS—FEMALES

Measurement		No.	Range	Mean	S.D.	V.
Age		27	20– 59	39.60 ± 1.27	9.75 ± .89	24.62 ± 2.26
Weight	(lb.)	27	69–176	114.94 ± 2.45	18.84 ± 1.73	16.39 ± 1.50
Stature	(cm.)	28	139–159	148.79 ± .50	3.93 ± .35	2.64 ± .24
Sitting Height	(cm.)	28	72– 85	78.50 ± .38	2.98 ± .27	3.80 ± .34
Trunk Height	(cm.)	28	42– 55	49.14 ± .38	3.02 ± .27	6.15 ± .55
Upper Arm Length	(cm.)	28	24– 31	27.50 ± .22	1.74 ± .16	6.33 ± .57
Lower Arm Length	(cm.)	28	19– 25	21.64 ± .17	1.34 ± .12	6.19 ± .56
Hand Length	(cm.)	28	15– 18	16.46 ± .11	.87 ± .08	5.29 ± .48
Upper Leg Length	(cm.)	28	25– 44	34.36 ± .47	3.68 ± .33	10.71 ± .97
Lower Leg Length	(cm.)	28	28– 35	31.71 ± .24	1.85 ± .17	5.83 ± .53
Total Leg Length	(cm.)	28	61– 82	71.00 ± .45	3.50 ± .32	4.93 ± .44
Biacromion	(cm.)	28	35– 42	37.11 ± .22	1.74 ± .16	4.69 ± .42
Cristal Breadth	(cm.)	28	27– 36	29.57 ± .28	2.23 ± .20	7.54 ± .68
Chest Breadth	(cm.)	27	22– 31	26.00 ± .26	2.00 ± .18	7.69 ± .71
Head Length	(mm.)	21	170–201	181.46 ± 1.15	7.78 ± .81	4.29 ± .45
Head Breadth	(mm.)	28	137–158	147.58 ± .65	5.08 ± .46	3.44 ± .31
Head Height	(cm.)	28	11– 15	13.14 ± .13	.99 ± .09	7.53 ± .68
Minimum Frontal Diameter	(mm.)	28	97–120	110.21 ± .71	5.55 ± .50	5.04 ± .45
Bizygomatic Diameter	(mm.)	28	122–151	136.17 ± .76	6.00 ± .54	4.41 ± .40
Bigonial Diameter	(mm.)	28	97–129	108.71 ± .83	6.48 ± .58	5.96 ± .54
Total Face Height	(mm.)	28	100–129	114.17 ± .77	6.06 ± .55	5.31 ± .48
Upper Face Height	(mm.)	28	63– 86	75.36 ± .66	5.18 ± .47	6.87 ± .62
Forehead Height	(mm.)	28	42– 73	56.94 ± .89	7.00 ± .63	12.29 ± 1.11
Nose Height	(mm.)	28	42– 57	49.64 ± .41	3.18 ± .29	6.41 ± .58
Nose Length	(mm.)	28	40– 53	47.58 ± .41	3.18 ± .29	6.68 ± .60

		N	Range	Mean ±	S.D. ±	V ±
Nose Salient	(mm.)	28	8– 17	12.59 ± .26	2.02 ± .19	16.04 ± 1.47
Nose Breadth	(mm.)	28	30– 39	33.28 ± .32	2.52 ± .23	7.57 ± .68
Inter-Ocular	(mm.)	28	26– 36	29.61 ± .36	2.86 ± .26	9.66 ± .87
Bi-Ocular	(mm.)	28	86–109	98.42 ± .55	4.32 ± .39	4.39 ± .40
Index						
Relative Shoulder Breadth		28	23– 28	24.86 ± .17	1.32 ± .12	5.31 ± .48
Relative Hip Breadth		28	18– 23	19.86 ± .19	1.52 ± .14	7.65 ± .69
Shoulder-Hip		28	71– 88	78.83 ± .55	4.35 ± .39	5.52 ± .50
Relative Sitting Height		28	47– 55	52.54 ± .21	1.66 ± .15	3.16 ± .28
Relative Trunk Height		28	28– 36	33.07 ± .24	1.85 ± .17	5.59 ± .50
Brachial		28	71– 93	78.86 ± .57	4.48 ± .40	5.68 ± .51
Tibio-Femoral		28	70–124	94.15 ± 1.39	10.90 ± .98	11.58 ± 1.04
Inter-Membral		28	80–103	92.58 ± .62	4.86 ± .44	5.25 ± .47
Cephalic		21	74– 93	81.26 ± .55	3.74 ± .39	4.60 ± .48
Length-Height		21	62– 87	72.78 ± .89	6.03 ± .63	8.29 ± .86
Breadth-Height		28	74–103	88.78 ± .80	6.30 ± .57	7.10 ± .64
Cephalo-Facial		28	83– 98	92.00 ± .41	3.20 ± .29	3.48 ± .31
Fronto-Parietal		28	68– 79	74.78 ± .35	2.76 ± .25	3.69 ± .33
Zygo-Frontal		28	74– 89	81.00 ± .41	3.20 ± .29	3.95 ± .36
Zygo-Gonial		28	74– 87	79.92 ± .43	3.34 ± .30	4.18 ± .38
Facial		28	69– 95	84.04 ± .65	5.13 ± .46	6.10 ± .55
Upper Facial		28	46– 66	55.79 ± .64	5.01 ± .45	8.98 ± .81
Nasal		28	54– 89	68.22 ± .99	7.74 ± .70	11.35 ± 1.02
Nose Salient-Height		27	19– 33	25.67 ± .43	3.30 ± .30	12.86 ± 1.18
Nose Length-Height		28	92–103	96.78 ± .32	2.48 ± .22	2.56 ± .23

TABLE 76

MEANS OF YAMAGUCHI IMMIGRANTS—FEMALES

Measurement		No.	Range	Mean	S.D.	V.
Age		18	20– 64	42.30 ± 1.94	12.20 ± 1.37	28.84 ± 3.24
Weight	(lb.)	16	81–164	114.22 ± 3.26	19.32 ± 2.30	16.91 ± 2.02
Stature	(cm.)	18	136–153	146.99 ± .69	4.35 ± .49	2.96 ± .33
Sitting Height	(cm.)	18	72– 83	76.50 ± .35	2.20 ± .25	2.88 ± .32
Trunk Height	(cm.)	18	44– 55	47.62 ± .43	2.70 ± .29	5.67 ± .64
Upper Arm Length	(cm.)	18	24– 31	27.89 ± .31	1.97 ± .22	7.06 ± .79
Lower Arm Length	(cm.)	18	20– 23	21.67 ± .14	.88 ± .10	4.06 ± .46
Hand Length	(cm.)	18	16– 17	16.50 ± .08	.50 ± .06	3.03 ± .34
Upper Leg Length	(cm.)	18	25– 44	34.06 ± .75	4.70 ± .53	13.80 ± 1.55
Lower Leg Length	(cm.)	18	27– 35	30.67 ± .32	2.00 ± .22	6.52 ± .73
Total Leg Length	(cm.)	18	63– 78	70.84 ± .67	4.22 ± .47	5.96 ± .67
Biacromion	(cm.)	18	34– 39	36.72 ± .22	1.41 ± .16	3.84 ± .43
Cristal Breadth	(cm.)	17	26– 35	30.12 ± .41	2.52 ± .29	8.37 ± .97
Chest Breadth	(cm.)	17	23– 33	26.24 ± .39	2.39 ± .28	9.11 ± 1.05
Head Length	(mm.)	11	176–189	181.04 ± .80	3.92 ± .56	2.17 ± .31
Head Breadth	(mm.)	18	137–158	145.94 ± .92	5.76 ± .65	3.95 ± .44
Head Height	(cm.)	18	10– 15	12.78 ± .19	1.22 ± .14	9.55 ± 1.07
Minimum Frontal Diameter	(mm.)	18	103–120	109.82 ± .82	5.16 ± .58	4.70 ± .53
Bizygomatic Diameter	(mm.)	17	119–151	136.23 ± 1.12	6.84 ± .79	5.02 ± .58
Bigonial Diameter	(mm.)	18	94–120	108.32 ± .89	5.61 ± .63	5.18 ± .58
Total Face Height	(mm.)	18	103–123	114.68 ± .84	5.31 ± .60	4.63 ± .52
Upper Face Height	(mm.)	18	69– 82	76.00 ± .53	3.34 ± .38	4.39 ± .49
Forehead Height	(mm.)	18	42– 77	61.06 ± 1.50	9.44 ± 1.06	15.46 ± 1.74
Nose Height	(mm.)	18	40– 53	47.72 ± .57	3.60 ± .40	7.54 ± .85
Nose Length	(mm.)	18	30– 53	45.38 ± .75	4.74 ± .53	10.45 ± 1.17

		N	Range			
Nose Salient	(mm.)	18	7– 16	12.17 ± .37	2.34 ± .26	19.23 ± 2.16
Nose Breadth	(mm.)	18	26– 39	32.06 ± .47	2.94 ± .33	9.17 ± 1.03
Inter-Ocular	(mm.)	18	23– 36	29.61 ± .60	3.77 ± .42	12.73 ± 1.43
Bi-Ocular	(mm.)	18	90–107	100.62 ± .69	4.34 ± .49	4.31 ± .48
Index						
Relative Shoulder Breadth		18	23– 28	24.94 ± .21	1.30 ± .15	5.21 ± .59
Relative Hip Breadth		17	16– 25	20.62 ± .33	2.00 ± .23	9.70 ± 1.12
Shoulder-Hip		17	68– 94	81.72 ± 1.02	6.21 ± .72	7.60 ± .88
Relative Sitting Height		18	50– 55	51.94 ± .26	1.65 ± .19	3.18 ± .36
Relative Trunk Height		18	30– 38	32.39 ± .34	2.11 ± .24	6.51 ± .73
Brachial		18	71– 92	78.16 ± .78	4.90 ± .55	6.27 ± .70
Tibio-Femoral		18	70–139	91.15 ± 2.53	15.90 ± 1.79	17.44 ± 1.96
Inter-Membral		18	86–103	93.62 ± .79	4.96 ± .56	5.30 ± .60
Cephalic		11	76– 87	79.96 ± .60	2.96 ± .43	3.70 ± .53
Length-Height		11	60– 83	71.78 ± 1.24	6.10 ± .88	8.50 ± 1.22
Breadth-Height		18	70–109	87.38 ± 1.41	8.84 ± .99	10.12 ± 1.14
Cephalo-Facial		17	85– 96	92.92 ± .44	2.72 ± .31	2.93 ± .34
Fronto-Parietal		18	66– 83	75.16 ± .57	3.58 ± .40	4.76 ± .54
Zygo-Frontal		17	72– 91	80.74 ± .68	4.16 ± .48	5.15 ± .60
Zygo-Gonial		17	72– 89	79.20 ± .54	3.28 ± .38	4.14 ± .48
Facial		17	75– 95	84.64 ± .86	5.25 ± .61	6.20 ± .72
Upper Facial		17	52– 60	56.36 ± .41	2.52 ± .29	4.47 ± .52
Nasal		18	54– 83	67.50 ± 1.25	7.86 ± .88	11.64 ± 1.31
Nose Salient-Height		18	13– 39	25.49 ± .97	6.09 ± .68	23.89 ± 2.69
Nose Length-Height		18	76– 99	95.28 ± .81	5.08 ± .57	5.33 ± .60

TABLE 77

MEANS OF KYUSHU IMMIGRANTS—FEMALES

Measurement		No.	Range	Mean	S.D.	V.
Age		14	20– 54	35.95 ± 1.57	8.70 ± 1.11	24.20 ± 3.08
Weight	(lb.)	15	81–176	117.70 ± 3.47	19.92 ± 2.45	16.92 ± 2.08
Stature	(cm.)	16	142–156	149.57 ± .57	3.39 ± .40	2.27 ± .27
Sitting Height	(cm.)	16	74– 85	80.38 ± .46	2.70 ± .32	3.36 ± .40
Trunk Height	(cm.)	16	46– 55	50.74 ± .43	2.54 ± .30	5.01 ± .60
Upper Arm Length	(cm.)	16	25– 32	28.25 ± .29	1.71 ± .20	6.05 ± .72
Lower Arm Length	(cm.)	16	20– 24	21.62 ± .20	1.17 ± .14	5.41 ± .64
Hand Length	(cm.)	16	16– 18	16.75 ± .13	.75 ± .09	4.48 ± .53
Upper Leg Length	(cm.)	16	27– 40	33.50 ± .56	3.32 ± .40	9.91 ± 1.18
Lower Leg Length	(cm.)	15	29– 33	31.00 ± .19	1.10 ± .14	3.55 ± .44
Total Leg Length	(cm.)	16	63– 78	69.88 ± .61	3.62 ± .43	5.18 ± .62
Biacromion	(cm.)	16	35– 43	37.88 ± .36	2.12 ± .25	5.60 ± .67
Cristal Breadth	(cm.)	16	28– 35	30.56 ± .34	2.00 ± .24	6.54 ± .78
Chest Breadth	(cm.)	16	22– 32	26.38 ± .44	2.62 ± .31	9.93 ± 1.18
Head Length	(mm.)	14	178–197	185.92 ± .76	4.20 ± .54	2.26 ± .29
Head Breadth	(mm.)	16	137–158	145.50 ± .52	3.10 ± .37	2.13 ± .25
Head Height	(cm.)	15	11– 15	12.73 ± .18	1.06 ± .13	8.33 ± 1.03
Minimum Frontal Diameter	(mm.)	16	97–120	110.36 ± .96	5.70 ± .68	5.16 ± .62
Bizygomatic Diameter	(mm.)	16	125–148	135.57 ± .98	5.82 ± .69	4.29 ± .51
Bigonial Diameter	(mm.)	16	97–123	109.64 ± 1.34	7.92 ± .94	7.22 ± .86
Total Face Height	(mm.)	16	100–129	117.50 ± 1.13	6.72 ± .80	5.72 ± .68
Upper Face Height	(mm.)	16	59– 90	74.26 ± 1.39	8.24 ± .98	11.10 ± 1.32
Forehead Height	(mm.)	16	64– 75	67.43 ± .48	2.85 ± .34	4.23 ± .50
Nose Height	(mm.)	16	44– 57	49.12 ± .63	3.72 ± .44	7.57 ± .90
Nose Length	(mm.)	16	42– 55	47.38 ± .65	3.88 ± .46	8.19 ± .98

Nose Salient	(mm.)	16	9– 15	12.62 ± .25	1.50 ± .18	11.89 ± 1.42
Nose Breadth	(mm.)	16	30– 39	33.62 ± .41	2.44 ± .29	7.26 ± .87
Inter-Ocular	(mm.)	16	25– 36	30.25 ± .42	2.51 ± .30	8.30 ± .99
Bi-Ocular	(mm.)	16	92–105	98.50 ± .56	3.32 ± .40	3.37 ± .40
Index						
Relative Shoulder Breadth		16	23– 30	25.38 ± .25	1.50 ± .18	5.91 ± .70
Relative Hip Breadth		16	16– 23	19.74 ± .29	1.72 ± .20	8.71 ± 1.04
Shoulder-Hip		16	74– 91	80.82 ± .70	4.17 ± .50	5.16 ± .62
Relative Sitting Height		16	51– 57	53.25 ± .30	1.75 ± .21	3.29 ± .39
Relative Trunk Height		16	32– 36	33.69 ± .26	1.57 ± .19	4.66 ± .56
Brachial		16	69– 88	76.62 ± .83	4.90 ± .58	6.40 ± .76
Tibio-Femoral		15	75–114	93.35 ± 1.70	9.75 ± 1.20	10.44 ± 1.29
Inter-Membral		16	88–105	95.62 ± .71	4.24 ± .51	4.43 ± .53
Cephalic		14	72– 89	78.78 ± .89	4.94 ± .63	6.27 ± .80
Length-Height		13	58– 83	69.12 ± 1.25	6.68 ± .88	9.66 ± 1.28
Breadth-Height		15	74–103	87.96 ± 1.24	7.10 ± .87	8.07 ± .99
Cephalo-Facial		16	85– 98	92.62 ± .61	3.60 ± .43	3.89 ± .46
Fronto-Parietal		16	66– 83	75.88 ± .71	4.22 ± .50	5.56 ± .66
Zygo-Frontal		16	72– 87	81.38 ± .71	4.24 ± .51	5.21 ± .62
Zygo-Gonial		16	72– 89	80.88 ± .74	4.36 ± .52	5.39 ± .64
Facial		16	75– 98	87.07 ± .81	4.83 ± .58	5.55 ± .66
Upper Facial		16	43– 69	56.57 ± 1.03	6.12 ± .73	10.82 ± 1.29
Nasal		16	54– 83	69.12 ± 1.38	8.20 ± .98	11.86 ± 1.41
Nose Salient-Height		16	16– 33	25.82 ± .63	3.75 ± .45	14.52 ± 1.73
Nose Length-Height		16	90–101	96.26 ± .45	2.64 ± .31	2.74 ± .33

TABLE 78

MEANS OF 'OTHER JAPAN' IMMIGRANTS—FEMALES

Measurement		No.	Range	Mean	S.D.	V.
Age		16	20–54	34.50 ± 1.40	8.30 ± .99	24.06 ± 2.87
Weight	(lb.)	12	81–152	112.54 ± 3.79	19.44 ± 2.68	17.27 ± 2.38
Stature	(cm.)	16	139–156	147.14 ± .82	4.86 ± .58	3.30 ± .39
Sitting Height	(cm.)	16	72–85	78.26 ± .52	3.08 ± .37	3.94 ± .47
Trunk Height	(cm.)	16	44–57	49.26 ± .48	2.82 ± .34	5.72 ± .68
Upper Arm Length	(cm.)	16	26–31	27.94 ± .23	1.35 ± .16	4.83 ± .58
Lower Arm Length	(cm.)	16	19–25	22.00 ± .23	1.37 ± .16	6.23 ± .74
Hand Length	(cm.)	16	15–18	16.62 ± .13	.78 ± .09	4.69 ± .56
Upper Leg Length	(cm.)	15	25–38	32.96 ± .60	3.46 ± .43	10.50 ± 1.29
Lower Leg Length	(cm.)	16	28–36	31.56 ± .38	2.24 ± .27	7.10 ± .85
Total Leg Length	(cm.)	16	61–76	69.12 ± .60	3.54 ± .42	5.12 ± .61
Biacromion	(cm.)	16	33–40	36.56 ± .34	2.03 ± .24	5.55 ± .66
Cristal Breadth	(cm.)	12	25–35	29.75 ± .46	2.35 ± .32	7.90 ± 1.09
Chest Breadth	(cm.)	12	22–29	25.50 ± .41	2.10 ± .29	8.24 ± 1.13
Head Length	(mm.)	15	174–199	182.76 ± 1.14	6.56 ± .81	3.59 ± .44
Head Breadth	(mm.)	16	141–154	148.26 ± .62	3.66 ± .44	2.47 ± .29
Head Height	(cm.)	16	11–14	12.06 ± .15	.90 ± .11	7.46 ± .89
Minimum Frontal Diameter	(mm.)	16	100–120	111.32 ± .78	4.62 ± .55	4.15 ± .49
Bizygomatic Diameter	(mm.)	16	128–160	138.36 ± 1.29	7.65 ± .91	5.53 ± .66
Bigonial Diameter	(mm.)	16	100–114	109.25 ± .63	3.75 ± .45	3.43 ± .41
Total Face Height	(mm.)	16	97–120	113.93 ± 1.05	6.24 ± .74	5.48 ± .65
Upper Face Height	(mm.)	16	63–84	74.88 ± .98	5.82 ± .69	7.77 ± .93
Forehead Height	(mm.)	16	46–73	59.50 ± 1.17	6.92 ± .82	11.63 ± 1.39
Nose Height	(mm.)	16	40–55	48.38 ± .65	3.84 ± .46	7.94 ± .95
Nose Length	(mm.)	16	34–55	45.26 ± .87	5.14 ± .61	11.36 ± 1.35

Nose Salient	(mm.)	16	9– 18	13.25 ± .48	2.84 ± .34	21.43 ± 2.56
Nose Breadth	(mm.)	16	28– 39	33.74 ± .48	2.82 ± .34	8.36 ± 1.00
Inter-Ocular	(mm.)	16	27– 38	31.62 ± .52	3.10 ± .37	9.80 ± 1.17
Bi-Ocular	(mm.)	16	90–109	101.00 ± .90	5.32 ± .63	5.27 ± .63
Index						
Relative Shoulder Breadth		16	23– 28	24.74 ± .20	1.20 ± .14	4.85 ± .58
Relative Hip Breadth		12	16– 23	20.00 ± .36	1.86 ± .26	9.30 ± 1.28
Shoulder–Hip		12	71– 88	79.74 ± 1.02	5.25 ± .72	6.58 ± .91
Relative Sitting Height		16	50– 57	52.94 ± .32	1.89 ± .23	3.57 ± .43
Relative Trunk Height		16	31– 37	33.38 ± .27	1.62 ± .19	4.85 ± .58
Brachial		16	69– 86	78.74 ± .64	3.80 ± .45	4.83 ± .58
Tibio-Femoral		15	75–134	96.35 ± 2.64	15.15 ± 1.87	15.72 ± 1.94
Inter-Membral		16	88–113	96.50 ± 1.02	6.04 ± .72	6.26 ± .75
Cephalic		15	76– 89	81.04 ± .59	3.38 ± .42	4.17 ± .51
Length-Height		15	58– 81	65.84 ± .95	5.44 ± .67	8.26 ± 1.02
Breadth-Height		16	72– 99	81.50 ± 1.13	6.70 ± .80	8.22 ± .98
Cephalo-Facial		16	87–104	93.26 ± .69	4.12 ± .49	4.42 ± .53
Fronto-Parietal		16	68– 79	74.88 ± .40	2.36 ± .28	3.15 ± .38
Zygo-Frontal		16	74– 87	80.50 ± .60	3.54 ± .42	4.40 ± .52
Zygo-Gonial		16	72– 87	79.38 ± .43	2.54 ± .30	3.20 ± .38
Facial		16	75– 92	82.75 ± .83	4.92 ± .59	5.95 ± .71
Upper Facial		16	46– 66	54.50 ± .88	5.19 ± .62	9.52 ± 1.14
Nasal		16	58– 89	70.26 ± 1.46	8.64 ± 1.03	12.30 ± 1.47
Nose Salient-Height		16	19– 42	27.86 ± 1.12	6.63 ± .79	23.80 ± 2.84
Nose Length-Height		16	84–101	93.88 ± .94	5.56 ± .66	5.92 ± .71

TABLE 79

DIFFERENCES OF HIROSHIMA IMMIGRANTS AND TOTAL IMMIGRANTS—FEMALES

Measurement	Difference	x p.e.
Age	1.10 ± 1.30	.85
Weight	1.92 ± 2.51	.76
Stature	.27 ± .57	.47
Sitting Height	− .34 ± .44	.77
Trunk Height	− .42 ± .42	1.00
Upper Arm Length	− .32 ± .23	1.39
Lower Arm Length	− .10 ± .16	.62
Hand Length	− .14 ± .10	1.40
Upper Leg Length	.64 ± .52	1.23
Lower Leg Length	.22 ± .25	.88
Total Leg Length	.78 ± .50	1.56
Biacromion	.11 ± .25	.44
Cristal Breadth	− .41 ± .29	1.41
Chest Breadth	− .08 ± .31	.26
Head Length	−1.36 ± .98	1.39
Head Breadth	.60 ± .70	.86
Head Height (cm.)	.32 ± .15	2.13
Minimum Frontal Diameter	− .03 ± .67	.04
Bizygomatic Diameter	− .03 ± .83	.04
Bigonial Diameter	− .36 ± .79	.46
Total Face Height	−1.29 ± .82	1.57
Upper Face Height	.16 ± .82	.20
Forehead Height	−1.44 ± .93	1.55
Nose Height	.64 ± .48	1.33
Nose Length	1.00 ± .57	1.75
Nose Salient	− .26 ± .32	.81
Nose Breadth	.06 ± .34	.18
Inter-Ocular	− .62 ± .40	1.55
Bi-Ocular	− .72 ± .56	1.29
Index		
Relative Shoulder Breadth	.04 ± .16	.25
Relative Hip Breadth	− .14 ± .19	.74
Shoulder-Hip	−1.90 ± .65	2.92
Relative Sitting Height	− .24 ± .24	1.00
Relative Trunk Height	− .20 ± .25	.80
Brachial	.56 ± .62	.90
Tibio-Femoral	− .75 ± 1.79	.42
Inter-Membral	−1.88 ± .72	2.61
Cephalic	.70 ± .61	1.15
Length-Height	2.26 ± .96	2.35
Breadth-Height	1.60 ± 1.00	1.60

[TABLE 79—*continued*]

DIFFERENCES OF HIROSHIMA IMMIGRANTS AND TOTAL IMMIGRANTS—FEMALES

Index	Difference	x p.e.
Cephalo-Facial	− .38 ± .45	.84
Fronto-Parietal	− .16 ± .42	.38
Zygo-Frontal	.06 ± .45	.13
Zygo-Gonial	− .24 ± .47	.51
Facial	−1.11 ± .71	1.56
Upper Facial	− .36 ± .67	.54
Nasal	− .34 ± 1.03	.33
Nose Salient-Height	− .72 ± .70	1.03
Nose Length-Height	1.34 ± .47	2.85

TABLE 80

DIFFERENCES OF YAMAGUCHI IMMIGRANTS AND TOTAL IMMIGRANTS—FEMALES

Measurement	Difference	x p.e.
Age	3.80 ± 1.60	2.38
Weight	1.20 ± 3.26	.37
Stature	−1.53 ± .71	2.15
Sitting Height	−2.34 ± .55	4.25
Trunk Height	−1.94 ± .52	3.73
Upper Arm Length	.07 ± .28	.25
Lower Arm Length	− .07 ± .20	.35
Hand Length	− .10 ± .13	.77
Upper Leg Length	.34 ± .65	.52
Lower Leg Length	− .82 ± .32	2.56
Total Leg Length	.62 ± .62	1.00
Biacromion	− .28 ± .31	.90
Cristal Breadth	.14 ± .38	.37
Chest Breadth	.16 ± .39	.41
Head Length	−1.78 ± 1.36	1.31
Head Breadth	−1.04 ± .87	1.20
Head Height (cm.)	− .04 ± .18	.22
Minimum Frontal Diameter	− .42 ± .83	.51
Bizygomatic Diameter	.03 ± 1.07	.03
Bigonial Diameter	− .75 ± .99	.76
Total Face Height	− .78 ± 1.02	.76
Upper Face Height	.80 ± 1.02	.78
Forehead Height	2.68 ± 1.16	2.31
Nose Height	−1.28 ± .60	2.13
Nose Length	−1.20 ± .71	1.69
Nose Salient	− .68 ± .39	1.74
Nose Breadth	−1.16 ± .43	2.70
Inter-Ocular	− .62 ± .50	1.24
Bi-Ocular	1.48 ± .80	1.85
Index		
Relative Shoulder Breadth	.12 ± .21	.57
Relative Hip Breadth	.62 ± .28	2.21
Shoulder-Hip	.99 ± .83	1.19
Relative Sitting Height	− .84 ± .31	2.71
Relative Trunk Height	− .88 ± .30	2.93
Brachial	− .14 ± .77	.18
Tibio-Femoral	−3.75 ± 2.23	1.68
Inter-Membral	− .84 ± .90	.93
Cephalic	− .60 ± .84	.71
Length-Height	1.26 ± 1.33	.95
Breadth-Height	.20 ± 1.25	.16

[TABLE 80—*continued*]

DIFFERENCES OF YAMAGUCHI IMMIGRANTS AND TOTAL IMMIGRANTS—FEMALES

Index	Difference	x p.e.
Cephalo-Facial	.54 ± .58	.93
Fronto-Parietal	.22 ± .53	.42
Zygo-Frontal	− .20 ± .57	.35
Zygo-Gonial	− .96 ± .61	1.57
Facial	− .51 ± .91	.56
Upper Facial	.21 ± .86	.24
Nasal	−1.06 ± 1.28	.83
Nose Salient-Height	− .90 ± .86	1.05
Nose Length-Height	− .16 ± .68	.27

TABLE 81

DIFFERENCES OF KYUSHU IMMIGRANTS AND TOTAL IMMIGRANTS—FEMALES

Measurement	Difference	x p.e.
Age	−2.55 ± 1.81	1.41
Weight	4.68 ± 3.36	1.39
Stature	1.05 ± .75	1.40
Sitting Height	1.54 ± .58	2.66
Trunk Height	1.18 ± .55	2.15
Upper Arm Length	.43 ± .30	1.43
Lower Arm Length	− .12 ± .22	.55
Hand Length	.15 ± .14	1.07
Upper Leg Length	− .22 ± .69	.32
Lower Leg Length	− .49 ± .35	1.40
Total Leg Length	− .34 ± .66	.52
Biacromion	.88 ± .33	2.67
Cristal Breadth	.58 ± .39	1.49
Chest Breadth	.30 ± .40	.75
Head Length	3.10 ± 1.20	2.58
Head Breadth	−1.48 ± .92	1.61
Head Height (cm.)	− .09 ± .20	.45
Minimum Frontal Diameter	.12 ± .89	.13
Bizygomatic Diameter	− .63 ± 1.10	.57
Bigonial Diameter	.57 ± 1.05	.54
Total Face Height	2.04 ± 1.08	1.89
Upper Face Height	− .94 ± 1.08	.87
Forehead Height	9.05 ± 1.23	7.36
Nose Height	.12 ± .64	.19
Nose Length	.80 ± .76	1.05
Nose Salient	− .23 ± .41	.56
Nose Breadth	.40 ± .45	.89
Inter-Ocular	.02 ± .53	.04
Bi-Ocular	− .64 ± .85	.75
Index		
Relative Shoulder Breadth	.56 ± .22	2.55
Relative Hip Breadth	− .26 ± .29	.90
Shoulder-Hip	.09 ± .86	.10
Relative Sitting Height	.47 ± .32	1.47
Relative Trunk Height	.42 ± .34	1.24
Brachial	−1.68 ± .82	2.05
Tibio-Femoral	−1.55 ± 2.45	.63
Inter-Membral	1.16 ± .95	1.22
Cephalic	−1.78 ± .74	2.41
Length-Height	−1.40 ± 1.22	1.15
Breadth-Height	.78 ± 1.37	.57

[TABLE 81—*continued*]

DIFFERENCES OF KYUSHU IMMIGRANTS AND TOTAL IMMIGRANTS—FEMALES

Index	Difference	x p.e.
Cephalo-Facial	.24 ± .59	.41
Fronto-Parietal	.94 ± .56	1.68
Zygo-Frontal	.44 ± .59	.75
Zygo-Gonial	.72 ± .62	1.16
Facial	1.92 ± .94	2.04
Upper Facial	.42 ± .89	.47
Nasal	.56 ± 1.36	.41
Nose Salient-Height	− .57 ± .91	.63
Nose Length-Height	.82 ± .73	1.12

TABLE 82

DIFFERENCES OF 'OTHER JAPAN' IMMIGRANTS AND TOTAL
IMMIGRANTS—FEMALES

Measurement	Difference	x p.e.
Age	−4.00 ± 1.69	2.37
Weight	− .48 ± 3.76	.13
Stature	−1.38 ± .75	1.84
Sitting Height	− .58 ± .58	1.00
Trunk Height	− .30 ± .55	.55
Upper Arm Length	.12 ± .27	.44
Lower Arm Length	.26 ± .22	1.18
Hand Length	.02 ± .14	.14
Upper Leg Length	− .76 ± .71	1.07
Lower Leg Length	.07 ± .34	.21
Total Leg Length	1.10 ± .66	1.67
Biacromion	− .44 ± .33	1.33
Cristal Breadth	− .23 ± .45	.51
Chest Breadth	− .58 ± .47	1.23
Head Length	− .06 ± 1.16	.05
Head Breadth	1.28 ± .92	1.39
Head Height (cm.)	− .76 ± .19	4.00
Minimum Frontal Diameter	1.08 ± .89	1.21
Bizygomatic Diameter	2.16 ± 1.10	1.96
Bigonial Diameter	.18 ± 1.05	.17
Total Face Height	−1.53 ± 1.08	1.42
Upper Face Height	− .32 ± 1.08	.30
Forehead Height	1.12 ± 1.23	.91
Nose Height	− .62 ± .64	.97
Nose Length	−1.32 ± .76	1.74
Nose Salient	.40 ± .41	.98
Nose Breadth	.52 ± .45	1.16
Inter-Ocular	1.39 ± .53	2.62
Bi-Ocular	1.86 ± .85	2.19
Index		
Relative Shoulder Breadth	− .08 ± .22	.36
Relative Hip Breadth	.00 ± .34	.00
Shoulder-Hip	− .99 ± .99	1.00
Relative Sitting Height	.16 ± .32	.50
Relative Trunk Height	.11 ± .34	.32
Brachial	.44 ± .82	.54
Tibio-Femoral	1.45 ± 2.45	.59
Inter-Membral	2.04 ± .95	2.15
Cephalic	.48 ± .72	.67
Length-Height	−4.68 ± 1.14	4.11

[TABLE 82—*continued*]

DIFFERENCES OF 'OTHER JAPAN' IMMIGRANTS AND TOTAL
IMMIGRANTS—FEMALES

Index	Difference	x p.e.
Breadth-Height	-5.68 ± 1.33	4.27
Cephalo-Facial	$.88 \pm .59$	1.49
Fronto-Parietal	$- .06 \pm .56$	.11
Zygo-Frontal	$- .44 \pm .59$	.75
Zygo-Gonial	$- .78 \pm .62$	1.26
Facial	$-2.40 \pm .94$	2.55
Upper Facial	$-1.65 \pm .89$	1.85
Nasal	1.70 ± 1.36	1.25
Nose Salient-Height	$1.47 \pm .91$	1.62
Nose Length-Height	$-1.56 \pm .73$	2.14

TABLE 83

DISTRIBUTION OF THE X P.E.'S OF THE DIFFERENCES BETWEEN THE PREFECTURAL GROUPS OF FEMALE IMMIGRANTS AND THE TOTAL FEMALE IMMIGRANTS

		0–.99	1.00–1.99	2.00–2.99	3.00–3.99	4.00–4.99	5.00–5.99	6.00–X
Hiroshima Immigrants	Measurements	14	13	1	0	0	0	0
Total Immigrants	Indices	11	5	4	0	0	0	0
Yamaguchi Immigrants	Measurements	14	7	5	1	1	0	0
Total Immigrants	Indices	13	4	3	0	0	0	0
Kyushu Immigrants	Measurements	14	9	4	0	0	0	1
Total Immigrants	Indices	9	7	4	0	0	0	0
'Other Japan' Immigrants	Measurements	12	13	2	0	1	0	0
Total Immigrants	Indices	9	6	3	0	2	0	0

TABLE 84

DIFFERENCES OF MEANS OF IMMIGRANT FEMALES BY PREFECTURE

Hiroshima
Yamaguchi

Measurement	Difference	x p.e.
Age	2.70 ± 2.32	1.16
Weight	− .72 ± 4.08	.18
Stature	−1.80 ± .85	2.12
Sitting Height	−2.00 ± .52	3.85
Trunk Height	−1.52 ± .57	2.67
Upper Arm Length	.39 ± .38	1.03
Lower Arm Length	.03 ± .22	.14
Hand Length	.04 ± .14	.29
Upper Leg Length	− .30 ± .89	.34
Lower Leg Length	−1.04 ± .40	2.60
Total Leg Length	− .16 ± .81	.20
Biacromion	− .39 ± .31	1.26
Cristal Breadth	.55 ± .50	1.10
Chest Breadth	.24 ± .47	.51
Head Length	− .42 ± 1.40	.30
Head Breadth	−1.64 ± 1.13	1.45
Head Height	− .36 ± .23	1.57
Minimum Frontal Diameter	− .39 ± 1.09	.36
Bizygomatic Diameter	.06 ± 1.35	.04
Bigonial Diameter	− .39 ± 1.22	.32
Total Face Height	.51 ± 1.14	.45
Upper Face Height	.64 ± .85	.75
Forehead Height	4.12 ± 1.74	2.37
Nose Height	−1.92 ± .70	2.74
Nose Length	−2.20 ± .85	2.59
Nose Salient	− .42 ± .45	.93
Nose Breadth	−1.22 ± .57	2.14
Inter-Ocular	.00 ± .70	.00
Bi-Ocular	2.20 ± .88	2.50
Index		
Relative Shoulder Breadth	.08 ± .27	.30
Relative Hip Breadth	.76 ± .38	2.00
Shoulder-Hip	2.89 ± 1.16	2.49
Relative Sitting Height	− .60 ± .33	1.82
Relative Trunk Height	− .68 ± .42	1.62
Brachial	− .70 ± .97	.72
Tibio-Femoral	−3.00 ± 2.89	1.04
Inter-Membral	1.04 ± 1.00	1.04

[*Continued*]

[TABLE 84—*continued*]

DIFFERENCES OF MEANS OF IMMIGRANT FEMALES BY PREFECTURE

Hiroshima
——————
Yamaguchi

Index	Difference	x p.e.
Cephalic	$-1.30 \pm .81$	1.60
Length-Height	-1.00 ± 1.53	.65
Breadth-Height	-1.40 ± 1.62	.86
Cephalo-Facial	$.92 \pm .60$	1.53
Fronto-Parietal	$.38 \pm .67$	.57
Zygo-Frontal	$-.26 \pm .79$	.33
Zygo-Gonial	$-.72 \pm .69$	1.04
Facial	$.60 \pm 1.08$	.56
Upper Facial	$.57 \pm .76$	.75
Nasal	$-.72 \pm 1.59$	.45
Nose Salient-Height	$-.18 \pm 1.06$	.17
Nose Length-Height	$-1.50 \pm .87$	1.72

TABLE 85

DIFFERENCES OF MEANS OF IMMIGRANT FEMALES BY PREFECTURE

Hiroshima
Kyushu

Measurement	Difference	x p.e.
Age	3.65 ± 2.02	1.81
Weight	− 2.76 ± 4.25	.65
Stature	− .78 ± .76	1.03
Sitting Height	− 1.88 ± .60	3.13
Trunk Height	− 1.60 ± .57	2.81
Upper Arm Length	− .75 ± .36	2.08
Lower Arm Length	.02 ± .26	.08
Hand Length	− .29 ± .17	1.71
Upper Leg Length	.86 ± .73	1.18
Lower Leg Length	.71 ± .31	2.29
Total Leg Length	1.12 ± .76	1.47
Biacromion	− .77 ± .42	1.83
Cristal Breadth	− .99 ± .44	2.25
Chest Breadth	− .38 ± .51	.74
Head Length	− 4.46 ± 1.38	3.23
Head Breadth	2.08 ± .83	2.51
Head Height	.41 ± .22	1.86
Minimum Frontal Diameter	− .15 ± 1.19	.13
Bizygomatic Diameter	.60 ± 1.24	.48
Bigonial Diameter	− .93 ± 1.57	.59
Total Face Height	− 3.33 ± 1.37	2.43
Upper Face Height	1.10 ± 1.54	.71
Forehead Height	−10.49 ± 1.01	10.39
Nose Height	.52 ± .75	.69
Nose Length	.20 ± .77	.26
Nose Salient	− .03 ± .36	.08
Nose Breadth	− .34 ± .52	.65
Inter-Ocular	− .64 ± .55	1.16
Bi-Ocular	− .08 ± .78	.10
Index		
Relative Shoulder Breadth	− .52 ± .30	1.73
Relative Hip Breadth	.12 ± .35	.34
Shoulder-Hip	− 1.99 ± .89	2.24
Relative Sitting Height	− .71 ± .37	1.92
Relative Trunk Height	− .62 ± .35	1.77
Brachial	2.24 ± 1.00	2.24
Tibio-Femoral	.80 ± 2.20	.36
Inter-Membral	− 3.04 ± .94	3.23

[Continued]

[TABLE 85—*continued*]

DIFFERENCES OF MEANS OF IMMIGRANT FEMALES BY PREFECTURE

Hiroshima
—————
Kyushu

Index	Difference	x p.e.
Cephalic	2.48 ± 1.04	2.38
Length-Height	3.66 ± 1.53	2.39
Breadth-Height	.82 ± 1.48	.55
Cephalo-Facial	— .62 ± .73	.85
Fronto-Parietal	— 1.10 ± .79	1.39
Zygo-Frontal	— .38 ± .82	.46
Zygo-Gonial	— .96 ± .86	1.12
Facial	— 3.03 ± 1.04	2.91
Upper Facial	— .78 ± 1.21	.64
Nasal	— .90 ± 1.70	.53
Nose Salient-Height	— .15 ± .76	.20
Nose Length-Height	.52 ± .55	.95

TABLE 86

DIFFERENCES OF MEANS OF IMMIGRANT FEMALES BY PREFECTURE

Hiroshima
'Other Japan'

Measurement	Difference	x p.e.
Age	5.10 ± 1.90	2.68
Weight	2.40 ± 4.51	.53
Stature	1.65 ± .96	1.72
Sitting Height	.24 ± .64	.38
Trunk Height	− .12 ± .61	.20
Upper Arm Length	− .44 ± .32	1.38
Lower Arm Length	− .36 ± .29	1.24
Hand Length	− .16 ± .17	.94
Upper Leg Length	1.40 ± .76	1.84
Lower Leg Length	.15 ± .45	.33
Total Leg Length	1.88 ± .75	2.51
Biacromion	.55 ± .40	1.38
Cristal Breadth	− .18 ± .54	.33
Chest Breadth	.50 ± .49	1.02
Head Length	−1.30 ± 1.62	.80
Head Breadth	− .68 ± .90	.76
Head Height	1.08 ± .20	5.40
Minimum Frontal Diameter	−1.11 ± 1.05	1.06
Bizygomatic Diameter	−2.19 ± 1.50	1.46
Bigonial Diameter	− .54 ± 1.04	.52
Total Face Height	.24 ± 1.30	.18
Upper Face Height	.48 ± 1.18	.41
Forehead Height	−2.56 ± 1.47	1.74
Nose Height	1.26 ± .77	1.64
Nose Length	2.32 ± .96	2.42
Nose Salient	− .66 ± .55	1.20
Nose Breadth	− .46 ± .58	.79
Inter-Ocular	−2.01 ± .63	3.19
Bi-Ocular	−2.58 ± 1.05	2.46

Index		
Relative Shoulder Breadth	.12 ± .26	.46
Relative Hip Breadth	− .14 ± .41	.34
Shoulder-Hip	− .91 ± 1.16	.78
Relative Sitting Height	− .40 ± .38	1.05
Relative Trunk Height	− .31 ± .36	.86
Brachial	.12 ± .86	.14
Tibio-Femoral	−2.20 ± 2.98	.74
Inter-Membral	−3.92 ± 1.19	3.29

[*Continued*]

[TABLE 86—*continued*]

DIFFERENCES OF MEANS OF IMMIGRANT FEMALES BY PREFECTURE

Hiroshima
'Other Japan'

Index	Difference	x p.e.
Cephalic	.22 ± .81	.27
Length-Height	6.94 ± 1.30	5.34
Breadth-Height	7.28 ± 1.39	5.24
Cephalo-Facial	−1.26 ± .80	1.58
Fronto-Parietal	− .10 ± .53	.19
Zygo-Frontal	.50 ± .73	.68
Zygo-Gonial	.54 ± .61	.89
Facial	1.29 ± 1.05	1.23
Upper Facial	1.29 ± 1.09	1.18
Nasal	−2.04 ± 1.76	1.16
Nose Salient-Height	−2.19 ± 1.20	1.82
Nose Length-Height	2.90 ± .99	2.93

TABLE 87

DIFFERENCES OF MEANS OF IMMIGRANT FEMALES BY PREFECTURE

Yamaguchi
Kyushu

Measurement	Difference	x p.e.
Age	6.35 ± 2.50	2.54
Weight	−3.48 ± 4.76	.73
Stature	−2.58 ± .89	2.90
Sitting Height	−3.88 ± .58	6.69
Trunk Height	−3.12 ± .61	5.11
Upper Arm Length	− .36 ± .42	.86
Lower Arm Length	.05 ± .24	.21
Hand Length	− .25 ± .15	1.67
Upper Leg Length	.56 ± .94	.60
Lower Leg Length	− .33 ± .37	.89
Total Leg Length	.96 ± .91	1.05
Biacromion	−1.16 ± .42	2.76
Cristal Breadth	− .44 ± .53	.83
Chest Breadth	− .14 ± .59	.24
Head Length	−4.88 ± 1.10	4.44
Head Breadth	.44 ± 1.06	.42
Head Height	.05 ± .26	.19
Minimum Frontal Diameter	− .54 ± 1.26	.43
Bizygomatic Diameter	.66 ± 1.49	.44
Bigonial Diameter	−1.32 ± 1.61	.82
Total Face Height	−2.82 ± 1.41	2.00
Upper Face Height	1.74 ± 1.49	1.17
Forehead Height	−6.37 ± 1.57	4.06
Nose Height	−1.40 ± .85	1.65
Nose Length	−2.00 ± .99	2.02
Nose Salient	− .45 ± .45	1.00
Nose Breadth	−1.56 ± .62	2.52
Inter-Ocular	− .64 ± .73	.88
Bi-Ocular	2.12 ± .89	2.38
Index		
Relative Shoulder Breadth	− .44 ± .33	1.33
Relative Hip Breadth	.88 ± .44	2.00
Shoulder-Hip	.90 ± 1.24	.73
Relative Sitting Height	−1.31 ± .40	3.28
Relative Trunk Height	−1.30 ± .43	3.02
Brachial	1.54 ± 1.14	1.35
Tibio-Femoral	−2.20 ± 3.05	.72
Inter-Membral	−2.00 ± 1.06	1.89

[*Continued*]

[TABLE 87—*continued*]

DIFFERENCES OF MEANS OF IMMIGRANT FEMALES BY PREFECTURE

<u>Yamaguchi</u>
<u>Kyushu</u>

Index	Difference	x p.e.
Cephalic	1.18 ± 1.07	1.10
Length-Height	2.66 ± 1.76	1.51
Breadth-Height	− .58 ± 1.88	.31
Cephalo-Facial	.30 ± .75	.40
Fronto-Parietal	− .72 ± .91	.79
Zygo-Frontal	− .64 ± .98	.65
Zygo-Gonial	−1.68 ± .92	1.83
Facial	−2.43 ± 1.18	2.06
Upper Facial	− .21 ± 1.11	.19
Nasal	−1.62 ± 1.86	.87
Nose Salient-Height	− .33 ± 1.16	.28
Nose Length-Height	− .98 ± .93	1.05

TABLE 88

DIFFERENCES OF MEANS OF IMMIGRANT FEMALES BY PREFECTURE

Yamaguchi
'Other Japan'

Measurement	Difference	x p.e.
Age	7.80 ± 2.39	3.26
Weight	1.68 ± 5.00	.34
Stature	− .15 ± 1.07	.14
Sitting Height	−1.76 ± .63	2.79
Trunk Height	−1.64 ± .64	2.56
Upper Arm Length	− .05 ± .39	.13
Lower Arm Length	− .33 ± .27	1.22
Hand Length	− .12 ± .15	.80
Upper Leg Length	1.10 ± .96	1.15
Lower Leg Length	− .89 ± .50	1.78
Total Leg Length	1.72 ± .90	1.91
Biacromion	.16 ± .40	.40
Cristal Breadth	.37 ± .62	.60
Chest Breadth	.74 ± .57	1.30
Head Length	−1.72 ± 1.39	1.24
Head Breadth	−2.32 ± 1.11	2.09
Head Height	.72 ± .24	3.00
Minimum Frontal Diameter	−1.50 ± 1.13	1.33
Bizygomatic Diameter	−2.13 ± 1.71	1.25
Bigonial Diameter	− .93 ± 1.09	.85
Total Face Height	.75 ± 1.35	.56
Upper Face Height	1.12 ± 1.11	1.01
Forehead Height	1.56 ± 1.90	.82
Nose Height	− .66 ± .86	.77
Nose Length	.12 ± 1.15	.10
Nose Salient	−1.08 ± .61	1.77
Nose Breadth	−1.68 ± .67	2.51
Inter-Ocular	−2.01 ± .79	2.54
Bi-Ocular	− .38 ± 1.14	.33

Index		
Relative Shoulder Breadth	.20 ± .29	.69
Relative Hip Breadth	.62 ± .49	1.27
Shoulder-Hip	1.98 ± 1.44	1.38
Relative Sitting Height	−1.00 ± .41	2.44
Relative Trunk Height	− .99 ± .43	2.30
Brachial	− .58 ± 1.01	.57
Tibio-Femoral	−5.20 ± 3.66	1.42
Inter-Membral	−2.88 ± 1.29	2.23

[*Continued*]

[TABLE 88—*continued*]

DIFFERENCES OF MEANS OF IMMIGRANT FEMALES BY PREFECTURE

Yamaguchi
'Other Japan'

Index	Difference	x p.e.
Cephalic	−1.08 ± .84	1.29
Length-Height	5.94 ± 1.56	3.81
Breadth-Height	5.88 ± 1.81	3.25
Cephalo-Facial	− .34 ± .82	.41
Fronto-Parietal	.28 ± .70	.40
Zygo-Frontal	.24 ± .91	.26
Zygo-Gonial	− .18 ± .69	.26
Facial	1.89 ± 1.20	1.58
Upper Facial	1.86 ± .97	1.92
Nasal	−2.76 ± 1.92	1.44
Nose Salient-Height	−2.37 ± 1.48	1.60
Nose Length-Height	1.40 ± 1.24	1.13

TABLE 89

DIFFERENCES OF MEANS OF IMMIGRANT FEMALES BY PREFECTURE

Kyushu
'Other Japan'

Measurement	Difference	x p.e.
Age	1.45 ± 2.10	.69
Weight	5.16 ± 5.14	1.00
Stature	2.43 ± 1.00	2.43
Sitting Height	2.12 ± .69	3.07
Trunk Height	1.48 ± .64	2.31
Upper Arm Length	.31 ± .37	.84
Lower Arm Length	— .38 ± .30	1.27
Hand Length	.13 ± .18	.72
Upper Leg Length	.54 ± .82	.66
Lower Leg Length	— .56 ± .42	1.33
Total Leg Length	.76 ± .86	.88
Biacromion	1.32 ± .50	2.64
Cristal Breadth	.81 ± .57	1.42
Chest Breadth	.88 ± .60	1.47
Head Length	3.16 ± 1.37	2.31
Head Breadth	—2.76 ± .81	3.41
Head Height	.67 ± .23	2.91
Minimum Frontal Diameter	— .96 ± 1.24	.77
Bizygomatic Diameter	—2.79 ± 1.62	1.72
Bigonial Diameter	.39 ± 1.48	.26
Total Face Height	3.57 ± 1.54	2.32
Upper Face Height	— .62 ± 1.70	.36
Forehead Height	7.93 ± 1.26	6.29
Nose Height	.74 ± .91	.81
Nose Length	2.12 ± 1.09	1.94
Nose Salient	— .63 ± .54	1.17
Nose Breadth	— .12 ± .63	.19
Inter-Ocular	—1.37 ± .67	2.04
Bi-Ocular	—2.50 ± 1.06	2.36
Index		
Relative Shoulder Breadth	.64 ± .32	2.00
Relative Hip Breadth	— .26 ± .46	.57
Shoulder-Hip	1.08 ± 1.24	.87
Relative Sitting Height	.31 ± .44	.70
Relative Trunk Height	.31 ± .37	.84
Brachial	—2.12 ± 1.05	2.02
Tibio-Femoral	—3.00 ± 3.14	.96
Inter-Membral	— .88 ± 1.24	.71

[Continued]

[TABLE 89—*continued*]

DIFFERENCES OF MEANS OF IMMIGRANT FEMALES BY PREFECTURE

Kyushu
'Other Japan'

Index	Difference	x p.e.
Cephalic	−2.26 ± 1.07	2.11
Length-Height	3.28 ± 1.57	2.09
Breadth-Height	6.46 ± 1.68	3.85
Cephalo-Facial	− .64 ± .92	.70
Fronto-Parietal	1.00 ± .81	1.23
Zygo-Frontal	.88 ± .93	.95
Zygo-Gonial	1.50 ± .86	1.74
Facial	4.32 ± 1.16	3.72
Upper Facial	2.07 ± 1.36	1.52
Nasal	−1.14 ± 2.01	.57
Nose Salient-Height	−2.04 ± 1.28	1.59
Nose Length-Height	2.38 ± 1.04	2.29

TABLE 90

DISTRIBUTION OF THE X P.E.'S OF THE DIFFERENCES BETWEEN THE VARIOUS PREFECTURAL GROUPS OF FEMALE IMMIGRANTS

		0–99	1.00–1.99	2.00–2.99	3.00–3.99	4.00–4.99	5.00–5.99	6.00–X
Hiroshima / Yamaguchi	Measurements	14	5	8	1	0	0	0
	Indices	10	8	2	0	0	0	0
Hiroshima / Kyushu	Measurements	12	7	6	2	0	0	1
	Indices	9	5	5	1	0	0	0
Hiroshima / 'Other Japan'	Measurements	12	11	3	1	0	1	0
	Indices	10	6	1	1	0	2	0
Yamaguchi / Kyushu	Measurements	13	5	6	0	2	1	1
	Indices	9	7	2	2	0	0	0
Yamaguchi / 'Other Japan'	Measurements	12	10	5	1	0	0	0
	Indices	6	9	3	2	0	0	0
Kyushu / 'Other Japan'	Measurements	9	8	8	2	0	0	1
	Indices	9	4	5	2	0	0	0

TABLE 91

MEANS OF HIROSHIMA HAWAIIAN BORN—FEMALES

Measurement		No.	Range	Mean	S.D.	V.
Age		22	20– 39	23.35 ± .50	3.45 ± .35	14.78 ± 1.50
Weight	(lb.)	19	81–140	111.62 ± 1.89	12.24 ± 1.34	10.97 ± 1.20
Stature	(cm.)	22	139–162	150.77 ± .74	5.16 ± .52	3.42 ± .35
Sitting Height	(cm.)	22	74– 85	79.32 ± .36	2.52 ± .26	3.18 ± .32
Trunk Height	(cm.)	22	42– 63	50.22 ± .60	4.20 ± .43	8.36 ± .85
Upper Arm Length	(cm.)	22	24– 31	27.68 ± .25	1.72 ± .17	6.21 ± .63
Lower Arm Length	(cm.)	21	19– 25	21.48 ± .21	1.44 ± .15	6.70 ± .70
Hand Length	(cm.)	22	14– 18	16.36 ± .12	.83 ± .08	5.07 ± .52
Upper Leg Length	(cm.)	22	27– 42	35.04 ± .58	4.00 ± .41	11.42 ± 1.16
Lower Leg Length	(cm.)	22	26– 35	32.05 ± .32	2.25 ± .23	7.02 ± .71
Total Leg Length	(cm.)	22	61– 80	71.96 ± .62	4.30 ± .44	5.98 ± .61
Biacromion	(cm.)	22	33– 39	36.14 ± .41	2.82 ± .29	7.80 ± .79
Cristal Breadth	(cm.)	21	24– 31	27.52 ± .30	2.04 ± .21	7.41 ± .77
Chest Breadth	(cm.)	21	22– 27	23.95 ± .21	1.40 ± .15	5.85 ± .61
Head Length	(mm.)	22	166–197	177.68 ± .86	5.96 ± .61	3.35 ± .34
Head Breadth	(mm.)	22	133–162	149.14 ± .94	6.52 ± .66	4.37 ± .44
Head Height	(cm.)	22	11– 16	13.00 ± .19	1.32 ± .13	10.15 ± 1.03
Minimum Frontal Diameter	(mm.)	22	100–114	107.81 ± .50	3.51 ± .36	3.26 ± .33
Bizygomatic Diameter	(mm.)	22	122–145	133.50 ± .75	5.25 ± .53	3.93 ± .40
Bigonial Diameter	(mm.)	22	94–117	104.69 ± .67	4.69 ± .48	4.41 ± .45
Total Face Height	(mm.)	22	103–129	114.50 ± .94	6.51 ± .66	5.69 ± .58
Upper Face Height	(mm.)	22	59– 84	75.69 ± .85	5.94 ± .60	7.85 ± .80
Forehead Height	(mm.)	22	46– 69	56.22 ± .85	5.88 ± .60	10.46 ± 1.06
Nose Height	(mm.)	22	38– 53	47.68 ± .55	3.80 ± .39	7.97 ± .81
Nose Length	(mm.)	20	34– 53	45.70 ± .65	4.30 ± .46	9.41 ± 1.00

Index		N	Range	Mean ± SE	± SE	± SE
Nose Salient	(mm.)	22	9– 16	12.91 ± .22	1.56 ± .16	12.08 ± 1.23
Nose Breadth	(mm.)	22	28– 35	31.96 ± .26	1.84 ± .19	5.76 ± .59
Inter-Ocular	(mm.)	22	26– 37	31.86 ± .39	2.73 ± .28	8.57 ± .87
Bi-Ocular	(mm.)	22	92–109	100.14 ± .69	4.78 ± .49	4.77 ± .48
Relative Shoulder Breadth		22	21– 26	23.96 ± .15	1.04 ± .11	4.34 ± .44
Relative Hip Breadth		21	16– 21	18.50 ± .18	1.24 ± .13	6.70 ± .70
Shoulder-Hip		21	68– 82	75.72 ± .53	3.57 ± .37	4.71 ± .49
Relative Sitting Height		22	48– 56	52.32 ± .28	1.96 ± .20	3.75 ± .38
Relative Trunk Height		22	29– 42	33.27 ± .39	2.72 ± .28	8.18 ± .83
Brachial		21	69– 88	77.70 ± .74	5.02 ± .52	6.46 ± .67
Tibio-Femoral		22	75–124	92.45 ± 1.76	12.25 ± 1.25	13.25 ± 1.35
Inter-Membral		21	82–101	91.26 ± .75	5.08 ± .53	5.57 ± .58
Cephalic		22	76– 93	84.22 ± .62	4.28 ± .44	5.08 ± .52
Length-Height		22	60– 89	73.04 ± 1.02	7.06 ± .72	9.67 ± .98
Breadth-Height		22	70–103	87.32 ± 1.32	9.20 ± .94	10.54 ± 1.07
Cephalo-Facial		22	81– 96	89.60 ± .43	2.98 ± .30	3.33 ± .34
Fronto-Parietal		22	66– 81	72.40 ± .46	3.22 ± .33	4.45 ± .45
Zygo-Frontal		22	74– 89	80.40 ± .49	3.44 ± .35	4.28 ± .44
Zygo-Gonial		22	68– 85	78.50 ± .61	4.22 ± .43	5.38 ± .55
Facial		22	72– 98	85.81 ± .79	5.52 ± .56	6.43 ± .65
Upper Facial		22	43– 66	56.69 ± .71	4.95 ± .50	8.73 ± .89
Nasal		22	54– 89	67.96 ± 1.10	7.66 ± .78	11.27 ± 1.15
Nose Salient-Height		22	19– 42	27.08 ± .69	4.83 ± .49	17.84 ± 1.81
Nose Length-Height		20	86–101	95.20 ± .54	3.60 ± .38	3.78 ± .40

TABLE 92

MEANS OF YAMAGUCHI HAWAIIAN BORN—FEMALES

Measurement		No.	Range	Mean ±	S.D. ±	V. ±
Age		24	20– 39	23.90 ± .47	3.45 ± .34	14.44 ± 1.41
Weight	(lb.)	24	81–152	101.98 ± 2.00	14.52 ± 1.41	14.24 ± 1.39
Stature	(cm.)	24	142–165	150.38 ± .71	5.19 ± .51	3.45 ± .34
Sitting Height	(cm.)	24	72– 87	78.92 ± .54	3.92 ± .38	4.97 ± .48
Trunk Height	(cm.)	24	42– 57	49.34 ± .46	3.36 ± .33	6.81 ± .66
Upper Arm Length	(cm.)	24	24– 32	28.08 ± .24	1.73 ± .17	6.16 ± .60
Lower Arm Length	(cm.)	24	20– 25	21.88 ± .17	1.23 ± .12	5.62 ± .55
Hand Length	(cm.)	24	14– 18	16.08 ± .10	.75 ± .07	4.66 ± .45
Upper Leg Length	(cm.)	24	29– 42	35.16 ± .39	2.80 ± .27	7.96 ± .77
Lower Leg Length	(cm.)	24	27– 36	32.08 ± .28	2.00 ± .19	6.23 ± .61
Total Leg Length	(cm.)	24	65– 80	71.26 ± .45	3.28 ± .32	4.60 ± .45
Biacromion	(cm.)	24	33– 40	36.04 ± .23	1.69 ± .16	4.69 ± .46
Cristal Breadth	(cm.)	24	24– 32	28.04 ± .33	2.42 ± .24	8.63 ± .84
Chest Breadth	(cm.)	24	21– 31	24.08 ± .31	2.23 ± .22	9.26 ± .90
Head Length	(mm.)	23	168–193	178.76 ± .80	5.70 ± .57	3.19 ± .32
Head Breadth	(mm.)	24	133–164	148.84 ± .83	6.02 ± .59	4.04 ± .39
Head Height	(cm.)	24	11– 15	13.25 ± .14	1.05 ± .10	7.92 ± .77
Minimum Frontal Diameter	(mm.)	24	100–123	109.64 ± .73	5.28 ± .51	4.82 ± .47
Bizygomatic Diameter	(mm.)	24	122–151	133.62 ± .89	6.48 ± .63	4.85 ± .47
Bigonial Diameter	(mm.)	24	91–117	103.76 ± .88	6.42 ± .62	6.19 ± .60
Total Face Height	(mm.)	24	100–126	113.36 ± .78	5.64 ± .55	4.98 ± .48
Upper Face Height	(mm.)	24	65– 84	76.26 ± .58	4.20 ± .41	5.51 ± .54
Forehead Height	(mm.)	24	38– 81	56.18 ± 1.13	8.20 ± .80	14.60 ± 1.42
Nose Height	(mm.)	24	42– 53	48.08 ± .38	2.78 ± .27	5.78 ± .56
Nose Length	(mm.)	24	40– 51	45.74 ± .34	2.44 ± .24	5.33 ± .52

Nose Salient	(mm.)	24	9– 18	12.67 ± .28	2.01 ± .20	15.86 ± 1.54
Nose Breadth	(mm.)	24	26– 37	31.42 ± .30	2.16 ± .21	6.87 ± .67
Inter-Ocular	(mm.)	24	25– 36	31.38 ± .37	2.69 ± .26	8.57 ± .83
Bi-Ocular	(mm.)	24	94–109	100.00 ± .62	4.48 ± .44	4.48 ± .44
Index						
Relative Shoulder Breadth		24	21– 28	24.00 ± .17	1.20 ± .12	5.00 ± .49
Relative Hip Breadth		24	16– 21	18.66 ± .21	1.50 ± .15	8.04 ± .78
Shoulder-Hip		24	65– 88	77.64 ± .67	4.86 ± .47	6.26 ± .61
Relative Sitting Height		24	49– 56	52.58 ± .24	1.73 ± .17	3.29 ± .32
Relative Trunk Height		24	29– 37	32.75 ± .25	1.83 ± .18	5.59 ± .54
Brachial		24	69– 88	78.16 ± .64	4.64 ± .45	5.94 ± .58
Tibio-Femoral		24	75–114	92.20 ± 1.41	10.25 ± 1.00	11.12 ± 1.08
Inter-Membral		24	82–101	92.84 ± .65	4.74 ± .46	5.11 ± .50
Cephalic		23	76– 91	84.06 ± .51	3.64 ± .36	4.33 ± .43
Length-Height		23	62– 89	73.98 ± .93	6.62 ± .66	8.95 ± .89
Breadth-Height		24	72–105	88.50 ± .95	6.92 ± .67	7.82 ± .76
Cephalo-Facial		24	83– 98	89.34 ± .46	3.32 ± .32	3.72 ± .36
Fronto-Parietal		24	66– 81	73.26 ± .48	3.46 ± .34	4.72 ± .46
Zygo-Frontal		24	74– 91	82.00 ± .50	3.66 ± .36	4.46 ± .43
Zygo-Gonial		24	72– 83	77.50 ± .36	2.58 ± .25	3.33 ± .32
Facial		24	69– 95	84.76 ± .69	5.04 ± .49	5.95 ± .58
Upper Facial		24	52– 66	56.87 ± .54	3.93 ± .38	6.91 ± .67
Nasal		24	52– 79	65.58 ± .81	5.86 ± .57	8.94 ± .87
Nose Salient-Height		24	19– 36	26.36 ± .48	3.51 ± .34	13.32 ± 1.30
Nose Length-Height		24	90– 99	95.34 ± .32	2.30 ± .22	2.41 ± .23

TABLE 93

MEANS OF KYUSHU HAWAIIAN BORN—FEMALES

Measurement		No.	Range	Mean		S.D.		V.	
Age		16	20– 34	24.80 ±	.60	3.55 ±	.42	14.31 ±	1.71
Weight	(lb.)	15	81–140	104.14 ±	2.38	13.68 ±	1.68	13.14 ±	1.62
Stature	(cm.)	17	142–159	149.18 ±	.66	4.05 ±	.47	2.71 ±	.31
Sitting Height	(cm.)	17	74– 85	78.50 ±	.49	3.00 ±	.35	3.82 ±	.44
Trunk Height	(cm.)	17	40– 53	48.74 ±	.56	3.42 ±	.40	7.02 ±	.81
Upper Arm Length	(cm.)	17	25– 32	28.53 ±	.26	1.58 ±	.18	5.54 ±	.64
Lower Arm Length	(cm.)	17	19– 24	21.35 ±	.22	1.33 ±	.15	6.23 ±	.72
Hand Length	(cm.)	17	15– 18	16.12 ±	.12	.76 ±	.08	4.71 ±	.54
Upper Leg Length	(cm.)	17	27– 40	34.32 ±	.51	3.14 ±	.36	9.15 ±	1.06
Lower Leg Length	(cm.)	17	28– 34	31.59 ±	.26	1.57 ±	.18	4.97 ±	.57
Total Leg Length	(cm.)	17	63– 76	70.56 ±	.54	3.30 ±	.38	4.68 ±	.54
Biacromion	(cm.)	17	32– 40	36.47 ±	.29	1.79 ±	.21	4.91 ±	.57
Cristal Breadth	(cm.)	17	26– 31	28.18 ±	.27	1.66 ±	.19	5.89 ±	.68
Chest Breadth	(cm.)	17	21– 27	24.59 ±	.24	1.46 ±	.17	5.94 ±	.69
Head Length	(mm.)	15	166–189	176.38 ±	.94	5.40 ±	.66	3.06 ±	.38
Head Breadth	(mm.)	17	137–158	147.50 ±	.76	4.66 ±	.54	3.16 ±	.37
Head Height	(cm.)	17	11– 16	12.30 ±	.41	2.48 ±	.29	20.16 ±	2.33
Minimum Frontal Diameter	(mm.)	17	100–117	108.23 ±	.72	4.38 ±	.51	4.05 ±	.47
Bizygomatic Diameter	(mm.)	17	125–145	133.59 ±	.79	4.83 ±	.56	3.62 ±	.42
Bigonial Diameter	(mm.)	17	97–117	105.59 ±	.83	5.07 ±	.59	4.80 ±	.56
Total Face Height	(mm.)	17	100–126	114.23 ±	1.05	6.42 ±	.74	5.62 ±	.65
Upper Face Height	(mm.)	17	63– 86	77.62 ±	.83	5.06 ±	.59	6.52 ±	.75
Forehead Height	(mm.)	17	42– 77	55.74 ±	1.52	9.28 ±	1.07	16.65 ±	1.93
Nose Height	(mm.)	17	46– 57	48.86 ±	.46	2.84 ±	.33	5.81 ±	.67
Nose Length	(mm.)	17	42– 55	46.98 ±	.53	3.26 ±	.38	6.94 ±	.80

Index		N	Range			
Nose Salient	(mm.)	17	9– 16	12.94 ± .32	1.98 ± .23	15.30 ± 1.77
Nose Breadth	(mm.)	17	28– 39	32.74 ± .47	2.90 ± .34	8.86 ± 1.02
Inter-Ocular	(mm.)	17	26– 37	30.88 ± .48	2.95 ± .34	9.55 ± 1.10
Bi-Ocular	(mm.)	17	90–109	98.26 ± .85	5.18 ± .60	5.27 ± .61
Index						
Relative Shoulder Breadth		17	21– 28	24.44 ± .23	1.40 ± .16	5.73 ± .66
Relative Hip Breadth		17	16– 21	18.86 ± .20	1.24 ± .14	6.57 ± .76
Shoulder-Hip		17	68– 85	77.46 ± .72	4.41 ± .51	5.69 ± .93
Relative Sitting Height		17	50– 56	52.59 ± .26	1.61 ± .19	3.06 ± .35
Relative Trunk Height		17	26– 36	32.65 ± .38	2.33 ± .27	7.14 ± .83
Brachial		17	67– 84	75.38 ± .71	4.32 ± .50	5.73 ± .66
Tibio-Femoral		17	75–114	92.90 ± 1.51	9.25 ± 1.07	9.96 ± 1.15
Inter-Membral		17	86–103	93.44 ± .78	4.76 ± .55	5.09 ± .59
Cephalic		15	78– 89	83.96 ± .50	2.88 ± .35	3.43 ± .42
Length-Height		15	62– 91	71.84 ± 1.26	7.22 ± .89	10.05 ± 1.24
Breadth-Height		17	72–105	85.20 ± 1.23	7.52 ± .87	8.83 ± 1.02
Cephalo-Facial		17	87– 96	90.44 ± .41	2.48 ± .29	2.74 ± .32
Fronto-Parietal		17	68– 77	73.20 ± .37	2.28 ± .26	3.11 ± .36
Zygo-Frontal		17	76– 87	80.86 ± .35	2.14 ± .25	2.65 ± .31
Zygo-Gonial		17	74– 85	78.98 ± .48	2.96 ± .34	3.75 ± .43
Facial		17	75– 92	85.36 ± .77	4.71 ± .54	5.52 ± .64
Upper Facial		17	49– 66	57.95 ± .53	3.24 ± .39	5.06 ± .60
Nasal		17	58– 83	67.08 ± 1.08	6.62 ± .77	9.87 ± 1.14
Nose Salient-Height		17	19– 33	26.54 ± .66	4.02 ± .46	15.15 ± 1.75
Nose Length-Height		17	92–101	96.14 ± .38	2.30 ± .27	2.39 ± .28

TABLE 94

MEANS OF 'OTHER JAPAN' HAWAIIAN BORN—FEMALES

Measurement		No.	Range	Mean	S.D.	V.
Age		16	20– 49	26.05 ± 1.12	6.65 ± .79	25.53 ± 3.04
Weight	(lb.)	16	81–140	104.50 ± 2.27	13.44 ± 1.60	12.86 ± 1.53
Stature	(cm.)	16	145–162	151.82 ± .73	4.32 ± .52	2.85 ± .34
Sitting Height	(cm.)	16	74– 85	79.26 ± .45	2.64 ± .31	3.33 ± .40
Trunk Height	(cm.)	16	46– 53	49.88 ± .33	1.96 ± .23	3.93 ± .47
Upper Arm Length	(cm.)	16	26– 31	28.12 ± .25	1.50 ± .18	5.33 ± .64
Lower Arm Length	(cm.)	16	20– 23	21.81 ± .14	.81 ± .10	3.71 ± .44
Hand Length	(cm.)	16	15– 18	16.38 ± .14	.86 ± .10	5.25 ± .63
Upper Leg Length	(cm.)	16	29– 38	34.88 ± .41	2.42 ± .29	6.94 ± .83
Lower Leg Length	(cm.)	16	27– 35	32.38 ± .30	1.80 ± .21	5.56 ± .66
Total Leg Length	(cm.)	16	67– 78	72.26 ± .43	2.54 ± .30	3.52 ± .30
Biacromion	(cm.)	16	34– 38	36.12 ± .21	1.27 ± .15	3.52 ± .42
Cristal Breadth	(cm.)	16	23– 32	28.38 ± .43	2.57 ± .31	9.06 ± 1.08
Chest Breadth	(cm.)	16	22– 28	24.38 ± .30	1.76 ± .21	7.22 ± .86
Head Length	(mm.)	15	170–199	178.76 ± 1.18	6.76 ± .83	3.78 ± .47
Head Breadth	(mm.)	16	143–162	149.62 ± .75	4.44 ± .53	2.97 ± .35
Head Height	(cm.)	16	12– 15	13.06 ± .16	.97 ± .12	7.43 ± .89
Minimum Frontal Diameter	(mm.)	16	103–117	110.57 ± .51	3.03 ± .36	2.74 ± .33
Bizygomatic Diameter	(mm.)	16	128–157	136.32 ± 1.06	6.27 ± .75	4.60 ± .55
Bigonial Diameter	(mm.)	16	91–120	105.86 ± .96	5.70 ± .68	5.38 ± .64
Total Face Height	(mm.)	16	103–123	113.36 ± .88	5.19 ± .62	4.58 ± .55
Upper Face Height	(mm.)	16	71– 86	76.88 ± .61	3.64 ± .43	4.73 ± .56
Forehead Height	(mm.)	16	46– 73	54.50 ± 1.13	6.72 ± .80	12.33 ± 1.47
Nose Height	(mm.)	16	40– 59	49.00 ± .68	4.02 ± .48	8.20 ± .98
Nose Length	(mm.)	16	38– 55	46.38 ± .65	3.84 ± .46	8.28 ± .99

Nose Salient	(mm.)	16	9– 15	11.75 ± .26	1.56 ± .19	13.28 ± 1.58
Nose Breadth	(mm.)	16	28– 39	32.12 ± .41	2.46 ± .29	7.66 ± .91
Inter-Ocular	(mm.)	16	26– 38	32.44 ± .58	3.45 ± .41	10.64 ± 1.27
Bi-Ocular	(mm.)	16	90–103	98.38 ± .66	3.90 ± .46	3.96 ± .47
Index						
Relative Shoulder Breadth		16	21– 26	23.88 ± .21	1.26 ± .15	5.28 ± .63
Relative Hip Breadth		16	14– 21	18.74 ± .31	1.86 ± .22	9.93 ± 1.18
Shoulder-Hip		16	62– 88	78.75 ± .94	5.55 ± .66	7.05 ± .84
Relative Sitting Height		16	51– 55	52.38 ± .21	1.22 ± .15	2.33 ± .28
Relative Trunk Height		16	32– 35	32.88 ± .17	.99 ± .12	3.01 ± .36
Brachial		16	71– 86	78.50 ± .64	3.82 ± .46	4.87 ± .58
Tibio-Femoral		16	80–114	92.95 ± 1.37	8.15 ± .97	8.77 ± 1.05
Inter-Membral		16	86–101	91.62 ± .65	3.88 ± .46	4.23 ± .50
Cephalic		15	74– 87	82.64 ± .56	3.22 ± .40	3.90 ± .48
Length-Height		15	60– 85	73.56 ± 1.18	6.76 ± .83	9.19 ± 1.13
Breadth-Height		16	76–101	88.26 ± 1.10	6.52 ± .78	7.39 ± .88
Cephalo-Facial		16	83–106	92.38 ± .76	4.52 ± .54	4.89 ± .58
Fronto-Parietal		16	66– 79	74.50 ± .60	3.54 ± .42	4.75 ± .57
Zygo-Frontal		16	64– 85	81.00 ± .78	4.62 ± .55	5.70 ± .68
Zygo-Gonial		16	68– 85	77.74 ± .72	4.30 ± .51	5.53 ± .66
Facial		16	66– 92	82.75 ± .91	5.37 ± .64	6.49 ± .77
Upper Facial		16	49– 63	56.75 ± .55	3.27 ± .39	5.76 ± .69
Nasal		16	56– 83	66.12 ± 1.10	6.52 ± .78	9.86 ± 1.18
Nose Salient-Height		16	19– 30	24.86 ± .54	3.18 ± .38	12.79 ± 1.52
Nose Length-Height		16	88–101	95.74 ± .61	3.60 ± .43	3.76 ± .45

TABLE 95

DIFFERENCES OF HIROSHIMA HAWAIIAN BORN AND TOTAL
HAWAIIAN BORN—FEMALES

Measurement	Difference	x p.e.
Age	−1.20 ± .66	1.82
Weight	8.32 ± 2.19	3.80
Stature	.54 ± .69	.78
Sitting Height	.44 ± .44	1.00
Trunk Height	.64 ± .50	1.28
Upper Arm Length	− .33 ± .24	1.38
Lower Arm Length	− .13 ± .19	.68
Hand Length	.15 ± .12	1.25
Upper Leg Length	.28 ± .48	.58
Lower Leg Length	.08 ± .27	.30
Total Leg Length	.66 ± .51	1.29
Biacromion	.01 ± .25	.04
Cristal Breadth	− .59 ± .33	1.79
Chest Breadth	− .28 ± .28	1.00
Head Length	− .40 ± .87	.46
Head Breadth	.14 ± .80	.18
Head Height (cm.)	− .10 ± .17	.59
Minimum Frontal Diameter	−1.20 ± .62	1.94
Bizygomatic Diameter	− .57 ± .83	.69
Bigonial Diameter	− .57 ± .82	.70
Total Face Height	.78 ± .87	.90
Upper Face Height	− .57 ± .69	.83
Forehead Height	.44 ± 1.05	.42
Nose Height	− .68 ± .47	1.45
Nose Length	− .48 ± .51	.94
Nose Salient	.29 ± .26	1.12
Nose Breadth	.00 ± .34	.00
Inter-Ocular	.18 ± .43	.42
Bi-Ocular	.82 ± .64	1.28
Index		
Relative Shoulder Breadth	− .14 ± .18	.78
Relative Hip Breadth	− .26 ± .22	1.18
Shoulder-Hip	−2.04 ± .71	2.87
Relative Sitting Height	− .18 ± .24	.75
Relative Trunk Height	.29 ± .31	.94
Brachial	.28 ± .66	.42
Tibio-Femoral	− .30 ± 1.51	.20
Inter-Membral	−1.18 ± .67	1.76
Cephalic	.42 ± .51	.82
Length-Height	− .54 ± .98	.55

[TABLE 95—*continued*]

DIFFERENCES OF HIROSHIMA HAWAIIAN BORN AND TOTAL
HAWAIIAN BORN—FEMALES

Index	Difference	x p.e.
Breadth-Height	$-$ .58 $\pm$ 1.14	.51
Cephalo-Facial	$-$ .52 $\pm$ .51	1.02
Fronto-Parietal	$-$ .84 $\pm$ .46	1.83
Zygo-Frontal	$-$ .80 $\pm$ .51	1.57
Zygo-Gonial	.02 $\pm$ .52	.04
Facial	1.11 $\pm$ .77	1.44
Upper Facial	$-$ .21 $\pm$ .57	.37
Nasal	1.50 $\pm$ .93	1.61
Nose Salient-Height	.84 $\pm$ .57	1.47
Nose Length-Height	$-$ .42 $\pm$ .44	.95

TABLE 96

DIFFERENCES OF YAMAGUCHI HAWAIIAN BORN AND TOTAL
HAWAIIAN BORN—FEMALES

Measurement	Difference	x p.e.
Age	− .65 ± .63	1.03
Weight	−1.32 ± 1.95	.68
Stature	.15 ± .66	.23
Sitting Height	.04 ± .42	.10
Trunk Height	− .24 ± .48	.50
Upper Arm Length	.07 ± .23	.30
Lower Arm Length	.27 ± .18	1.50
Hand Length	− .13 ± .11	1.18
Upper Leg Length	.40 ± .46	.87
Lower Leg Length	.11 ± .26	.42
Total Leg Length	− .04 ± .49	.08
Biacromion	− .09 ± .24	.38
Cristal Breadth	− .07 ± .31	.23
Chest Breadth	− .15 ± .26	.58
Head Length	.68 ± .85	.80
Head Breadth	− .16 ± .77	.21
Head Height (cm.)	.15 ± .16	.94
Minimum Frontal Diameter	.63 ± .59	1.07
Bizygomatic Diameter	− .45 ± .79	.57
Bigonial Diameter	−1.50 ± .78	1.92
Total Face Height	− .36 ± .83	.43
Upper Face Height	.00 ± .66	.00
Forehead Height	.40 ± 1.00	.40
Nose Height	− .28 ± .45	.62
Nose Length	− .44 ± .47	.94
Nose Salient	.05 ± .25	.20
Nose Breadth	− .54 ± .32	1.69
Inter-Ocular	− .30 ± .42	.71
Bi-Ocular	.68 ± .61	1.11
Index		
Relative Shoulder Breadth	− .10 ± .17	.59
Relative Hip Breadth	− .10 ± .21	.48
Shoulder-Hip	− .12 ± .66	.18
Relative Sitting Height	.08 ± .23	.35
Relative Trunk Height	− .23 ± .30	.77
Brachial	.74 ± .62	1.19
Tibio-Femoral	− .55 ± 1.45	.38
Inter-Membral	.40 ± .63	.63
Cephalic	.26 ± .50	.52
Length-Height	.40 ± .96	.42

[TABLE 96—*continued*]

DIFFERENCES OF YAMAGUCHI HAWAIIAN BORN AND TOTAL
HAWAIIAN BORN—FEMALES

Index	Difference	x p.e.
Breadth-Height	.60 ± 1.09	.55
Cephalo-Facial	−.78 ± .49	1.59
Fronto-Parietal	.02 ± .44	.05
Zygo-Frontal	.80 ± .48	1.67
Zygo-Gonial	−.98 ± .50	1.96
Facial	.06 ± .74	.08
Upper Facial	−.03 ± .55	.05
Nasal	−.88 ± .89	.99
Nose Salient-Height	.12 ± .55	.22
Nose Length-Height	−.28 ± .40	.70

TABLE 97

DIFFERENCES OF KYUSHU HAWAIIAN BORN AND TOTAL
HAWAIIAN BORN—FEMALES

Measurement	Difference	x p.e.
Age	.25 ± .78	.32
Weight	.84 ± 2.47	.34
Stature	−1.05 ± .79	1.33
Sitting Height	− .38 ± .50	.76
Trunk Height	− .84 ± .57	1.47
Upper Arm Length	.52 ± .27	1.93
Lower Arm Length	− .26 ± .21	1.24
Hand Length	− .09 ± .13	.69
Upper Leg Length	− .44 ± .55	.80
Lower Leg Length	− .38 ± .31	1.23
Total Leg Length	− .74 ± .59	1.25
Biacromion	.34 ± .29	1.17
Cristal Breadth	.07 ± .37	.19
Chest Breadth	.36 ± .31	1.16
Head Length	−1.70 ± 1.05	1.62
Head Breadth	−1.50 ± .91	1.65
Head Height (cm.)	− .80 ± .19	4.21
Minimum Frontal Diameter	− .78 ± .70	1.11
Bizygomatic Diameter	− .48 ± .94	.51
Bigonial Diameter	.33 ± .93	.35
Total Face Height	.51 ± .99	.52
Upper Face Height	1.36 ± .78	1.74
Forehead Height	− .04 ± 1.19	.03
Nose Height	.50 ± .54	.93
Nose Length	.80 ± .55	1.45
Nose Salient	.32 ± .30	1.07
Nose Breadth	.78 ± .39	2.00
Inter-Ocular	− .80 ± .49	1.63
Bi-Ocular	−1.06 ± .72	1.47
Index		
Relative Shoulder Breadth	.34 ± .20	1.70
Relative Hip Breadth	.10 ± .25	.40
Shoulder-Hip	− .30 ± .79	.38
Relative Sitting Height	.09 ± .28	.32
Relative Trunk Height	− .33 ± .36	.92
Brachial	−2.04 ± .73	2.79
Tibio-Femoral	.15 ± 1.72	.09
Inter-Membral	1.00 ± .75	1.33
Cephalic	.16 ± .62	.26
Length-Height	−1.74 ± 1.19	1.46

[TABLE 97—*continued*]

DIFFERENCES OF KYUSHU HAWAIIAN BORN AND TOTAL
HAWAIIAN BORN—FEMALES

Index	Difference	x p.e.
Breadth-Height	−2.70 ± 1.30	2.08
Cephalo-Facial	.32 ± .58	.55
Fronto-Parietal	− .04 ± .53	.08
Zygo-Frontal	− .34 ± .58	.59
Zygo-Gonial	.50 ± .59	.85
Facial	.66 ± .88	.75
Upper Facial	1.05 ± .65	1.62
Nasal	.62 ± 1.06	.58
Nose Salient-Height	.30 ± .65	.46
Nose Length-Height	.52 ± .48	1.08

TABLE 98

DIFFERENCES OF 'OTHER JAPAN' HAWAIIAN BORN AND TOTAL
HAWAIIAN BORN—FEMALES

Measurement	Difference	x p.e.
Age	1.50 ± .78	1.92
Weight	1.20 ± 2.39	.50
Stature	1.59 ± .81	1.96
Sitting Height	.38 ± .52	.73
Trunk Height	.30 ± .58	.52
Upper Arm Length	.11 ± .28	.39
Lower Arm Length	.20 ± .22	.91
Hand Length	.17 ± .14	1.21
Upper Leg Length	.12 ± .57	.21
Lower Leg Length	.41 ± .32	1.28
Total Leg Length	.96 ± .60	1.60
Biacromion	− .01 ± .30	.03
Cristal Breadth	.27 ± .38	.71
Chest Breadth	.15 ± .32	.47
Head Length	.68 ± 1.05	.65
Head Breadth	.62 ± .94	.66
Head Height (cm.)	− .04 ± .20	.20
Minimum Frontal Diameter	1.56 ± .72	2.17
Bizygomatic Diameter	2.25 ± .97	2.32
Bigonial Diameter	.60 ± .96	.62
Total Face Height	− .36 ± 1.02	.35
Upper Face Height	.62 ± .81	.77
Forehead Height	−1.28 ± 1.23	1.04
Nose Height	.64 ± .55	1.16
Nose Length	.20 ± .57	.35
Nose Salient	− .87 ± .31	2.81
Nose Breadth	.16 ± .40	.40
Inter-Ocular	.76 ± .51	1.49
Bi-Ocular	− .94 ± .75	1.25
Index		
Relative Shoulder Breadth	− .22 ± .21	1.05
Relative Hip Breadth	− .02 ± .25	.08
Shoulder-Hip	.99 ± .81	1.22
Relative Sitting Height	− .12 ± .28	.43
Relative Trunk Height	− .10 ± .37	.27
Brachial	1.08 ± .76	1.42
Tibio-Femoral	.20 ± 1.77	.11
Inter-Membral	− .82 ± .77	1.06
Cephalic	−1.16 ± .62	1.87
Length-Height	− .02 ± 1.19	.02

[TABLE 98—*continued*]

DIFFERENCES OF 'OTHER JAPAN' HAWAIIAN BORN AND TOTAL
HAWAIIAN BORN—FEMALES

Index	Difference	x p.e.
Breadth-Height	.36 ± 1.34	.27
Cephalo-Facial	2.26 ± .60	3.77
Fronto-Parietal	1.26 ± .54	2.33
Zygo-Frontal	− .20 ± .59	.34
Zygo-Gonial	− .74 ± .61	1.21
Facial	−1.95 ± .91	2.14
Upper Facial	− .15 ± .67	.22
Nasal	− .34 ± 1.10	.31
Nose Salient-Height	−1.38 ± .67	2.06
Nose Length-Height	.12 ± .50	.24

TABLE 99

DISTRIBUTION OF THE X P.E.'S OF THE DIFFERENCES BETWEEN THE PREFECTURAL GROUPS OF HAWAIIAN BORN FEMALES AND THE TOTAL HAWAIIAN BORN FEMALES

		0–.99	1.00–1.99	2.00–2.99	3.00–3.99	4.00–4.99	5.00–5.99	6.00–X
Hiroshima Hawaiian Born	Measurements	16	11	0	1	0	0	0
Total Hawaiian Born	Indices	11	8	1	0	0	0	0
Yamaguchi Hawaiian Born	Measurements	22	6	0	0	0	0	0
Total Hawaiian Born	Indices	16	4	0	0	0	0	0
Kyushu Hawaiian Born	Measurements	10	16	1	0	1	0	0
Total Hawaiian Born	Indices	13	5	2	0	0	0	0
'Other Japan' Hawaiian Born	Measurements	17	8	3	0	0	0	0
Total Hawaiian Born	Indices	10	6	3	1	0	0	0

TABLE 100

DIFFERENCES OF MEANS OF HAWAIIAN BORN FEMALES BY PREFECTURE

Hiroshima
Yamaguchi

Measurement	Difference	x p.e.
Age	.55 ± .69	.80
Weight	−9.64 ± 2.75	3.51
Stature	− .39 ± 1.02	.38
Sitting Height	− .40 ± .65	.62
Trunk Height	− .88 ± .76	1.16
Upper Arm Length	.40 ± .35	1.14
Lower Arm Length	.40 ± .27	1.48
Hand Length	− .28 ± .16	1.75
Upper Leg Length	.12 ± .70	.17
Lower Leg Length	.03 ± .43	.07
Total Leg Length	− .70 ± .77	.91
Biacromion	− .10 ± .47	.21
Cristal Breadth	.52 ± .45	1.16
Chest Breadth	.13 ± .37	.35
Head Length	1.08 ± 1.17	.92
Head Breadth	− .30 ± 1.25	.24
Head Height	.25 ± .24	1.04
Minimum Frontal Diameter	1.83 ± .88	2.08
Bizygomatic Diameter	.12 ± 1.16	.10
Bigonial Diameter	− .93 ± 1.10	.85
Total Face Height	−1.14 ± 1.22	.93
Upper Face Height	.57 ± 1.03	.55
Forehead Height	− .04 ± 1.41	.03
Nose Height	.40 ± .67	.60
Nose Length	.04 ± .73	.05
Nose Salient	− .24 ± .36	.67
Nose Breadth	− .54 ± .40	1.35
Inter-Ocular	− .48 ± .54	.89
Bi-Ocular	− .14 ± .93	.15
Index		
Relative Shoulder Breadth	.04 ± .23	.17
Relative Hip Breadth	.16 ± .28	.57
Shoulder-Hip	1.92 ± .85	2.26
Relative Sitting Height	.26 ± .37	.70
Relative Trunk Height	− .52 ± .46	1.13
Brachial	.46 ± .98	.47
Tibio-Femoral	− .25 ± 2.26	.11
Inter-Membral	1.58 ± .99	1.60

[Continued]

[TABLE 100—*continued*]

DIFFERENCES OF MEANS OF HAWAIIAN BORN FEMALES BY PREFECTURE

Hiroshima
Yamaguchi

Index	Difference	x p.e.
Cephalic	— .16 ± .80	.20
Length-Height	.94 ± 1.38	.68
Breadth-Height	1.18 ± 1.62	.73
Cephalo-Facial	— .26 ± .63	.41
Fronto-Parietal	.86 ± .66	1.30
Zygo-Frontal	1.60 ± .70	2.29
Zygo-Gonial	—1.00 ± .71	1.41
Facial	—1.05 ± 1.05	1.00
Upper Facial	.18 ± .89	.20
Nasal	—2.38 ± 1.37	1.74
Nose Salient-Height	— .72 ± .84	.86
Nose Length-Height	.14 ± .63	.22

TABLE 101

DIFFERENCES OF MEANS OF HAWAIIAN BORN FEMALES BY PREFECTURE

Hiroshima
Kyushu

Measurement	Difference	x p.e.
Age	$-1.45 \pm .78$	1.86
Weight	7.48 ± 3.04	2.46
Stature	$1.59 \pm .99$	1.61
Sitting Height	$.82 \pm .61$	1.34
Trunk Height	$1.48 \pm .82$	1.80
Upper Arm Length	$- .85 \pm .36$	2.36
Lower Arm Length	$.13 \pm .30$	.43
Hand Length	$.24 \pm .17$	1.41
Upper Leg Length	$.72 \pm .77$	.94
Lower Leg Length	$.46 \pm .41$	1.12
Total Leg Length	$1.40 \pm .82$	1.71
Biacromion	$- .33 \pm .50$	.66
Cristal Breadth	$- .66 \pm .40$	1.65
Chest Breadth	$- .64 \pm .32$	2.00
Head Length	1.30 ± 1.27	1.02
Head Breadth	1.64 ± 1.21	1.36
Head Height	$.70 \pm .45$	1.56
Minimum Frontal Diameter	$- .42 \pm .88$	.48
Bizygomatic Diameter	$- .09 \pm 1.09$	.08
Bigonial Diameter	$- .90 \pm 1.07$	.84
Total Face Height	$.27 \pm 1.41$	.19
Upper Face Height	-1.93 ± 1.19	1.62
Forehead Height	$.48 \pm 1.74$	.28
Nose Height	$-1.18 \pm .72$	1.64
Nose Length	$-1.28 \pm .84$	1.52
Nose Salient	$- .03 \pm .39$	.08
Nose Breadth	$- .78 \pm .54$	1.44
Inter-Ocular	$.98 \pm .62$	1.58
Bi-Ocular	1.88 ± 1.10	1.71

Index		
Relative Shoulder Breadth	$- .48 \pm .27$	1.78
Relative Hip Breadth	$- .36 \pm .27$	1.33
Shoulder-Hip	$-1.74 \pm .89$	1.96
Relative Sitting Height	$- .27 \pm .38$	.71
Relative Trunk Height	$.62 \pm .54$	1.15
Brachial	2.32 ± 1.02	2.27
Tibio-Femoral	$- .45 \pm 2.32$	.19
Inter-Membral	-2.18 ± 1.08	2.02

[Continued]

[TABLE 101—*continued*]

DIFFERENCES OF MEANS OF HAWAIIAN BORN FEMALES BY PREFECTURE

$$\frac{\text{Hiroshima}}{\text{Kyushu}}$$

Index	Difference	x p.e.
Cephalic	.26 ± .80	.32
Length-Height	1.20 ± 1.62	.74
Breadth-Height	2.12 ± 1.81	1.17
Cephalo-Facial	− .84 ± .59	1.42
Fronto-Parietal	− .80 ± .59	1.36
Zygo-Frontal	− .46 ± .60	.77
Zygo-Gonial	− .48 ± .78	.62
Facial	.45 ± 1.10	.41
Upper Facial	−1.26 ± .89	1.42
Nasal	.88 ± 1.54	.57
Nose Salient-Height	.54 ± .95	.57
Nose Length-Height	− .94 ± .66	1.42

TABLE 102

DIFFERENCES OF MEANS OF HAWAIIAN BORN FEMALES BY PREFECTURE

Hiroshima
'Other Japan'

Measurement	Difference	x p.e.
Age	−2.70 ± 1.22	2.21
Weight	7.12 ± 2.95	2.41
Stature	−1.05 ± 1.04	1.01
Sitting Height	.06 ± .58	.10
Trunk Height	.34 ± .68	.50
Upper Arm Length	− .44 ± .35	1.26
Lower Arm Length	− .33 ± .25	1.32
Hand Length	− .02 ± .18	.11
Upper Leg Length	.16 ± .71	.23
Lower Leg Length	− .33 ± .44	.75
Total Leg Length	− .30 ± .75	.40
Biacromion	.02 ± .46	.04
Cristal Breadth	− .86 ± .52	1.65
Chest Breadth	− .43 ± .37	1.16
Head Length	−1.08 ± 1.46	.74
Head Breadth	− .48 ± 1.20	.40
Head Height	− .06 ± .25	.24
Minimum Frontal Diameter	−2.76 ± ,71	3.89
Bizygomatic Diameter	−2.82 ± 1.30	2.17
Bigonial Diameter	−1.17 ± 1.17	1.00
Total Face Height	1.14 ± 1.29	.88
Upper Face Height	−1.19 ± 1.04	1.14
Forehead Height	1.72 ± 1.41	1.22
Nose Height	−1.32 ± .87	1.52
Nose Length	− .68 ± .92	.74
Nose Salient	1.16 ± .34	3.41
Nose Breadth	− .16 ± .49	.33
Inter-Ocular	− .58 ± .70	.83
Bi-Ocular	1.76 ± .95	1.85

Index		
Relative Shoulder Breadth	.08 ± .26	.31
Relative Hip Breadth	− .24 ± .36	.67
Shoulder-Hip	−3.03 ± 1.08	2.81
Relative Sitting Height	− .06 ± .35	.17
Relative Trunk Height	.39 ± .43	.91
Brachial	− .80 ± .98	.82
Tibio-Femoral	− .50 ± 2.23	.22
Inter-Membral	− .36 ± .99	.36

[*Continued*]

[TABLE 102—*continued*]

DIFFERENCES OF MEANS OF HAWAIIAN BORN FEMALES BY PREFECTURE

Hiroshima
'Other Japan'

Index	Difference	x p.e.
Cephalic	1.58 ± .84	1.88
Length-Height	− .52 ± 1.56	.33
Breadth-Height	− .94 ± 1.72	.55
Cephalo-Facial	−2.78 ± .87	3.20
Fronto-Parietal	−2.10 ± .76	2.76
Zygo-Frontal	− .60 ± .92	.65
Zygo-Gonial	.76 ± .94	.81
Facial	3.06 ± 1.20	2.55
Upper Facial	− .06 ± .90	.07
Nasal	1.84 ± 1.56	1.18
Nose Salient-Height	2.22 ± .88	2.52
Nose Length-Height	− .54 ± .81	.67

TABLE 103

DIFFERENCES OF MEANS OF HAWAIIAN BORN FEMALES BY PREFECTURE

Yamaguchi
Kyushu

Measurement	Difference	x p.e.
Age	— .90 ± .76	1.18
Weight	—2.16 ± 3.11	.69
Stature	1.20 ± .97	1.24
Sitting Height	.42 ± .73	.58
Trunk Height	.60 ± .72	.83
Upper Arm Length	— .45 ± .35	1.29
Lower Arm Length	.53 ± .28	1.89
Hand Length	— .04 ± .16	.25
Upper Leg Length	.84 ± .64	1.31
Lower Leg Length	.49 ± .38	1.29
Total Leg Length	.70 ± .70	1.00
Biacromion	— .43 ± .37	1.16
Cristal Breadth	— .14 ± .43	.33
Chest Breadth	— .51 ± .39	1.31
Head Length	2.38 ± 1.23	1.93
Head Breadth	1.34 ± 1.13	1.19
Head Height	.95 ± .43	2.21
Minimum Frontal Diameter	1.41 ± 1.02	1.38
Bizygomatic Diameter	.03 ± 1.19	.03
Bigonial Diameter	—1.83 ± 1.21	1.51
Total Face Height	— .87 ± 1.31	.66
Upper Face Height	—1.36 ± 1.01	1.35
Forehead Height	.44 ± 1.89	.23
Nose Height	— .78 ± .60	1.30
Nose Length	—1.24 ± .63	1.97
Nose Salient	— .27 ± .43	.63
Nose Breadth	—1.32 ± .56	2.36
Inter-Ocular	.50 ± .61	.82
Bi-Ocular	1.74 ± 1.05	1.66
Index		
Relative Shoulder Breadth	— .44 ± .29	1.52
Relative Hip Breadth	— .20 ± .29	.69
Shoulder-Hip	.18 ± .98	.18
Relative Sitting Height	— .01 ± .35	.03
Relative Trunk Height	.10 ± .45	.22
Brachial	2.78 ± .96	2.90
Tibio-Femoral	— .70 ± 2.07	.34
Inter-Membral	— .60 ± 1.01	.59

[*Continued*]

[TABLE 103—*continued*]

DIFFERENCES OF MEANS OF HAWAIIAN BORN FEMALES BY PREFECTURE

Yamaguchi
—————
Kyushu

Index	Difference	x p.e.
Cephalic	.10 ± .71	.14
Length-Height	2.14 ± 1.57	1.36
Breadth-Height	3.30 ± 1.56	2.12
Cephalo-Facial	−1.10 ± .62	1.77
Fronto-Parietal	.06 ± .61	.10
Zygo-Frontal	1.14 ± .61	1.87
Zygo-Gonial	−1.48 ± .60	2.47
Facial	−. 60 ± 1.03	.58
Upper Facial	−1.08 ± .76	1.42
Nasal	−1.50 ± 1.35	1.11
Nose Salient-Height	− .18 ± .82	.22
Nose Length-Height	− .80 ± .50	1.60

TABLE 104

DIFFERENCES OF MEANS OF HAWAIIAN BORN FEMALES BY PREFECTURE

Yamaguchi
'Other Japan'

Measurement	Difference	x p.e.
Age	−2.15 ± 1.22	1.76
Weight	−2.52 ± 3.02	.83
Stature	−1.44 ± 1.02	1.41
Sitting Height	− .34 ± .70	.49
Trunk Height	− .54 ± .57	.95
Upper Arm Length	− .04 ± .35	.11
Lower Arm Length	.07 ± .22	.32
Hand Length	− .30 ± .17	1.76
Upper Leg Length	.28 ± .57	.49
Lower Leg Length	− .30 ± .41	.73
Total Leg Length	−1.00 ± .62	1.61
Biacromion	− .08 ± .31	.26
Cristal Breadth	− .34 ± .54	.63
Chest Breadth	− .30 ± .43	.70
Head Length	.00 ± 1.42	.00
Head Breadth	− .78 ± 1.12	.70
Head Height	.19 ± .21	.90
Minimum Frontal Diameter	− .93 ± .89	1.04
Bizygomatic Diameter	−2.70 ± 1.39	1.94
Bigonial Diameter	−2.10 ± 1.30	1.62
Total Face Height	.00 ± 1.17	.00
Upper Face Height	− .62 ± .84	.74
Forehead Height	1.68 ± 1.60	1.05
Nose Height	− .92 ± .78	1.18
Nose Length	− .64 ± .73	.88
Nose Salient	.92 ± .38	2.42
Nose Breadth	− .70 ± .51	1.37
Inter-Ocular	−1.06 ± .69	1.54
Bi-Ocular	1.62 ± .91	1.78

Index		
Relative Shoulder Breadth	.12 ± .27	.44
Relative Hip Breadth	− .08 ± .37	.22
Shoulder-Hip	−1.11 ± 1.15	.97
Relative Sitting Height	.20 ± .32	.62
Relative Trunk Height	− .13 ± .30	.43
Brachial	− .34 ± .90	.38
Tibio-Femoral	− .75 ± 1.96	.38
Inter-Membral	1.22 ± .92	1.33

[*Continued*]

[TABLE 104—*continued*]

DIFFERENCES OF MEANS OF HAWAIIAN BORN FEMALES BY PREFECTURE

Yamaguchi
'Other Japan'

Index	Difference	x p.e.
Cephalic	1.42 ± .76	1.87
Length-Height	.42 ± 1.50	.28
Breadth-Height	.24 ± 1.45	.17
Cephalo-Facial	−3.04 ± .89	3.42
Fronto-Parietal	−1.24 ± .77	1.61
Zygo-Frontal	1.00 ± .93	1.08
Zygo-Gonial	− .24 ± .80	.30
Facial	2.01 ± 1.14	1.76
Upper Facial	.12 ± .77	.16
Nasal	− .54 ± 1.37	.39
Nose Salient-Height	1.50 ± .72	2.08
Nose Length-Height	− .40 ± .69	.58

TABLE 105

DIFFERENCES OF MEANS OF HAWAIIAN BORN FEMALES BY PREFECTURE

Kyushu
'Other Japan'

Measurement	Difference	x p.e.
Age	—1.25 ± 1.27	.98
Weight	— .36 ± 3.29	.11
Stature	—2.64 ± .80	3.30
Sitting Height	— .76 ± .67	1.13
Trunk Height	—1.14 ± .65	1.75
Upper Arm Length	.41 ± .36	1.14
Lower Arm Length	— .46 ± .26	1.77
Hand Length	— .26 ± .18	1.44
Upper Leg Length	— .56 ± .65	.86
Lower Leg Length	— .79 ± .40	1.98
Total Leg Length	—1.70 ± .69	2.46
Biacromion	.35 ± .36	.97
Cristal Breadth	— .20 ± .51	.39
Chest Breadth	.21 ± .38	.55
Head Length	—2.38 ± 1.51	1.58
Head Breadth	—2.12 ± 1.07	1.98
Head Height	— .76 ± .44	1.73
Minimum Frontal Diameter	—2.34 ± .88	2.66
Bizygomatic Diameter	—2.73 ± 1.32	2.07
Bigonial Diameter	— .27 ± 1.27	.21
Total Face Height	.87 ± 1.37	.64
Upper Face Height	.74 ± 1.03	.72
Forehead Height	1.24 ± 1.89	.66
Nose Height	— .14 ± .82	.17
Nose Length	.60 ± .84	.71
Nose Salient	1.19 ± .41	2.90
Nose Breadth	.62 ± .62	1.00
Inter-Ocular	—1.56 ± .75	2.08
Bi-Ocular	— .12 ± 1.08	.11

Index		
Relative Shoulder Breadth	.56 ± .31	1.81
Relative Hip Breadth	.12 ± .37	.32
Shoulder-Hip	—1.29 ± 1.18	1.09
Relative Sitting Height	.21 ± .33	.64
Relative Trunk Height	— .23 ± .42	.55
Brachial	—3.12 ± .96	3.25
Tibio-Femoral	— .05 ± 2.04	.02
Inter-Membral	1.82 ± 1.01	1.80

[Continued]

[TABLE 105—*continued*]

DIFFERENCES OF MEANS OF HAWAIIAN BORN FEMALES BY PREFECTURE

Kyushu

'Other Japan'

Index	Difference	x. p.e.
Cephalic	1.32 ± .75	1.76
Length-Height	−1.72 ± 1.73	.99
Breadth-Height	−3.06 ± 1.65	1.85
Cephalo-Facial	−1.94 ± .86	2.26
Fronto-Parietal	−1.30 ± .70	1.86
Zygo-Frontal	− .14 ± .85	.16
Zygo-Gonial	1.24 ± .87	1.43
Facial	2.61 ± 1.19	2.19
Upper Facial	1.20 ± .76	1.58
Nasal	.96 ± 1.54	.62
Nose Salient-Height	1.68 ± .85	1.98
Nose Length-Height	.40 ± .72	.56

TABLE 106

DISTRIBUTION OF THE X P.E.'S OF THE DIFFERENCES BETWEEN THE VARIOUS PREFECTURAL GROUPS OF HAWAIIAN BORN FEMALES

		0–.99	1.00–1.99	2.00–2.99	3.00–3.99	4.00–4.99	5.00–5.99	6.00–X
Hiroshima	Measurements	19	7	1	1	0	0	0
Yamaguchi	Indices	12	6	2	0	0	0	0
Hiroshima	Measurements	9	16	3	0	0	0	0
Kyushu	Indices	9	9	2	0	0	0	0
Hiroshima	Measurements	14	10	2	2	0	0	0
'Other Japan'	Indices	13	2	4	1	0	0	0
Yamaguchi	Measurements	10	16	2	0	0	0	0
Kyushu	Indices	10	7	3	0	0	0	0
Yamaguchi	Measurements	16	11	1	0	0	0	0
'Other Japan'	Indices	13	5	1	1	0	0	0
Kyushu	Measurements	12	10	5	1	0	0	0
'Other Japan'	Indices	8	9	2	1	0	0	0

TABLE 107

$$\frac{\text{Yamaguchi Sedentes}}{\text{Total Immigrants}}\text{—Males}$$

Measurement	Difference	x p.e.
Weight	−5.00 ± 1.99	2.51
Stature	− .39 ± .65	.60
Sitting Height	2.20 ± .42	5.24
Trunk Height	2.34 ± .38	6.16
Upper Arm Length	.13 ± .22	.59
Lower Arm Length	− .45 ± .20	2.25
Hand Length	− .22 ± .13	1.69
Upper Leg Length	−2.64 ± .45	5.87
Lower Leg Length	− .71 ± .23	3.09
Total Leg Length	−2.58 ± .46	5.61
Biacromion	− .70 ± .20	3.50
Cristal Breadth	.93 ± .19	4.89
Chest Breadth	− .36 ± .17	2.12
Chest Depth	.15 ± .20	.75
Head Length	− .04 ± .76	.05
Head Breadth	.62 ± .55	1.13
Head Height	− .92 ± .13	7.08
Minimum Frontal Diameter	−1.77 ± .58	3.05
Bizygomatic Diameter	− .09 ± .52	.17
Bigonial Diameter	−3.42 ± .67	5.10
Total Face Height	−3.48 ± .81	4.30
Upper Face Height	−8.46 ± .51	16.59
Forehead Height	2.92 ± .90	3.24
Nose Height	−1.32 ± .34	3.88
Nose Length	−2.90 ± .40	7.25
Nose Salient	1.26 ± .27	4.67
Nose Breadth	1.76 ± .33	5.33
Inter-Ocular	.93 ± .31	3.00
Bi-Ocular	− .94 ± .64	1.47

Index		
Relative Shoulder Breadth	− .38 ± .14	2.71
Relative Hip Breadth	.76 ± .13	5.85
Shoulder-Hip	3.33 ± .45	7.40
Relative Sitting Height	1.46 ± .20	7.30
Relative Trunk Height	1.66 ± .19	8.74
Thoracic	1.56 ± .75	2.08
Brachial	−2.06 ± .59	3.49
Tibio-Femoral	4.80 ± 1.31	3.66
Inter-Membral	2.38 ± .55	4.33
Cephalic	.56 ± .53	1.06

[TABLE 107—*continued*]

$$\frac{\text{Yamaguchi Sedentes}}{\text{Total Immigrants}}\text{—Males}$$

Index	Difference	x p.e.
Length-Height	−4.94 ± .70	7.06
Breadth-Height	−6.48 ± .88	7.36
Cephalo-Facial	− .46 ± .35	1.31
Fronto-Parietal	− .94 ± .41	2.29
Zygo-Frontal	− .90 ± .31	2.90
Zygo-Gonial	−2.10 ± .32	6.56
Facial	−2.52 ± .64	3.94
Upper Facial	−5.52 ± .51	10.82
Nasal	5.08 ± .82	6.20
Nose Salient-Height	2.91 ± .47	6.19
Nose Length-Height	−3.20 ± .37	8.65

TABLE 108

$$\frac{\text{Hiroshima Sedentes}}{\text{Total Immigrants}}\text{—Males}$$

Measurement	Difference	x p.e.
Weight	−6.30 ± 1.38	4.57
Stature	− .54 ± .51	1.06
Sitting Height	1.04 ± .38	2.74
Trunk Height	.92 ± .32	2.88
Upper Arm Length	− .19 ± .17	1.12
Lower Arm Length	− .32 ± .14	2.29
Hand Length	− .48 ± .09	5.33
Upper Leg Length	−1.28 ± .32	4.00
Lower Leg Length	−1.40 ± .19	7.37
Total Leg Length	−1.88 ± .40	4.70
Biacromion	− .89 ± .17	5.24
Cristal Breadth	− .11 ± .16	.69
Chest Breadth	−1.04 ± .15	6.93
Chest Depth	.17 ± .13	1.31
Head Length	− .44 ± .59	.75
Head Breadth	−1.48 ± .49	3.02
Head Height	− .81 ± .10	8.10
Minimum Frontal Diameter	− .27 ± .50	.54
Bizygomatic Diameter	−1.32 ± .28	4.71
Bigonial Diameter	−1.71 ± .50	3.42
Total Face Height	−3.36 ± .63	5.33
Upper Face Height	−8.96 ± .45	19.91
Forehead Height	.44 ± .75	.59
Nose Height	− .78 ± .38	2.05
Nose Length	−2.04 ± .39	5.23
Nose Salient	.57 ± .22	2.59
Nose Breadth	.32 ± .28	1.14
Inter-Ocular	.56 ± .31	1.81
Bi-Ocular	−1.34 ± .52	2.58
Index		
Relative Shoulder Breadth	− .46 ± .12	3.83
Relative Hip Breadth	.14 ± .11	1.27
Shoulder-Hip	1.59 ± .44	3.61
Relative Sitting Height	.94 ± .18	5.22
Relative Trunk Height	.74 ± .18	4.11
Thoracic	3.58 ± .47	7.62
Brachial	− .88 ± .32	2.75
Tibio-Femoral	−1.10 ± .46	2.39
Inter-Membral	.84 ± .51	1.65
Cephalic	− .54 ± .31	1.74

[TABLE 108—*continued*]

$$\frac{\text{Hiroshima Sedentes}}{\text{Total Immigrants}}\text{—Males}$$

Index	Difference	x p.e.
Length-Height	$-3.94 \pm .56$	7.04
Breadth-Height	$-4.46 \pm .70$	6.37
Cephalo-Facial	$- .88 \pm .27$	3.26
Fronto-Parietal	$.74 \pm .32$	2.31
Zygo-Frontal	$1.20 \pm .34$	3.53
Zygo-Gonial	$- .50 \pm .33$	1.52
Facial	$-1.74 \pm .50$	3.48
Upper Facial	$-5.97 \pm .35$	17.06
Nasal	$1.48 \pm .76$	1.95
Nose Salient-Height	$1.59 \pm .41$	3.88
Nose Length-Height	$-2.74 \pm .32$	8.56

TABLE 109

$$\frac{\text{Kyushu Sedentes}}{\text{Total Immigrants}}\text{—Males}$$

Measurement	Difference	x p.e.
Weight	2.80 ± 2.25	1.24
Stature	2.28 ± .81	2.81
Sitting Height	3.04 ± .53	5.74
Trunk Height	2.78 ± .42	6.62
Upper Arm Length	1.18 ± .26	4.54
Lower Arm Length	− .25 ± .18	1.39
Hand Length	− .39 ± .10	3.90
Upper Leg Length	−2.12 ± .44	4.82
Lower Leg Length	.26 ± .29	.90
Total Leg Length	− .70 ± .58	1.21
Biacromion	− .28 ± .23	1.22
Cristal Breadth	1.64 ± .21	7.81
Chest Breadth	.97 ± .17	5.71
Chest Depth	.42 ± .18	2.33
Head Length	−1.60 ± 1.37	1.17
Head Breadth	−1.76 ± .59	2.98
Head Height	− .46 ± .14	3.29
Minimum Frontal Diameter	−4.68 ± .80	5.85
Bizygomatic Diameter	− .81 ± .73	1.11
Bigonial Diameter	−3.33 ± .60	5.55
Total Face Height	−4.23 ± .85	4.98
Upper Face Height	−9.54 ± .60	15.90
Forehead Height	− .60 ± 1.30	.46
Nose Height	− .88 ± .39	2.26
Nose Length	−2.10 ± .41	5.12
Nose Salient	1.66 ± .25	6.64
Nose Breadth	.98 ± .36	2.72
Inter-Ocular	1.96 ± .49	4.00
Bi-Ocular	−2.04 ± .70	2.91
Index		
Relative Shoulder Breadth	.92 ± .16	5.75
Relative Hip Breadth	.90 ± .18	5.00
Shoulder-Hip	3.44 ± .67	5.13
Relative Sitting Height	1.08 ± .23	4.70
Relative Trunk Height	1.22 ± .25	4.88
Thoracic	−1.12 ± .64	1.75
Brachial	−4.14 ± .65	6.37
Tibio-Femoral	6.55 ± 1.44	4.55
Inter-Membral	2.14 ± .42	5.10
Cephalic	− .50 ± .55	.91

[TABLE 109—*continued*]

$$\frac{\text{Kyushu Sedentes}}{\text{Total Immigrants}}\text{—Males}$$

Index	Difference	x p.e.
Length-Height	−2.22 ± .82	2.71
Breadth-Height	−2.30 ± .93	2.47
Cephalo-Facial	.56 ± .54	1.04
Fronto-Parietal	−2.12 ± .52	4.08
Zygo-Frontal	−2.74 ± .52	5.27
Zygo-Gonial	−1.98 ± .52	3.81
Facial	−2.34 ± .61	3.84
Upper Facial	−6.39 ± .40	15.98
Nasal	2.58 ± .98	2.63
Nose Salient-Height	3.72 ± .57	6.53
Nose Length-Height	−2.14 ± .40	5.35

TABLE 110

$$\frac{\text{'Other Japan' Sedentes}}{\text{Total Immigrants}}\text{—Males}$$

Measurement	Difference	x p.e.
Weight	−4.20 ± 2.22	1.89
Stature	−1.53 ± .70	2.19
Sitting Height	.02 ± .45	.04
Trunk Height	.80 ± .50	1.60
Upper Arm Length	− .37 ± .25	1.48
Lower Arm Length	− .17 ± .17	1.00
Hand Length	.05 ± .09	.56
Upper Leg Length	− .86 ± .47	1.83
Lower Leg Length	− .96 ± .30	3.20
Total Leg Length	−1.44 ± .55	2.62
Biacromion	− .70 ± .31	2.26
Cristal Breadth	− .46 ± .31	1.48
Chest Breadth	.10 ± .23	.43
Chest Depth	.59 ± .20	2.95
Head Length	3.82 ± .47	8.13
Head Breadth	.70 ± .74	.95
Head Height	− .26 ± .18	1.44
Minimum Frontal Diameter	4.74 ± .63	7.52
Bizygomatic Diameter	2.10 ± .66	3.18
Bigonial Diameter	1.08 ± .59	1.83
Total Face Height	−2.04 ± 1.02	2.00
Upper Face Height	−7.52 ± .66	11.36
Forehead Height	3.96 ± 1.40	2.83
Nose Height	−1.32 ± .43	3.07
Nose Length	−1.66 ± .42	3.95
Nose Salient	.15 ± .29	.52
Nose Breadth	− .14 ± .37	.38
Inter-Ocular	2.00 ± .49	4.08
Bi-Ocular	.68 ± .45	1.51

Index		
Relative Shoulder Breadth	− .18 ± .23	.78
Relative Hip Breadth	− .10 ± .20	.50
Shoulder-Hip	.45 ± .72	.62
Relative Sitting Height	.48 ± .25	1.92
Relative Trunk Height	.71 ± .27	2.63
Thoracic	1.96 ± .67	2.93
Brachial	.48 ± .60	.80
Tibio-Femoral	− .10 ± 1.29	.08
Inter-Membral	1.58 ± .66	2.39
Cephalic	−1.22 ± .48	2.54

[TABLE 110—*continued*]

'Other Japan' Sedentes
———————————————————————Males
Total Immigrants

Index	Difference	x p.e.
Length-Height	−2.62 ± .91	2.88
Breadth-Height	−2.16 ± 1.17	1.85
Cephalo-Facial	1.08 ± .51	2.12
Fronto-Parietal	2.72 ± .48	5.67
Zygo-Frontal	1.90 ± .45	4.22
Zygo-Gonial	− .18 ± .46	.39
Facial	− .15 ± .79	.19
Upper Facial	−6.21 ± .52	11.94
Nasal	1.40 ± .98	1.43
Nose Salient-Height	1.02 ± .59	1.73
Nose Length-Height	−1.16 ± .38	3.05

TABLE III

DISTRIBUTION OF THE X P.E.'S OF THE DIFFERENCES BETWEEN THE PREFECTURAL GROUPS OF MALE SEDENTES AND THE TOTAL MALE IMMIGRANTS

		0–.99	1.00–1.99	2.00–2.99	3.00–3.99	4.00–4.99	5.00–5.99	6.00–X
Yamaguchi Sedentes	Measurements	5	3	3	6	3	5	4
Total Immigrants	Indices	0	2	4	3	1	1	10
Hiroshima Sedentes	Measurements	4	5	6	2	4	4	4
Total Immigrants	Indices	0	5	3	6	1	1	5
Kyushu Sedentes	Measurements	2	6	6	2	4	5	4
Total Immigrants	Indices	1	2	3	2	4	6	3
'Other Japan' Sedentes	Measurements	6	9	6	4	1	0	3
Total Immigrants	Indices	7	4	6	1	1	1	1

TABLE 112

$$\frac{\text{Yamaguchi Sedentes}}{\text{Total Immigrants}}\text{—Females}$$

Measurement	Difference	x p.e.
Weight	−2.52 ± 4.42	.57
Stature	−1.20 ± .71	1.69
Sitting Height	1.28 ± .48	2.67
Trunk Height	2.06 ± .49	4.20
Upper Arm Length	− .76 ± .24	3.17
Lower Arm Length	− .74 ± .28	2.64
Hand Length	− .35 ± .13	2.69
Upper Leg Length	−1.22 ± .72	1.69
Lower Leg Length	−2.80 ± .28	10.00
Total Leg Length	−2.84 ± .65	4.37
Biacromion	− .56 ± .35	1.60
Cristal Breadth	− .04 ± .31	.13
Chest Width	− .39 ± .35	1.11
Head Length	−3.26 ± .94	3.47
Head Width	.28 ± .61	.46
Head Height	− .94 ± .25	3.76
Minimum Frontal Diameter	−3.81 ± .85	4.48
Bizygomatic Diameter	−1.56 ± .64	2.44
Bigonial Diameter	−7.50 ± .91	8.24
Total Face Height	−4.32 ± 1.11	3.89
Upper Face Height	−8.32 ± .94	8.85
Forehead Height	.12 ± 1.35	.09
Nose Height	−2.26 ± .61	3.70
Nose Length	−3.32 ± .68	4.88
Nose Salient	.90 ± .28	3.21
Nose Width	.04 ± .25	.16
Inter-Ocular	.58 ± .45	1.29
Bi-Ocular	−2.52 ± .77	3.27
Index		
Relative Shoulder Breadth	.06 ± .22	.27
Relative Hip Breadth	.38 ± .26	1.46
Shoulder-Hip	1.20 ± .85	1.41
Relative Sitting Height	1.60 ± .33	4.85
Relative Trunk Height	1.85 ± .39	4.74
Brachial	− .68 ± .80	.85
Tibio-Femoral	−6.35 ± 2.19	2.90
Inter-Membral	1.42 ± .82	1.73
Cephalic	1.54 ± .52	2.96
Length-Height	−4.56 ± 1.50	3.04
Breadth-Height	−6.44 ± 1.77	3.64

[*Continued*]

[TABLE 112—*continued*]

$$\frac{\text{Yamaguchi Sedentes}}{\text{Total Immigrants}}\text{—Females}$$

Index	Difference	x p.e.
Cephalo-Facial	−1.42 ± .39	3.64
Fronto-Parietal	−2.82 ± .55	5.13
Zygo-Frontal	−1.94 ± .60	3.23
Zygo-Gonial	−5.04 ± .78	6.46
Facial	−3.15 ± .75	4.20
Upper Facial	−6.33 ± .69	9.17
Nasal	2.82 ± 1.04	2.71
Nose Salient-Height	2.79 ± .57	4.89
Nose Length-Height	−3.18 ± .72	4.42

TABLE 113

$$\frac{\text{Hiroshima Sedentes}}{\text{Total Immigrants}}\text{—Females}$$

Measurement	Difference	x p.e.
Weight	− 13.08 ± 2.09	6.26
Stature	− 2.52 ± .65	3.88
Sitting Height	− .26 ± .48	.54
Trunk Height	1.16 ± .40	2.90
Upper Arm Length	− .86 ± .22	3.91
Lower Arm Length	− .55 ± .17	3.24
Hand Length	− .49 ± .12	4.08
Upper Leg Length	− .30 ± .47	.64
Lower Leg Length	− 2.79 ± .28	9.96
Total Leg Length	− 2.80 ± .48	5.83
Biacromion	− 1.81 ± .21	8.62
Cristal Breadth	− 1.63 ± .25	6.52
Chest Width	− .86 ± .27	3.19
Head Length	.20 ± .87	.23
Head Width	− 1.92 ± .74	2.59
Head Height	− .52 ± .19	2.74
Minimum Frontal Diameter	.66 ± .61	1.08
Bizygomatic Diameter	− .87 ± .72	1.21
Bigonial Diameter	− 5.40 ± .82	6.59
Total Face Height	− 2.91 ± 1.02	2.85
Upper Face Height	− 4.52 ± .70	6.46
Forehead Height	− 1.36 ± 1.01	1.35
Nose Height	− .36 ± .48	.75
Nose Length	− 1.20 ± .53	2.26
Nose Salient	.41 ± .29	1.41
Nose Width	.40 ± .38	1.05
Inter-Ocular	1.65 ± .41	4.02
Bi-Ocular	− 1.88 ± .74	2.54
Index		
Relative Shoulder Breadth	− .80 ± .17	4.71
Relative Hip Breadth	− .58 ± .18	3.22
Shoulder-Hip	.03 ± .67	.04
Relative Sitting Height	1.03 ± .26	3.96
Relative Trunk Height	1.40 ± .26	5.38
Brachial	.98 ± .68	1.44
Tibio-Femoral	− 6.95 ± 1.84	3.78
Inter-Membral	.92 ± .72	1.28
Cephalic	− 1.02 ± .58	1.76
Length-Height	− 2.88 ± 1.13	2.55
Breadth-Height	− 2.30 ± 1.38	1.67

[*Continued*]

[TABLE 113—*continued*]

$$\frac{\text{Hiroshima Sedentes}}{\text{Total Immigrants}}\text{—Females}$$

Index	Difference	x p.e.
Cephalo-Facial	1.04 ± .46	2.26
Fronto-Parietal	1.64 ± .52	3.15
Zygo-Frontal	.90 ± .52	1.73
Zygo-Gonial	− 3.66 ± .53	6.91
Facial	− 1.71 ± .80	2.14
Upper Facial	− 4.05 ± .56	7.23
Nasal	.38 ± 1.03	.37
Nose Salient-Height	.60 ± .60	1.00
Nose Length-Height	− 1.38 ± .57	2.42

TABLE 114

$$\frac{\text{Kyushu Sedentes}}{\text{Total Immigrants}}\text{—Females}$$

Measurement	Difference	x p.e.
Weight	−6.48 ± 3.27	1.98
Stature	−1.68 ± .87	1.93
Sitting Height	1.10 ± .56	1.96
Trunk Height	2.50 ± .46	5.43
Upper Arm Length	.01 ± .22	.05
Lower Arm Length	− .68 ± .17	4.00
Hand Length	− .77 ± .13	5.92
Upper Leg Length	−1.66 ± .53	3.13
Lower Leg Length	−1.88 ± .23	8.17
Total Leg Length	−3.28 ± .65	5.05
Biacromion	.17 ± .22	.77
Cristal Breadth	− .09 ± .33	.27
Chest Width	1.48 ± .36	4.11
Head Length	.16 ± 1.21	.13
Head Width	−3.14 ± .86	3.65
Head Height	− .76 ± .16	4.75
Minimum Frontal Diameter	−2.73 ± .58	4.71
Bizygomatic Diameter	−2.52 ± .79	3.19
Bigonial Diameter	−7.08 ± .83	8.53
Total Face Height	−3.96 ± .98	4.04
Upper Face Height	−5.58 ± .70	7.97
Forehead Height	− .20 ± 1.29	.16
Nose Height	−2.16 ± .52	4.15
Nose Length	−2.64 ± .65	4.06
Nose Salient	.32 ± .25	1.28
Nose Width	.50 ± .36	1.39
Inter-Ocular	.94 ± .52	1.81
Bi-Ocular	−1.76 ± .75	2.35
Index		
Relative Shoulder Breadth	.68 ± .17	4.00
Relative Hip Breadth	.38 ± .24	1.58
Shoulder-Hip	− .39 ± .79	.49
Relative Sitting Height	1.61 ± .27	5.96
Relative Trunk Height	2.34 ± .25	9.36
Brachial	−2.46 ± .56	4.39
Tibio-Femoral	−1.25 ± 1.84	.68
Inter-Membral	2.26 ± .85	2.66
Cephalic	−2.18 ± .69	3.16
Length-Height	−4.02 ± 1.02	3.94
Breadth-Height	−2.56 ± 1.11	2.31

[*Continued*]

[TABLE 114—*continued*]

$$\frac{\text{Kyushu Sedentes}}{\text{Total Immigrants}}\text{—Females}$$

Index	Difference	x p.e.
Cephalo-Facial	.78 ± .64	1.22
Fronto-Parietal	.12 ± .59	.20
Zygo-Frontal	− .78 ± .48	1.63
Zygo-Gonial	−3.78 ± .55	6.87
Facial	−1.47 ± .85	1.73
Upper Facial	−4.14 ± .61	6.79
Nasal	3.72 ± 1.08	3.44
Nose Salient-Height	1.77 ± .56	3.16
Nose Length-Height	−1.16 ± .73	1.59

TABLE 115

'Other Japan' Sedentes
—————————————————— —Females
Total Immigrants

Measurement	Difference	x p.e.
Weight	−5.28 ± 2.63	2.01
Stature	−3.45 ± .79	4.37
Sitting Height	−2.72 ± .56	4.86
Trunk Height	− .68 ± .53	1.28
Upper Arm Length	− .82 ± .36	2.28
Lower Arm Length	− .80 ± .25	3.20
Hand Length	− .29 ± .12	2.42
Upper Leg Length	.16 ± .58	.28
Lower Leg Length	−1.80 ± .40	4.50
Total Leg Length	−2.34 ± .60	3.90
Biacromion	−1.06 ± .31	3.42
Cristal Breadth	−1.42 ± .34	4.18
Chest Width	− .70 ± .30	2.33
Head Length	.74 ± 1.51	.49
Head Width	−1.10 ± .90	1.22
Head Height	.12 ± .27	.44
Minimum Frontal Diameter	.33 ± .79	.42
Bizygomatic Diameter	−3.45 ± .78	4.42
Bigonial Diameter	−7.71 ± .95	8.12
Total Face Height	−1.71 ± 1.11	1.54
Upper Face Height	−3.20 ± .76	4.21
Forehead Height	2.36 ± 1.35	1.75
Nose Height	.26 ± .70	.37
Nose Length	.04 ± .65	.06
Nose Salient	− .35 ± .32	1.09
Nose Width	−1.22 ± .50	2.44
Inter-Ocular	− .67 ± .48	1.40
Bi-Ocular	−2.14 ± .64	3.34

Index		
Relative Shoulder Breadth	.30 ± .26	1.15
Relative Hip Breadth	− .12 ± .26	.46
Shoulder-Hip	−1.41 ± .74	1.91
Relative Sitting Height	.03 ± .30	.10
Relative Trunk Height	.54 ± .34	1.59
Brachial	2.96 ± .95	3.12
Tibio-Femoral	−6.35 ± 1.97	3.22
Inter-Membral	−1.34 ± .90	1.49
Cephalic	− .86 ± .98	.88
Length-Height	− .28 ± 1.74	.16
Breadth-Height	.94 ± 1.82	.52

[*Continued*]

[TABLE 115—*continued*]

'Other Japan' Sedentes
———————————————— —Females
Total Immigrants

Index	Difference	x p.e.
Cephalo-Facial	$-1.38 \pm .46$	3.00
Fronto-Parietal	$.94 \pm .47$	2.00
Zygo-Frontal	$2.32 \pm .51$	4.55
Zygo-Gonial	$-3.66 \pm .79$	4.63
Facial	$.21 \pm .81$	.26
Upper Face Height	$-1.83 \pm .63$	2.90
Nasal	-2.82 ± 1.32	2.14
Nose Salient-Height	$- .96 \pm .69$	1.39
Nose Length-Height	$.18 \pm .44$	.41

TABLE 116

DISTRIBUTION OF THE X P.E.'S OF THE DIFFERENCES BETWEEN THE PREFECTURAL GROUPS OF FEMALE SEDENTES AND THE TOTAL FEMALE IMMIGRANTS

		0–.99	1.00–1.99	2.00–2.99	3.00–3.99	4.00–4.99	5.00–5.99	6.00–X
Yamaguchi Sedentes	Measurements	5	5	4	7	4	0	3
Total Immigrants	Indices	2	3	3	4	5	1	2
Hiroshima Sedentes	Measurements	4	5	6	4	2	1	6
Total Immigrants	Indices	2	6	4	4	1	1	2
Kyushu Sedentes	Measurements	5	6	1	3	7	3	3
Total Immigrants	Indices	3	5	2	4	2	1	3
'Other Japan' Sedentes	Measurements	6	6	5	4	6	0	1
Total Immigrants	Indices	7	5	3	3	2	0	0

TABLE 117

DIFFERENCES OF YAMAGUCHI IMMIGRANTS FROM YAMAGUCHI SEDENTES—MALES

Measurement	Difference	x p.e.
Age	6.55 ± 1.89	3.47
Weight	−2.10 ± 2.44	.86
Stature	.54 ± .83	.65
Sitting Height	−1.38 ± .64	2.16
Trunk Height	−1.72 ± .52	3.31
Upper Arm Length	− .13 ± .30	.43
Lower Arm Length	.11 ± .23	.48
Hand Length	.28 ± .14	2.00
Upper Leg Length	2.74 ± .55	4.98
Lower Leg Length	.83 ± .30	2.77
Total Leg Length	2.34 ± .65	3.60
Biacromion	.31 ± .28	1.11
Cristal Breadth	−1.90 ± .22	8.64
Chest Breadth	− .08 ± .21	.38
Chest Depth	− .98 ± .26	3.77
Head Length	−2.44 ± .98	2.49
Head Breadth	.60 ± .82	.73
Head Height (cm.)	1.30 ± .19	6.84
Minimum Frontal Diameter	1.62 ± .82	1.98
Bizygomatic Diameter	−1.08 ± .74	1.46
Bigonial Diameter	3.21 ± .90	3.57
Total Face Height	4.23 ± 1.00	4.23
Upper Face Height	9.82 ± .70	14.03
Forehead Height	−2.12 ± 1.20	1.77
Nose Height	1.40 ± .40	3.50
Nose Length	3.16 ± .52	6.08
Nose Salient	−1.28 ± .36	3.56
Nose Breadth	−1.58 ± .40	3.95
Inter-Ocular	−1.64 ± .52	3.15
Bi-Ocular	1.20 ± .90	1.33
Index		
Relative Shoulder Breadth	.06 ± .19	.32
Relative Hip Breadth	−1.32 ± .17	7.76
Shoulder-Hip	−5.25 ± .55	9.55
Relative Sitting Height	−1.14 ± .33	3.45
Relative Trunk Height	−1.40 ± .27	5.19
Thoracic	−3.50 ± .97	3.61
Brachial	1.26 ± .74	1.70
Tibio-Femoral	−4.85 ± 1.52	3.19
Inter-Membral	−2.72 ± .74	3.68
Cephalic	1.00 ± .69	1.45

[TABLE 117—*continued*]

DIFFERENCES OF YAMAGUCHI IMMIGRANTS FROM YAMAGUCHI SEDENTES—MALES

Index	Difference	x p.e.
Length-Height	7.44 ± 1.09	6.83
Breadth-Height	8.50 ± 1.21	7.02
Cephalo-Facial	− .98 ± .46	2.13
Fronto-Parietal	.44 ± .52	.85
Zygo-Frontal	1.40 ± .47	2.98
Zygo-Gonial	2.34 ± .45	5.20
Facial	3.72 ± .84	4.43
Upper Facial	6.99 ± .64	10.92
Nasal	−4.80 ± 1.00	4.80
Nose Salient-Height	−2.97 ± .63	4.71
Nose Length-Height	3.30 ± .50	6.60

TABLE 118

DIFFERENCES OF HIROSHIMA IMMIGRANTS FROM HIROSHIMA SEDENTES—MALES

Measurement	Difference	x p.e.
Age	8.35 ± 1.38	6.05
Weight	4.60 ± 1.94	2.37
Stature	− .24 ± .69	.35
Sitting Height	−2.06 ± .45	4.58
Trunk Height	−1.62 ± .39	4.15
Upper Arm Length	.07 ± .23	.30
Lower Arm Length	.55 ± .19	2.89
Hand Length	.47 ± .11	4.27
Upper Leg Length	1.76 ± .42	4.19
Lower Leg Length	1.25 ± .24	5.21
Total Leg Length	2.02 ± .55	3.67
Biacromion	.67 ± .22	3.05
Cristal Breadth	.32 ± .21	1.52
Chest Breadth	.89 ± .20	4.45
Chest Depth	.10 ± .21	.48
Head Length	− .56 ± .77	.73
Head Breadth	1.46 ± .61	2.39
Head Height (cm.)	.73 ± .13	5.62
Minimum Frontal Diameter	.06 ± .72	.08
Bizygomatic Diameter	2.10 ± .53	3.96
Bigonial Diameter	2.34 ± .73	3.21
Total Face Height	2.37 ± .80	2.96
Upper Face Height	8.26 ± .63	13.11
Forehead Height	− .56 ± 1.01	.55
Nose Height	.26 ± .50	.52
Nose Length	1.36 ± .55	2.47
Nose Salient	− .65 ± .28	2.32
Nose Breadth	− .22 ± .38	.58
Inter-Ocular	− .85 ± .41	2.07
Bi-Ocular	2.44 ± .75	3.25
Index		
Relative Shoulder Breadth	.50 ± .15	3.33
Relative Hip Breadth	.06 ± .15	.40
Shoulder-Hip	−1.31 ± .58	2.26
Relative Sitting Height	−1.27 ± .23	5.52
Relative Trunk Height	− .96 ± .23	4.17
Thoracic	−2.16 ± .65	3.32
Brachial	1.96 ± .57	3.44
Tibio-Femoral	− .75 ± .69	1.09
Inter-Membral	−1.00 ± .58	1.72
Cephalic	1.02 ± .38	2.68

[TABLE 118—*continued*]

DIFFERENCES OF HIROSHIMA IMMIGRANTS FROM HIROSHIMA SEDENTES—MALES

Index	Difference	x p.e.
Length-Height	3.96 ± .70	5.66
Breadth-Height	3.94 ± .94	4.19
Cephalo-Facial	1.42 ± .36	3.94
Fronto-Parietal	− .78 ± .43	1.81
Zygo-Frontal	−1.56 ± .44	3.55
Zygo-Gonial	.58 ± .45	1.29
Facial	.72 ± .67	1.07
Upper Facial	5.25 ± .49	10.71
Nasal	− .66 ± .90	.73
Nose Salient-Height	−1.32 ± .50	2.64
Nose Length-Height	4.52 ± .44	10.27

TABLE 119

Measurement	Difference	x p.e.
Age	10.65 ± 1.91	5.58
Weight	1.10 ± 2.76	.40
Stature	− 2.13 ± .90	2.37
Sitting Height	− 3.00 ± .60	5.00
Trunk Height	− 3.04 ± .49	6.20
Upper Arm Length	− 1.11 ± .31	3.58
Lower Arm Length	.11 ± .23	.48
Hand Length	.52 ± .13	4.00
Upper Leg Length	1.80 ± .49	3.67
Lower Leg Length	.04 ± .34	.12
Total Leg Length	.78 ± .63	1.24
Biacromion	.56 ± .28	2.00
Cristal Breadth	− 1.57 ± .32	4.91
Chest Breadth	− .71 ± .24	2.96
Chest Depth	− .20 ± .23	.87
Head Length	4.08 ± 1.48	2.76
Head Breadth	.84 ± .73	1.15
Head Height (cm.)	.35 ± .26	1.35
Minimum Frontal Diameter	5.10 ± .91	5.60
Bizygomatic Diameter	1.35 ± .79	1.71
Bigonial Diameter	2.97 ± .82	3.62
Total Face Height	4.47 ± .99	4.52
Upper Face Height	10.08 ± .70	14.40
Forehead Height	1.00 ± 1.48	.68
Nose Height	1.04 ± .47	2.21
Nose Length	2.32 ± .48	4.83
Nose Salient	− 1.91 ± .30	6.37
Nose Breadth	− .86 ± .45	1.91
Inter-Ocular	− 1.30 ± .54	2.41
Bi-Ocular	.64 ± .82	.78

Index		
Relative Shoulder Breadth	− .82 ± .21	3.90
Relative Hip Breadth	− .80 ± .25	3.20
Shoulder-Hip	− 4.04 ± .82	4.93
Relative Sitting Height	− 1.11 ± .26	4.27
Relative Trunk Height	− 1.34 ± .28	4.79
Thoracic	1.64 ± .82	2.00
Brachial	3.50 ± .80	4.38
Tibio-Femoral	− 5.35 ± 1.49	3.59
Inter-Membral	− 2.10 ± .56	3.75
Cephalic	− 1.04 ± .67	1.55

[TABLE 119—*continued*]

DIFFERENCES OF KYUSHU IMMIGRANTS FROM KYUSHU SEDENTES—MALES

Index	Difference	x p.e.
Length-Height	.00 ± .95	.00
Breadth-Height	1.06 ± 1.15	.92
Cephalo-Facial	.56 ± .61	.92
Fronto-Parietal	2.46 ± .63	3.90
Zygo-Frontal	2.28 ± .63	3.62
Zygo-Gonial	1.52 ± .63	2.41
Facial	1.83 ± .71	2.58
Upper Facial	6.51 ± .53	12.28
Nasal	— 2.84 ± 1.15	2.47
Nose Salient-Height	— 4.11 ± .65	6.32
Nose Length-Height	2.28 ± .50	4.56

TABLE 120

DIFFERENCES OF 'OTHER JAPAN' IMMIGRANTS FROM
'OTHER JAPAN' SEDENTES—MALES

Measurement	Difference	x p.e.
Age	−4.50 ± 2.12	2.12
Weight	5.70 ± 2.55	2.24
Stature	2.55 ± .91	2.80
Sitting Height	.26 ± .62	.42
Trunk Height	− .54 ± .63	.86
Upper Arm Length	.61 ± .26	2.35
Lower Arm Length	.50 ± .21	2.38
Hand Length	− .13 ± .14	.93
Upper Leg Length	.96 ± .58	1.66
Lower Leg Length	.92 ± .34	2.71
Total Leg Length	2.00 ± .68	2.94
Biacromion	.73 ± .37	1.97
Cristal Breadth	.95 ± .35	2.71
Chest Breadth	.15 ± .27	.56
Chest Depth	− .52 ± .25	2.08
Head Length	−2.70 ± .73	3.70
Head Breadth	−1.64 ± .88	1.86
Head Height (cm.)	.49 ± .23	2.13
Minimum Frontal Diameter	−5.31 ± .77	6.90
Bizygomatic Diameter	−2.61 ± .77	3.39
Bigonial Diameter	−2.10 ± .86	2.44
Total Face Height	1.47 ± 1.25	1.18
Upper Face Height	6.68 ± .86	7.77
Forehead Height	−5.56 ± 1.57	3.54
Nose Height	.82 ± .60	1.37
Nose Length	1.80 ± .61	2.95
Nose Salient	− .11 ± .39	.28
Nose Breadth	.00 ± .47	.00
Inter-Ocular	−1.46 ± .64	2.28
Bi-Ocular	− .94 ± .68	1.38
Index		
Relative Shoulder Breadth	.04 ± .26	.15
Relative Hip Breadth	.22 ± .24	.92
Shoulder-Hip	1.38 ± .89	1.55
Relative Sitting Height	− .57 ± .31	1.84
Relative Trunk Height	− .74 ± .33	2.24
Thoracic	−2.42 ± .81	2.99
Brachial	− .28 ± .73	.38
Tibio-Femoral	1.00 ± 1.57	.64
Inter-Membral	−1.40 ± .81	1.73

[TABLE 120—*continued*]

DIFFERENCES OF 'OTHER JAPAN' IMMIGRANTS FROM
'OTHER JAPAN' SEDENTES—MALES

Index	Difference	x p.e.
Cephalic	.28 ± .57	.49
Length-Height	3.46 ± 1.20	2.88
Breadth-Height	4.60 ± 1.45	3.17
Cephalo-Facial	−1.14 ± .56	2.04
Fronto-Parietal	−2.56 ± .58	4.41
Zygo-Frontal	−1.74 ± .52	3.35
Zygo-Gonial	− .20 ± .58	.34
Facial	.36 ± .94	.38
Upper Facial	5.70 ± .61	9.34
Nasal	−1.48 ± 1.31	1.13
Nose Salient-Height	−1.11 ± .75	1.48
Nose Length-Height	1.56 ± .47	3.32

TABLE 121

DISTRIBUTION OF THE X P.E.'S OF THE DIFFERENCES BETWEEN MALE IMMIGRANTS AND SEDENTES BY PREFECTURE

		0–99	1.00–1.99	2.00–2.99	3.00–3.99	4.00–4.99	5.00–5.99	6.00–X
Yamaguchi Immigrants	Measurements	6	5	4	8	2	0	4
Yamaguchi Sedentes	Indices	2	2	2	4	3	2	6
Hiroshima Immigrants	Measurements	8	1	7	5	5	2	1
Hiroshima Sedentes	Indices	2	5	3	5	2	2	2
Kyushu Immigrants	Measurements	6	5	6	3	4	2	3
Kyushu Sedentes	Indices	3	1	4	6	5	0	2
'Other Japan' Immigrants	Measurements	6	6	12	3	0	0	2
'Other Japan' Sedentes	Indices	7	5	4	3	1	0	1

TABLE 122

DIFFERENCES OF YAMAGUCHI HAWAIIAN BORN FROM YAMAGUCHI
IMMIGRANTS—MALES

Measurement	Difference	x p.e.
Age	−18.35 ± 1.33	13.80
Weight	10.50 ± 2.31	4.55
Stature	4.50 ± .74	6.08
Sitting Height	1.72 ± .61	2.82
Trunk Height	.80 ± .49	1.63
Upper Arm Length	1.15 ± .26	4.42
Lower Arm Length	1.18 ± .19	6.21
Hand Length	− .09 ± .11	.82
Upper Leg Length	.72 ± .44	1.64
Lower Leg Length	1.00 ± .30	3.33
Total Leg Length	2.70 ± .60	4.50
Biacromion	1.53 ± .27	5.67
Cristal Breadth	.17 ± .23	.74
Chest Breadth	− .17 ± .21	.81
Chest Depth	.12 ± .25	.48
Head Length	.46 ± .87	.53
Head Breadth	.80 ± .81	.99
Head Height (cm.)	.08 ± .18	.44
Minimum Frontal Diameter	− .33 ± .82	.40
Bizygomatic Diameter	.57 ± .73	.78
Bigonial Diameter	− .39 ± .87	.45
Total Face Height	− 2.16 ± .81	2.67
Upper Face Height	− 1.00 ± .71	1.41
Forehead Height	− .36 ± 1.11	.32
Nose Height	− .10 ± .41	.24
Nose Length	− .76 ± .51	1.49
Nose Salient	.56 ± .33	1.70
Nose Breadth	− .98 ± .40	2.45
Inter-Ocular	1.19 ± .53	2.25
Bi-Ocular	.06 ± .82	.07
Index		
Relative Shoulder Breadth	.22 ± .19	1.16
Relative Hip Breadth	− .44 ± .18	2.44
Shoulder-Hip	− 2.22 ± .56	3.96
Relative Sitting Height	− .35 ± .31	1.13
Relative Trunk Height	− .40 ± .25	1.60
Thoracic	1.12 ± .85	1.32
Brachial	.28 ± .67	.42
Tibio-Femoral	1.55 ± 1.20	1.29
Inter-Membral	.10 ± .64	.16

[Continued]

[TABLE 122—*continued*]

DIFFERENCES OF YAMAGUCHI HAWAIIAN BORN FROM YAMAGUCHI
IMMIGRANTS—MALES

Index	Difference	x p.e.
Cephalic	.40 ± .59	.68
Length-Height	.80 ± 1.07	.75
Breadth-Height	− .28 ± 1.15	.24
Cephalo-Facial	− .14 ± .44	.32
Fronto-Parietal	− .62 ± .51	1.22
Zygo-Frontal	− .34 ± .49	.69
Zygo-Gonial	.14 ± .46	.30
Facial	− 1.62 ± .72	2.25
Upper Facial	− .96 ± .56	1.71
Nasal	− 2.06 ± .92	2.24
Nose Salient-Height	1.23 ± .62	1.98
Nose Length-Height	− 1.16 ± .48	2.42

TABLE 123

DIFFERENCES OF HIROSHIMA HAWAIIAN BORN FROM HIROSHIMA
IMMIGRANTS—MALES

Measurement	Difference	x p.e.
Age	−17.95 ± 1.08	16.62
Weight	3.20 ± 2.54	1.26
Stature	4.14 ± .79	5.24
Sitting Height	3.08 ± .51	6.04
Trunk Height	1.92 ± .46	4.17
Upper Arm Length	1.61 ± .25	6.44
Lower Arm Length	.82 ± .20	4.10
Hand Length	.02 ± .12	.17
Upper Leg Length	− 1.12 ± .51	2.20
Lower Leg Length	1.47 ± .30	4.90
Total Leg Length	.80 ± .62	1.29
Biacromion	.85 ± .24	3.54
Cristal Breadth	− .86 ± .27	3.19
Chest Breadth	− .24 ± .26	.92
Chest Depth	− .87 ± .30	2.90
Head Length	− 4.10 ± .88	4.66
Head Breadth	2.58 ± .73	3.53
Head Height (cm.)	.29 ± .17	1.71
Minimum Frontal Diameter	.06 ± .81	.07
Bizygomatic Diameter	− 1.86 ± .76	2.45
Bigonial Diameter	− 2.40 ± .92	2.61
Total Face Height	− .06 ± .86	.07
Upper Face Height	1.74 ± .72	2.42
Forehead Height	2.00 ± 1.10	1.82
Nose Height	.86 ± .54	1.59
Nose Length	.78 ± .57	1.37
Nose Salient	.01 ± .32	.03
Nose Breadth	− 1.06 ± .46	2.30
Inter-Ocular	2.06 ± .54	3.81
Bi-Ocular	− 2.10 ± .84	2.50
Index		
Relative Shoulder Breadth	− .02 ± .16	.12
Relative Hip Breadth	− 1.02 ± .19	5.37
Shoulder-Hip	− 3.07 ± .67	4.58
Relative Sitting Height	.71 ± .25	2.84
Relative Trunk Height	.33 ± .26	1.27
Thoracic	− 2.56 ± .81	3.16
Brachial	− 1.54 ± .73	2.11
Tibio-Femoral	7.60 ± 1.24	6.13
Inter-Membral	2.68 ± .55	4.87

[Continued]

[TABLE 123—*continued*]

DIFFERENCES OF HIROSHIMA HAWAIIAN BORN FROM HIROSHIMA
IMMIGRANTS—MALES

Index	Difference	x p.e.
Cephalic	3.02 ± .52	5.81
Length-Height	3.08 ± .90	3.42
Breadth-Height	.36 ± 1.13	.32
Cephalo-Facial	— 2.68 ± .42	6.38
Fronto-Parietal	— 1.08 ± .51	2.12
Zygo-Frontal	.94 ± .47	2.00
Zygo-Gonial	— .58 ± .52	1.12
Facial	.69 ± .70	.99
Upper Facial	1.68 ± .56	3.00
Nasal	— 3.24 ± .92	3.52
Nose Salient-Height	— .54 ± .64	.84
Nose Length-Height	— 2.66 ± .43	6.19

TABLE 124

DIFFERENCES OF KYUSHU HAWAIIAN BORN FROM KYUSHU IMMIGRANTS—MALES

Measurement	Difference	x p.e.
Age	−14.80 ± 1.18	12.54
Weight	1.00 ± 2.98	.34
Stature	4.38 ± .86	5.09
Sitting Height	2.18 ± .60	3.63
Trunk Height	1.32 ± .56	2.36
Upper Arm Length	1.24 ± .34	3.65
Lower Arm Length	1.11 ± .29	3.83
Hand Length	− .34 ± .14	2.43
Upper Leg Length	.68 ± .47	1.45
Lower Leg Length	.93 ± .32	2.91
Total Leg Length	2.36 ± .60	3.93
Biacromion	.94 ± .30	3.13
Cristal Breadth	− .14 ± .37	.38
Chest Breadth	− .37 ± .41	.90
Chest Depth	− .76 ± .28	2.71
Head Length	− 4.30 ± 1.14	3.77
Head Breadth	2.70 ± .84	3.21
Head Height (cm.)	.37 ± .24	1.54
Minimum Frontal Diameter	− 1.56 ± .66	2.36
Bizygomatic Diameter	− 2.25 ± .68	3.31
Bigonial Diameter	− .18 ± .81	.22
Total Face Height	− 2.31 ± .86	2.69
Upper Face Height	− .56 ± .74	.76
Forehead Height	− 2.16 ± 1.24	1.74
Nose Height	− .14 ± .49	.29
Nose Length	− .20 ± .50	.40
Nose Salient	.79 ± .34	2.32
Nose Breadth	− 1.92 ± .42	4.57
Inter-Ocular	− .14 ± .50	.28
Bi-Ocular	1.02 ± .76	1.34
Index		
Relative Shoulder Breadth	− .08 ± .19	.42
Relative Hip Breadth	− .88 ± .23	3.83
Shoulder-Hip	− 1.83 ± .70	2.61
Relative Sitting Height	− .15 ± .27	.56
Relative Trunk Height	− .18 ± .29	.62
Thoracic	− 1.88 ± .92	2.04
Brachial	.42 ± .76	.55
Tibio-Femoral	1.75 ± 1.02	1.72
Inter-Membral	− 1.02 ± .74	1.38
Cephalic	3.50 ± .67	5.22

[Continued]

[TABLE 124—*continued*]

DIFFERENCES OF KYUSHU HAWAIIAN BORN FROM KYUSHU IMMIGRANTS—MALES

Index	Difference	x p.e.
Length-Height	4.76 ± .85	5.60
Breadth-Height	1.90 ± 1.09	1.74
Cephalo-Facial	− 3.18 ± .43	7.40
Fronto-Parietal	− 1.64 ± .52	3.15
Zygo-Frontal	.90 ± .52	1.73
Zygo-Gonial	1.08 ± .48	2.25
Facial	.21 ± .69	.30
Upper Facial	.21 ± .62	.34
Nasal	− 3.76 ± 1.02	3.69
Nose Salient-Height	.48 ± .62	.77
Nose Length-Height	− .84 ± .47	1.79

TABLE 125

DISTRIBUTION OF THE x P.E.'S OF THE DIFFERENCES BETWEEN HAWAIIAN BORN AND IMMIGRANT MALES BY PREFECTURE

	0–.99	1.00–1.99	2.00–2.99	3.00–3.99	4.00–4.99	5.00–5.99	6.00–X
Yamaguchi Hawaiian Born { Measurements	13	5	4	1	3	1	2
Yamaguchi Immigrants { Indices	8	8	4	1	0	0	0
Hiroshima Hawaiian Born { Measurements	5	6	7	4	4	1	2
Hiroshima Immigrants { Indices	4	2	4	4	2	2	3
Kyushu Hawaiian Born { Measurements	8	4	7	8	1	1	0
Kyushu Immigrants { Indices	7	5	3	3	0	2	1

TABLE 126

DIFFERENCES OF YAMAGUCHI HAWAIIAN BORN FROM YAMAGUCHI
SEDENTES—MALES

Measurement	Difference	x p.e.
Age	− 11.80 ± 1.53	7.71
Weight	8.40 ± 2.42	3.47
Stature	5.04 ± .76	6.63
Sitting Height	.34 ± .50	.68
Trunk Height	− .92 ± .44	2.09
Upper Arm Length	1.02 ± .24	4.25
Lower Arm Length	1.29 ± .22	5.86
Hand Length	.19 ± .14	1.36
Upper Leg Length	3.46 ± .49	7.06
Lower Leg Length	1.83 ± .30	6.10
Total Leg Length	5.04 ± .53	9.51
Biacromion	1.84 ± .24	7.67
Cristal Breadth	− 1.73 ± .23	7.52
Chest Breadth	− .25 ± .20	1.25
Chest Depth	− .86 ± .24	3.58
Head Length	− 1.98 ± .86	2.30
Head Breadth	1.40 ± .67	2.09
Head Height (cm.)	1.38 ± .16	8.62
Minimum Frontal Diameter	1.29 ± .72	1.79
Bizygomatic Diameter	− .51 ± .64	.80
Bigonial Diameter	2.82 ± .81	3.48
Total Face Height	2.07 ± .88	2.35
Upper Face Height	8.82 ± .63	14.00
Forehead Height	− 2.48 ± 1.04	2.38
Nose Height	1.30 ± .42	3.10
Nose Length	2.40 ± .49	4.90
Nose Salient	− .72 ± .32	2.25
Nose Breadth	− 2.56 ± .40	6.40
Inter-Ocular	− .45 ± .37	1.22
Bi-Ocular	1.26 ± .71	1.77
Index		
Relative Shoulder Breadth	.28 ± .16	1.75
Relative Hip Breadth	− 1.76 ± .16	11.00
Shoulder-Hip	− 7.47 ± .54	13.83
Relative Sitting Height	− 1.49 ± .23	6.48
Relative Trunk Height	− 1.80 ± .22	8.18
Thoracic	− 2.38 ± .88	2.70
Brachial	1.54 ± .68	2.26
Tibio-Femoral	− 3.30 ± 1.49	2.21
Inter-Membral	− 2.62 ± .60	4.37

[TABLE 126—*continued*]

DIFFERENCES OF YAMAGUCHI HAWAIIAN BORN FROM YAMAGUCHI
SEDENTES—MALES

Index	Difference	x p.e.
Cephalic	1.40 ± .59	2.37
Length-Height	8.24 ± .83	9.93
Breadth-Height	8.22 ± 1.04	7.90
Cephalo-Facial	− 1.12 ± .42	2.67
Fronto-Parietal	− .18 ± .52	.35
Zygo-Frontal	1.06 ± .39	2.72
Zygo-Gonial	2.48 ± .38	6.53
Facial	2.10 ± .71	2.96
Upper Facial	6.03 ± .58	10.40
Nasal	− 6.86 ± .97	7.07
Nose Salient-Height	− 1.74 ± .59	2.95
Nose Length-Height	2.14 ± .45	4.76

TABLE 127

DIFFERENCES OF HIROSHIMA HAWAIIAN BORN FROM HIROSHIMA
SEDENTES—MALES

Measurement	Difference	x p.e.
Age	− 9.60 ± 1.14	8.42
Weight	7.80 ± 2.25	3.47
Stature	3.90 ± .73	5.34
Sitting Height	1.02 ± .52	1.96
Trunk Height	.30 ± .46	.65
Upper Arm Length	1.68 ± .23	7.30
Lower Arm Length	1.37 ± .17	8.06
Hand Length	.49 ± .13	3.77
Upper Leg Length	.64 ± .49	1.31
Lower Leg Length	2.72 ± .29	9.38
Total Leg Length	2.82 ± .58	4.86
Biacromion	1.52 ± .22	6.91
Cristal Breadth	− .54 ± .25	2.16
Chest Breadth	.65 ± .23	2.83
Chest Depth	− .77 ± .26	2.96
Head Length	− 4.66 ± .82	5.68
Head Breadth	4.04 ± .70	5.77
Head Height (cm.)	1.02 ± .16	6.38
Minimum Frontal Diameter	.12 ± .70	.17
Bizygomatic Diameter	.24 ± .58	.41
Bigonial Diameter	− .06 ± .78	.08
Total Face Height	2.31 ± .84	2.75
Upper Face Height	10.00 ± .64	15.62
Forehead Height	1.44 ± .99	1.45
Nose Height	1.12 ± .52	2.15
Nose Length	2.14 ± .51	4.20
Nose Salient	− .64 ± .31	2.06
Nose Breadth	− 1.28 ± .42	3.05
Inter-Ocular	1.21 ± .50	2.42
Bi-Ocular	.34 ± .70	.49
Index		
Relative Shoulder Breadth	.48 ± .15	3.20
Relative Hip Breadth	− .96 ± .16	6.00
Shoulder-Hip	− 4.38 ± .62	7.06
Relative Sitting Height	− .56 ± .25	2.24
Relative Trunk Height	− .63 ± .26	2.42
Thoracic	− 4.72 ± .72	6.56
Brachial	.42 ± .53	.79
Tibio-Femoral	6.85 ± 1.05	6.52
Inter-Membral	1.68 ± .62	2.71

[TABLE 127—*continued*]

DIFFERENCES OF HIROSHIMA HAWAIIAN BORN FROM HIROSHIMA
SEDENTES—MALES

Index	Difference	x p.e.
Cephalic	4.04 ± .48	8.42
Length-Height	7.04 ± .84	8.38
Breadth-Height	4.30 ± 1.03	4.17
Cephalo-Facial	− 1.26 ± .37	3.41
Fronto-Parietal	− 1.86 ± .46	4.04
Zygo-Frontal	− .62 ± .45	1.38
Zygo-Gonial	.00 ± .47	.00
Facial	1.41 ± .64	2.20
Upper Facial	6.93 ± .49	14.14
Nasal	− 3.90 ± .97	4.02
Nose Salient-Height	− 1.86 ± .64	2.91
Nose Length-Height	1.86 ± .39	4.77

TABLE 128

DIFFERENCES OF KYUSHU HAWAIIAN BORN FROM KYUSHU
SEDENTES—MALES

Measurement	Difference	x p.e.
Age	−4.15 ± 1.73	2.40
Weight	2.10 ± 3.16	.66
Stature	2.25 ± 1.05	2.14
Sitting Height	− .82 ± .70	1.17
Trunk Height	−1.72 ± .61	2.82
Upper Arm Length	.13 ± .36	.36
Lower Arm Length	1.22 ± .28	4.36
Hand Length	.18 ± .14	1.29
Upper Leg Length	2.48 ± .57	4.35
Lower Leg Length	.97 ± .36	2.69
Total Leg Length	3.14 ± .74	4.24
Biacromion	1.50 ± .31	4.84
Cristal Breadth	−1.71 ± .31	5.52
Chest Breadth	−1.08 ± .39	2.79
Chest Depth	− .96 ± .27	3.56
Head Length	− . 22 ± 1.63	.13
Head Breadth	3.54 ± .85	4.16
Head Height (cm.)	.72 ± .16	4.50
Minimum Frontal Diameter	3.54 ± .86	4.12
Bizygomatic Diameter	− .90 ± .89	1.01
Bigonial Diameter	2.79 ± .71	3.93
Total Face Height	2.16 ± 1.00	2.16
Upper Face Height	−9.52 ± .81	11.75
Forehead Height	−1.16 ± 1.54	.75
Nose Height	.90 ± .51	1.76
Nose Length	2.12 ± .53	4.00
Nose Salient	−1.12 ± .36	3.11
Nose Breadth	−2.78 ± .44	6.32
Inter-Ocular	−1.44 ± .62	2.32
Bi-Ocular	1.66 ± .84	1.98
Index		
Relative Shoulder Breadth	− .90 ± .18	5.00
Relative Hip Breadth	−1.68 ± .23	7.30
Shoulder-Hip	−5.87 ± .78	7.53
Relative Sitting Height	−1.26 ± .30	4.20
Relative Trunk Height	−1.52 ± .33	4.61
Thoracic	− .24 ± .91	.26
Brachial	3.92 ± .81	4.84
Tibio-Femoral	−3.60 ± 1.60	2.25
Inter-Membral	−3.12 ± .69	4.52

[TABLE 128—*continued*]

DIFFERENCES OF KYUSHU HAWAIIAN BORN FROM KYUSHU
SEDENTES—MALES

Index	Difference	x p.e.
Cephalic	2.46 ± .73	3.37
Length-Height	4.76 ± .97	4.91
Breadth-Height	2.96 ± 1.13	2.62
Cephalo-Facial	−2.62 ± .58	4.52
Fronto-Parietal	.82 ± .59	1.39
Zygo-Frontal	3.18 ± .60	5.30
Zygo-Gonial	2.60 ± .56	4.64
Facial	2.04 ± .78	2.62
Upper Facial	6.72 ± .59	11.39
Nasal	−6.60 ± 1.17	5.64
Nose Salient-Height	−3.63 ± .73	4.97
Nose Length-Height	1.44 ± .50	2.88

TABLE 129

DISTRIBUTION OF THE X P.E.'S OF THE DIFFERENCES BETWEEN MALE HAWAIIAN BORN AND SEDENTES BY PREFECTURE

		0-.99	1.00-1.99	2.00-2.99	3.00-3.99	4.00-4.99	5.00-5.99	6.00-X
Yamaguchi Hawaiian Born	Measurements	2	5	6	4	2	1	9
Yamaguchi Sedentes	Indices	1	1	8	0	2	0	9
Hiroshima Hawaiian Born	Measurements	5	3	7	3	2	3	6
Hiroshima Sedentes	Indices	2	1	5	2	4	0	7
Kyushu Hawaiian Born	Measurements	4	5	6	3	8	1	2
Kyushu Sedentes	Indices	1	1	4	1	8	3	3

TABLE 130

DIFFERENCES OF YAMAGUCHI IMMIGRANTS FROM YAMAGUCHI
SEDENTES—FEMALES

Measurement	Difference	x p.e.
Age	2.20 ± 2.67	.82
Weight	3.72 ± 5.29	.70
Stature	− .33 ± .94	.35
Sitting Height	−3.62 ± .54	6.70
Trunk Height	−4.00 ± .61	6.56
Upper Arm Length	.83 ± .37	2.24
Lower Arm Length	.67 ± .30	2.23
Hand Length	.25 ± .14	1.79
Upper Leg Length	1.56 ± 1.00	1.56
Lower Leg Length	1.98 ± .40	4.95
Total Leg Length	3.46 ± .89	3.89
Biacromion	.28 ± .39	.72
Cristal Breadth	.18 ± .49	.37
Chest Breadth	.55 ± .49	1.12
Head Length	1.48 ± 1.12	1.32
Head Breadth	−1.32 ± 1.04	1.27
Head Height (cm.)	.90 ± .31	2.90
Minimum Frontal Diameter	3.39 ± 1.12	3.03
Bizygomatic Diameter	1.59 ± 1.20	1.32
Bigonial Diameter	6.75 ± 1.20	5.62
Total Face Height	3.54 ± 1.32	2.68
Upper Face Height	9.12 ± .98	9.31
Forehead Height	2.56 ± 1.95	1.31
Nose Height	.98 ± .79	1.24
Nose Length	2.12 ± .97	2.19
Nose Salient	−1.58 ± .43	3.67
Nose Breadth	−1.20 ± .50	2.40
Inter-Ocular	−1.20 ± .72	1.67
Bi-Ocular	4.00 ± .98	4.08

Index		
Relative Shoulder Breadth	.06 ± .29	.21
Relative Hip Breadth	.24 ± .40	.60
Shoulder-Hip	− .21 ± 1.28	.16
Relative Sitting Height	−2.44 ± .40	6.10
Relative Trunk Height	−2.73 ± .50	5.46
Brachial	.54 ± 1.06	.51
Tibio-Femoral	2.60 ± 3.19	.82
Inter-Membral	−2.26 ± 1.07	2.11
Cephalic	−2.14 ± .73	2.93
Length-Height	5.82 ± 1.88	3.10

[Continued]

[TABLE 130—*continued*]

DIFFERENCES OF YAMAGUCHI IMMIGRANTS FROM YAMAGUCHI
SEDENTES—FEMALES

Index	Difference	x p.e.
Breadth-Height	6.64 ± 2.19	3.03
Cephalo-Facial	1.96 ± .53	3.70
Fronto-Parietal	3.04 ± .76	4.00
Zygo-Frontal	1.74 ± .91	1.91
Zygo-Gonial	4.08 ± .92	4.43
Facial	2.64 ± 1.07	2.47
Upper Facial	6.54 ± .71	9.21
Nasal	−3.88 ± 1.53	2.54
Nose Salient-Height	−3.69 ± 1.06	3.48
Nose Length-Height	3.02 ± 1.04	2.90

TABLE 131

DIFFERENCES OF HIROSHIMA IMMIGRANTS FROM HIROSHIMA
SEDENTES—FEMALES

Measurement	Difference	x p.e.
Age	.00 ± 2.16	.00
Weight	5.00 ± 2.86	1.75
Stature	2.79 ± .76	3.67
Sitting Height	− .08 ± .57	.14
Trunk Height	−1.58 ± .50	3.16
Upper Arm Length	.54 ± .29	1.86
Lower Arm Length	.45 ± .22	2.05
Hand Length	.35 ± .15	2.33
Upper Leg Length	.94 ± .60	1.57
Lower Leg Length	3.01 ± .34	8.85
Total Leg Length	3.58 ± .60	5.97
Biacromion	1.92 ± .27	7.11
Cristal Breadth	1.22 ± .33	3.70
Chest Breadth	.78 ± .33	2.36
Head Length	−1.56 ± 1.35	1.16
Head Breadth	2.52 ± .91	2.77
Head Height (cm.)	.84 ± .21	4.00
Minimum Frontal Diameter	− .69 ± .86	.80
Bizygomatic Diameter	.84 ± .94	.89
Bigonial Diameter	5.04 ± 1.09	4.62
Total Face Height	1.62 ± 1.19	1.36
Upper Face Height	4.68 ± .85	5.51
Forehead Height	− .08 ± 1.24	.06
Nose Height	1.00 ± .57	1.75
Nose Length	2.20 ± .59	3.73
Nose Salient	− .67 ± .35	1.91
Nose Breadth	− .34 ± .46	.74
Inter-Ocular	−2.27 ± .50	4.54
Bi-Ocular	1.16 ± .85	1.36
Index		
Relative Shoulder Breadth	.84 ± .23	3.65
Relative Hip Breadth	.44 ± .23	1.91
Shoulder-Hip	−1.93 ± .78	2.47
Relative Sitting Height	−1.27 ± .30	4.23
Relative Trunk Height	−1.60 ± .33	4.85
Brachial	− .42 ± .82	.51
Tibio-Femoral	6.20 ± 2.08	2.98
Inter-Membral	−2.80 ± .87	3.22
Cephalic	1.72 ± .73	2.36
Length-Height	5.14 ± 1.34	3.84

[Continued]

[TABLE 131—*continued*]

DIFFERENCES OF HIROSHIMA IMMIGRANTS FROM HIROSHIMA
SEDENTES—FEMALES

Index	Difference	x p.e.
Breadth-Height	3.90 ± 1.50	2.60
Cephalo-Facial	−1.42 ± .57	2.49
Fronto-Parietal	−1.80 ± .59	3.05
Zygo-Frontal	− .84 ± .62	1.35
Zygo-Gonial	3.42 ± .63	5.43
Facial	.60 ± .96	.62
Upper Facial	3.69 ± .77	4.79
Nasal	− .72 ± 1.31	.55
Nose Salient-Height	−1.32 ± .63	2.10
Nose Length-Height	2.72 ± .58	4.69

TABLE 132

DIFFERENCES OF KYUSHU IMMIGRANTS FROM KYUSHU SEDENTES—FEMALES

Measurement	Difference	x p.e.
Age	− .65 ± 2.60	.25
Weight	11.16 ± 4.54	2.46
Stature	2.73 ± .99	2.76
Sitting Height	.44 ± .69	.64
Trunk Height	− 1.32 ± .59	2.24
Upper Arm Length	.42 ± .34	1.24
Lower Arm Length	.56 ± .24	2.33
Hand Length	.92 ± .18	5.11
Upper Leg Length	1.44 ± .71	2.03
Lower Leg Length	1.39 ± .26	5.35
Total Leg Length	2.94 ± .85	3.46
Biacromion	.71 ± .40	1.78
Cristal Breadth	.67 ± .44	1.52
Chest Breadth	− 1.18 ± .54	2.19
Head Length	2.94 ± 1.33	2.21
Head Breadth	1.66 ± .93	1.78
Head Height (cm.)	.67 ± .23	2.91
Minimum Frontal Diameter	2.85 ± 1.06	2.69
Bizygomatic Diameter	1.89 ± 1.17	1.62
Bigonial Diameter	7.65 ± 1.52	5.03
Total Face Height	6.00 ± 1.42	4.23
Upper Face Height	4.64 ± 1.49	3.11
Forehead Height	9.25 ± 1.27	7.28
Nose Height	2.28 ± .77	2.96
Nose Length	3.44 ± .86	4.00
Nose Salient	− .55 ± .31	1.77
Nose Breadth	− .10 ± .51	.20
Inter-Ocular	− .92 ± .63	1.46
Bi-Ocular	1.12 ± .87	1.29
Index		
Relative Shoulder Breadth	− .12 ± .29	.41
Relative Hip Breadth	− .64 ± .35	1.83
Shoulder-Hip	.48 ± .99	.48
Relative Sitting Height	− 1.14 ± .38	3.00
Relative Trunk Height	− 1.92 ± .33	5.82
Brachial	.78 ± .94	.83
Tibio-Femoral	− .30 ± 2.29	.13
Inter-Membral	− 1.10 ± 1.04	1.06
Cephalic	.40 ± 1.08	.37
Length-Height	2.62 ± 1.53	1.71
Breadth-Height	3.34 ± 1.57	2.13

[Continued]

[TABLE 132—*continued*]

DIFFERENCES OF KYUSHU IMMIGRANTS FROM KYUSHU SEDENTES—FEMALES

Measurement	Difference	x p.e.
Cephalo-Facial	− .54 ± .85	.64
Fronto-Parietal	.82 ± .89	.92
Zygo-Frontal	1.22 ± .82	1.49
Zygo-Gonial	4.50 ± .88	5.11
Facial	3.39 ± 1.10	3.08
Upper Facial	4.56 ± 1.14	4.00
Nasal	− 3.16 ± 1.66	1.90
Nose Salient-Height	− 2.34 ± .75	3.12
Nose Length-Height	1.98 ± .81	2.44

TABLE 133

DIFFERENCES OF 'OTHER JAPAN' IMMIGRANTS FROM 'OTHER JAPAN'
SEDENTES—FEMALES

Measurement	Difference	x p.e.
Age	-6.55 ± 2.31	2.84
Weight	4.80 ± 4.37	1.10
Stature	2.07 ± 1.10	1.88
Sitting Height	$2.14 \pm .73$	2.93
Trunk Height	$.38 \pm .68$	.56
Upper Arm Length	$.94 \pm .41$	2.29
Lower Arm Length	$1.06 \pm .33$	3.21
Hand Length	$.31 \pm .16$	1.94
Upper Leg Length	$- .92 \pm .78$	1.18
Lower Leg Length	$1.87 \pm .53$	3.53
Total Leg Length	$1.24 \pm .81$	1.53
Biacromion	$.62 \pm .44$	1.41
Cristal Breadth	$1.19 \pm .54$	2.20
Chest Breadth	$.12 \pm .48$	.25
Head Length	$- .80 \pm 1.82$	.44
Head Breadth	2.38 ± 1.03	2.31
Head Height (cm.)	$- .88 \pm .30$	2.93
Minimum Frontal Diameter	$.75 \pm 1.05$	.71
Bizygomatic Diameter	5.61 ± 1.44	3.90
Bigonial Diameter	7.89 ± 1.06	7.44
Total Face Height	$.18 \pm 1.46$	.12
Upper Face Height	2.88 ± 1.15	2.50
Forehead Height	-1.24 ± 1.71	.73
Nose Height	$- .88 \pm .92$	.96
Nose Length	-1.36 ± 1.04	1.31
Nose Salient	$.75 \pm .55$	1.36
Nose Breadth	$1.74 \pm .66$	2.64
Inter-Ocular	$2.06 \pm .67$	3.07
Bi-Ocular	4.00 ± 1.05	3.81
Index		
Relative Shoulder Breadth	$- .38 \pm .31$	1.23
Relative Hip Breadth	$.12 \pm .43$	.28
Shoulder-Hip	$.42 \pm 1.20$	.35
Relative Sitting Height	$.13 \pm .42$	.31
Relative Trunk Height	$- .43 \pm .41$	1.05
Brachial	-2.52 ± 1.10	2.29
Tibio-Femoral	7.80 ± 3.14	2.48
Inter-Membral	3.38 ± 1.30	2.60
Cephalic	1.34 ± 1.10	1.22
Length-Height	-4.40 ± 1.91	2.30

[*Continued*]

[TABLE 133—*continued*]

DIFFERENCES OF 'OTHER JAPAN' IMMIGRANTS FROM 'OTHER JAPAN'
SEDENTES—FEMALES

Index	Difference	x p.e.
Breadth-Height	−6.62 ± 2.07	3.20
Cephalo-Facial	2.26 ± .79	2.86
Fronto-Parietal	−1.00 ± .57	1.75
Zygo-Frontal	−2.76 ± .75	3.68
Zygo-Gonial	2.88 ± .86	3.35
Facial	−2.61 ± 1.09	2.39
Upper Facial	.18 ± 1.01	.18
Nasal	4.52 ± 1.90	2.38
Nose Salient-Height	2.43 ± 1.26	1.93
Nose Length-Height	−1.74 ± .99	1.76

TABLE 134

DISTRIBUTION OF THE X P.E.'S OF THE DIFFERENCES BETWEEN THE FEMALE IMMIGRANTS AND SEDENTES BY PREFECTURE

		0–99	1.00–1.99	2.00–2.99	3.00–3.99	4.00–4.99	5.00–5.99	6.00–X
Yamaguchi Immigrants	Measurements	4	9	6	3	2	1	3
Yamaguchi Sedentes	Indices	5	1	5	4	2	1	2
Hiroshima Immigrants	Measurements	5	8	4	4	3	2	2
Hiroshima Sedentes	Indices	3	2	6	4	4	1	0
Kyushu Immigrants	Measurements	2	8	10	2	2	3	1
Kyushu Sedentes	Indices	7	5	2	3	1	2	0
'Other Japan' Immigrants	Measurements	7	8	7	5	0	0	1
'Other Japan' Sedentes	Indices	4	6	7	3	0	0	0

TABLE 135

DIFFERENCES OF YAMAGUCHI HAWAIIAN BORN FROM YAMAGUCHI
IMMIGRANTS—FEMALES

Measurement	Difference	x p.e.
Age	−18.40 ± 1.99	9.25
Weight	−12.24 ± 3.82	3.20
Stature	3.39 ± .99	3.42
Sitting Height	2.42 ± .64	3.78
Trunk Height	1.72 ± .63	2.73
Upper Arm Length	.19 ± .39	.49
Lower Arm Length	.21 ± .22	.95
Hand Length	− .42 ± .13	3.23
Upper Leg Length	1.10 ± .85	1.29
Lower Leg Length	1.41 ± .43	3.28
Total Leg Length	.42 ± .81	.52
Biacromion	− .68 ± .32	2.12
Cristal Breadth	− 2.08 ± .53	3.92
Chest Breadth	− 2.16 ± .50	4.32
Head Length	− 2.28 ± 1.13	2.02
Head Breadth	2.90 ± 1.24	2.34
Head Height (cm.)	.47 ± .24	1.96
Minimum Frontal Diameter	− .18 ± 1.10	.16
Bizygomatic Diameter	− 2.61 ± 1.43	1.82
Bigonial Diameter	− 4.56 ± 1.25	3.65
Total Face Height	− 1.32 ± 1.14	1.16
Upper Face Height	.26 ± .79	.33
Forehead Height	− 4.88 ± 1.88	2.60
Nose Height	.36 ± .68	.53
Nose Length	.36 ± .82	.44
Nose Salient	.50 ± .46	1.09
Nose Breadth	− .64 ± .56	1.14
Inter-Ocular	1.77 ± .70	2.53
Bi-Ocular	− .62 ± .93	.67
Index		
Relative Shoulder Breadth	− .94 ± .27	3.48
Relative Hip Breadth	− 1.96 ± .39	5.03
Shoulder-Hip	− 4.08 ± 1.22	3.34
Relative Sitting Height	.64 ± .35	1.83
Relative Trunk Height	.36 ± .42	.86
Brachial	.00 ± 1.01	.00
Tibio-Femoral	1.05 ± 2.90	.36
Inter-Membral	− .78 ± 1.02	.76
Cephalic	4.10 ± .79	5.19
Length-Height	2.20 ± 1.55	1.42

[TABLE 135—*continued*]

DIFFERENCES OF YAMAGUCHI HAWAIIAN BORN FROM YAMAGUCHI
IMMIGRANTS—FEMALES

Index	Difference	x p.e.
Breadth-Height	1.12 ± 1.70	.66
Cephalo-Facial	− 3.58 ± .64	5.59
Fronto-Parietal	− 1.90 ± .75	2.53
Zygo-Frontal	1.26 ± .84	1.50
Zygo-Gonial	− 1.70 ± .65	2.62
Facial	.12 ± 1.49	.08
Upper Facial	.51 ± .68	.75
Nasal	− 1.92 ± 1.49	1.29
Nose Salient-Height	.87 ± 1.08	.81
Nose Length-Height	.06 ± .87	.07

TABLE 136

DIFFERENCES OF HIROSHIMA HAWAIIAN BORN FROM HIROSHIMA
IMMIGRANTS—FEMALES

Measurement	Difference	x p.e.
Age	−16.25 ± 1.36	11.95
Weight	− 3.32 ± 3.09	1.07
Stature	1.98 ± .89	2.22
Sitting Height	.82 ± .52	1.58
Trunk Height	1.08 ± .71	1.52
Upper Arm Length	.18 ± .33	.55
Lower Arm Length	− .16 ± .27	.59
Hand Length	− .10 ± .16	.62
Upper Leg Length	.68 ± .75	.91
Lower Leg Length	.34 ± .40	.85
Total Leg Length	.96 ± .77	1.25
Biacromion	− .97 ± .47	2.06
Cristal Breadth	− 2.05 ± .41	5.00
Chest Breadth	− 2.05 ± .33	6.21
Head Length	− 3.78 ± 1.44	2.62
Head Breadth	1.56 ± 1.14	1.37
Head Height (cm.)	− .14 ± .23	.61
Minimum Frontal Diameter	− 2.40 ± .87	2.76
Bizygomatic Diameter	− 2.67 ± 1.07	2.50
Bigonial Diameter	− 4.02 ± 1.07	3.76
Total Face Height	.33 ± 1.22	.27
Upper Face Height	.33 ± 1.08	.31
Forehead Height	− .72 ± 1.23	.59
Nose Height	− 1.96 ± .69	2.84
Nose Length	− 1.88 ± .77	2.44
Nose Salient	.32 ± .34	.94
Nose Breadth	− 1.32 ± .41	3.22
Inter-Ocular	2.25 ± .53	4.25
Bi-Ocular	1.72 ± .88	1.95
Index		
Relative Shoulder Breadth	− .90 ± .23	3.91
Relative Hip Breadth	− 1.36 ± .26	5.23
Shoulder-Hip	− 3.11 ± .76	4.09
Relative Sitting Height	− .22 ± .35	.63
Relative Trunk Height	.20 ± .46	.43
Brachial	− 1.16 ± .93	1.25
Tibio-Femoral	− 1.70 ± 2.24	.76
Inter-Membral	− 1.32 ± .97	1.36
Cephalic	2.96 ± .83	3.57
Length-Height	.26 ± 1.35	.19

[TABLE 136—*continued*]

DIFFERENCES OF HIROSHIMA HAWAIIAN BORN FROM HIROSHIMA
IMMIGRANTS—FEMALES

Index	Difference	x p.e.
Breadth-Height	− 1.46 ± 1.54	.95
Cephalo-Facial	− 2.40 ± .59	4.07
Fronto-Parietal	− 2.38 ± .58	4.10
Zygo-Frontal	− .60 ± .64	.94
Zygo-Gonial	− 1.42 ± .75	1.89
Facial	1.77 ± 1.02	1.74
Upper Facial	.90 ± .96	.94
Nasal	− .26 ± 1.48	.18
Nose Salient-Height	1.41 ± .81	1.74
Nose Length-Height	− 1.58 ± .63	2.51

TABLE 137

DIFFERENCES OF KYUSHU HAWAIIAN BORN FROM KYUSHU
IMMIGRANTS—FEMALES

Measurement	Difference	x p.e.
Age	-11.15 ± 1.68	6.64
Weight	-13.56 ± 4.21	3.22
Stature	$- .39 \pm .87$	.45
Sitting Height	$- 1.88 \pm .67$	2.81
Trunk Height	$- 2.00 \pm .71$	2.82
Upper Arm Length	$.28 \pm .39$	.72
Lower Arm Length	$- .27 \pm .30$	.90
Hand Length	$- .63 \pm .18$	3.50
Upper Leg Length	$.82 \pm .76$	1.08
Lower Leg Length	$.59 \pm .32$	1.84
Total Leg Length	$.68 \pm .81$	.84
Biacromion	$- 1.41 \pm .46$	3.07
Cristal Breadth	$- 2.38 \pm .43$	5.53
Chest Breadth	$- 1.79 \pm .50$	3.58
Head Length	$- 9.54 \pm 1.21$	7.88
Head Breadth	$2.00 \pm .92$	2.17
Head Height (cm.)	$- .43 \pm .45$	.96
Minimum Frontal Diameter	$- 2.13 \pm 1.20$	1.78
Bizygomatic Diameter	$- 1.98 \pm 1.26$	1.57
Bigonial Diameter	$- 4.05 \pm 1.57$	2.58
Total Face Height	$- 3.27 \pm 1.54$	2.12
Upper Face Height	3.36 ± 1.62	2.07
Forehead Height	-11.69 ± 1.59	7.35
Nose Height	$- .26 \pm .78$	.33
Nose Length	$- .40 \pm .84$	.48
Nose Salient	$.32 \pm .41$	.78
Nose Breadth	$- .88 \pm .62$	1.42
Inter-Ocular	$.63 \pm .64$	.98
Bi-Ocular	$- .24 \pm 1.02$	.24
Index		
Relative Shoulder Breadth	$- .94 \pm .34$	2.76
Relative Hip Breadth	$- .88 \pm .35$	2.51
Shoulder-Hip	$- 3.36 \pm 1.00$	3.36
Relative Sitting Height	$- .66 \pm .40$	1.65
Relative Trunk Height	$- 1.04 \pm .46$	2.26
Brachial	$- 1.24 \pm 1.09$	1.14
Tibio-Femoral	$- .45 \pm 2.27$	.20
Inter-Membral	$- 2.18 \pm 1.05$	2.08
Cephalic	5.18 ± 1.02	5.08
Length-Height	2.72 ± 1.77	1.54

[TABLE 137—*continued*]

DIFFERENCES OF KYUSHU HAWAIIAN BORN FROM KYUSHU
IMMIGRANTS—FEMALES

Index	Difference	x p.e.
Breadth-Height	— 2.76 ± 1.75	1.58
Cephalo-Facial	— 2.18 ± .73	2.99
Fronto-Parietal	— 2.68 ± .80	3.35
Zygo-Frontal	— .52 ± .79	.66
Zygo-Gonial	— 1.90 ± .88	2.16
Facial	— 1.71 ± 1.12	1.53
Upper Facial	1.38 ± 1.16	1.19
Nasal	— 2.04 ± 1.75	1.17
Nose Salient-Height	.72 ± .91	.79
Nose Length-Height	— .12 ± .59	.20

TABLE 138

DIFFERENCES OF 'OTHER JAPAN' HAWAIIAN BORN FROM 'OTHER JAPAN'
IMMIGRANTS—FEMALES

Measurement	Difference	x p.e.
Age	−8.45 ± 1.79	4.72
Weight	−8.04 ± 4.42	1.82
Stature	4.68 ± 1.10	4.25
Sitting Height	1.00 ± .69	1.45
Trunk Height	.62 ± .58	1.07
Upper Arm Length	.18 ± .34	.53
Lower Arm Length	− .19 ± .27	.70
Hand Length	− .24 ± .19	1.26
Upper Leg Length	1.92 ± .73	2.63
Lower Leg Length	.82 ± .48	1.71
Total Leg Length	3.14 ± .74	4.24
Biacromion	− .44 ± .40	1.10
Cristal Breadth	−1.37 ± .63	2.17
Chest Breadth	−1.12 ± .51	2.20
Head Length	−4.00 ± 1.64	2.44
Head Breadth	1.36 ± .97	1.40
Head Height (cm.)	1.00 ± .22	4.55
Minimum Frontal Diameter	− .75 ± .93	.81
Bizygomatic Diameter	−2.04 ± 1.67	1.22
Bigonial Diameter	−3.39 ± 1.74	1.95
Total Face Height	− .57 ± 1.37	.42
Upper Face Height	2.00 ± 1.15	1.74
Forehead Height	−5.00 ± 1.63	3.07
Nose Height	.62 ± .94	.66
Nose Length	1.12 ± 1.09	1.03
Nose Salient	−1.50 ± .55	2.73
Nose Breadth	−1.62 ± .63	2.57
Inter-Ocular	.82 ± .78	1.05
Bi-Ocular	−2.62 ± 1.12	2.34
Index		
Relative Shoulder Breadth	− .86 ± .29	2.97
Relative Hip Breadth	−1.26 ± .48	2.62
Shoulder-Hip	− .99 ± 1.39	.71
Relative Sitting Height	− .56 ± .38	1.47
Relative Trunk Height	− .50 ± .32	1.56
Brachial	− .24 ± .90	.27
Tibio-Femoral	−3.40 ± 2.97	1.14
Inter-Membral	−4.88 ± 1.21	4.03
Cephalic	1.60 ± .81	1.98
Length-Height	7.72 ± 1.51	5.11

[TABLE 138—*continued*]

DIFFERENCES OF 'OTHER JAPAN' HAWAIIAN BORN FROM 'OTHER JAPAN'
IMMIGRANTS—FEMALES

Index	Difference	x p.e.
Breadth-Height	6.76 ± 1.58	4.28
Cephalo-Facial	− .88 ± 1.02	.86
Fronto-Parietal	− .38 ± .72	.53
Zygo-Frontal	.50 ± .98	.51
Zygo-Gonial	−1.64 ± .84	1.95
Facial	.00 ± 1.23	.00
Upper Facial	2.25 ± 1.04	2.16
Nasal	−4.14 ± 1.83	2.26
Nose Salient-Height	−3.00 ± 1.24	2.42
Nose Length-Height	1.86 ± 1.12	1.66

TABLE 139

DISTRIBUTION OF THE X P.E.'S OF THE DIFFERENCES BETWEEN HAWAIIAN BORN AND IMMIGRANT FEMALES BY PREFECTURE

		0–99	1.00–1.99	2.00–2.99	3.00–3.99	4.00–4.99	5.00–5.99	6.00–X
Yamaguchi Hawaiian Born	Measurements	8	6	6	7	1	0	0
Yamaguchi Immigrants	Indices	9	4	2	2	0	3	0
Hiroshima Hawaiian Born	Measurements	10	6	7	2	1	1	1
Hiroshima Immigrants	Indices	8	5	1	2	3	1	0
Kyushu Hawaiian Born	Measurements	10	5	6	4	0	1	2
Kyushu Immigrants	Indices	4	7	6	2	0	1	0
'Other Japan' Hawaiian Born	Measurements	5	12	7	1	3	0	0
'Other Japan' Immigrants	Indices	6	6	5	0	2	1	0

TABLE 140

DIFFERENCES OF YAMAGUCHI HAWAIIAN BORN FROM YAMAGUCHI
SEDENTES—FEMALES

Measurement	Difference	x p.e.
Age	−16.20 ± 1.90	8.53
Weight	− 8.52 ± 4.62	1.84
Stature	3.06 ± .96	3.19
Sitting Height	− 1.20 ± .68	1.76
Trunk Height	− 2.28 ± .63	3.62
Upper Arm Length	1.02 ± .32	3.19
Lower Arm Length	.88 ± .31	2.84
Hand Length	− .17 ± .15	1.13
Upper Leg Length	2.66 ± .77	3.45
Lower Leg Length	3.39 ± .37	9.16
Total Leg Length	3.88 ± .74	5.24
Biacromion	− .40 ± .39	1.03
Cristal Breadth	− 1.90 ± .42	4.52
Chest Breadth	− 1.61 ± .43	3.74
Head Length	− .80 ± 1.12	.71
Head Breadth	1.58 ± .96	1.65
Head Height (cm.)	1.37 ± .28	4.89
Minimum Frontal Diameter	3.21 ± 1.05	3.06
Bizygomatic Diameter	− 1.02 ± .99	1.03
Bigonial Diameter	2.19 ± 1.19	1.84
Total Face Height	2.22 ± 1.28	1.73
Upper Face Height	9.38 ± 1.00	9.38
Forehead Height	− 2.32 ± 1.69	1.37
Nose Height	1.34 ± .67	2.00
Nose Length	2.48 ± .70	3.54
Nose Salient	− 1.08 ± .36	3.00
Nose Breadth	− 1.84 ± .34	5.41
Inter-Ocular	.57 ± .54	1.06
Bi-Ocular	3.38 ± .93	3.63
Index		
Relative Shoulder Breadth	− .88 ± .26	3.38
Relative Hip Breadth	− 1.72 ± .30	5.73
Shoulder-Hip	− 4.29 ± 1.02	4.21
Relative Sitting Height	− 1.80 ± .38	4.74
Relative Trunk Height	− 2.37 ± .44	5.39
Brachial	.54 ± .96	.56
Tibio-Femoral	3.65 ± 2.41	1.51
Inter-Membral	− 3.04 ± .97	3.13
Cephalic	1.96 ± .65	3.02
Length-Height	8.02 ± 1.69	4.75

[*Continued*]

[TABLE 140—*continued*]

DIFFERENCES OF YAMAGUCHI HAWAIIAN BORN FROM YAMAGUCHI
SEDENTES—FEMALES

Index	Difference	x p.e.
Breadth-Height	7.76 ± 1.93	4.02
Cephalo-Facial	− 1.62 ± .55	2.95
Fronto-Parietal	1.14 ± .69	1.65
Zygo-Frontal	3.00 ± .78	3.85
Zygo-Gonial	2.38 ± .82	2.90
Facial	2.76 ± .94	2.94
Upper Facial	7.05 ± .79	8.92
Nasal	− 5.80 ± 1.20	4.83
Nose Salient-Height	− 2.82 ± .64	4.41
Nose Length-Height	3.08 ± .72	4.28

TABLE 141

DIFFERENCES OF HIROSHIMA HAWAIIAN BORN FROM HIROSHIMA
SEDENTES—FEMALES

Measurement	Difference	x p.e.
Age	−16.25 ± 1.82	8.93
Weight	11.68 ± 2.40	4.87
Stature	4.77 ± .93	5.13
Sitting Height	.74 ± .55	1.35
Trunk Height	− .50 ± .68	.74
Upper Arm Length	.72 ± .31	2.32
Lower Arm Length	.29 ± .25	1.16
Hand Length	.25 ± .16	1.56
Upper Leg Length	1.62 ± .69	2.35
Lower Leg Length	3.35 ± .40	8.38
Total Leg Length	4.54 ± .74	6.14
Biacromion	.95 ± .44	2.16
Cristal Breadth	− .83 ± .35	2.37
Chest Breadth	− 1.27 ± .29	4.38
Head Length	− 5.34 ± 1.11	4.81
Head Breadth	4.08 ± 1.14	3.58
Head Height (cm.)	.70 ± .25	2.80
Minimum Frontal Diameter	− 3.09 ± .70	4.41
Bizygomatic Diameter	− 1.83 ± .93	1.97
Bigonial Diameter	1.02 ± .97	1.05
Total Face Height	1.95 ± 1.31	1.49
Upper Face Height	5.01 ± 1.00	5.01
Forehead Height	− .80 ± 1.22	.66
Nose Height	− .96 ± .68	1.41
Nose Length	.32 ± .78	.41
Nose Salient	− .35 ± .33	1.06
Nose Breadth	− 1.66 ± .42	3.95
Inter-Ocular	− .02 ± .52	.04
Bi-Ocular	2.88 ± .95	3.03
Index		
Relative Shoulder Breadth	− .06 ± .21	.29
Relative Hip Breadth	− .92 ± .22	4.18
Shoulder-Hip	− 5.04 ± .77	6.55
Relative Sitting Height	− 1.49 ± .36	4.14
Relative Trunk Height	− 1.40 ± .45	3.11
Brachial	− 1.58 ± .95	1.66
Tibio-Femoral	4.50 ± 2.35	1.91
Inter-Membral	− 4.12 ± .97	4.25
Cephalic	4.68 ± .78	6.00
Length-Height	5.40 ± 1.43	3.78

[Continued]

[TABLE 141—*continued*]

DIFFERENCES OF HIROSHIMA HAWAIIAN BORN FROM HIROSHIMA
SEDENTES—FEMALES

Index	Difference	x p.e.
Breadth-Height	2.44 ± 1.83	1.33
Cephalo-Facial	− 3.82 ± .58	6.59
Fronto-Parietal	− 4.18 ± .66	6.33
Zygo-Frontal	− 1.44 ± .67	2.15
Zygo-Gonial	2.00 ± .76	2.63
Facial	2.37 ± 1.05	2.26
Upper Facial	4.59 ± .82	5.60
Nasal	− .98 ± 1.40	.70
Nose Salient-Height	.09 ± .83	.11
Nose Length-Height	1.14 ± .72	1.58

TABLE 142

DIFFERENCES OF KYUSHU HAWAIIAN BORN FROM KYUSHU
SEDENTES—FEMALES

Measurement	Difference	x p.e.
Age	−11.80 ± 2.15	5.49
Weight	− 2.40 ± 3.77	.64
Stature	2.34 ± 1.04	2.25
Sitting Height	− 1.44 ± .71	2.03
Trunk Height	− 3.32 ± .69	4.81
Upper Arm Length	.70 ± .32	2.19
Lower Arm Length	.29 ± .26	1.12
Hand Length	.29 ± .17	1.71
Upper Leg Length	2.26 ± .67	3.37
Lower Leg Length	1.98 ± .32	6.19
Total Leg Length	3.62 ± .80	4.52
Biacromion	− .70 ± .34	2.06
Cristal Breadth	− 1.71 ± .39	4.38
Chest Breadth	− 2.97 ± .39	7.62
Head Length	− 6.60 ± 1.44	4.58
Head Breadth	3.66 ± 1.08	3.39
Head Height (cm.)	.24 ± .43	.56
Minimum Frontal Diameter	.72 ± .85	.85
Bizygomatic Diameter	− .09 ± 1.01	.09
Bigonial Diameter	3.60 ± 1.09	3.30
Total Face Height	2.73 ± 1.36	2.01
Upper Face Height	8.00 ± .99	8.08
Forehead Height	− 2.44 ± 1.92	1.27
Nose Height	2.02 ± .64	3.16
Nose Length	3.04 ± .78	3.90
Nose Salient	− .23 ± .37	.62
Nose Breadth	− .98 ± .56	1.75
Inter-Ocular	− .29 ± .67	.43
Bi-Ocular	.88 ± 1.08	.81
Index		
Relative Shoulder Breadth	− 1.06 ± .27	3.93
Relative Hip Breadth	− 1.52 ± .28	5.43
Shoulder-Hip	− 2.88 ± 1.00	2.88
Relative Sitting Height	− 1.80 ± .35	5.14
Relative Trunk Height	− 2.96 ± .43	6.88
Brachial	− .46 ± .84	.55
Tibio-Femoral	− .75 ± 2.16	.35
Inter-Membral	− 3.28 ± 1.09	3.01
Cephalic	5.58 ± .79	7.06
Length-Height	5.34 ± 1.54	3.47

[*Continued*]

[TABLE 142—*continued*]

DIFFERENCES OF KYUSHU HAWAIIAN BORN FROM KYUSHU
SEDENTES—FEMALES

Index	Difference	x p.e.
Breadth-Height	.58 ± 1.56	.37
Cephalo-Facial	− 2.72 ± .72	3.78
Fronto-Parietal	− 1.86 ± .65	2.86
Zygo-Frontal	.70 ± .54	1.30
Zygo-Gonial	2.60 ± .68	3.82
Facial	1.68 ± 1.08	1.56
Upper Facial	5.94 ± .72	8.25
Nasal	− 5.20 ± 1.42	3.66
Nose Salient-Height	− 1.62 ± .78	2.08
Nose Length-Height	1.86 ± .77	2.42

TABLE 143

DIFFERENCES OF 'OTHER JAPAN' HAWAIIAN BORN FROM 'OTHER JAPAN'
SEDENTES—FEMALES

Measurement	Difference	x p.e.
Age	−15.00 ± 2.15	6.98
Weight	− 3.24 ± 3.15	1.03
Stature	6.75 ± 1.03	6.55
Sitting Height	3.14 ± .68	4.62
Trunk Height	1.00 ± .58	1.72
Upper Arm Length	1.12 ± .42	2.67
Lower Arm Length	.87 ± .27	3.22
Hand Length	.07 ± .17	.41
Upper Leg Length	1.00 ± .65	1.54
Lower Leg Length	2.69 ± .48	5.60
Total Leg Length	4.38 ± .69	6.35
Biacromion	.18 ± .35	.51
Cristal Breadth	− .18 ± .52	.35
Chest Breadth	− 1.00 ± .38	2.63
Head Length	− 4.80 ± 1.85	2.59
Head Breadth	3.74 ± 1.11	3.37
Head Height (cm.)	.12 ± .31	.39
Minimum Frontal Diameter	.00 ± .87	.00
Bizygomatic Diameter	3.57 ± 1.23	2.90
Bigonial Diameter	4.50 ± 1.28	3.52
Total Face Height	− .39 ± 1.35	.29
Upper Face Height	4.88 ± .86	5.67
Forehead Height	− 6.24 ± 1.69	3.69
Nose Height	− .26 ± .94	.28
Nose Length	− .24 ± .86	.28
Nose Salient	− .75 ± .37	2.03
Nose Breadth	.12 ± .62	.19
Inter-Ocular	2.88 ± .72	4.00
Bi-Ocular	1.38 ± .85	1.62
Index		
Relative Shoulder Breadth	− 1.24 ± .32	3.88
Relative Hip Breadth	− 1.14 ± .39	2.92
Shoulder-Hip	− .57 ± 1.14	.50
Relative Sitting Height	− .43 ± .34	1.26
Relative Trunk Height	− .93 ± .35	2.66
Brachial	− 2.76 ± 1.10	2.51
Tibio-Femoral	4.40 ± 2.18	2.18
Inter-Membral	− 1.50 ± 1.04	1.44
Cephalic	2.94 ± 1.09	2.70
Length-Height	3.32 ± 2.04	1.63

[Continued]

[TABLE 143—*continued*]

DIFFERENCES OF 'OTHER JAPAN' HAWAIIAN BORN FROM 'OTHER JAPAN'
SEDENTES—FEMALES

Index	Difference	x p.e.
Breadth-Height	.14 ± 2.06	.07
Cephalo-Facial	1.38 ± .82	1.68
Fronto-Parietal	— 1.38 ± .73	1.89
Zygo-Frontal	— 2.26 ± .90	2.51
Zygo-Gonial	1.24 ± 1.04	1.19
Facial	— 2.61 ± 1.15	2.27
Upper Facial	2.43 ± .75	3.24
Nasal	.38 ± 1.63	.23
Nose Salient-Height	— .57 ± .79	.72
Nose Length-Height	.12 ± .69	.17

TABLE 144

DISTRIBUTION OF THE X P.E.'S OF THE DIFFERENCES BETWEEN FEMALE HAWAIIAN BORN AND SEDENTES BY PREFECTURE

		0–.99	1.00–1.99	2.00–2.99	3.00–3.99	4.00–4.99	5.00–5.99	6.00–X
Yamaguchi Hawaiian Born	Measurements	1	10	2	9	2	2	3
Yamaguchi Sedentes	Indices	1	2	3	4	7	2	1
Hiroshima Hawaiian Born	Measurements	4	8	5	3	4	2	2
Hiroshima Sedentes	Indices	3	4	3	2	3	1	4
Kyushu Hawaiian Born	Measurements	7	4	5	5	4	0	3
Kyushu Sedentes	Indices	3	2	4	6	0	2	3
'Other Japan' Hawaiian Born	Measurements	9	4	5	4	2	2	2
'Other Japan' Sedentes	Indices	5	6	7	2	0	0	0

TABLE 145

UNWEIGHTED MEANS OF THE POOLED PREFECTURAL GROUPS OF MALE SEDENTES AND IMMIGRANTS, TOGETHER WITH A COMPARISON OF THEIR DIFFERENCES AND THOSE DERIVED FROM THE TOTAL WEIGHTED SERIES

Measurement	Unweighted Means of Pooled Prefectures Male Sedentes	Unweighted Means of Pooled Prefectures Male Immigrants	Difference between Pooled Means	Difference between Total, Unweighted Means
Weight	120.83	123.15	2.32	4.20
Stature	158.68	158.86	.18	.33
Sitting Height	84.68	83.13	−1.55	−1.40
Trunk Height	54.33	52.60	−1.73	−1.54
Upper Arm Length	29.56	29.42	−.14	−.03
Lower Arm Length	23.18	23.50	.32	.33
Hand Length	17.54	17.83	.29	.33
Upper Leg Length	35.80	37.61	1.81	1.74
Lower Leg Length	31.95	32.71	.76	.94
Total Leg Length	73.91	75.70	1.79	1.80
Biacromion	39.64	40.21	.57	.75
Cristal Width	30.04	29.49	−.55	−.31
Chest Width	27.59	27.65	.06	.40
Chest Depth	20.62	20.22	−.40	−.33
Head Length	189.82	189.41	−.41	−.32
Head Width	152.24	152.56	.32	.82
Head Height (cm.)	12.80	13.52	.72	.68
Minimum Frontal Diameter	112.15	112.51	.36	.54
Bizygomatic Diameter	142.32	142.26	−.06	.60

Bigonial Diameter	109.84	111.44	1.60	2.25
Total Face Height	119.95	123.09	3.14	3.57
Upper Face Height	72.78	81.49	8.71	8.74
Forehead Height	61.06	59.25	—1.81	—1.48
Nose Height	50.59	51.47	.88	1.12
Nose Length	48.07	50.23	2.16	2.36
Nose Salient	14.84	13.85	—.99	—.70
Nose Width	36.53	35.87	—.66	—.70
Inter-Ocular	31.90	30.59	—1.31	—1.08
Bi-Ocular	99.91	100.75	.84	1.26
Index				
Relative Shoulder Breadth	25.28	25.22	—.06	.38
Relative Hip Breadth	19.03	18.57	.46	—.34
Shoulder-Hip	75.61	73.31	—2.30	—2.19
Relative Sitting Height	53.36	52.34	—1.02	—1.00
Relative Trunk Height	34.22	33.11	—1.11	—1.03
Thoracic	74.74	73.13	—1.61	—2.40
Brachial	78.53	80.14	1.61	1.40
Tibio-Femoral	90.04	87.55	—2.49	—1.55
Inter-Membral	95.28	93.47	—1.81	—1.44
Cephalic	80.30	80.61	.31	.50
Length-Height	67.39	71.11	3.72	3.76
Breadth-Height	84.05	88.58	4.53	4.18
Cephalo-Facial	93.20	93.16	—.04	—.14
Fronto-Parietal	73.72	73.61	—.11	.22
Zygo-Frontal	78.93	79.02	.09	—.08

[Continued]

[TABLE 145—*continued*]

UNWEIGHTED MEANS OF THE POOLED PREFECTURAL GROUPS OF MALE SEDENTES AND IMMIGRANTS, TOGETHER WITH A COMPARISON OF THEIR DIFFERENCES AND THOSE DERIVED FROM THE TOTAL WEIGHTED SERIES

Index	Unweighted Means of Pooled Prefectures Male Sedentes	Unweighted Means of Pooled Prefectures Male Immigrants	Difference between Pooled Means	Difference between Total, Unweighted Means
Zygo-Gonial	77.19	78.25	1.06	1.14
Facial	84.84	86.50	1.66	2.28
Upper Facial	51.33	57.44	6.11	5.94
Nasal	72.28	69.83	−2.45	−2.80
Nose Salient-Height	29.24	26.86	−2.38	−2.01
Nose Length-Height	95.51	98.43	2.92	2.68

TABLE 146

UNWEIGHTED MEANS OF THE POOLED PREFECTURAL GROUPS OF FEMALE SEDENTES AND IMMIGRANTS, TOGETHER WITH A COMPARISON OF THEIR DIFFERENCES AND THOSE DERIVED FROM THE TOTAL WEIGHTED SERIES

Measurement	Unweighted Means of Pooled Prefectures Male Sedentes	Unweighted Means of Pooled Prefectures Male Immigrants	Difference between Pooled Means	Difference between Total Weighted Means
Weight	106.18	114.85	8.67	8.64
Stature	146.31	148.12	1.81	2.52
Sitting Height	78.69	78.41	− .28	− .02
Trunk Height	50.82	49.19	−1.63	−1.40
Upper Arm Length	27.21	27.90	.69	.94
Lower Arm Length	21.05	21.73	.68	.73
Hand Length	16.13	16.58	.45	.50
Upper Leg Length	32.97	33.72	.75	1.04
Lower Leg Length	29.17	31.24	2.07	2.40
Total Leg Length	67.41	70.21	2.80	3.14
Biacromion	36.19	37.07	.88	.95
Cristal Width	29.19	30.00	.81	.88
Chest Width	25.96	26.03	.07	.23
Head Length	182.28	182.80	.52	.42
Head Width	145.51	146.82	1.31	1.74
Head Height (cm.)	12.30	12.68	.38	.61
Minimum Frontal Diameter	108.85	110.43	1.58	1.29

[Continued]

[TABLE 146—continued]

UNWEIGHTED MEANS OF THE POOLED PREFECTURAL GROUPS OF FEMALE SEDENTES AND IMMIGRANTS, TOGETHER WITH A COMPARISON OF THEIR DIFFERENCES AND THOSE DERIVED FROM THE TOTAL WEIGHTED SERIES

Measurement	Unweighted Means of Pooled Prefectures Male Sedentes	Unweighted Means of Pooled Prefectures Male Immigrants	Difference between Pooled Means	Difference between Total Weighted Means
Bizygomatic Diameter	134.10	136.58	2.48	1.98
Bigonial Diameter	102.15	108.98	6.83	6.66
Total Face Height	112.24	115.07	2.83	3.54
Upper Face Height	69.80	75.13	5.33	5.62
Forehead Height	58.61	61.23	2.62	—.20
Nose Height	47.87	48.72	.85	1.20
Nose Length	44.80	46.40	1.60	1.88
Nose Salient	13.17	12.66	—.51	—.40
Nose Width	33.15	33.18	.03	.04
Inter-Ocular	30.86	30.27	—.59	—.84
Bi-Ocular	97.07	99.64	2.57	2.64
Index				
Relative Shoulder Width	24.88	24.98	.10	.02
Relative Hip Width	20.02	20.06	.04	.06
Shoulder-Hip	80.59	80.28	—.31	—.09
Relative Sitting Height	53.85	52.67	—1.18	—1.27
Relative Trunk Height	34.80	33.13	—1.67	—1.66
Brachial	78.50	78.10	.40	.32

Tibio-Femoral	89.68	93.75	4.07	4.65
Inter-Membral	95.28	94.58	— .70	—1.08
Cephalic	79.93	80.26	.33	.84
Length-Height	67.59	69.88	2.29	3.38
Breadth-Height	84.59	86.41	1.82	3.10
Cephalo-Facial	92.14	92.70	.56	— .06
Fronto-Parietal	74.91	75.18	.27	— .26
Zygo-Frontal	81.07	80.91	— .16	— .20
Zygo-Gonial	76.13	79.85	3.72	3.88
Facial	83.62	84.63	1.01	1.80
Upper Facial	52.06	55.81	3.75	4.11
Nasal	69.59	68.78	— .81	—1.20
Nose Salient-Height	27.44	26.21	—1.23	—1.23
Nose Length-Height	94.06	95.55	1.49	1.52

TABLE 147

JAPANESE ADULT MALES

Age Groups by Decades

WEIGHT

	No.	Range	Mean	p.e.	S.D.	p.e.	V.	p.e.
20-29								
Hawaiian Born	142	91-180	126.30 ±	.84	14.80 ±	.59	11.72 ±	.47
Immigrants	33	91-180	125.50 ±	2.01	17.10 ±	1.42	13.63 ±	1.13
Sedentes	65	91-150	121.50 ±	.97	11.60 ±	.69	9.55 ±	.56
30-39								
Hawaiian Born	39	91-230	131.40 ±	3.03	28.10 ±	2.15	21.38 ±	1.63
Immigrants	42	101-150	123.60 ±	1.31	12.60 ±	.93	10.19 ±	.75
Sedentes	26	101-150	122.40 ±	1.40	10.60 ±	1.01	8.66 ±	.81
40-49								
Hawaiian Born	4	91-160	125.50		—		—	
Immigrants	59	91-170	124.30 ±	1.35	15.40 ±	.96	12.39 ±	.77
Sedentes	26	91-160	119.00 ±	1.97	14.90 ±	1.39	12.52 ±	1.17
50-59								
Hawaiian Born	0	—	—		—		—	
Immigrants	34	81-180	122.60 ±	2.53	21.90 ±	1.79	17.86 ±	1.46
Sedentes	16	81-140	114.50 ±	2.60	15.40 ±	1.84	13.47 ±	1.61
60-64								
Hawaiian Born	0	—	—		—		—	
Immigrants	7	111-150	125.50		—		—	
Sedentes	10	81-160	112.50 ±	4.16	19.50 ±	2.94	17.33 ±	2.61

STATURE

	No.	Range	Mean	p.e.	S.D.	p.e.	V.	p.e.
20-29								
Hawaiian Born	144	151-177	163.22 ±	.28	5.04 ±	.20	3.09 ±	.12
Immigrants	34	151-171	160.04 ±	.59	5.07 ±	.41	3.17 ±	.26
Sedentes	71	145-174	158.81 ±	.40	4.98 ±	.28	3.14 ±	.18
30-39								
Hawaiian Born	40	148-174	161.36 ±	.64	6.00 ±	.45	3.72 ±	.28
Immigrants	42	148-174	159.65 ±	.49	4.74 ±	.35	2.97 ±	.22
Sedentes	35	151-174	160.40 ±	.58	5.10 ±	.41	3.18 ±	.26
40-49								
Hawaiian Born	4	157-168	163.25		—		—	
Immigrants	60	145-171	159.05 ±	.42	4.83 ±	.30	3.04 ±	.19
Sedentes	33	148-168	158.09 ±	.59	5.04 ±	.42	3.19 ±	.26
50-59								
Hawaiian Born	0	—	—		—		—	
Immigrants	36	145-174	156.92 ±	.65	5.76 ±	.46	3.67 ±	.29
Sedentes	19	148-165	155.33 ±	.71	4.56 ±	.50	2.94 ±	.32
60-64								
Hawaiian Born	0	—	—		—		—	
Immigrants	7	148-162	154.58		—		—	
Sedentes	13	145-165	154.76 ±	1.02	5.46 ±	.72	3.53 ±	.47

[Continued]

[TABLE 147—continued]

JAPANESE ADULT MALES

Age Groups by Decades

SITTING HEIGHT

	No.	Range	Mean ± p.e.	S.D. ± p.e.	V. ± p.e.
20–29					
Hawaiian Born	143	76– 95	85.76 ± .21	3.70 ± .15	4.31 ± .17
Immigrants	34	76– 99	84.02 ± .46	4.00 ± .33	4.76 ± .39
Sedentes	71	74– 93	84.16 ± .28	3.44 ± .19	4.09 ± .23
30–39					
Hawaiian Born	40	78– 91	84.46 ± .39	3.62 ± .27	4.29 ± .32
Immigrants	42	76– 91	83.70 ± .33	3.18 ± .23	3.80 ± .28
Sedentes	35	74– 95	86.32 ± .47	4.14 ± .33	4.80 ± .39
40–49					
Hawaiian Born	4	80– 89	85.50	—	—
Immigrants	60	76– 91	82.96 ± .30	3.40 ± .21	4.10 ± .25
Sedentes	33	76– 91	84.56 ± .39	3.32 ± .28	3.93 ± .33
50–59					
Hawaiian Born	0	—	—	—	—
Immigrants	36	76– 93	82.38 ± .45	4.02 ± .32	4.88 ± .39
Sedentes	19	76– 89	83.24 ± .52	3.38 ± .37	4.06 ± .44
60–64					
Hawaiian Born	0	—	—	—	—
Immigrants	7	76– 89	80.22	—	—
Sedentes	13	74– 89	83.12 ± .80	4.26 ± .56	5.13 ± .68

TRUNK HEIGHT

	No.	Range	Mean ± p.e.	S.D. ± p.e.	V. ± p.e.
20–29					
Hawaiian Born	143	46– 63	54.32 ± .19	3.34 ± .13	6.15 ± .25
Immigrants	34	44– 57	52.20 ± .40	3.46 ± .28	6.63 ± .54
Sedentes	71	46– 65	54.00 ± .24	2.98 ± .17	5.52 ± .31
30–39					
Hawaiian Born	40	46– 61	53.40 ± .34	3.22 ± .24	6.03 ± .45
Immigrants	42	48– 61	53.08 ± .31	3.00 ± .22	5.65 ± .42
Sedentes	35	44– 63	55.46 ± .45	3.98 ± .32	7.19 ± .58
40–49					
Hawaiian Born	4	50– 57	54.50	—	—
Immigrants	60	46– 59	52.66 ± .28	3.18 ± .20	6.04 ± .37
Sedentes	32	46– 59	54.26 ± .31	2.60 ± .22	4.79 ± .40
50–59					
Hawaiian Born	0	—	—	—	—
Immigrants	36	44– 61	52.34 ± .41	3.68 ± .29	7.03 ± .56
Sedentes	19	46– 59	53.02 ± .55	3.54 ± .39	6.68 ± .73
60–64					
Hawaiian Born	0	—	—	—	—
Immigrants	7	48– 57	50.50	—	—
Sedentes	13	44– 59	53.26 ± .77	4.12 ± .54	7.74 ± 1.02

[Continued]

[TABLE 147—*Continued*]

JAPANESE ADULT MALES

Age Groups by Decades

UPPER ARM LENGTH

	No.	Range	Mean	p.e.	S.D.	p.e.	V.	p.e.
20–29								
Hawaiian Born	143	26– 35	30.62 ±	.10	1.74 ±	.07	5.68 ±	.23
Immigrants	34	27– 33	29.88 ±	.17	1.49 ±	.12	4.99 ±	.41
Sedentes	71	25– 34	29.83 ±	.15	1.82 ±	.10	6.10 ±	.35
30–39								
Hawaiian Born	39	27– 34	30.13 ±	.20	1.85 ±	.14	6.14 ±	.47
Immigrants	42	25– 33	29.00 ±	.17	1.59 ±	.12	5.48 ±	.40
Sedentes	35	25– 33	29.57 ±	.18	1.59 ±	.13	5.38 ±	.43
40–49								
Hawaiian Born	4	30– 31	30.75				—	
Immigrants	60	27– 33	29.47 ±	.13	1.50 ±	.09	5.09 ±	.31
Sedentes	34	25– 31	28.91 ±	.20	1.69 ±	.14	5.85 ±	.48
50–59								
Hawaiian Born	0	—	—		—		—	
Immigrants	36	25– 34	29.28 ±	.25	2.26 ±	.18	7.72 ±	.61
Sedentes	19	25– 31	28.58 ±	.25	1.63 ±	.18	5.70 ±	.62
60–64								
Hawaiian Born	0	—	—		—		—	
Immigrants	7	28– 31	29.00		—		—	
Sedentes	13	23– 32	29.08 ±	.40	2.13 ±	.28	7.32 ±	.97

LOWER ARM LENGTH

	No.	Range	Mean	p.e.	S.D.	p.e.	V.	p.e.
20–29								
Hawaiian Born	144	20– 28	24.36 ±	.08	1.45 ±	.06	5.95 ±	.24
Immigrants	34	20– 30	23.94 ±	.23	1.95 ±	.16	8.15 ±	.67
Sedentes	71	19– 26	23.24 ±	.11	1.41 ±	.08	6.07 ±	.34
30–39								
Hawaiian Born	39	20– 28	24.10 ±	.20	1.88 ±	.14	7.80 ±	.60
Immigrants	42	20– 26	23.38 ±	.13	1.22 ±	.09	5.22 ±	.38
Sedentes	35	20– 25	23.20 ±	.15	1.33 ±	.11	5.73 ±	.46
40–49								
Hawaiian Born	4	23– 26	24.50		—		—	
Immigrants	60	20– 26	23.47 ±	.11	1.31 ±	.08	5.58 ±	.34
Sedentes	34	20– 27	23.21 ±	.17	1.43 ±	.12	6.16 ±	.50
50–59								
Hawaiian Born	0	—	—		—		—	
Immigrants	36	20– 28	23.22 ±	.21	1.87 ±	.15	8.05 ±	.64
Sedentes	19	19– 25	22.63 ±	.21	1.35 ±	.15	5.97 ±	.65
60–64								
Hawaiian Born	0	—	—		—		—	
Immigrants	7	21– 24	23.00		—		—	
Sedentes	13	21– 26	23.08 ±	.24	1.27 ±	.17	5.50 ±	.73

[Continued]

[TABLE 147—continued]

JAPANESE ADULT MALES
Age Groups by Decades

HAND LENGTH

	No.	Range	Mean	p.e.	S.D.	p.e.	V.	p.e.
20–29								
Hawaiian Born	144	15– 20	17.79 ±	.05	.84 ±	.04	4.72 ±	.19
Immigrants	34	15– 19	17.56 ±	.11	.95 ±	.08	5.41 ±	.44
Sedentes	71	15– 20	17.39 ±	.07	.90 ±	.05	5.18 ±	.29
30–39								
Hawaiian Born	40	16– 20	17.92 ±	.10	.98 ±	.07	5.47 ±	.41
Immigrants	42	17– 19	17.81 ±	.07	.66 ±	.05	3.71 ±	.27
Sedentes	35	16– 19	17.54 ±	.10	.84 ±	.07	4.79 ±	.39
40–49								
Hawaiian Born	4	17– 18	17.75		—		—	
Immigrants	60	16– 19	17.90 ±	.06	.68 ±	.04	3.80 ±	.23
Sedentes	34	16– 20	17.71 ±	.10	.89 ±	.07	5.03 ±	.41
50–59								
Hawaiian Born	0	—	—		—		—	
Immigrants	36	16– 20	17.89 ±	.11	1.02 ±	.08	5.70 ±	.45
Sedentes	19	16– 18	17.37 ±	.10	.66 ±	.07	3.80 ±	.42
60–64								
Hawaiian Born	0	—	—		—		—	
Immigrants	7	17– 20	17.86		—		—	
Sedentes	13	16– 19	17.15 ±	.16	.87 ±	.12	5.07 ±	.67

UPPER LEG LENGTH

	No.	Range	Mean	p.e.	S.D.	p.e.	V.	p.e.
20–29								
Hawaiian Born	142	29– 46	37.88 ±	.18	3.16 ±	.13	8.34 ±	.33
Immigrants	33	31– 42	37.08 ±	.34	2.86 ±	.24	7.71 ±	.64
Sedentes	70	29– 46	36.56 ±	.27	3.40 ±	.19	9.30 ±	.53
30–39								
Hawaiian Born	40	29– 46	37.20 ±	.35	3.28 ±	.25	8.82 ±	.67
Immigrants	42	31– 44	37.70 ±	.27	2.64 ±	.19	7.00 ±	.52
Sedentes	35	29– 44	35.68 ±	.36	3.14 ±	.25	8.80 ±	.71
40–49								
Hawaiian Born	4	35– 40	37.50		—		—	
Immigrants	60	29– 46	37.86 ±	.28	3.22 ±	.20	8.50 ±	.52
Sedentes	33	27– 42	34.90 ±	.36	3.06 ±	.25	8.77 ±	.73
50–59								
Hawaiian Born	0	—	—		—		—	
Immigrants	36	33– 46	37.22 ±	.38	3.38 ±	.27	9.08 ±	.72
Sedentes	19	29– 40	34.76 ±	.48	3.12 ±	.34	8.98 ±	.98
60–64								
Hawaiian Born	0	—	—		—		—	
Immigrants	7	35– 42	37.78		—		—	
Sedentes	13	31– 42	35.66 ±	.68	3.64 ±	.48	10.21 ±	1.35

[Continued]

[TABLE 147—*continued*]

JAPANESE ADULT MALES

Age Groups by Decades

LOWER LEG LENGTH

	No.	Range	Mean	p.e.	S.D.	p.e.	V.	p.e.
20–29								
Hawaiian Born	144	29– 42	33.88 ±	.12	2.15 ±	.09	6.33 ±	.25
Immigrants	34	28– 38	33.35 ±	.25	2.17 ±	.18	6.51 ±	.53
Sedentes	71	28– 36	31.92 ±	.14	1.74 ±	.10	5.45 ±	.31
30–39								
Hawaiian Born	40	30– 39	34.18 ±	.22	2.04 ±	.15	5.97 ±	.45
Immigrants	42	28– 38	32.81 ±	.22	2.11 ±	.16	6.43 ±	.47
Sedentes	35	28– 37	32.14 ±	.25	2.23 ±	.18	6.94 ±	.56
40–49								
Hawaiian Born	4	33– 34	33.25		—		—	
Immigrants	60	28– 36	32.63 ±	.15	1.69 ±	.10	5.18 ±	.32
Sedentes	33	27– 37	31.85 ±	.25	2.15 ±	.18	6.75 ±	.56
50–59								
Hawaiian Born	0	—			—		—	
Immigrants	36	29– 37	32.19 ±	.20	1.74 ±	.14	5.41 ±	.43
Sedentes	19	28– 35	30.68 ±	.27	1.75 ±	.19	5.70 ±	.62
60–64								
Hawaiian Born	0	—			—		—	
Immigrants	7	29– 32	31.00		—		—	
Sedentes	13	28– 33	30.54 ±	.26	1.39 ±	.18	4.55 ±	.60

TOTAL LEG LENGTH

	No.	Range	Mean ± p.e.	S.D. ± p.e.	V. ± p.e.
20–29					
Hawaiian Born	143	65– 88	77.52 ± .22	3.90 ± .16	5.03 ± .20
Immigrants	33	69– 84	76.22 ± .43	3.64 ± .30	4.78 ± .40
Sedentes	71	67– 84	74.60 ± .31	3.86 ± .22	5.17 ± .29
30–39					
Hawaiian Born	40	69– 90	77.20 ± .51	4.82 ± .36	6.24 ± .47
Immigrants	42	67– 86	75.60 ± .36	3.50 ± .26	4.63 ± .34
Sedentes	35	65– 84	74.02 ± .41	3.58 ± .29	4.84 ± .39
40–49					
Hawaiian Born	4	73– 78	76.50	—	—
Immigrants	60	69– 88	75.86 ± .34	3.90 ± .24	5.14 ± .32
Sedentes	33	63– 84	73.50 ± 44	3.76 ± .31	5.12 ± .42
50–59					
Hawaiian Born	0	—	—	—	—
Immigrants	36	67– 86	74.72 ± .53	4.70 ± .37	6.29 ± .50
Sedentes	19	67– 80	72.02 ± .56	3.60 ± .39	5.00 ± .55
60–64					
Hawaiian Born	0	—	—	—	—
Immigrants	7	71– 80	74.64	—	—
Sedentes	13	63– 80	71.66 ± .83	4.46 ± .59	6.22 ± .82

[Continued]

[TABLE 147—continued]

JAPANESE ADULT MALES

Age Groups by Decades

BIACROMION

	No.	Range	Mean ± p.e.		S.D. ± p.e.		V. ± p.e.	
20–29								
Hawaiian Born	143	37– 47	41.31 ±	.10	1.75 ±	.07	4.24 ±	.17
Immigrants	34	36– 46	40.71 ±	.24	2.09 ±	.17	5.13 ±	.42
Sedentes	71	37– 44	39.79 ±	.13	1.60 ±	.09	4.02 ±	.23
30–39								
Hawaiian Born	40	38– 45	41.50 ±	.21	1.99 ±	.15	4.80 ±	.36
Immigrants	42	38– 44	40.40 ±	.17	1.68 ±	.12	4.16 ±	.31
Sedentes	35	37– 44	39.71 ±	.22	1.89 ±	.15	4.76 ±	.38
40–49								
Hawaiian Born	4	37– 44	41.00		—		—	
Immigrants	60	37– 44	40.30 ±	.15	1.73 ±	.11	4.29 ±	.26
Sedentes	33	35– 44	39.52 ±	.24	2.03 ±	.17	5.14 ±	.43
50–59								
Hawaiian Born	0	—	—		—		—	
Immigrants	36	35– 43	39.83 ±	.22	1.95 ±	.16	4.90 ±	.39
Sedentes	19	36– 42	39.00 ±	.25	1.62 ±	.18	4.15 ±	.45
60–64								
Hawaiian Born	0	—	—		—		—	
Immigrants	7	38– 42	40.00		—		—	
Sedentes	13	35– 43	38.38 ±	.41	2.17 ±	.29	5.65 ±	.75

CRISTAL BREADTH

	No.	Range	Mean p.e.	S.D. p.e.	V. p.e.
20–29					
Hawaiian Born	144	25– 34	29.09 ± .10	1.86 ± .07	6.39 ± .25
Immigrants	34	25– 34	29.62 ± .23	2.00 ± .16	6.75 ± .55
Sedentes	70	25– 33	29.93 ± .13	1.67 ± .10	5.58 ± .32
30–39					
Hawaiian Born	40	26– 36	29.72 ± .25	2.33 ± .18	7.84 ± .59
Immigrants	42	25– 32	29.26 ± .19	1.79 ± .13	6.12 ± .45
Sedentes	35	26– 33	29.60 ± .18	1.62 ± .13	5.47 ± .44
40–49					
Hawaiian Born	4	27– 32	29.25	—	—
Immigrants	60	25– 36	29.62 ± .17	1.97 ± .12	6.65 ± .41
Sedentes	34	26– 33	30.06 ± .19	1.68 ± .14	5.59 ± .46
50–59					
Hawaiian Born	0	—	—	—	—
Immigrants	36	25– 35	29.56 ± .24	2.13 ± .17	7.21 ± .57
Sedentes	19	26– 33	29.53 ± .33	2.14 ± .23	7.25 ± .79
60–64					
Hawaiian Born	0	—	—	—	—
Immigrants	7	29– 34	30.43	—	—
Sedentes	13	28– 33	30.08 ± .32	1.69 ± .22	5.62 ± .74

[Continued]

[TABLE 147—continued]

JAPANESE ADULT MALES

Age Groups by Decades

CHEST BREADTH

	No.	Range	Mean	p.e.	S.D.	p.e.	V.	p.e.
20–29								
Hawaiian Born	144	23– 33	27.13 ±	.09	1.55 ±	.06	5.71 ±	.23
Immigrants	34	24– 32	27.38 ±	.19	1.66 ±	.14	6.06 ±	.50
Sedentes	71	24– 30	27.37 ±	.11	1.41 ±	.08	5.15 ±	.29
30–39								
Hawaiian Born	40	24– 35	27.58 ±	.28	2.66 ±	.20	9.64 ±	.73
Immigrants	42	24– 31	27.62 ±	.17	1.63 ±	.12	5.90 ±	.43
Sedentes	35	25– 30	27.51 ±	.15	1.34 ±	.11	4.87 ±	.39
40–49								
Hawaiian Born	4	25– 39	29.75		—		—	
Immigrants	60	25– 32	27.90 ±	.14	1.60 ±	.10	5.73 ±	.35
Sedentes	34	22– 30	27.12 ±	.21	1.83 ±	.15	6.75 ±	.55
50–59								
Hawaiian Born	0	—	—		—		—	
Immigrants	36	24– 33	27.47 ±	.21	1.91 ±	.15	6.95 ±	.55
Sedentes	19	22– 30	27.00 ±	.28	1.81 ±	.20	6.70 ±	.73
60–64								
Hawaiian Born	0	—	—		—		—	
Immigrants	7	27– 31	28.71		—		—	
Sedentes	13	25– 30	26.85 ±	.30	1.61 ±	.21	6.00 ±	.79

CHEST DEPTH

	No.	Range	Mean	p.e.	S.D.	p.e.	V.	p.e.
20–29								
Hawaiian Born	143	16– 25	19.52 ±	.09	1.61 ±	.06	8.25 ±	.33
Immigrants	34	15– 27	19.68 ±	.24	2.05 ±	.17	10.42 ±	.85
Sedentes	71	17– 23	20.32 ±	.09	1.17 ±	.07	5.76 ±	.33
30–39								
Hawaiian Born	40	17– 27	20.15 ±	.24	2.25 ±	.17	11.17 ±	.84
Immigrants	42	18– 23	19.79 ±	.14	1.32 ±	.10	6.67 ±	.49
Sedentes	34	19– 23	20.68 ±	.13	1.10 ±	.09	5.32 ±	.44
40–49								
Hawaiian Born	4	16– 22	19.25		—		—	
Immigrants	60	16– 24	20.35 ±	.16	1.83 ±	.11	8.99 ±	.55
Sedentes	34	18– 25	20.94 ±	.15	1.26 ±	.10	6.02 ±	.49
50–59								
Hawaiian Born	0	—	—		—		—	
Immigrants	36	16– 24	21.00 ±	.21	1.84 ±	.15	8.76 ±	.70
Sedentes	18	18– 26	21.00 ±	.29	1.85 ±	.21	8.81 ±	.99
60–64								
Hawaiian Born	0	—	—		—		—	
Immigrants	7	20– 24	22.00		—		—	
Sedentes	12	18– 23	20.67 ±	.29	1.49 ±	.21	7.21 ±	.99

[Continued]

[TABLE 147—*continued*]

JAPANESE ADULT MALES

Age Groups by Decades

HEAD LENGTH

	No.	Range	Mean	p.e.	S.D.	p.e.	V.	p.e.
20–29								
Hawaiian Born	143	172–205	186.72 ±	.37	6.52 ±	.26	3.49 ±	.14
Immigrants	34	174–203	187.62 ±	.86	7.40 ±	.61	3.94 ±	.32
Sedentes	71	166–207	188.08 ±	.53	6.58 ±	.37	3.50 ±	.20
30–39								
Hawaiian Born	40	168–199	185.26 ±	.70	6.56 ±	.49	3.54 ±	.27
Immigrants	42	176–205	188.12 ±	.58	5.56 ±	.41	2.96 ±	.22
Sedentes	35	178–213	191.36 ±	.86	7.56 ±	.61	3.95 ±	.32
40–49								
Hawaiian Born	4	186–197	193.00		——		——	
Immigrants	60	176–205	191.26 ±	.50	5.76 ±	.35	3.01 ±	.19
Sedentes	34	174–207	190.20 ±	.69	5.94 ±	.49	3.12 ±	.26
50–59								
Hawaiian Born	0	——	——		——		——	
Immigrants	36	172–199	189.12 ±	.72	6.40 ±	.51	3.38 ±	.27
Sedentes	19	178–207	190.92 ±	1.10	7.10 ±	.78	3.72 ±	.41
60–64								
Hawaiian Born	0	——	——		——		——	
Immigrants	7	184–205	192.22		——		——	
Sedentes	13	184–201	189.58 ±	.89	4.74 ±	.63	2.50 ±	.33

HEAD BREADTH

	No.	Range	Mean ± p.e.	S.D. ± p.e.	V. ± p.e.
20–29					
Hawaiian Born	144	139–168	154.98 ± .32	5.70 ± .23	3.68 ± .15
Immigrants	34	143–170	151.56 ± .61	5.24 ± .43	3.46 ± .28
Sedentes	71	141–164	151.28 ± .36	4.54 ± .26	3.00 ± .17
30–39					
Hawaiian Born	40	147–174	155.40 ± .65	6.14 ± .46	3.95 ± .30
Immigrants	42	143–168	154.12 ± .62	5.94 ± .44	3.85 ± .28
Sedentes	35	143–164	153.72 ± .53	4.68 ± .38	3.04 ± .24
40–49					
Hawaiian Born	4	149–162	155.00	—	—
Immigrants	60	143–168	152.84 ± .43	4.92 ± .30	3.22 ± .20
Sedentes	34	131–160	151.44 ± .70	6.02 ± .49	3.98 ± .33
50–59					
Hawaiian Born	0	—	—	—	—
Immigrants	36	143–162	152.22 ± .59	5.28 ± .42	3.47 ± .28
Sedentes	19	141–158	152.14 ± .74	4.78 ± .52	3.14 ± .34
60–64					
Hawaiian Born	0	—	—	—	—
Immigrants	7	147–158	151.78	—	—
Sedentes	13	143–162	151.34 ± .89	4.74 ± .63	3.13 ± .41

[Continued]

[TABLE 147—continued]

JAPANESE ADULT MALES
Age Groups by Decades

HEAD HEIGHT (cm.)

	No.	Range	Mean ± p.e.	S.D. ± p.e.	V. ± p.e.
20-29					
Hawaiian Born	140	11- 16	13.74 ± .06	1.10 ± .04	8.01 ± .32
Immigrants	34	11- 16	13.68 ± .15	1.26 ± .10	9.21 ± .75
Sedentes	71	10- 15	12.54 ± .08	.97 ± .05	7.74 ± .44
30-39					
Hawaiian Born	39	12- 15	13.59 ± .11	.98 ± .07	7.21 ± .55
Immigrants	42	11- 16	13.60 ± .13	1.25 ± .09	9.19 ± .68
Sedentes	35	11- 15	13.00 ± .14	1.20 ± .10	9.23 ± .74
40-49					
Hawaiian Born	4	12- 14	12.75	—	—
Immigrants	58	11- 16	13.28 ± .10	1.10 ± .07	8.28 ± .52
Sedentes	34	11- 16	12.68 ± .12	1.02 ± .08	8.04 ± .66
50-59					
Hawaiian Born	0	—	—	—	—
Immigrants	36	11- 16	13.22 ± .13	1.16 ± .09	8.77 ± .70
Sedentes	19	11- 15	13.21 ± .19	1.20 ± .13	9.08 ± .99
60-64					
Hawaiian Born	0	—	—	—	—
Immigrants	7	12- 14	13.14	—	—
Sedentes	13	11- 15	12.54 ± .23	1.22 ± .16	9.73 ± 1.29

MINIMUM FRONTAL DIAMETER

	No.	Range	Mean	p.e.	S.D.	p.e.	V.	p.e.
20–29								
Hawaiian Born	144	97–126	112.22 ±	.27	4.74 ±	.19	4.22 ±	.17
Immigrants	34	100–123	114.23 ±	.61	5.25 ±	.43	4.60 ±	.38
Sedentes	71	94–123	111.35 ±	.42	5.31 ±	.30	4.77 ±	.27
30–39								
Hawaiian Born	40	103–123	113.75 ±	.58	5.43 ±	.41	4.77 ±	.36
Immigrants	42	103–123	112.85 ±	.51	4.86 ±	.36	4.31 ±	.32
Sedentes	35	100–123	113.87 ±	.57	5.04 ±	.41	4.43 ±	.36
40–49								
Hawaiian Born	4	106–111	108.50		—		—	
Immigrants	60	100–126	113.30 ±	.46	5.31 ±	.33	4.69 ±	.29
Sedentes	34	100–123	111.23 ±	.61	5.31 ±	.43	4.77 ±	.39
50–59								
Hawaiian Born	0	—	—		—		—	
Immigrants	36	97–123	112.34 ±	.71	6.36 ±	.51	5.66 ±	.45
Sedentes	18	100–129	113.51 ±	1.12	7.02 ±	.79	6.18 ±	.69
60–64								
Hawaiian Born	0	—	—		—		—	
Immigrants	7	106–123	112.58		—		—	
Sedentes	13	100–123	112.07 ±	1.07	5.70 ±	.75	5.09 ±	.67

[Continued]

[TABLE 147—*continued*]

JAPANESE ADULT MALES

Age Groups by Decades

BIZYGOMATIC DIAMETER

	No.	Range	Mean	p.e.	S.D.	p.e.	V.	p.e.
20–29								
Hawaiian Born	143	125–160	141.36 ±	.29	5.10 ±	.20	3.61 ±	.14
Immigrants	34	125–151	140.37 ±	.59	5.13 ±	.42	3.65 ±	.30
Sedentes	71	131–151	141.03 ±	.36	4.47 ±	.25	3.17 ±	.18
30–39								
Hawaiian Born	40	131–156	141.60 ±	.63	5.94 ±	.45	4.19 ±	.32
Immigrants	42	134–154	142.80 ±	.46	4.41 ±	.32	3.09 ±	.23
Sedentes	35	131–154	143.49 ±	.54	4.77 ±	.38	3.32 ±	.27
40–49								
Hawaiian Born	4	131–145	139.50					
Immigrants	59	134–154	143.04 ±	.34	3.93 ±	.24	2.75 ±	.17
Sedentes	34	128–157	142.05 ±	.61	5.31 ±	.43	3.74 ±	.31
50–59								
Hawaiian Born	0	—	—		—		—	
Immigrants	36	128–154	142.41 ±	.66	5.88 ±	.47	4.13 ±	.33
Sedentes	19	131–151	140.52 ±	.69	4.47 ±	.49	3.18 ±	.35
60–64								
Hawaiian Born	0	—	—		—		—	
Immigrants	7	140–151	143.13					
Sedentes	13	134–148	141.93 ±	.63	3.39 ±	.45	2.39 ±	.32

BIGONIAL DIAMETER

	No.	Range	Mean ± p.e.	S.D. ± p.e.	V. ± p.e.
20–29					
Hawaiian Born	144	88–126	110.93 ± .31	5.46 ± .22	4.92 ± .20
Immigrants	34	97–123	110.63 ± .58	5.04 ± .41	4.56 ± .37
Sedentes	71	97–123	108.32 ± .42	5.31 ± .30	4.90 ± .28
30–39					
Hawaiian Born	40	97–126	111.05 ± .72	6.72 ± .51	6.05 ± .46
Immigrants	42	97–126	111.86 ± .62	5.94 ± .44	5.31 ± .39
Sedentes	35	100–123	110.87 ± .53	4.68 ± .38	4.22 ± .34
40–49					
Hawaiian Born	4	100–117	110.00	—	—
Immigrants	60	97–129	112.01 ± .57	6.57 ± .40	5.87 ± .36
Sedentes	34	97–123	110.45 ± .64	5.49 ± .45	4.97 ± .41
50–59					
Hawaiian Born	0	—	—	—	—
Immigrants	36	97–129	111.41 ± .79	6.99 ± .56	6.27 ± .50
Sedentes	19	97–120	109.67 ± .75	4.86 ± .53	4.43 ± .48
60–64					
Hawaiian Born	0	—	—	—	—
Immigrants	7	106–123	114.71	—	—
Sedentes	13	100–117	108.86 ± .78	4.17 ± .55	3.83 ± .51

[Continued]

[TABLE 147—continued]

JAPANESE ADULT MALES

Age Groups by Decades

TOTAL FACE HEIGHT

	No.	Range	Mean	p.e.	S.D.	p.e.	V.	p.e.
20–29								
Hawaiian Born	143	106–138	121.82 ±	.33	5.79 ±	.23	4.75 ±	.19
Immigrants	33	115–135	123.55 ±	.55	4.65 ±	.39	3.76 ±	.31
Sedentes	71	103–135	118.67 ±	.51	6.33 ±	.36	5.33 ±	.30
30–39								
Hawaiian Born	39	109–135	121.46 ±	.59	5.43 ±	.41	4.47 ±	.34
Immigrants	42	106–138	124.79 ±	.62	5.97 ±	.44	4.78 ±	.35
Sedentes	35	109–141	122.69 ±	.81	7.14 ±	.58	5.82 ±	.47
40–49								
Hawaiian Born	4	115–132	122.75		—		—	
Immigrants	60	109–141	123.14 ±	.54	6.21 ±	.38	5.04 ±	.31
Sedentes	34	103–132	118.64 ±	.74	6.39 ±	.52	5.39 ±	.44
50–59								
Hawaiian Born	0	—	—		—		—	
Immigrants	36	106–138	122.00 ±	.68	6.03 ±	.48	4.94 ±	.39
Sedentes	19	103–132	119.15 ±	1.00	6.48 ±	.71	5.44 ±	.60
60–64								
Hawaiian Born	0	—	—		—		—	
Immigrants	7	112–132	123.29		—		—	
Sedentes	13	103–129	120.14 ±	1.39	7.41 ±	.98	6.17 ±	.82

UPPER FACE HEIGHT

	No.	Range	Mean	p.e.	S.D.	p.e.	V.	p.e.
20–29								
Hawaiian Born	143	67– 94	81.48 ±	.27	4.72 ±	.19	5.79 ±	.23
Immigrants	34	69– 86	79.38 ±	.50	4.36 ±	.36	5.49 ±	.45
Sedentes	71	63– 86	72.14 ±	.33	4.18 ±	.24	5.79 ±	.33
30–39								
Hawaiian Born	40	69– 92	81.70 ±	.59	5.54 ±	.42	6.78 ±	.51
Immigrants	42	71– 94	82.12 ±	.51	4.86 ±	.36	5.92 ±	.44
Sedentes	35	65– 88	73.56 ±	.56	4.94 ±	.40	6.72 ±	.54
40–49								
Hawaiian Born	4	77– 92	86.50		—		—	
Immigrants	60	67– 94	82.00 ±	.40	4.62 ±	.28	5.63 ±	.35
Sedentes	34	65– 82	71.92 ±	.47	4.08 ±	.33	5.67 ±	.46
50–59								
Hawaiian Born	0	—	—		—		—	
Immigrants	36	71– 96	80.88 ±	.57	5.04 ±	.40	6.23 ±	.50
Sedentes	19	65– 84	73.50 ±	.74	4.76 ±	.52	6.48 ±	.71
60–64								
Hawaiian Born	0	—	—		—		—	
Immigrants	7	71– 94	84.36		—		—	
Sedentes	13	65– 78	73.66 ±	.70	3.72 ±	.49	5.05 ±	.67

[Continued]

[TABLE 147—continued]

JAPANESE ADULT MALES

Age Groups by Decades

FOREHEAD HEIGHT

	No.	Range	Mean ± p.e.	S.D. ± p.e.	V. ± p.e.
20–29					
Hawaiian Born	143	38– 77	58.90 ± .39	6.92 ± .28	11.75 ± .47
Immigrants	34	38– 73	55.38 ± .92	7.96 ± .65	14.37 ± 1.18
Sedentes	70	42– 77	59.62 ± .57	7.08 ± .40	11.88 ± .68
30–39					
Hawaiian Born	40	38– 81	59.82 ± .96	9.04 ± .68	15.11 ± 1.14
Immigrants	42	46– 77	60.54 ± .64	6.16 ± .45	10.18 ± .75
Sedentes	33	42– 77	62.66 ± .99	8.44 ± .70	13.47 ± 1.12
40–49					
Hawaiian Born	4	50– 69	60.50	—	—
Immigrants	60	42– 81	61.22 ± .76	8.68 ± .53	14.18 ± .87
Sedentes	29	42– 77	62.26 ± .95	7.56 ± .67	12.14 ± 1.08
50–59					
Hawaiian Born	0	—	—	—	—
Immigrants	34	42– 77	59.02 ± .90	7.80 ± .64	13.22 ± 1.08
Sedentes	16	50– 77	63.02 ± 1.04	6.16 ± .73	9.77 ± 1.16
60–64					
Hawaiian Born	0	—	—	—	—
Immigrants	7	50– 69	58.34	—	—
Sedentes	10	38– 69	55.90 ± 1.89	8.84 ± 1.33	15.81 ± 2.38

NOSE HEIGHT

	No.	Range	Mean	p.e.	S.D.	p.e.	V.	p.e.
20–29								
Hawaiian Born	144	44– 61	51.68 ±	.18	3.12 ±	.12	6.04 ±	.24
Immigrants	34	42– 63	51.08 ±	.52	4.46 ±	.36	8.73 ±	.71
Sedentes	71	40– 61	50.42 ±	.27	3.32 ±	.19	6.58 ±	.37
30–39								
Hawaiian Born	40	40– 61	52.10 ±	.45	4.18 ±	.32	8.02 ±	.60
Immigrants	40	44– 59	52.00 ±	.33	3.10 ±	.23	5.96 ±	.45
Sedentes	35	44– 63	51.12 ±	.44	3.84 ±	.31	7.51 ±	.61
40–49								
Hawaiian Born	4	46– 61	53.50		—		—	
Immigrants	60	44– 59	51.64 ±	.27	3.10 ±	.19	6.00 ±	.37
Sedentes	34	44– 59	50.26 ±	.30	2.60 ±	.21	5.17 ±	.42
50–59								
Hawaiian Born	0	—	—		—		—	
Immigrants	36	44– 61	51.94 ±	.39	3.46 ±	.28	6.66 ±	.53
Sedentes	19	42– 57	50.40 ±	.59	3.82 ±	.42	7.58 ±	.83
60–64								
Hawaiian Born	0	—	—		—		—	
Immigrants	7	44– 57	50.50		—		—	
Sedentes	13	44– 57	50.50 ±	.61	3.24 ±	.43	6.42 ±	.85

[Continued]

[TABLE 147—continued]

JAPANESE ADULT MALES

Age Groups by Decades

NOSE LENGTH

	No.	Range	Mean	p.e.	S.D.	p.e.	V.	p.e.
20–29								
Hawaiian Born	144	40– 59	50.04 ±	.19	3.38 ±	.13	6.75 ±	.27
Immigrants	34	40– 63	49.32 ±	.53	4.56 ±	.37	9.25 ±	.76
Sedentes	71	40– 59	47.46 ±	.28	3.46 ±	.20	7.29 ±	.41
30–39								
Hawaiian Born	40	40– 59	50.66 ±	.43	4.06 ±	.31	8.01 ±	.60
Immigrants	40	44– 59	50.74 ±	.35	3.30 ±	.25	6.50 ±	.49
Sedentes	35	42– 61	48.90 ±	.46	4.04 ±	.33	8.26 ±	.67
40–49								
Hawaiian Born	4	42– 57	51.00		—		—	
Immigrants	60	40– 57	50.24 ±	.33	3.76 ±	.23	7.48 ±	.46
Sedentes	34	40– 57	47.98 ±	.33	2.88 ±	.24	6.00 ±	.49
50–59								
Hawaiian Born	0	—	—		—		—	
Immigrants	36	44– 57	50.66 ±	.39	3.48 ±	.28	6.87 ±	.55
Sedentes	19	32– 55	47.44 ±	.76	4.92 ±	.54	10.37 ±	1.13
60–64								
Hawaiian Born	0	—	—		—		—	
Immigrants	7	40– 55	48.78		—		—	
Sedentes	13	38– 55	47.74 ±	.79	4.20 ±	.56	8.80 ±	1.16

NOSE SALIENT

	No.	Range	Mean	p.e.	S.D.	p.e.	V.	p.e.
20–29								
Hawaiian Born	144	9– 21	14.10 ±	.13	2.39 ±	.10	16.95 ±	.68
Immigrants	34	10– 19	14.09 ±	.27	2.33 ±	.19	16.54 ±	1.35
Sedentes	71	10– 21	14.89 ±	.15	1.93 ±	.11	12.96 ±	.73
30–39								
Hawaiian Born	40	10– 19	14.18 ±	.24	2.29 ±	.17	16.15 ±	1.22
Immigrants	40	9– 19	14.25 ±	.25	2.30 ±	.17	16.14 ±	1.22
Sedentes	35	9– 22	14.66 ±	.28	2.42 ±	.20	16.51 ±	1.33
40–49								
Hawaiian Born	4	11– 16	14.00		—		—	
Immigrants	59	9– 18	13.69 ±	.18	2.07 ±	.13	15.12 ±	.94
Sedentes	34	11– 17	14.06 ±	.19	1.68 ±	.14	11.95 ±	.98
50–59								
Hawaiian Born	0		—		—		—	
Immigrants	36	11– 19	14.08 ±	.20	1.75 ±	.14	12.43 ±	.99
Sedentes	19	9– 19	14.47 ±	.46	2.98 ±	.33	20.59 ±	2.25
60–64								
Hawaiian Born	0		—		—		—	
Immigrants	7	9– 15	12.14		—		—	
Sedentes	13	10– 21	14.54 ±	.57	3.03 ±	.40	20.84 ±	2.76

[Continued]

[TABLE 147—continued]

JAPANESE ADULT MALES

Age Groups by Decades

NOSE BREADTH

	No.	Range	Mean ± p.e.	S.D. ± p.e.	V. ± p.e.
20–29					
Hawaiian Born	144	28– 43	34.56 ± .15	2.66 ± .11	7.70 ± .31
Immigrants	34	26– 39	34.26 ± .34	2.90 ± .24	8.46 ± .69
Sedentes	71	30– 41	36.10 ± .20	2.56 ± .14	7.09 ± .40
30–39					
Hawaiian Born	40	28– 41	34.46 ± .34	3.18 ± .24	9.23 ± .70
Immigrants	40	30– 39	34.66 ± .22	2.06 ± .16	5.94 ± .45
Sedentes	35	32– 43	37.12 ± .25	2.18 ± .18	5.87 ± .47
40–49					
Hawaiian Born	4	30– 39	35.00	—	—
Immigrants	60	30– 43	36.06 ± .23	2.60 ± .16	7.21 ± .44
Sedentes	34	30– 43	36.26 ± .37	3.24 ± .26	8.94 ± .73
50–59					
Hawaiian Born	0	—	—	—	—
Immigrants	36	30– 43	37.84 ± .33	2.94 ± .23	7.77 ± .62
Sedentes	19	28– 43	36.40 ± .53	3.40 ± .37	9.34 ± 1.02
60–64					
Hawaiian Born	0	—	—	—	—
Immigrants	7	30– 43	37.36	—	—
Sedentes	13	32– 41	37.74 ± .52	2.78 ± .37	7.37 ± .97

INTER-OCULAR

	No.	Range	Mean	p.e.	S.D.	p.e.	V.	p.e.
20-29								
Hawaiian Born	144	23- 41	31.50 ±	.19	3.43 ±	.14	10.89 ±	.43
Immigrants	34	22- 38	30.88 ±	.44	3.84 ±	.31	12.44 ±	1.02
Sedentes	71	25- 37	31.80 ±	.21	2.62 ±	.15	8.24 ±	.47
30-39								
Hawaiian Born	40	23- 40	30.98 ±	.38	3.57 ±	.27	11.52 ±	.87
Immigrants	42	26- 42	31.52 ±	.34	3.27 ±	.24	10.37 ±	.76
Sedentes	35	26- 39	31.09 ±	.39	3.41 ±	.27	10.97 ±	.88
40-49								
Hawaiian Born	4	25- 33	28.75		—		—	
Immigrants	60	22- 38	30.32 ±	.30	3.50 ±	.22	11.54 ±	.71
Sedentes	34	26- 44	31.85 ±	.38	3.26 ±	.27	10.24 ±	.84
50-59								
Hawaiian Born	0	—	—		—		—	
Immigrants	36	21- 36	29.58 ±	.38	3.38 ±	.27	11.43 ±	.91
Sedentes	19	27- 36	31.74 ±	.34	2.20 ±	.24	6.93 ±	.76
60-64								
Hawaiian Born	0	—	—		—		—	
Immigrants	7	25- 36	30.43		—		—	
Sedentes	13	24- 36	31.23 ±	.65	3.45 ±	.46	11.05 ±	1.46

[Continued]

[TABLE 147—continued]

JAPANESE ADULT MALES

Age Groups by Decades

BI-OCULAR

	No.	Range	Mean ± p.e.	S.D. ± p.e.	V. ± p.e.
20–29					
Hawaiian Born	144	84–113	100.34 ± .28	5.02 ± .20	5.00 ± .20
Immigrants	34	82–111	99.98 ± .76	6.54 ± .53	6.54 ± .53
Sedentes	71	86–109	99.26 ± .37	4.60 ± .26	4.63 ± .26
30–39					
Hawaiian Born	39	86–113	99.58 ± .56	5.22 ± .40	5.24 ± .40
Immigrants	42	86–117	100.98 ± .58	5.62 ± .41	5.57 ± .41
Sedentes	35	88–111	100.22 ± .54	4.76 ± .38	4.75 ± .38
40–49					
Hawaiian Born	4	98–109	102.00	—	—
Immigrants	60	88–111	100.76 ± .45	5.18 ± .32	5.14 ± .32
Sedentes	34	92–111	100.32 ± .61	5.28 ± .43	5.26 ± .43
50–59					
Hawaiian Born	0	—	—	—	—
Immigrants	36	88–119	101.66 ± .78	6.94 ± .55	6.83 ± .54
Sedentes	19	86–107	98.82 ± .74	4.78 ± .52	4.84 ± .53
60–64					
Hawaiian Born	0	—	—	—	—
Immigrants	7	96–109	100.22	—	—
Sedentes	13	88–109	98.66 ± 1.14	6.10 ± .81	6.18 ± .82

RELATIVE SHOULDER BREADTH

	No.	Range	Mean	p.e.	S.D.	p.e.	V.	p.e.
20–29								
Hawaiian Born	143	23– 28	25.28 ±	.06	1.06 ±	.04	4.19 ±	.17
Immigrants	34	23– 30	25.38 ±	.18	1.54 ±	.13	6.07 ±	.50
Sedentes	71	21– 28	24.94 ±	.10	1.22 ±	.07	4.89 ±	.28
30–39								
Hawaiian Born	40	23– 28	25.74 ±	.13	1.22 ±	.09	4.74 ±	.36
Immigrants	42	23– 28	25.30 ±	.14	1.38 ±	.10	5.45 ±	.40
Sedentes	35	21– 28	24.70 ±	.15	1.28 ±	.10	5.18 ±	.42
40–49								
Hawaiian Born	4	23– 28	25.50		—		—	
Immigrants	60	23– 28	25.34 ±	.10	1.16 ±	.07	4.58 ±	.28
Sedentes	32	21– 28	25.00 ±	.16	1.32 ±	.11	5.28 ±	.45
50–59								
Hawaiian Born	0	—	—		—		—	
Immigrants	36	23– 30	25.12 ±	.15	1.32 ±	.10	5.25 ±	.42
Sedentes	19	23– 28	25.08 ±	.19	1.24 ±	.14	4.94 ±	.54
60–64								
Hawaiian Born	0	—	—		—		—	
Immigrants	7	25– 28	25.78		—		—	
Sedentes	13	23– 28	24.88 ±	.22	1.20 ±	.16	4.82 ±	.64

[Continued]

[TABLE 147—continued]

JAPANESE ADULT MALES

Age Groups by Decades

RELATIVE HIP BREADTH

	No.	Range	Mean	p.e.	S.D.	p.e.	V.	p.e.
20-29								
Hawaiian Born	143	14– 21	17.80 ±	.07	1.22 ±	.05	6.85 ±	.27
Immigrants	34	16– 21	18.62 ±	.14	1.18 ±	.10	6.34 ±	.52
Sedentes	71	16– 21	18.04 ±	.09	1.08 ±	.06	5.99 ±	.34
30-39								
Hawaiian Born	40	16– 21	18.26 ±	.15	1.38 ±	.10	7.56 ±	.57
Immigrants	42	14– 21	18.36 ±	.15	1.42 ±	.10	7.73 ±	.57
Sedentes	35	16– 21	18.50 ±	.12	1.08 ±	.09	5.84 ±	.47
40-49								
Hawaiian Born	4	16– 19	17.50		—		—	
Immigrants	60	14– 23	18.50 ±	.13	1.46 ±	.09	7.89 ±	.49
Sedentes	33	16– 21	19.16 ±	.14	1.16 ±	.10	6.05 ±	.50
50-59								
Hawaiian Born	0	—			—		—	
Immigrants	36	16– 23	18.84 ±	.16	1.46 ±	.12	7.75 ±	.62
Sedentes	19	16– 21	18.92 ±	.24	1.54 ±	.17	8.14 ±	.89
60-64								
Hawaiian Born	0	—			—		—	
Immigrants	7	18– 21	19.64		—		—	
Sedentes	13	18– 21	19.42 ±	.19	1.00 ±	.13	5.15 ±	.68

SHOULDER-HIP INDEX

	No.	Range	Mean	p.e.	S.D.	p.e.	V.	p.e.
20–29								
Hawaiian Born	143	62– 79	70.35 ±	.24	4.32 ±	.17	6.14 ±	.24
Immigrants	34	65– 97	73.50 ±	.66	5.70 ±	.47	7.76 ±	.63
Sedentes	71	65– 88	75.12 ±	.34	4.23 ±	.24	5.63 ±	.32
30–39								
Hawaiian Born	40	62– 85	71.64 ±	.51	4.74 ±	.36	6.62 ±	.50
Immigrants	42	59– 82	72.42 ±	.49	4.71 ±	.35	6.50 ±	.48
Sedentes	35	62– 82	74.82 ±	.48	4.23 ±	.34	5.65 ±	.46
40–49								
Hawaiian Born	4	68– 73	70.50		—		—	
Immigrants	60	62– 88	73.26 ±	.39	4.44 ±	.27	6.06 ±	.37
Sedentes	33	68– 85	76.08 ±	.48	4.11 ±	.34	5.40 ±	.45
50–59								
Hawaiian Born	0	—	—		—		—	
Immigrants	36	62– 82	74.16 ±	.49	4.35 ±	.35	5.87 ±	.47
Sedentes	19	68– 88	75.96 ±	.78	5.07 ±	.55	6.67 ±	.73
60–64								
Hawaiian Born	0	—	—		—		—	
Immigrants	7	71– 82	76.29		—		—	
Sedentes	13	71– 85	78.69 ±	.67	3.57 ±	.47	4.54 ±	.60

[Continued]

[TABLE 147—continued]

JAPANESE ADULT MALES

Age Groups by Decades

RELATIVE SITTING HEIGHT

	No.	Range	Mean	p.e.	S.D.	p.e.	V.	p.e.
20-29								
Hawaiian Born	143	48–58	52.53 ±	.10	1.73 ±	.07	3.29 ±	.13
Immigrants	34	49–61	52.53 ±	.24	2.06 ±	.17	3.92 ±	.32
Sedentes	71	48–56	52.97 ±	.14	1.69 ±	.10	3.19 ±	.18
30-39								
Hawaiian Born	40	47–56	52.20 ±	.21	1.99 ±	.15	3.81 ±	.29
Immigrants	42	48–55	52.48 ±	.16	1.55 ±	.11	2.95 ±	.22
Sedentes	35	49–58	53.83 ±	.21	1.86 ±	.15	3.46 ±	.28
40-49								
Hawaiian Born	4	51–54	52.75					
Immigrants	60	47–56	52.20 ±	.15	1.73 ±	.11	3.31 ±	.20
Sedentes	33	49–57	53.48 ±	.19	1.62 ±	.13	3.03 ±	.25
50-59								
Hawaiian Born	0	—	—		—		—	
Immigrants	36	48–57	52.42 ±	.23	2.02 ±	.16	3.85 ±	.31
Sedentes	19	50–56	53.63 ±	.28	1.81 ±	.20	3.37 ±	.37
60-64								
Hawaiian Born	0	—	—		—		—	
Immigrants	7	50–55	52.14					
Sedentes	13	50–56	53.62 ±	.36	1.94 ±	.26	3.62 ±	.48

RELATIVE TRUNK HEIGHT

	No.	Range	Mean	p.e.	S.D.	p.e.	V.	p.e.
20–29								
Hawaiian Born	143	29– 38	33.21 ±	.10	1.79 ±	.07	5.39 ±	.21
Immigrants	34	29– 36	32.91 ±	.17	1.50 ±	.12	4.56 ±	.37
Sedentes	71	30– 39	33.87 ±	.13	1.66 ±	.09	4.90 ±	.28
30–39								
Hawaiian Born	40	29– 37	33.00 ±	.19	1.79 ±	.13	5.42 ±	.41
Immigrants	42	30– 36	33.24 ±	.16	1.51 ±	.11	4.54 ±	.33
Sedentes	35	29– 39	34.43 ±	.24	2.10 ±	.17	6.10 ±	.49
40–49								
Hawaiian Born	4	32– 35	33.75		—		—	
Immigrants	60	29– 36	33.15 ±	.15	1.67 ±	.10	5.04 ±	.31
Sedentes	32	30– 38	34.50 ±	.20	1.68 ±	.14	4.87 ±	.41
50–59								
Hawaiian Born	0		—		—		—	
Immigrants	36	28– 38	33.28 ±	.23	2.09 ±	.17	6.28 ±	.50
Sedentes	19	30– 38	34.11 ±	.30	1.94 ±	.21	5.69 ±	.62
60–64								
Hawaiian Born	0		—		—		—	
Immigrants	7	31– 35	32.86		—		—	
Sedentes	13	30– 37	34.38 ±	.41	2.17 ±	.29	6.31 ±	.83

[Continued]

[TABLE 147—continued]

JAPANESE ADULT MALES

Age Groups by Decades

THORACIC INDEX

	No.	Range	Mean	p.e.	S.D.	p.e.	V.	p.e.
20–29								
Hawaiian Born	143	54– 85	71.96 ±	.31	5.56 ±	.22	7.73 ±	.31
Immigrants	34	60– 85	71.86 ±	.68	5.90 ±	.48	8.21 ±	.67
Sedentes	71	64– 89	74.20 ±	.37	4.66 ±	.26	6.28 ±	.36
30–39								
Hawaiian Born	40	58– 85	73.10 ±	.60	5.58 ±	.42	7.63 ±	.58
Immigrants	42	62– 81	71.74 ±	.48	4.60 ±	.34	6.41 ±	.47
Sedentes	34	68– 89	75.20 ±	.50	4.34 ±	.35	5.77 ±	.47
40–49								
Hawaiian Born	4	56– 73	65.50					
Immigrants	60	58– 85	72.80 ±	.49	5.66 ±	.35	7.77 ±	.48
Sedentes	34	66– 91	77.32 ±	.59	5.10 ±	.42	6.60 ±	.54
50–59								
Hawaiian Born	0	—	—		—		—	
Immigrants	36	62– 89	76.34 ±	.58	5.14 ±	.41	6.73 ±	.53
Sedentes	18	66– 93	77.72 ±	.97	6.12 ±	.69	7.87 ±	.88
60–64								
Hawaiian Born	0	—	—		—		—	
Immigrants	7	72– 81	76.22					
Sedentes	12	62– 87	77.50 ±	1.32	6.76 ±	.93	8.72 ±	1.20

BRACHIAL INDEX

	No.	Range	Mean	p.e.	S.D.	p.e.	V.	p.e.
20–29								
Hawaiian Born	143	69– 90	79.70 ±	.24	4.28 ±	.17	5.37 ±	.21
Immigrants	34	69– 92	80.02 ±	.57	4.90 ±	.40	6.12 ±	.50
Sedentes	71	67– 86	78.12 ±	.36	4.50 ±	.25	5.76 ±	.33
30–39								
Hawaiian Born	39	69– 90	80.26 ±	.56	5.20 ±	.40	6.48 ±	.49
Immigrants	42	71– 90	80.78 ±	.53	5.08 ±	.37	6.29 ±	.46
Sedentes	35	69– 88	78.64 ±	.50	4.40 ±	.35	5.60 ±	.45
40–49								
Hawaiian Born	4	73– 84	79.50		—		—	
Immigrants	60	67– 90	79.84 ±	.44	5.06 ±	.31	6.34 ±	.39
Sedentes	34	71– 90	80.26 ±	.55	4.72 ±	.39	5.88 ±	.48
50–59								
Hawaiian Born	0	—	—		—		—	
Immigrants	36	63– 90	80.00 ±	.71	6.28 ±	.50	7.85 ±	.62
Sedentes	19	71– 90	79.40 ±	.68	4.42 ±	.48	5.57 ±	.61
60–64								
Hawaiian Born	0	—	—		—		—	
Immigrants	7	75– 86	79.50		—		—	
Sedentes	12	71– 88	78.00 ±	.98	5.04 ±	.69	6.46 ±	.89

[Continued]

[TABLE 147—continued]

JAPANESE ADULT MALES

Age Groups by Decades

TIBIO-FEMORAL INDEX

	No.	Range	Mean	p.e.	S.D.	p.e.	V.	p.e.
20–29								
Hawaiian Born	142	70–124	93.50 ±	.48	8.50 ±	.34	9.09 ±	.36
Immigrants	33	75–119	90.80 ±	1.18	10.05 ±	.83	11.07 ±	.92
Sedentes	70	60–114	88.00 ±	.77	9.60 ±	.55	10.91 ±	.62
30–39								
Hawaiian Born	40	80–119	92.75 ±	.92	8.65 ±	.65	9.33 ±	.70
Immigrants	42	70–104	87.25 ±	.78	7.50 ±	.56	8.60 ±	.64
Sedentes	35	60–114	90.45 ±	1.28	11.25 ±	.91	12.44 ±	1.00
40–49								
Hawaiian Born	4	85– 94	88.25		—		—	
Immigrants	60	65–109	86.65 ±	.71	8.15 ±	.50	9.41 ±	.58
Sedentes	33	70–114	90.50 ±	1.16	9.90 ±	.82	10.94 ±	.91
50–59								
Hawaiian Born	0	—	—		—		—	
Immigrants	36	70–109	86.85 ±	.93	8.30 ±	.66	9.56 ±	.76
Sedentes	19	70–109	89.35 ±	1.47	9.50 ±	1.04	10.63 ±	1.16
60–64								
Hawaiian Born	0	—	—		—		—	
Immigrants	7	70– 89	82.70		—		—	
Sedentes	13	75–114	87.00 ±	1.80	9.60 ±	1.27	11.03 ±	1.46

INTER-MEMBRAL INDEX

	No.	Range	Mean	p.e.	S.D.	p.e.	V.	p.e.
20–29								
Hawaiian Born	142	82–107	94.00 ±	.24	4.30 ±	.17	4.57 ±	.18
Immigrants	33	86–117	93.66 ±	.69	5.84 ±	.48	6.24 ±	.52
Sedentes	71	80–107	94.30 ±	.39	4.86 ±	.28	5.15 ±	.29
30–39								
Hawaiian Born	39	83–101	93.38 ±	.36	3.36 ±	.26	3.60 ±	.27
Immigrants	42	84–101	92.92 ±	.40	3.80 ±	.28	4.09 ±	.30
Sedentes	35	78–109	95.30 ±	.61	5.32 ±	.43	5.58 ±	.45
40–49								
Hawaiian Born	4	90–99	95.00		—		—	
Immigrants	60	84–107	93.40 ±	.39	4.50 ±	.28	4.82 ±	.30
Sedentes	33	82–103	95.04 ±	.57	4.86 ±	.40	5.11 ±	.42
50–59								
Hawaiian Born	0	—	—		—		—	
Immigrants	36	84–105	94.00 ±	.49	4.38 ±	.35	4.66 ±	.37
Sedentes	19	86–105	95.56 ±	.73	4.70 ±	.51	4.92 ±	.54
60–64								
Hawaiian Born	0	—	—		—		—	
Immigrants	7	90–103	94.22		—		—	
Sedentes	13	90–105	96.80 ±	.80	4.28 ±	.57	8.94 ±	1.18

[Continued]

[TABLE 147—continued]

JAPANESE ADULT MALES
Age Groups by Decades

CEPHALIC INDEX

	No.	Range	Mean ± p.e.	S.D. ± p.e.	V. ± p.e.
20–29					
Hawaiian Born	144	74–101	83.34 ± .24	4.26 ± .17	5.11 ± .20
Immigrants	34	72– 93	81.02 ± .50	4.32 ± .35	5.33 ± .44
Sedentes	71	74– 87	80.34 ± .27	3.36 ± .19	4.18 ± .24
30–39					
Hawaiian Born	40	74– 93	83.90 ± .43	4.02 ± .30	4.79 ± .36
Immigrants	42	74– 95	81.84 ± .44	4.20 ± .31	5.13 ± .38
Sedentes	35	70– 89	80.56 ± .44	3.86 ± .31	4.79 ± .39
40–49					
Hawaiian Born	4	76– 83	80.50	—	—
Immigrants	60	72– 89	80.10 ± .31	3.56 ± .22	4.44 ± .27
Sedentes	34	68– 97	79.86 ± .50	4.30 ± .35	5.38 ± .44
50–59					
Hawaiian Born	0	—	—	—	—
Immigrants	36	72– 89	80.44 ± .42	3.78 ± .30	4.70 ± .37
Sedentes	19	72– 89	80.18 ± .57	3.68 ± .40	4.59 ± .50
60–64					
Hawaiian Born	0	—	—	—	—
Immigrants	7	74– 83	78.78	—	—
Sedentes	13	76– 85	79.74 ± .54	2.90 ± .38	3.64 ± .48

LENGTH-HEIGHT INDEX

	No.	Range	Mean	p.e.	S.D.	p.e.	V.	p.e.
20–29								
Hawaiian Born	141	56– 91	73.60 ±	.35	6.14 ±	.25	8.34 ±	.34
Immigrants	34	56– 87	72.80 ±	.75	6.46 ±	.53	8.87 ±	.73
Sedentes	71	56– 79	66.56 ±	.43	5.38 ±	.30	8.08 ±	.46
30–39								
Hawaiian Born	39	60– 85	73.32 ±	.62	5.70 ±	.44	7.77 ±	.59
Immigrants	42	58– 87	71.92 ±	.77	7.42 ±	.55	10.32 ±	.76
Sedentes	35	56– 79	68.04 ±	.64	5.62 ±	.45	8.26 ±	.67
40–49								
Hawaiian Born	4	60– 75	66.00		—		—	
Immigrants	58	58– 85	67.50 ±	.56	6.32 ±	.40	9.36 ±	.59
Sedentes	33	56– 79	66.08 ±	.57	4.88 ±	.41	7.38 ±	.61
50–59								
Hawaiian Born	0	—	—		—		—	
Immigrants	36	58– 89	70.22 ±	.71	6.36 ±	.51	9.06 ±	.72
Sedentes	19	54– 81	69.34 ±	1.04	6.70 ±	.73	9.66 ±	1.06
60–64								
Hawaiian Born	0	—	—		—		—	
Immigrants	7	58– 75	68.50		—		—	
Sedentes	13	58– 77	66.34 ±	1.10	5.90 ±	.78	8.89 ±	1.18

[Continued]

[TABLE 147—*continued*]

JAPANESE ADULT MALES

Age Groups by Decades

BREADTH-HEIGHT INDEX

	No.	Range	Mean	p.e.	S.D.	p.e.	V.	p.e.
20–29								
Hawaiian Born	140	68–107	88.78 ±	.40	7.06 ±	.28	7.95 ±	.32
Immigrants	34	76–105	90.14 ±	.90	7.78 ±	.64	8.63 ±	.71
Sedentes	71	66– 99	82.80 ±	.53	6.56 ±	.37	7.92 ±	.45
30–39								
Hawaiian Born	39	70–101	87.26 ±	.78	7.22 ±	.55	8.27 ±	.63
Immigrants	42	68–107	88.36 ±	.87	8.34 ±	.61	9.44 ±	.69
Sedentes	35	68– 97	84.62 ±	.88	7.76 ±	.63	9.17 ±	.74
40–49								
Hawaiian Born	4	74– 93	82.50		—		—	
Immigrants	58	70–111	86.88 ±	.70	7.86 ±	.49	9.05 ±	.57
Sedentes	33	70– 99	83.04 ±	.74	6.28 ±	.52	7.56 ±	.63
50–59								
Hawaiian Born	0	—	—		—		—	
Immigrants	36	70–107	87.22 ±	.82	7.30 ±	.58	8.37 ±	.67
Sedentes	19	74–105	86.92 ±	1.23	7.94 ±	.87	9.13 ±	1.00
60–64								
Hawaiian Born	0	—	—		—		—	
Immigrants	7	78– 95	86.50		—		—	
Sedentes	13	68–101	83.26 ±	1.53	8.20 ±	1.08	9.85 ±	1.30

CEPHALO-FACIAL INDEX

	No.	Range	Mean	p.e.	S.D.	p.e.	V.	p.e.
20–29								
Hawaiian Born	143	83–102	91.24 ±	.16	2.92 ±	.12	3.20 ±	.13
Immigrants	34	83–98	92.56 ±	.36	3.12 ±	.26	3.37 ±	.28
Sedentes	71	87–100	93.34 ±	.24	2.96 ±	.17	3.17 ±	.18
30–39								
Hawaiian Born	40	85–100	90.94 ±	.33	3.12 ±	.24	3.43 ±	.26
Immigrants	42	87–102	92.50 ±	.30	2.90 ±	.21	3.14 ±	.23
Sedentes	35	87–100	93.16 ±	.31	2.72 ±	.22	2.92 ±	.24
40–49								
Hawaiian Born	4	87–92	89.50		—		—	
Immigrants	59	85–102	93.44 ±	.26	2.92 ±	.18	3.12 ±	.19
Sedentes	34	85–108	93.50 ±	.46	3.96 ±	.32	4.24 ±	.35
50–59								
Hawaiian Born	0	—	—		—		—	
Immigrants	36	85–102	93.62 ±	.48	4.24 ±	.34	4.53 ±	.36
Sedentes	19	85–98	92.34 ±	.45	2.92 ±	.32	3.16 ±	.35
60–64								
Hawaiian Born	0	—	—		—		—	
Immigrants	7	91–98	94.36 ±	.61	—		—	
Sedentes	13	89–100	93.96 ±	.46	3.24 ±	.43	3.45 ±	.46

[Continued]

[TABLE 147—continued]

JAPANESE ADULT MALES

Age Groups by Decades

FRONTO-PARIETAL INDEX

	No.	Range	Mean ± p.e.	S.D. ± p.e.	V. ± p.e.
20–29					
Hawaiian Born	144	62– 83	72.48 ± .19	3.36 ± .13	4.64 ± .18
Immigrants	34	68– 79	73.56 ± .34	2.96 ± .24	4.02 ± .33
Sedentes	71	64– 83	73.82 ± .28	3.46 ± .20	4.69 ± .27
30–39					
Hawaiian Born	40	68– 83	73.26 ± .35	3.32 ± .25	4.53 ± .34
Immigrants	42	66– 81	73.36 ± .29	2.74 ± .20	3.74 ± .28
Sedentes	35	68– 79	73.88 ± .33	2.90 ± .23	3.93 ± .32
40–49					
Hawaiian Born	4	68– 73	70.00	—	—
Immigrants	60	62– 81	74.06 ± .34	3.90 ± .24	5.27 ± .32
Sedentes	34	66– 83	73.38 ± .42	3.64 ± .30	4.96 ± .41
50–59					
Hawaiian Born	0	—	—	—	—
Immigrants	36	64– 81	73.16 ± .45	3.98 ± .32	5.44 ± .43
Sedentes	18	68– 81	74.28 ± .67	4.20 ± .47	5.65 ± .64
60–64					
Hawaiian Born	0	—	—	—	—
Immigrants	7	68– 79	74.22	—	—
Sedentes	13	68– 81	74.50 ± .69	3.68 ± .49	4.94 ± .65

ZYGO-FRONTAL INDEX

	No.	Range	Mean ± p.e.	S.D. ± p.e.	V. ± p.e.
20–29					
Hawaiian Born	143	72– 87	79.52 ± .17	2.94 ± .12	3.70 ± .15
Immigrants	34	74– 87	79.50 ± .35	3.04 ± .25	3.82 ± .31
Sedentes	71	68– 87	78.96 ± .28	3.50 ± .20	4.43 ± .25
30–39					
Hawaiian Born	40	74– 87	80.30 ± .29	2.68 ± .20	3.34 ± .25
Immigrants	42	70– 85	79.16 ± .29	2.74 ± .20	3.46 ± .25
Sedentes	35	70– 87	79.18 ± .38	3.34 ± .27	4.22 ± .34
40–49					
Hawaiian Born	4	76– 81	78.00	—	—
Immigrants	59	72– 85	79.18 ± .24	2.70 ± .17	3.41 ± .21
Sedentes	34	70– 85	78.74 ± .40	3.46 ± .28	4.39 ± .36
50–59					
Hawaiian Born	0	—	—	—	—
Immigrants	36	62– 89	78.50 ± .52	4.66 ± .37	5.94 ± .47
Sedentes	18	74– 87	80.16 ± .49	3.08 ± .35	3.84 ± .43
60–64					
Hawaiian Born	0	—	—	—	—
Immigrants	7	74– 83	79.08	—	—
Sedentes	13	72– 85	79.26 ± .63	3.38 ± .45	4.26 ± .56

[Continued]

TABLE 147—continued]

JAPANESE ADULT MALES
Age Groups by Decades

ZYGO-GONIAL INDEX

	No.	Range	Mean	p.e.	S.D.	p.e.	V.	p.e.
20–29								
Hawaiian Born	143	68– 89	78.60 ±	.17	3.00 ±	.12	3.82 ±	.15
Immigrants	34	70– 85	78.62 ±	.35	3.06 ±	.25	3.89 ±	.32
Sedentes	71	64– 85	76.76 ±	.28	3.56 ±	.20	4.64 ±	.26
30–39								
Hawaiian Born	40	70– 83	78.54 ±	.32	3.04 ±	.23	3.87 ±	.29
Immigrants	42	72– 89	78.26 ±	.36	3.46 ±	.25	4.42 ±	.33
Sedentes	35	66– 83	77.18 ±	.40	3.54 ±	.29	4.59 ±	.37
40–49								
Hawaiian Born	4	72– 83	79.00		—		—	
Immigrants	59	70– 87	78.40 ±	.32	3.66 ±	.23	4.67 ±	.29
Sedentes	34	70– 89	77.98 ±	.43	3.74 ±	.31	4.80 ±	.39
50–59								
Hawaiian Born	0							
Immigrants	36	70– 87	78.06 ±	.43	3.80 ±	.30	4.87 ±	.39
Sedentes	19	72– 83	78.18 ±	.38	2.44 ±	.27	3.12 ±	.34
60–64								
Hawaiian Born	0							
Immigrants	7	76– 85	79.64		—		—	
Sedentes	13	72– 83	76.66 ±	.48	2.54 ±	.34	3.31 ±	.44

FACIAL INDEX

	No.	Range	Mean	p.e.	S.D.	p.e.	V.	p.e.
20–29								
Hawaiian Born	142	72– 98	86.11 ±	.25	4.41 ±	.18	5.12 ±	.20
Immigrants	33	78– 98	87.73 ±	.55	4.68 ±	.39	5.33 ±	.44
Sedentes	71	72– 95	83.95 ±	.38	4.80 ±	.27	5.72 ±	.32
30–39								
Hawaiian Born	39	75– 95	86.08 ±	.56	5.19 ±	.40	6.03 ±	.46
Immigrants	42	72– 98	87.07 ±	.47	4.47 ±	.33	5.13 ±	.38
Sedentes	35	75– 98	85.09 ±	.57	4.98 ±	.40	5.85 ±	.47
40–49								
Hawaiian Born	4	81– 92	88.00		—		—	
Immigrants	59	72–101	86.11 ±	.46	5.19 ±	.32	6.03 ±	.37
Sedentes	34	72– 98	83.77 ±	.71	6.12 ±	.50	7.31 ±	.60
50–59								
Hawaiian Born	0	—	—		—		—	
Immigrants	36	72– 98	85.57 ±	.59	5.22 ±	.41	6.10 ±	.48
Sedentes	19	72– 92	84.52 ±	.77	4.98 ±	.54	5.89 ±	.64
60–64								
Hawaiian Born	0	—	—		—		—	
Immigrants	7	78– 92	85.87		—		—	
Sedentes	13	75– 92	84.55 ±	.90	4.83 ±	.64	5.71 ±	.76

[Continued]

[TABLE 147—continued]

JAPANESE ADULT MALES

Age Groups by Decades

UPPER FACIAL INDEX

	No.	Range	Mean	p.e.	S.D.	p.e.	V.	p.e.
20-29								
Hawaiian Born	142	46- 69	57.53 ±	.22	3.81 ±	.15	6.62 ±	.26
Immigrants	34	46- 66	56.96 ±	.48	4.17 ±	.34	7.32 ±	.60
Sedentes	71	37- 63	51.32 ±	.31	3.90 ±	.22	7.60 ±	.43
30-39								
Hawaiian Born	40	49- 66	57.86 ±	.44	4.08 ±	.31	7.05 ±	.53
Immigrants	42	49- 66	57.65 ±	.36	3.42 ±	.25	5.93 ±	.44
Sedentes	35	43- 60	51.20 ±	.35	3.06 ±	.25	5.98 ±	.48
40-49								
Hawaiian Born	4	58- 69	62.75		—		—	
Immigrants	59	46- 69	57.53 ±	.36	4.05 ±	.25	7.04 ±	.44
Sedentes	34	43- 60	51.14 ±	.37	3.18 ±	.26	6.22 ±	.51
50-59								
Hawaiian Born	0	—	—		—		—	
Immigrants	36	46- 66	56.84 ±	.46	4.08 ±	.32	7.18 ±	.57
Sedentes	19	46- 63	52.37 ±	.59	3.84 ±	.42	7.33 ±	.80
60-64								
Hawaiian Born	0	—	—		—		—	
Immigrants	7	49- 66	58.58		—		—	
Sedentes	13	46- 57	51.62 ±	.52	2.79 ±	.37	5.40 ±	.71

NASAL INDEX

	No.	Range	Mean	p.e.	S.D.	p.e.	V.	p.e.
20–29								
Hawaiian Born	144	50– 83	66.98 ±	.34	6.02 ±	.24	8.99 ±	.36
Immigrants	34	50– 85	67.38 ±	.94	8.14 ±	.67	12.08 ±	.99
Sedentes	71	54– 93	71.72 ±	.56	7.02 ±	.40	9.79 ±	.55
30–39								
Hawaiian Born	40	50– 81	66.14 ±	.67	6.24 ±	.47	9.43 ±	.71
Immigrants	40	56– 81	67.00 ±	.57	5.36 ±	.40	8.00 ±	.60
Sedentes	35	56– 85	72.56 ±	.77	6.74 ±	.54	9.29 ±	.75
40–49								
Hawaiian Born	4	54– 77	67.00		—		—	
Immigrants	60	52– 85	70.16 ±	.60	6.90 ±	.42	9.83 ±	.61
Sedentes	34	54– 99	72.68 ±	1.02	8.80 ±	.72	12.11 ±	.99
50–59								
Hawaiian Born	0	—					—	
Immigrants	36	62– 95	73.16 ±	.70	6.24 ±	.50	8.53 ±	.68
Sedentes	19	56– 91	72.72 ±	1.45	9.40 ±	1.03	12.93 ±	1.41
60–64								
Hawaiian Born	0	—					—	
Immigrants	7	66– 89	74.22		—		—	
Sedentes	13	62– 91	74.96 ±	1.54	8.24 ±	1.09	10.99 ±	1.45

[Continued]

[TABLE 147—continued]

JAPANESE ADULT MALES

Age Groups by Decades

NOSE SALIENT-HEIGHT INDEX

	No.	Range	Mean	p.e.	S.D.	p.e.	V.	p.e.
20–29								
Hawaiian Born	144	16– 42	27.32 ±	.25	4.47 ±	.18	16.36 ±	.65
Immigrants	34	16– 36	27.68 ±	.51	4.38 ±	.36	15.82 ±	1.29
Sedentes	71	19– 42	29.69 ±	.31	3.93 ±	.22	13.24 ±	.75
30–39								
Hawaiian Born	40	16– 45	27.26 ±	.53	5.01 ±	.38	18.38 ±	1.39
Immigrants	40	19– 39	27.56 ±	.43	4.04 ±	.30	14.91 ±	1.12
Sedentes	35	19– 36	28.40 ±	.46	4.05 ±	.33	14.26 ±	1.15
40–49								
Hawaiian Born	4	22– 36	27.50		—		—	
Immigrants	59	16– 36	26.36 ±	.31	3.54 ±	.22	13.43 ±	.83
Sedentes	34	19– 33	27.77 ±	.39	3.33 ±	.27	11.99 ±	.98
50–59								
Hawaiian Born	0	—	—		—		—	
Immigrants	36	19– 33	27.32 ±	.36	3.21 ±	.26	11.75 ±	.93
Sedentes	19	19– 42	29.15 ±	.89	5.73 ±	.63	19.66 ±	2.15
60–64								
Hawaiian Born	0	—	—		—		—	
Immigrants	7	16– 30	23.42		—		—	
Sedentes	13	19– 42	26.00 ±	1.22	6.51 ±	.86	25.04 ±	3.31

NOSE LENGTH-HEIGHT INDEX

	No.	Range	Mean	p.e.	S.D.	p.e.	V.	p.e.
20–29								
Hawaiian Born	144	86–103	97.16 ±	.16	2.92 ±	.12	3.01 ±	.12
Immigrants	34	90–103	97.32 ±	.36	3.08 ±	.25	3.16 ±	.26
Sedentes	71	88–101	94.78 ±	.24	2.98 ±	.17	3.14 ±	.18
30–39								
Hawaiian Born	40	90–103	97.26 ±	.32	3.02 ±	.23	3.10 ±	.23
Immigrants	40	90–105	98.26 ±	.31	2.90 ±	.22	2.95 ±	.22
Sedentes	35	88–101	95.58 ±	.38	3.36 ±	.27	3.52 ±	.28
40–49								
Hawaiian Born	4	92–103	96.50		—		—	
Immigrants	60	86–105	97.86 ±	.31	3.54 ±	.22	3.62 ±	.22
Sedentes	34	90–103	95.98 ±	.34	2.96 ±	.24	3.08 ±	.25
50–59								
Hawaiian Born	0	—	—		—		—	
Immigrants	36	92–105	97.88 ±	.31	2.74 ±	.22	2.80 ±	.22
Sedentes	19	76–103	94.18 ±	.73	4.70 ±	.51	4.99 ±	.55
60–64								
Hawaiian Born	0	—	—		—		—	
Immigrants	7	90–101	96.78		—		—	
Sedentes	13	88–101	95.12 ±	.65	3.46 ±	.46	3.64 ±	.48

TABLE 148

MALE MANUAL LABORERS—SEDENTES

Measurement	No.	Range	Mean	p.e.	S.D.	p.e.	V.	p.e.
Age	38	20– 64	43.70 ± 1.29		11.80 ± .91		27.00 ± 2.09	
Weight	35	81–150	116.60 ± 1.72		15.10 ± 1.22		12.95 ± 1.04	
Stature	38	145–171	157.22 ± .60		5.46 ± .42		3.47 ± .27	
Sitting Height	38	74– 91	83.56 ± .42		3.88 ± .30		4.64 ± .36	
Trunk Height	37	44– 59	53.26 ± .39		3.56 ± .28		6.68 ± .52	
Upper Arm Length	38	23– 31	28.47 ± .20		1.79 ± .14		6.29 ± .49	
Lower Arm Length	38	22– 27	23.32 ± .13		1.22 ± .09		5.23 ± .40	
Hand Length	38	16– 20	17.61 ± .10		.88 ± .07		5.00 ± .39	
Upper Leg Length	38	29– 44	36.02 ± .33		3.00 ± .23		8.33 ± .64	
Lower Leg Length	38	27– 37	31.39 ± .26		2.41 ± .19		7.68 ± .59	
Total Leg Length	38	63– 84	73.40 ± .43		3.94 ± .30		5.37 ± .42	
Biacromion	37	35– 44	39.22 ± .27		2.41 ± .19		6.14 ± .48	
Cristal Breadth	38	25– 33	29.45 ± .22		2.03 ± .16		6.89 ± .53	
Chest Breadth	38	22– 30	26.89 ± .22		1.97 ± .15		7.33 ± .57	
Chest Depth	38	18– 25	20.76 ± .16		1.48 ± .11		7.13 ± .55	
Head Length	38	174–209	189.02 ± .72		6.62 ± .51		3.50 ± .27	
Head Breadth	38	141–164	151.66 ± .63		5.78 ± .45		3.81 ± .29	
Head Height (cm.)	38	11– 15	12.87 ± .14		1.26 ± .10		9.79 ± .76	
Minimum Frontal Diameter	38	100–129	114.26 ± .65		5.94 ± .46		5.20 ± .40	
Bizygomatic Diameter	38	128–157	141.39 ± .60		5.46 ± .42		3.86 ± .30	
Bigonial Diameter	38	100–123	110.48 ± .52		4.74 ± .37		4.29 ± .33	
Total Face Height	38	103–138	120.83 ± .75		6.87 ± .53		5.69 ± .44	
Upper Face Height	38	67– 82	73.72 ± .50		4.58 ± .35		6.21 ± .48	
Forehead Height	35	42– 77	61.54 ± .84		7.36 ± .59		11.96 ± .96	
Nose Height	38	44– 61	50.66 ± .40		3.62 ± .28		7.15 ± .55	

	N	Range	Mean ±	±	±
Nose Length	38	42– 57	48.72 ± .39	3.52 ± .27	7.22 ± .56
Nose Salient	38	10– 18	13.50 ± .22	2.00 ± .15	14.81 ± 1.15
Nose Breadth	38	28– 41	35.28 ± .32	2.90 ± .22	8.22 ± .64
Inter-Ocular	38	24– 44	31.55 ± .38	3.51 ± .27	11.13 ± .86
Bi-Ocular	38	86–109	98.24 ± .55	5.02 ± .39	5.11 ± .40
Index					
Relative Shoulder Breadth	37	21– 28	24.96 ± .18	1.58 ± .12	6.33 ± .50
Relative Hip Breadth	38	16– 21	18.72 ± .15	1.36 ± .11	7.26 ± .56
Shoulder-Hip	37	68– 88	75.72 ± .58	5.25 ± .41	6.93 ± .54
Relative Sitting Height	38	50– 57	53.21 ± .19	1.77 ± .14	3.33 ± .26
Relative Trunk Height	37	30– 38	33.97 ± .22	2.01 ± .16	5.92 ± .46
Thoracic	38	68– 91	77.40 ± .58	5.32 ± .41	6.87 ± .53
Brachial	37	73– 88	81.44 ± .41	3.68 ± .29	4.52 ± .35
Tibio-Femoral	38	65–104	87.00 ± .93	8.50 ± .66	9.77 ± .76
Inter-Membral	38	78–109	94.92 ± .55	5.04 ± .39	5.31 ± .41
Cephalic	38	74– 89	80.40 ± .39	3.52 ± .27	4.38 ± .34
Length-Height	38	56– 81	68.24 ± .65	5.98 ± .46	8.76 ± .68
Breadth-Height	38	68–105	84.82 ± .91	8.32 ± .64	9.81 ± .76
Cephalo-Facial	38	87–100	93.14 ± .32	2.94 ± .23	3.16 ± .24
Fronto-Parietal	38	66– 83	75.34 ± .38	3.48 ± .27	4.62 ± .36
Zygo-Frontal	38	70– 87	80.82 ± .40	3.68 ± .28	4.55 ± .35
Zygo-Gonial	38	70– 89	78.24 ± .41	3.78 ± .29	4.83 ± .37
Facial	38	72– 98	85.24 ± .64	5.82 ± .45	6.83 ± .53
Upper Facial	38	43– 60	52.13 ± .40	3.63 ± .28	6.96 ± .54
Nasal	38	54– 85	69.92 ± .82	7.52 ± .58	10.76 ± .83
Nose Salient-Height	38	19– 39	26.48 ± .44	4.05 ± .31	15.29 ± 1.18
Nose Length-Height	38	86–103	96.34 ± .40	3.64 ± .28	3.78 ± .29

TABLE 149

MALE MANUAL LABORERS—IMMIGRANTS

Measurement	No.	Range	Mean ± p.e.	S.D. ± p.e.	V. ± p.e.
Age	60	20– 64	41.00 ± .96	11.00 ± .68	26.83 ± 1.65
Weight	60	81–180	123.20 ± 1.41	16.20 ± 1.00	13.15 ± .81
Stature	60	145–171	157.79 ± .46	5.31 ± .33	3.37 ± .21
Sitting Height	60	76– 91	82.74 ± .30	3.46 ± .21	4.18 ± .26
Trunk Height	60	46– 59	52.20 ± .25	2.92 ± .18	5.59 ± .34
Upper Arm Length	60	26– 33	29.45 ± .14	1.62 ± .10	5.50 ± .34
Lower Arm Length	60	20– 26	23.47 ± .13	1.44 ± .09	6.14 ± .38
Hand Length	60	15– 20	17.92 ± .08	.88 ± .05	4.91 ± .30
Upper Leg Length	60	29– 42	36.86 ± .26	2.94 ± .18	7.98 ± .49
Lower Leg Length	60	28– 38	32.67 ± .17	1.97 ± .12	6.03 ± .37
Total Leg Length	60	67– 82	75.06 ± .30	3.40 ± .21	4.53 ± .28
Biacromion	60	36– 44	40.40 ± .16	1.83 ± .11	4.53 ± .28
Cristal Breadth	60	25– 34	29.63 ± .16	1.88 ± .12	6.34 ± .39
Chest Breadth	60	24– 33	27.55 ± .17	1.94 ± .12	7.04 ± .43
Chest Depth	60	16– 27	20.63 ± .17	1.93 ± .12	9.36 ± .58
Head Length	60	174–205	189.86 ± .62	7.08 ± .44	3.73 ± .23
Head Breadth	60	143–170	151.54 ± .48	5.54 ± .34	3.66 ± .23
Head Height (cm.)	60	11– 16	13.13 ± .11	1.24 ± .08	9.44 ± .58
Minimum Frontal Diameter	60	97–123	112.76 ± .52	5.94 ± .37	5.27 ± .32
Bizygomatic Diameter	60	125–154	141.96 ± .43	4.95 ± .30	3.49 ± .21
Bigonial Diameter	60	97–126	110.15 ± .53	6.12 ± .38	5.56 ± .34
Total Face Height	59	109–141	123.74 ± .66	7.56 ± .47	6.11 ± .38
Upper Face Height	60	69– 96	81.90 ± .42	4.86 ± .30	5.93 ± .37
Forehead Height	60	38– 81	58.50 ± .79	9.04 ± .56	15.45 ± .95
Nose Height	60	44– 63	51.90 ± .34	3.88 ± .24	7.48 ± .46

	N	Range	Mean		
Nose Length	60	42– 63	50.46 ± .37	4.20 ± .26	8.32 ± .51
Nose Salient	60	9– 19	13.80 ± .19	2.13 ± .13	15.43 ± .95
Nose Breadth	60	26– 43	34.96 ± .28	3.20 ± .20	9.15 ± .56
Inter-Ocular	60	22– 37	30.38 ± .28	3.22 ± .20	10.60 ± .65
Bi-Ocular	60	82–119	99.94 ± .53	6.12 ± .38	6.12 ± .38
Index					
Relative Shoulder Breadth	60	23– 30	25.60 ± .11	1.30 ± .08	5.08 ± .31
Relative Hip Breadth	60	16– 21	18.90 ± .11	1.24 ± .08	6.56 ± .40
Shoulder-Hip	60	62– 82	73.26 ± .34	3.87 ± .24	5.28 ± .32
Relative Sitting Height	60	49– 56	52.37 ± .13	1.44 ± .09	2.75 ± .17
Relative Trunk Height	60	30– 36	33.08 ± .12	1.37 ± .08	4.14 ± .25
Thoracic	60	58– 89	74.84 ± .52	5.96 ± .37	7.96 ± .49
Brachial	60	63– 90	79.86 ± .52	5.98 ± .37	7.49 ± .46
Tibio-Femoral	60	75–119	88.85 ± .79	9.05 ± .56	10.19 ± .63
Inter-Membral	60	86–107	94.36 ± .38	4.34 ± .27	4.60 ± .28
Cephalic	60	72– 93	80.06 ± .37	4.22 ± .26	5.27 ± .32
Length-Height	60	56– 85	69.20 ± .60	6.88 ± .42	9.94 ± .61
Breadth-Height	60	68–111	86.70 ± .74	8.54 ± .53	9.85 ± .61
Cephalo-Facial	60	83–102	93.66 ± .32	3.62 ± .22	3.86 ± .24
Fronto-Parietal	60	64– 81	74.14 ± .30	3.50 ± .22	4.72 ± .29
Zygo-Frontal	60	62– 89	79.14 ± .34	3.88 ± .24	4.90 ± .30
Zygo-Gonial	60	70– 83	77.50 ± .31	3.54 ± .22	4.57 ± .28
Facial	59	75–101	87.13 ± .45	5.13 ± .32	5.89 ± .37
Upper Facial	60	46– 69	58.01 ± .37	4.23 ± .26	7.29 ± .45
Nasal	60	50– 81	67.76 ± .65	7.42 ± .46	10.95 ± .67
Nose Salient-Height	60	16– 33	26.66 ± .31	3.60 ± .22	13.50 ± .83
Nose Length-Height	60	90–105	97.70 ± .25	2.92 ± .18	2.99 ± .18

TABLE 150

MALE SEDENTARY WORKERS—IMMIGRANTS

Measurement	No.	Range	Mean ± p.e.	S.D. ± p.e.	V. ± p.e.
Age	110	20– 64	40.15 ± .67	10.40 ± .47	25.90 ± 1.18
Weight	106	81–180	124.20 ± 1.09	16.60 ± .77	13.37 ± .62
Stature	110	145–174	159.26 ± .31	4.89 ± .22	3.07 ± .14
Sitting Height	110	76– 93	83.18 ± .22	3.46 ± .16	4.16 ± .19
Trunk Height	110	44– 61	52.84 ± .21	3.30 ± .15	6.25 ± .28
Upper Arm Length	110	25– 34	29.31 ± .11	1.74 ± .08	5.94 ± .27
Lower Arm Length	110	20– 30	23.44 ± .10	1.61 ± .07	6.87 ± .31
Hand Length	110	16– 19	17.84 ± .05	.79 ± .04	4.43 ± .20
Upper Leg Length	110	31– 46	37.98 ± .20	3.10 ± .14	8.16 ± .37
Lower Leg Length	110	28– 38	32.67 ± .12	1.89 ± .09	5.79 ± .26
Total Leg Length	110	67– 88	75.90 ± .27	4.20 ± .19	5.53 ± .25
Biacromion	110	35– 46	40.28 ± .12	1.86 ± .08	4.62 ± .21
Cristal Breadth	110	25– 36	29.49 ± .13	2.00 ± .09	6.78 ± .31
Chest Breadth	110	24– 32	27.69 ± .10	1.49 ± .07	5.38 ± .24
Chest Depth	110	15– 24	20.02 ± .11	1.74 ± .08	8.69 ± .40
Head Length	110	172–205	189.20 ± .39	6.00 ± .27	3.17 ± .14
Head Breadth	110	143–168	153.30 ± .33	5.06 ± .23	3.30 ± .15
Head Height (cm.)	108	12– 16	13.54 ± .07	1.13 ± .05	8.35 ± .38
Minimum Frontal Diameter	110	100–126	112.58 ± .33	5.19 ± .24	4.61 ± .21
Bizygomatic Diameter	109	128–154	142.41 ± .30	4.62 ± .21	3.24 ± .15
Bigonial Diameter	110	97–129	112.25 ± .40	6.21 ± .28	5.53 ± .25
Total Face Height	110	106–138	122.75 ± .39	6.00 ± .27	4.89 ± .22
Upper Face Height	110	67– 94	81.00 ± .31	4.84 ± .22	5.98 ± .27
Forehead Height	108	42– 77	59.94 ± .48	7.40 ± .34	12.35 ± .57
Nose Height	108	42– 59	51.54 ± .22	3.32 ± .15	6.44 ± .30

	N	Range			
Nose Length	108	40– 59	50.08 ± .24	3.74 ± .17	7.47 ± .34
Nose Salient	107	9– 19	14.02 ± .14	2.18 ± .10	2.04 ± .09
Nose Breadth	108	30– 43	36.18 ± .18	2.82 ± .13	7.79 ± .36
Inter-Ocular	110	21– 42	30.68 ± .24	3.77 ± .17	12.29 ± .56
Bi-Ocular	110	88–119	101.56 ± .37	5.72 ± .26	5.63 ± .26
Index					
Relative Shoulder Breadth	110	23– 30	25.18 ± .08	1.30 ± .06	5.16 ± .23
Relative Hip Breadth	110	14– 23	18.42 ± .09	1.42 ± .06	7.71 ± .35
Shoulder-Hip	110	59– 97	73.38 ± .33	5.19 ± .24	7.07 ± .32
Relative Sitting Height	110	47– 57	52.28 ± .12	1.85 ± .08	3.54 ± .16
Relative Trunk Height	110	28– 38	33.23 ± .12	1.80 ± .08	5.42 ± .25
Thoracic	110	60– 87	72.18 ± .33	5.14 ± .23	7.12 ± .32
Brachial	110	67– 92	80.20 ± .32	4.90 ± .22	6.11 ± .28
Tibio-Femoral	110	65–109	86.55 ± .49	7.55 ± .34	8.72 ± .40
Inter-Membral	110	84–117	92.96 ± .30	4.74 ± .22	5.10 ± .23
Cephalic	110	72– 95	81.00 ± .24	3.68 ± .17	4.54 ± .21
Length-Height	108	60– 89	71.54 ± .42	6.44 ± .30	9.00 ± .41
Breadth-Height	108	70–107	88.56 ± .48	7.44 ± .34	8.40 ± .39
Cephalo-Facial	109	85–102	92.76 ± .19	3.00 ± .14	3.23 ± .15
Fronto-Parietal	110	62– 81	73.36 ± .23	3.62 ± .16	4.93 ± .22
Zygo-Frontal	109	70– 85	79.06 ± .19	2.98 ± .14	3.77 ± .17
Zygo-Gonial	109	70– 89	78.80 ± .23	3.50 ± .16	4.44 ± .20
Facial	109	72– 98	86.17 ± .32	4.92 ± .22	5.71 ± .26
Upper Facial	109	46– 66	56.99 ± .23	3.60 ± .16	6.32 ± .29
Nasal	108	54– 95	70.48 ± .45	6.94 ± .32	9.85 ± .45
Nose Salient-Height	107	16– 39	27.20 ± .26	4.05 ± .19	14.89 ± .69
Nose Length-Height	108	86–105	97.72 ± .22	3.34 ± .15	3.42 ± .16

TABLE 151

MALE MANUAL LABORERS—HAWAIIAN BORN

Measurement	No.	Range	Mean	p.e.	S.D.	p.e.	V.	p.e.
Age	45	20– 44	27.00 ±	.54	5.40 ±	.38	20.00 ±	1.42
Weight	45	91–180	131.30 ±	1.70	16.90 ±	1.20	12.87 ±	.92
Stature	45	151–174	162.53 ±	.54	5.34 ±	.38	3.29 ±	.23
Sitting Height	45	78– 93	85.48 ±	.34	3.42 ±	.24	4.00 ±	.28
Trunk Height	45	46– 61	54.14 ±	.33	3.30 ±	.23	6.10 ±	.43
Upper Arm Length	44	27– 35	30.55 ±	.20	1.94 ±	.14	6.35 ±	.46
Lower Arm Length	44	22– 28	24.48 ±	.15	1.47 ±	.11	6.00 ±	.43
Hand Length	45	17– 20	17.96 ±	.08	.79 ±	.06	4.40 ±	.31
Upper Leg Length	45	31– 44	37.14 ±	.26	2.60 ±	.18	7.00 ±	.50
Lower Leg Length	45	30– 39	34.69 ±	.14	2.03 ±	.14	5.85 ±	.42
Total Leg Length	45	69– 88	77.06 ±	.37	3.68 ±	.26	4.78 ±	.34
Biacromion	45	38– 45	41.78 ±	.18	1.76 ±	.13	4.21 ±	.30
Cristal Breadth	45	26– 34	30.00 ±	.18	1.78 ±	.13	5.93 ±	.42
Chest Breadth	45	23– 39	27.49 ±	.25	2.50 ±	.18	9.09 ±	.65
Chest Depth	45	17– 25	20.20 ±	.18	1.83 ±	.13	9.06 ±	.64
Head Length	45	168–203	186.18 ±	.65	6.48 ±	.46	3.48 ±	.25
Head Breadth	45	139–170	155.82 ±	.62	6.16 ±	.44	3.95 ±	.28
Head Height (cm.)	45	11– 15	13.49 ±	.11	1.09 ±	.08	8.08 ±	.57
Minimum Frontal Diameter	45	103–123	113.27 ±	.47	4.65 ±	.33	4.11 ±	.29
Bizygomatic Diameter	45	125–151	142.20 ±	.45	4.50 ±	.32	3.16 ±	.22
Bigonial Diameter	45	100–126	111.86 ±	.50	4.95 ±	.35	4.43 ±	.31
Total Face Height	45	106–135	119.87 ±	.53	5.28 ±	.38	4.40 ±	.31
Upper Face Height	45	69– 92	79.54 ±	.45	4.52 ±	.32	5.68 ±	.40
Forehead Height	45	38– 77	59.14 ±	.78	7.72 ±	.55	13.05 ±	.93
Nose Height	45	42– 61	51.88 ±	.36	3.58 ±	.25	6.90 ±	.49

	N	Range	Mean ±	SD ±	CV ±
Nose Length	45	40– 59	49.84 ± .39	3.90 ± .28	7.82 ± .56
Nose Salient	45	9– 21	14.29 ± .26	2.58 ± .18	18.05 ± 1.28
Nose Breadth	45	28– 39	33.74 ± .27	2.72 ± .19	8.06 ± .57
Inter-Ocular	45	23– 38	30.96 ± .35	3.45 ± .25	11.14 ± .79
Bi-Ocular	45	84–113	99.88 ± .52	5.20 ± .37	5.21 ± .37
Index					
Relative Shoulder Breadth	45	23– 28	25.72 ± .11	1.14 ± .08	4.43 ± .31
Relative Hip Breadth	45	16– 21	18.36 ± .11	1.14 ± .08	6.21 ± .44
Shoulder-Hip	45	62– 82	71.88 ± .40	3.99 ± .28	5.55 ± .39
Relative Sitting Height	45	49– 55	52.47 ± .15	1.50 ± .11	2.86 ± .20
Relative Trunk Height	45	29– 37	33.16 ± .17	1.67 ± .12	5.04 ± .36
Thoracic	45	56– 85	73.52 ± .62	6.16 ± .44	8.38 ± .60
Brachial	44	69– 90	80.36 ± .51	5.04 ± .36	6.27 ± .45
Tibio-Femoral	45	75–119	93.80 ± .88	8.75 ± .62	9.33 ± .66
Inter-Membral	44	86–103	94.46 ± .36	3.56 ± .26	3.77 ± .27
Cephalic	45	74– 91	83.84 ± .39	3.88 ± .28	4.63 ± .33
Length-Height	45	58– 83	71.96 ± .63	6.28 ± .45	8.73 ± .62
Breadth-Height	45	70– 99	86.54 ± .67	6.68 ± .47	7.72 ± .55
Cephalo-Facial	45	83–102	91.18 ± .33	3.26 ± .23	3.58 ± .25
Fronto-Parietal	45	68– 83	72.76 ± .34	3.36 ± .24	4.62 ± .33
Zygo-Frontal	45	74– 85	79.84 ± .27	2.64 ± .19	3.31 ± .24
Zygo-Gonial	45	70– 89	78.98 ± .31	3.04 ± .22	3.85 ± .27
Facial	45	72– 92	84.40 ± .41	4.08 ± .29	4.83 ± .34
Upper Facial	45	49– 66	55.61 ± .37	3.66 ± .26	6.58 ± .47
Nasal	45	50– 83	65.38 ± .62	6.18 ± .44	9.45 ± .67
Nose Salient-Height	45	19– 45	27.74 ± .52	5.19 ± .37	18.71 ± 1.33
Nose Length-Height	45	88–101	96.42 ± .32	3.18 ± .23	3.30 ± .23

TABLE 152

MALE SEDENTARY WORKERS—HAWAIIAN BORN

Measurement	No.	Range	Mean	p.e.	S.D.	p.e.	V.	p.e.
Age	142	20– 49	25.90 ±	.30	5.30 ±	.21	20.46 ±	.82
Weight	139	91–230	126.10 ±	1.09	19.10 ±	.77	15.15 ±	.61
Stature	142	148–177	162.95 ±	.30	5.25 ±	.21	3.22 ±	.13
Sitting Height	141	78– 95	85.54 ±	.21	3.74 ±	.15	4.37 ±	.18
Trunk Height	141	46– 63	54.18 ±	.19	3.28 ±	.13	6.05 ±	.24
Upper Arm Length	141	26– 35	30.52 ±	.10	1.70 ±	.07	5.57 ±	.22
Lower Arm Length	142	20– 28	24.26 ±	.09	1.57 ±	.06	6.47 ±	.26
Hand Length	142	15– 20	17.77 ±	.05	.91 ±	.04	5.12 ±	.20
Upper Leg Length	140	29– 46	37.96 ±	.19	3.28 ±	.13	8.64 ±	.35
Lower Leg Length	142	29– 42	33.68 ±	.12	2.08 ±	.08	6.18 ±	.25
Total Leg Length	141	65– 90	77.60 ±	.24	4.20 ±	.17	5.41 ±	.22
Biacromion	142	37– 47	41.21 ±	.10	1.83 ±	.07	4.44 ±	.18
Cristal Breadth	142	25– 36	28.97 ±	.11	1.99 ±	.08	6.87 ±	.27
Chest Breadth	142	24– 35	27.21 ±	.11	1.88 ±	.08	6.91 ±	.28
Chest Depth	142	16– 27	19.48 ±	.10	1.75 ±	.07	8.98 ±	.36
Head Length	142	172–205	186.70 ±	.37	6.56 ±	.26	3.51 ±	.14
Head Breadth	142	143–174	154.86 ±	.32	5.64 ±	.23	3.64 ±	.15
Head Height (cm.)	137	11– 16	13.76 ±	.12	2.16 ±	.09	15.70 ±	.64
Minimum Frontal Diameter	142	97–126	112.19 ±	.28	4.98 ±	.20	4.44 ±	.18
Bizygomatic Diameter	141	128–160	141.12 ±	.31	5.52 ±	.22	3.91 ±	.16
Bigonial Diameter	142	88–126	110.60 ±	.34	5.97 ±	.24	5.40 ±	.22
Total Face Height	140	106–138	122.39 ±	.33	5.73 ±	.23	4.68 ±	.19
Upper Face Height	141	67– 94	82.28 ±	.28	4.96 ±	.20	6.03 ±	.24
Forehead Height	141	38– 81	59.06 ±	.37	6.56 ±	.26	11.11 ±	.45
Nose Height	142	44– 61	51.82 ±	.19	3.30 ±	.13	6.37 ±	.25

	N	Range			
Nose Length	142	40– 59	50.34 ± .20	3.48 ± .14	6.91 ± .28
Nose Salient	142	9– 19	14.08 ± .13	2.28 ± .09	16.19 ± .65
Nose Breadth	142	28– 43	34.80 ± .16	2.78 ± .11	7.99 ± .32
Inter-Ocular	142	23– 41	31.46 ± .20	3.50 ± .14	11.13 ± .45
Bi-Ocular	141	86–113	100.28 ± .29	5.02 ± .20	5.01 ± .20
Index					
Relative Shoulder Breadth	142	23– 28	25.28 ± .06	1.12 ± .04	4.43 ± .18
Relative Hip Breadth	142	14– 21	17.72 ± .07	1.24 ± .05	7.00 ± .28
Shoulder-Hip	142	62– 85	70.23 ± .25	4.44 ± .18	6.32 ± .25
Relative Sitting Height	141	47– 58	52.47 ± .11	1.87 ± .08	3.56 ± .14
Relative Trunk Height	141	29– 38	33.20 ± .10	1.81 ± .07	5.45 ± .22
Thoracic	142	54– 85	71.60 ± .31	5.42 ± .22	7.57 ± .30
Brachial	141	69– 90	79.66 ± .24	4.30 ± .17	5.40 ± .22
Tibio-Femoral	140	70–124	89.90 ± .46	8.05 ± .32	8.95 ± .36
Inter-Membral	140	82–107	93.68 ± .24	4.22 ± .17	4.50 ± .18
Cephalic	142	74– 93	83.14 ± .23	4.12 ± .16	4.96 ± .20
Length-Height	137	56– 91	73.78 ± .35	6.04 ± .25	8.19 ± .33
Breadth-Height	137	68–107	88.88 ± .40	6.86 ± .28	7.72 ± .31
Cephalo-Facial	141	85–100	91.12 ± .16	2.86 ± .11	3.14 ± .13
Fronto-Parietal	142	62– 83	72.48 ± .19	3.34 ± .13	4.61 ± .18
Zygo-Frontal	141	72– 87	79.54 ± .17	2.92 ± .12	3.67 ± .15
Zygo-Gonial	141	68– 85	78.44 ± .17	3.02 ± .12	3.85 ± .15
Facial	139	75– 98	86.71 ± .26	4.62 ± .19	5.33 ± .22
Upper Facial	140	46– 69	58.40 ± .22	3.78 ± .15	6.47 ± .26
Nasal	142	54– 83	67.26 ± .34	6.04 ± .24	8.98 ± .36
Nose Salient-Height	142	16– 36	27.20 ± .25	4.38 ± .18	16.10 ± .64
Nose Length-Height	142	86–103	97.38 ± .16	2.88 ± .12	2.96 ± .12

TABLE 153

DIFFERENCES OF MEANS OF MALE SEDENTES MANUAL LABORERS
FROM TOTAL MALE SEDENTES

Measurement	Difference	x p.e.
Age	8.15 ± 1.36	5.99
Weight	−3.20 ± 1.55	2.06
Stature	−1.17 ± .59	1.98
Sitting Height	− .94 ± .42	2.24
Trunk Height	− .90 ± .37	2.43
Upper Arm Length	− .93 ± .20	4.65
Lower Arm Length	.17 ± .15	1.13
Hand Length	.14 ± .10	1.40
Upper Leg Length	.24 ± .37	.65
Lower Leg Length	− .32 ± .22	1.45
Total Leg Length	− .36 ± .43	.84
Biacromion	− .31 ± .21	1.48
Cristal Breadth	− .40 ± .19	2.11
Chest Breadth	− .38 ± .17	2.24
Chest Depth	.14 ± .14	1.00
Head Length	− .68 ± .74	.92
Head Breadth	− .24 ± .55	.44
Head Height (cm.)	.14 ± .12	1.17
Minimum Frontal Diameter	2.16 ± .61	3.54
Bizygomatic Diameter	− .36 ± .52	.69
Bigonial Diameter	1.05 ± .57	1.84
Total Face Height	1.17 ± .74	1.58
Forehead Height	.68 ± .88	.66
Upper Face Height	1.06 ± .48	2.21
Nose Height	.12 ± .37	.32
Nose Length	.84 ± .41	2.05
Nose Salient	−1.13 ± .24	4.71
Nose Breadth	−1.22 ± .31	3.94
Inter-Ocular	− .07 ± .32	.22
Bi-Ocular	−1.32 ± .54	2.44
Index		
Relative Shoulder Breadth	.04 ± .14	.29
Relative Hip Breadth	− .22 ± .13	1.69
Shoulder-Hip	.12 ± .49	.24
Relative Sitting Height	− .16 ± .19	.84
Relative Trunk Height	− .20 ± .21	.95
Thoracic	1.76 ± .58	3.03
Brachial	2.66 ± .55	4.84
Tibio-Femoral	−2.05 ± 1.11	1.85
Inter-Membral	− .06 ± .54	.11

[TABLE 153—*continued*]

DIFFERENCES OF MEANS OF MALE SEDENTES MANUAL LABORERS
FROM TOTAL MALE SEDENTES

Index	Difference	x p.e.
Cephalic	.18 ± .40	.45
Length-Height	1.18 ± .62	1.90
Breadth-Height	1.10 ± .79	1.39
Cephalo-Facial	— .12 ± .35	.34
Fronto-Parietal	1.50 ± .38	3.95
Zygo-Frontal	1.68 ± .38	4.42
Zygo-Gonial	1.00 ± .38	2.63
Facial	.99 ± .57	1.74
Upper Facial	.72 ± .38	1.89
Nasal	—2.52 ± .85	2.96
Nose Salient-Height	—2.46 ± .47	5.23
Nose Length-Height	1.20 ± .39	3.08

TABLE 154

DIFFERENCES OF MEANS OF MALE IMMIGRANT MANUAL LABORERS
FROM TOTAL MALE IMMIGRANTS

Measurement	Difference	x p.e.
Age	.40 ± .94	.43
Weight	— .80 ± 1.44	.56
Stature	— .93 ± .45	2.07
Sitting Height	— .36 ± .32	1.12
Trunk Height	— .42 ± .28	1.50
Upper Arm Length	.08 ± .15	.53
Lower Arm Length	— .01 ± .14	.07
Hand Length	.12 ± .07	1.71
Upper Leg Length	— .66 ± .26	2.54
Lower Leg Length	.02 ± .17	.12
Total Leg Length	— .50 ± .34	1.47
Biacromion	.12 ± .16	.75
Cristal Breadth	.09 ± .17	.53
Chest Breadth	— .12 ± .15	.80
Chest Depth	.34 ± .16	2.12
Head Length	.48 ± .55	.87
Head Breadth	—1.18 ± .46	2.57
Head Height (cm.)	— .28 ± .10	2.80
Minimum Frontal Diameter	.12 ± .48	.25
Bizygomatic Diameter	— .39 ± .42	.93
Bigonial Diameter	—1.53 ± .55	2.78
Total Face Height	.51 ± .52	.98
Upper Face Height	.50 ± .43	1.16
Forehead Height	— .88 ± .70	1.26
Nose Height	.24 ± .30	.80
Nose Length	.22 ± .33	.67
Nose Salient	— .13 ± .19	.68
Nose Breadth	— .84 ± .26	3.23
Inter-Ocular	— .16 ± .31	.52
Bi-Ocular	— .88 ± .52	1.69
Index		
Relative Shoulder Breadth	.30 ± .11	2.73
Relative Hip Breadth	.30 ± .12	2.50
Shoulder-Hip	— .15 ± .42	.36
Relative Sitting Height	.00 ± .16	.00
Relative Trunk Height	— .06 ± .15	.40
Thoracic	1.60 ± .49	3.27
Brachial	— .32 ± .45	.71
Tibio-Femoral	1.35 ± .74	1.82
Inter-Membral	.82 ± .40	2.05

[TABLE 154—*continued*]

DIFFERENCES OF MEANS OF MALE IMMIGRANT MANUAL LABORERS
FROM TOTAL MALE IMMIGRANTS

Index	Difference	x p.e.
Cephalic	− .66 ± .34	1.94
Length-Height	−1.62 ± .59	2.75
Breadth-Height	−1.20 ± .69	1.74
Cephalo-Facial	.54 ± .29	1.86
Fronto-Parietal	.52 ± .31	1.68
Zygo-Frontal	.08 ± .29	.28
Zygo-Gonial	− .88 ± .31	2.84
Facial	.60 ± .44	1.36
Upper Facial	.66 ± .35	1.89
Nasal	−1.88 ± .62	3.03
Nose Salient-Height	− .27 ± .34	.79
Nose Length-Height	− .12 ± .28	.43

TABLE 155

DIFFERENCES OF MEANS OF MALE IMMIGRANT SEDENTARY WORKERS
FROM TOTAL MALE IMMIGRANTS

Measurement	Difference	x p.e.
Age	− .45 ± .69	.65
Weight	.20 ± 1.08	.19
Stature	.54 ± .33	1.64
Sitting Height	.08 ± .24	.33
Trunk Height	.22 ± .21	1.05
Upper Arm Length	− .06 ± .11	.55
Lower Arm Length	− .04 ± .10	.40
Hand Length	.03 ± .05	.60
Upper Leg Length	.46 ± .20	2.30
Lower Leg Length	.02 ± .13	.15
Total Leg Length	.34 ± .25	1.36
Biacromion	.00 ± .12	.00
Cristal Breadth	− .05 ± .13	.38
Chest Breadth	.02 ± .11	.18
Chest Depth	− .27 ± .12	2.25
Head Length	− .18 ± .41	.44
Head Breadth	.58 ± .34	1.71
Head Height (cm.)	.13 ± .08	1.62
Minimum Frontal Diameter	− .06 ± .35	.17
Bizygomatic Diameter	.06 ± .31	.19
Bigonial Diameter	.57 ± .41	1.39
Total Face Height	− .48 ± .38	1.26
Upper Face Height	− .40 ± .32	1.25
Forehead Height	.56 ± .52	1.08
Nose Height	− .12 ± .23	.52
Nose Length	− .16 ± .25	.64
Nose Salient	− .09 ± .14	.64
Nose Breadth	.38 ± .19	2.00
Inter-Ocular	.14 ± .23	.61
Bi-Ocular	.74 ± .38	1.95
Index		
Relative Shoulder Breadth	− .12 ± .08	1.50
Relative Hip Breadth	− .18 ± .09	2.00
Shoulder-Hip	− .03 ± .31	.10
Relative Sitting Height	− .09 ± .12	.75
Relative Trunk Height	.09 ± .11	.82
Thoracic	−1.06 ± .36	2.94
Brachial	.02 ± .33	.06
Tibio-Femoral	− .95 ± .55	1.73
Inter-Membral	− .58 ± .30	1.93

[TABLE 155—*continued*]

DIFFERENCES OF MEANS OF MALE IMMIGRANT SEDENTARY WORKERS
FROM TOTAL MALE IMMIGRANTS

Index	Difference	x p.e.
Cephalic	.28 ± .25	1.12
Length-Height	.72 ± .44	1.64
Breadth-Height	.66 ± .51	1.29
Cephalo-Facial	− .36 ± .21	1.71
Fronto-Parietal	− .26 ± .23	1.13
Zygo-Frontal	.00 ± .21	.00
Zygo-Gonial	.42 ± .23	1.83
Facial	− .36 ± .32	1.12
Upper Facial	− .36 ± .26	1.38
Nasal	.84 ± .46	1.83
Nose Salient-Height	.27 ± .26	1.04
Nose Length-Height	− .10 ± .20	.50

TABLE 156

DIFFERENCES OF MEANS OF MALE HAWAIIAN BORN MANUAL LABORERS
FROM TOTAL MALE HAWAIIAN BORN

Measurement	Difference	x p.e.
Age	.85 ± .54	1.57
Weight	3.90 ± 1.88	2.07
Stature	− .30 ± .53	.57
Sitting Height	.00 ± .37	.00
Trunk Height	.02 ± .33	.06
Upper Arm Length	.03 ± .18	.17
Lower Arm Length	.17 ± .16	1.06
Hand Length	.15 ± .09	1.67
Upper Leg Length	− .58 ± .31	1.87
Lower Leg Length	.76 ± .21	3.62
Total Leg Length	− .38 ± .41	.93
Biacromion	.43 ± .18	2.39
Cristal Breadth	.77 ± .20	3.85
Chest Breadth	.21 ± .21	1.00
Chest Depth	.35 ± .18	1.94
Head Length	− .36 ± .66	.55
Head Breadth	.72 ± .58	1.24
Head Height (cm.)	− .19 ± .11	1.73
Minimum Frontal Diameter	.81 ± .50	1.62
Bizygomatic Diameter	.84 ± .53	1.58
Bigonial Diameter	.93 ± .58	1.60
Total Face Height	−1.89 ± .57	3.32
Upper Face Height	−2.08 ± .50	4.16
Forehead Height	.04 ± .75	.05
Nose Height	.06 ± .34	.18
Nose Length	− .38 ± .36	1.06
Nose Salient	.17 ± .24	.71
Nose Breadth	− .82 ± .28	2.93
Inter-Ocular	− .37 ± .35	1.06
Bi-Ocular	− .26 ± .51	.51
Index		
Relative Shoulder Breadth	.34 ± .11	3.09
Relative Hip Breadth	.48 ± .12	4.00
Shoulder-Hip	1.26 ± .44	2.86
Relative Sitting Height	.01 ± .18	.06
Relative Trunk Height	− .02 ± .18	.11
Thoracic	1.46 ± .57	2.56
Brachial	.54 ± .46	1.17
Tibio-Femoral	2.85 ± .85	3.35
Inter-Membral	.56 ± .42	1.33

[TABLE 156—*continued*]

DIFFERENCES OF MEANS OF MALE HAWAIIAN BORN MANUAL LABORERS
FROM TOTAL MALE HAWAIIAN BORN

Index	Difference	x p.e.
Cephalic	.52 ± .41	1.27
Length-Height	−1.40 ± .62	2.26
Breadth-Height	−1.78 ± .72	2.47
Cephalo-Facial	.04 ± .30	.13
Fronto-Parietal	.18 ± .34	.53
Zygo-Frontal	.18 ± .29	.62
Zygo-Gonial	.38 ± .31	1.23
Facial	−1.74 ± .46	3.78
Upper Facial	−2.13 ± .40	5.32
Nasal	−1.44 ± .61	2.36
Nose Salient-Height	.42 ± .46	.91
Nose Length-Height	− .74 ± .30	2.47

TABLE 157

DIFFERENCES OF MEANS OF MALE HAWAIIAN BORN SEDENTARY WORKERS
FROM TOTAL MALE HAWAIIAN BORN

Measurement	Difference	x p.e.
Age	− .25 ± .30	.83
Weight	−1.30 ± 1.07	1.21
Stature	.12 ± .30	.40
Sitting Height	.06 ± .21	.29
Trunk Height	.06 ± .19	.32
Upper Arm Length	.00 ± .10	.00
Lower Arm Length	− .05 ± .09	.56
Hand Length	− .04 ± .05	.80
Upper Leg Length	.24 ± .18	1.33
Lower Leg Length	− .25 ± .12	2.08
Total Leg Length	.16 ± .23	.70
Biacromion	− .14 ± .10	1.40
Cristal Breadth	− .26 ± .11	2.36
Chest Breadth	− .07 ± .12	.58
Chest Depth	− .17 ± .10	1.70
Head Length	.16 ± .37	.43
Head Breadth	− .22 ± .33	.67
Head Height (cm.)	.08 ± .06	1.33
Minimum Frontal Diameter	− .27 ± .28	.96
Bizygomatic Diameter	− .24 ± .30	.80
Bigonial Diameter	− .33 ± .33	1.00
Total Face Height	.63 ± .32	1.97
Upper Face Height	.66 ± .28	2.36
Forehead Height	− .04 ± .42	.10
Nose Height	.00 ± .19	.00
Nose Length	.12 ± .20	.60
Nose Salient	− .04 ± .13	.31
Nose Breadth	.24 ± .16	1.50
Inter-Ocular	.13 ± .20	.65
Bi-Ocular	.14 ± .29	.48
Index		
Relative Shoulder Breadth	− .10 ± .06	1.67
Relative Hip Breadth	− .16 ± .07	2.29
Shoulder-Hip	− .39 ± .25	1.56
Relative Sitting Height	.01 ± .10	.10
Relative Trunk Height	.02 ± .10	.20
Thoracic	− .46 ± .32	1.44
Brachial	− .16 ± .25	.64
Tibio-Femoral	−1.05 ± .48	2.19
Inter-Membral	− .22 ± .23	.96

[TABLE 157—*continued*]

DIFFERENCES OF MEANS OF MALE HAWAIIAN BORN SEDENTARY WORKERS
FROM TOTAL MALE HAWAIIAN BORN

Index	Difference	x p.e.
Cephalic	− .18 ± .23	.78
Length-Height	.42 ± .36	1.17
Breadth-Height	.56 ± .41	1.37
Cephalo-Facial	− .02 ± .17	.12
Fronto-Parietal	− .10 ± .19	.53
Zygo-Frontal	− .12 ± .16	.75
Zygo-Gonial	− .16 ± .17	.94
Facial	.57 ± .26	2.19
Upper Facial	.66 ± .22	3.00
Nasal	.44 ± .35	1.26
Nose Salient-Height	− .12 ± .26	.46
Nose Length-Height	.22 ± .17	1.29

TABLE 158

DISTRIBUTION OF THE X P.E.'S OF THE DIFFERENCES BETWEEN OCCUPATIONAL AND TOTAL MALE GROUPS

		0–.99	1.00–1.99	2.00–2.99	3.00–3.99	4.00–4.99	5.00–5.99	6.00–X
Manual Laborers—Sedentes	Measurements	8	9	8	2	2	0	0
Total Sedentes	Indices	7	6	2	3	2	1	0
Manual Laborers—Immigrants	Measurements	15	7	6	1	0	0	0
Total Immigrants	Indices	7	7	5	2	0	0	0
Sedentary Workers—Immigrants	Measurements	16	10	3	0	0	0	0
Total Immigrants	Indices	6	13	2	0	0	0	0
Manual Laborers—Hawaiian Born	Measurements	10	12	3	3	1	0	0
Total Hawaiian Born	Indices	6	4	6	3	1	1	0
Sedentary Workers—Hawaiian Born	Measurements	18	8	3	0	0	0	0
Total Hawaiian Born	Indices	10	7	3	1	0	0	0

TABLE 159

Measurement	Difference	x p.e.
Age	− .85 ± 1.17	.73
Weight	1.00 ± 1.78	.56
Stature	1.47 ± .55	2.67
Sitting Height	.44 ± .37	1.19
Trunk Height	.64 ± .33	1.94
Upper Arm Length	− .14 ± .18	.78
Lower Arm Length	− .03 ± .16	.19
Hand Length	− .08 ± .09	.89
Upper Leg Length	1.12 ± .33	3.39
Lower Leg Length	.00 ± .21	.00
Total Leg Length	.84 ± .40	2.10
Biacromion	− .12 ± .20	.60
Cristal Breadth	− .14 ± .21	.67
Chest Breadth	.14 ± .20	.70
Chest Depth	− .61 ± .20	3.05
Head Length	− .66 ± .73	.90
Head Breadth	1.76 ± .58	3.03
Head Height (cm.)	.41 ± .13	3.15
Minimum Frontal Diameter	− .18 ± .62	.29
Bizygomatic Diameter	.45 ± .52	.87
Bigonial Diameter	2.10 ± .66	3.18
Total Face Height	− .99 ± .77	1.29
Upper Face Height	− .90 ± .52	1.73
Forehead Height	1.44 ± .92	1.57
Nose Height	− .36 ± .40	.90
Nose Length	− .38 ± .44	.86
Nose Salient	.22 ± .24	.92
Nose Breadth	1.22 ± .33	3.70
Inter-Ocular	.30 ± .37	.81
Bi-Ocular	1.62 ± .65	2.49
Index		
Relative Shoulder Breadth	− .42 ± .14	3.00
Relative Hip Breadth	− .48 ± .14ˈ	3.43
Shoulder-Hip	.12 ± .47	.26
Relative Sitting Height	− .09 ± .18	.50
Relative Trunk Height	.15 ± .17	.88
Thoracic	−2.66 ± .62	4.29
Brachial	.34 ± .61	.56
Tibio-Femoral	−2.30 ± .93	2.47
Inter-Membral	−1.40 ± .48	2.92

[Continued]

[TABLE 159—*continued*]

DIFFERENCES OF MEANS OF MALE IMMIGRANT SEDENTARY WORKERS
FROM MALE IMMIGRANT MANUAL LABORERS

Index	Difference	x p.e.
Cephalic	.94 ± .44	2.14
Length-Height	2.34 ± .73	3.21
Breadth-Height	1.86 ± .88	2.11
Cephalo-Facial	− .90 ± .37	2.43
Fronto-Parietal	− .78 ± .38	2.05
Zygo-Frontal	− .08 ± .39	.21
Zygo-Gonial	1.30 ± .39	3.33
Facial	− .96 ± .55	1.75
Upper Facial	−1.02 ± .44	2.32
Nasal	2.72 ± .79	3.44
Nose Salient-Height	.54 ± .40	1.35
Nose Length-Height	.02 ± .33	.06

TABLE 160

DIFFERENCES OF MEANS OF MALE HAWAIIAN BORN SEDENTARY WORKERS
FROM MALE HAWAIIAN BORN MANUAL LABORERS

Measurement	Difference	x p.e.
Age	−1.10 ± .62	1.77
Weight	−5.20 ± 2.02	2.57
Stature	.42 ± .62	.68
Sitting Height	.06 ± .40	.15
Trunk Height	.04 ± .38	.11
Upper Arm Length	− .03 ± .22	.14
Lower Arm Length	− .22 ± .17	1.29
Hand Length	− .19 ± .09	2.11
Upper Leg Length	.82 ± .32	2.56
Lower Leg Length	−1.01 ± .23	4.39
Total Leg Length	.54 ± .44	1.23
Biacromion	− .57 ± .21	2.71
Cristal Breadth	−1.03 ± .21	4.90
Chest Breadth	− .28 ± .27	1.04
Chest Depth	− .72 ± .21	3.43
Head Length	.52 ± .75	.69
Head Breadth	− .96 ± .70	1.37
Head Height (cm.)	.27 ± .16	1.69
Minimum Frontal Diameter	−1.08 ± .55	1.96
Bizygomatic Diameter	−1.08 ± .55	1.96
Bigonial Diameter	−1.26 ± .60	2.10
Total Face Height	2.52 ± .62	4.06
Upper Face Height	2.74 ± .53	5.17
Forehead Height	− .08 ± .86	.09
Nose Height	− .06 ± .41	.15
Nose Length	.50 ± .44	1.14
Nose Salient	− .21 ± .29	.72
Nose Breadth	1.06 ± .31	3.42
Inter-Ocular	.50 ± .40	1.25
Bi-Ocular	.40 ± .60	.67
Index		
Relative Shoulder Breadth	− .44 ± .13	3.38
Relative Hip Breadth	− .64 ± .13	4.92
Shoulder-Hip	−1.65 ± .47	3.51
Relative Sitting Height	.00 ± .19	.00
Relative Trunk Height	.04 ± .20	.20
Thoracic	−1.92 ± .69	2.78
Brachial	− .70 ± .56	1.25
Tibio-Femoral	−3.90 ± .99	3.94
Inter-Membral	− .78 ± .43	1.81

[*Continued*]

[TABLE 160—*continued*]

DIFFERENCES OF MEANS OF MALE HAWAIIAN BORN SEDENTARY WORKERS
FROM MALE HAWAIIAN BORN MANUAL LABORERS

Index	Difference	x p.e.
Cephalic	− .70 ± .45	1.56
Length-Height	1.82 ± .72	2.53
Breadth-Height	2.34 ± .78	3.00
Cephalo-Facial	− .06 ± .37	.16
Fronto-Parietal	− .28 ± .39	.72
Zygo-Frontal	− .30 ± .32	.94
Zygo-Gonial	− .54 ± .35	1.54
Facial	2.31 ± .49	4.71
Upper Facial	2.79 ± .43	6.49
Nasal	1.88 ± .71	2.65
Nose Salient-Height	− .54 ± .58	.93
Nose Length-Height	.96 ± .36	2.67

TABLE 161

DISTRIBUTIONS OF THE X P.E.'S OF THE DIFFERENCES BETWEEN MALE SEDENTARY WORKERS AND MALE MANUAL LABORERS

		0–.99	1.00–1.99	2.00–2.99	3.00–3.99	4.00–4.99	5.00–5.99	6.00–X
Immigrant Sedentary Workers	Measurements	15	5	3	6	0	0	0
Immigrant Manual Laborers	Indices	6	2	7	5	1	0	0
Hawaiian Born Sedentary Workers	Measurements	9	9	5	2	3	1	0
Hawaiian Born Manual Laborers	Indices	6	4	4	4	2	0	1

TABLE 162

DIFFERENCES OF MEANS OF MALE IMMIGRANT MANUAL LABORERS FROM
MALE SEDENTES MANUAL LABORERS

Measurement	Difference	x p.e.
Age	−2.70 ± 1.61	1.68
Weight	6.60 ± 2.22	2.97
Stature	.57 ± .76	.75
Sitting Height	− .82 ± .52	1.58
Trunk Height	−1.06 ± .46	2.30
Upper Arm Length	.98 ± .24	4.08
Lower Arm Length	.15 ± .18	.83
Hand Length	.31 ± .13	2.38
Upper Leg Length	.84 ± .42	2.00
Lower Leg Length	1.28 ± .31	4.13
Total Leg Length	1.66 ± .52	3.19
Biacromion	1.18 ± .31	3.81
Cristal Breadth	.18 ± .27	.67
Chest Breadth	.66 ± .28	2.36
Chest Depth	− .13 ± .23	.57
Head Length	.84 ± .95	.88
Head Breadth	− .12 ± .79	.15
Head Height (cm.)	.26 ± .18	1.44
Minimum Frontal Diameter	−1.50 ± .83	1.81
Bizygomatic Diameter	.57 ± .74	.77
Bigonial Diameter	− .33 ± .74	.45
Total Face Height	2.91 ± 1.00	2.91
Upper Face Height	8.18 ± .65	12.58
Forehead Height	−3.04 ± 1.15	2.64
Nose Height	1.24 ± .52	2.38
Nose Length	1.74 ± .54	3.22
Nose Salient	.30 ± .29	1.03
Nose Breadth	− .32 ± .43	.74
Inter-Ocular	−1.17 ± .47	2.49
Bi-Ocular	1.70 ± .76	2.24
Index		
Relative Shoulder Breadth	.64 ± .21	3.05
Relative Hip Breadth	.18 ± .19	.95
Shoulder-Hip	−2.46 ± .67	3.67
Relative Sitting Height	− .84 ± .23	3.65
Relative Trunk Height	− .89 ± .25	3.56
Thoracic	−2.56 ± .78	3.28
Brachial	−1.58 ± .66	2.39
Tibio-Femoral	1.85 ± 1.22	1.52
Inter-Membral	− .56 ± .67	.84

[TABLE 162—*continued*]

DIFFERENCES OF MEANS OF MALE IMMIGRANT MANUAL LABORERS FROM
MALE SEDENTES MANUAL LABORERS

Index	Difference	x p.e.
Cephalic	− .34 ± .54	.63
Length-Height	.96 ± .88	1.09
Breadth-Height	1.88 ± 1.17	1.61
Cephalo-Facial	.52 ± .45	1.16
Fronto-Parietal	−1.20 ± .48	2.50
Zygo-Frontal	−1.68 ± .52	3.23
Zygo-Gonial	− .74 ± .51	1.45
Facial	1.89 ± .78	2.42
Upper Facial	5.88 ± .54	10.89
Nasal	−2.16 ± 1.04	2.08
Nose Salient-Height	.18 ± .54	.33
Nose Length-Height	1.36 ± .47	2.89

TABLE 163

DIFFERENCES OF MEANS OF MALE HAWAIIAN BORN MANUAL LABORERS
FROM MALE IMMIGRANT MANUAL LABORERS

Measurement	Difference	x p.e.
Age	-14.00 ± 1.10	12.73
Weight	8.10 ± 2.21	3.67
Stature	$4.74 \pm .71$	6.68
Sitting Height	$2.74 \pm .45$	6.09
Trunk Height	$1.94 \pm .41$	4.73
Upper Arm Length	$1.10 \pm .24$	4.58
Lower Arm Length	$1.01 \pm .20$	5.05
Hand Length	$.04 \pm .11$	.36
Upper Leg Length	$.28 \pm .37$	.76
Lower Leg Length	$2.02 \pm .26$	7.77
Total Leg Length	$2.00 \pm .48$	4.17
Biacromion	$1.38 \pm .24$	5.75
Cristal Breadth	$.37 \pm .24$	1.54
Chest Breadth	$- .06 \pm .30$	.20
Chest Depth	$- .43 \pm .25$	1.72
Head Length	$- 3.68 \pm .90$	4.09
Head Breadth	$4.28 \pm .78$	5.49
Head Height (cm.)	$.36 \pm .16$	2.25
Minimum Frontal Diameter	$.51 \pm .70$	.73
Bizygomatic Diameter	$.24 \pm .62$	.39
Bigonial Diameter	$1.71 \pm .73$	2.34
Total Face Height	$- 3.87 \pm .85$	4.55
Upper Face Height	$- 2.36 \pm .62$	3.81
Forehead Height	$.64 \pm 1.11$	.58
Nose Height	$- .02 \pm .50$	.04
Nose Length	$- .62 \pm .54$	1.15
Nose Salient	$.49 \pm .32$	1.53
Nose Breadth	$- 1.22 \pm .39$	3.13
Inter-Ocular	$.58 \pm .45$	1.29
Bi-Ocular	$- .06 \pm .74$	.08
Index		
Relative Shoulder Breadth	$.12 \pm .16$	.75
Relative Hip Breadth	$- .54 \pm .16$	3.38
Shoulder-Hip	$- 1.38 \pm .52$	2.65
Relative Sitting Height	$.10 \pm .20$	.50
Relative Trunk Height	$.08 \pm .21$	.38
Thoracic	$- 1.32 \pm .81$	1.63
Brachial	$.50 \pm .73$	.68
Tibio-Femoral	4.95 ± 1.18	4.19
Inter-Membral	$.10 \pm .52$	.19

[TABLE 163—*continued*]

DIFFERENCES OF MEANS OF MALE HAWAIIAN BORN MANUAL LABORERS
FROM MALE IMMIGRANT MANUAL LABORERS

Index	Difference	x p.e.
Cephalic	3.78 ± .54	7.00
Length-Height	2.76 ± .87	3.17
Breadth-Height	− .16 ± 1.00	1.60
Cephalo-Facial	− 2.48 ± .46	5.39
Fronto-Parietal	− 1.38 ± .45	3.07
Zygo-Frontal	.70 ± .43	1.63
Zygo-Gonial	1.48 ± .44	3.36
Facial	− 2.73 ± .61	4.48
Upper Facial	− 2.40 ± .52	4.62
Nasal	− 2.38 ± .90	2.64
Nose Salient-Height	1.08 ± .61	1.77
Nose Length-Height	− 1.28 ± .41	3.12

TABLE 164

DIFFERENCES OF MEANS OF MALE HAWAIIAN BORN MANUAL LABORERS
FROM MALE SEDENTES MANUAL LABORERS

Measurement	Difference	x p.e.
Age	−16.70 ± 1.40	11.93
Weight	14.70 ± 2.42	6.07
Stature	5.31 ± .81	6.56
Sitting Height	1.92 ± .54	3.56
Trunk Height	.88 ± .51	1.73
Upper Arm Length	2.08 ± .28	7.43
Lower Arm Length	1.16 ± .20	5.80
Hand Length	.35 ± .13	2.69
Upper Leg Length	1.12 ± .42	2.67
Lower Leg Length	3.30 ± .30	11.00
Total Leg Length	3.66 ± .57	6.42
Biacromion	2.56 ± .32	8.00
Cristal Breadth	.55 ± .28	1.96
Chest Breadth	.60 ± .33	1.82
Chest Depth	− .56 ± .24	2.33
Head Length	− 2.84 ± .97	2.93
Head Breadth	4.16 ± .88	4.73
Head Height (cm.)	.62 ± .18	3.44
Minimum Frontal Diameter	− .99 ± .80	1.24
Bizygomatic Diameter	.81 ± .75	1.08
Bigonial Diameter	1.38 ± .72	1.92
Total Face Height	− .96 ± .92	1.04
Upper Face Height	5.82 ± .67	8.69
Forehead Height	− 2.40 ± 1.15	2.09
Nose Height	1.22 ± .54	2.26
Nose Length	1.12 ± .55	2.04
Nose Salient	.79 ± .34	2.32
Nose Breadth	− 1.54 ± .42	3.67
Inter-Ocular	− .59 ± .52	1.13
Bi-Ocular	1.64 ± .76	2.16
Index		
Relative Shoulder Breadth	.76 ± .21	3.62
Relative Hip Breadth	− .36 ± .19	1.89
Shoulder-Hip	− 3.84 ± .70	5.49
Relative Sitting Height	− .74 ± .24	3.08
Relative Trunk Height	− .81 ± .24	3.38
Thoracic	− 3.88 ± .85	4.56
Brachial	− 1.08 ± .65	1.66
Tibio-Femoral	6.80 ± 1.28	5.31
Inter-Membral	− .46 ± .66	.70

[TABLE 164—*continued*]

DIFFERENCES OF MEANS OF MALE HAWAIIAN BORN MANUAL LABORERS
FROM MALE SEDENTES MANUAL LABORERS

Index	Difference	x p.e.
Cephalic	3.44 ± .55	6.25
Length-Height	3.72 ± .91	4.09
Breadth-Height	1.72 ± 1.13	1.52
Cephalo-Facial	− 1.96 ± .46	4.26
Fronto-Parietal	− 2.58 ± .51	5.06
Zygo-Frontal	− .98 ± .48	2.04
Zygo-Gonial	.74 ± .51	1.45
Facial	− .84 ± .76	1.11
Upper Facial	3.48 ± .54	6.44
Nasal	− 4.54 ± 1.03	4.41
Nose Salient-Height	1.26 ± .68	1.85
Nose Length-Height	.08 ± .51	.16

TABLE 165

DIFFERENCES OF MEANS OF MALE HAWAIIAN BORN SEDENTARY WORKERS
FROM MALE IMMIGRANT SEDENTARY WORKERS

Measurement	Difference	x p.e.
Age	−14.25 ± .73	19.52
Weight	1.90 ± 1.54	1.23
Stature	3.69 ± .43	8.58
Sitting Height	2.36 ± .30	7.87
Trunk Height	1.34 ± .28	4.79
Upper Arm Length	1.21 ± .15	8.07
Lower Arm Length	.82 ± .13	6.31
Hand Length	− .07 ± .07	1.00
Upper Leg Length	− .02 ± .28	.07
Lower Leg Length	1.01 ± .17	5.94
Total Leg Length	1.70 ± .36	4.72
Biacromion	.93 ± .16	5.81
Cristal Breadth	− .52 ± .17	3.06
Chest Breadth	− .48 ± .15	3.20
Chest Depth	− .54 ± .15	3.60
Head Length	− 2.50 ± .54	4.63
Head Breadth	1.56 ± .46	3.39
Head Height (cm.)	.22 ± .14	1.57
Minimum Frontal Diameter	− .39 ± .43	.91
Bizygomatic Diameter	− 1.29 ± .43	3.00
Bigonial Diameter	− 1.65 ± .52	3.17
Total Face Height	− .36 ± .51	.71
Upper Face Height	1.28 ± .42	3.05
Forehead Height	− .88 ± .61	1.44
Nose Height	.28 ± .29	.97
Nose Length	.26 ± .31	.84
Nose Salient	.06 ± .19	.32
Nose Breadth	− 1.38 ± .24	5.75
Inter-Ocular	.78 ± .31	2.52
Bi-Ocular	− 1.28 ± .47	2.72
Index		
Relative Shoulder Breadth	.10 ± .10	1.00
Relative Hip Breadth	− .70 ± .11	6.36
Shoulder-Hip	− 3.15 ± .41	7.68
Relative Sitting Height	.19 ± .16	1.19
Relative Trunk Height	− .03 ± .16	.19
Thoracic	− .58 ± .45	1.29
Brachial	− .54 ± .40	1.35
Tibio-Femoral	3.35 ± .67	5.00
Inter-Membral	.72 ± .38	1.89

[TABLE 165—*continued*]

DIFFERENCES OF MEANS OF MALE HAWAIIAN BORN SEDENTARY WORKERS
FROM MALE IMMIGRANT SEDENTARY WORKERS

Index	Difference	x p.e.
Cephalic	2.14 ± .33	6.48
Length-Height	2.24 ± .55	4.07
Breadth-Height	.32 ± .62	.52
Cephalo-Facial	− 1.64 ± .25	6.56
Fronto-Parietal	− .88 ± .30	2.93
Zygo-Frontal	.48 ± .25	1.92
Zygo-Gonial	− .36 ± .29	1.24
Facial	.54 ± .41	1.32
Upper Facial	1.41 ± .32	4.41
Nasal	− 3.22 ± .56	5.75
Nose Salient-Height	.00 ± .36	.00
Nose Length-Height	− .34 ± .27	1.26

TABLE 166

DISTRIBUTIONS OF THE x P.E.'s OF THE DIFFERENCES BETWEEN MALE GROUPS OF SIMILAR OCCUPATION BUT OF DISSIMILAR ORIGIN

		0–99	1.00–1.99	2.00–2.99	3.00–3.99	4.00–4.99	5.00–5.99	6.00–X
Immigrant Manual Laborers	Measurements	9	4	10	3	2	0	1
Sedentes—Manual Laborers	Indices	4	5	5	6	0	0	1
Hawaiian Born Manual Laborers	Measurements	8	5	2	3	5	3	3
Immigrant Manual Laborers	Indices	5	4	2	5	3	1	1
Hawaiian Born Manual Laborers	Measurements	0	8	9	3	1	1	7
Sedentes—Manual Laborers	Indices	2	6	1	3	4	3	2
Hawaiian Born Sedentary Workers	Measurements	6	4	2	7	3	3	4
Immigrant Sedentary Workers	Indices	3	9	1	0	2	2	4

TABLE 167

OBSERVATIONS ON JAPANESE ADULT MALES

Birthplace

Group	Yamaguchi		Hiroshima		Kyushu Is.		'Other Japan'		Kauai, Niihau		Oahu		Maui, Molokai, Lanai		Hawaii		Total
	No.	%	No.	%	No.	%	No.	%	No.	%	No.	%	No.	%	No.	%	
Hawaiian Born	—		—		—		—		11	5.85	54	28.72	28	14.89	95	50.53	188
Immigrants	39	21.91	52	29.21	45	25.28	42	23.60	—		—		—		—		178
Sedentes	40	23.26	77	44.77	25	14.53	30	17.44	—		—		—		—		172

Father's Birthplace

Group	Yamaguchi		Hiroshima		Kyushu Is.		'Other Japan'		Total
	No.	%	No.	%	No.	%	No.	%	
Hawaiian Born	59	33.15	46	25.84	63	35.39	10	5.62	178
Immigrants	35	20.00	52	29.71	44	25.14	44	25.14	175
Sedentes	36	23.08	68	43.59	24	15.38	28	17.95	156

Mother's Birthplace

Group	Yamaguchi		Hiroshima		Kyushu Is.		'Other Japan'		Total
	No.	%	No.	%	No.	%	No.	%	
Hawaiian Born	56	40.88	41	29.93	33	24.09	7	5.11	137
Immigrants	35	21.47	48	29.45	41	25.15	39	23.93	163
Sedentes	36	22.50	72	45.00	23	14.38	29	18.12	160

[Continued]

[TABLE 167—*continued*]

OBSERVATIONS ON JAPANESE ADULT MALES

Skin Color, Cheek (*Von Luschan Scale*)

Group	6 No.	6 %	8 No.	8 %	9 No.	9 %	10 No.	10 %	11 No.	11 %	12 No.	12 %	13 No.	13 %	14 No.	14 %	Total
Hawaiian Born	—		—		1	.53	—		10	5.32	13	6.91	26	13.83	45	23.94	188
Immigrants	3	1.69	1	.56	1	.56	2	1.13	3	1.69	10	5.65	32	18.08	45	25.42	177
Sedentes	—		—		1	.58	7	4.07	10	5.81	22	12.79	40	23.26	41	23.84	172

Group	15 No.	15 %	16, 17 No.	16, 17 %	18 No.	18 %	19 No.	19 %	20 No.	20 %	21 No.	21 %	22 No.	22 %
Hawaiian Born	9	4.79	64	34.04	10	5.32	4	2.13	2	1.06	4	2.13	—	
Immigrants	11	6.21	44	24.86	10	5.65	7	3.95	4	2.26	2	1.13	2	1.13
Sedentes	16	9.30	24	13.95	5	2.91	4	2.33	1	.58	1	.58	—	

Skin Color, Arm (*Von Luschan Scale*)

Group	3 No.	3 %	4 No.	4 %	7 No.	7 %	8, 9 No.	8, 9 %	10 No.	10 %	11 No.	11 %	Total
Hawaiian Born	4	2.44	1	.61	26	15.85	52	31.71	36	21.95	27	16.46	164
Immigrants	2	1.23	—		27	16.67	44	27.16	44	27.16	28	17.28	162
Sedentes	2	2.17	—		11	11.96	21	22.83	31	33.70	17	18.48	92

Group	12 No.	12 %	13 No.	13 %	14 No.	14 %	15 No.	15 %	16, 17 No.	16, 17 %
Hawaiian Born	7	4.27	7	4.27	4	2.44	—		—	
Immigrants	11	6.79	3	1.85	2	1.23	—		1	.62
Sedentes	5	5.43	3	3.26	1	1.09	1	1.09	—	

Hair Form

Group	Straight		Low Waves		Medium Waves		Deep Waves		Frizzly		Total
	No.	%	No.	%	No.	%	No.	%	No.	%	
Hawaiian Born	128	68.09	42	22.34	13	6.91	4	2.13	1	.53	188
Immigrants	131	74.01	35	19.77	8	4.52	3	1.69	—	—	177
Sedentes	120	80.54	24	16.11	4	2.68	1	.67	—	—	149

Hair Texture

Group	Coarse		Medium		Fine		Total
	No.	%	No.	%	No.	%	
Hawaiian Born	54	28.72	125	66.49	9	4.79	188
Immigrants	91	51.12	80	44.94	7	3.93	178
Sedentes	97	59.15	54	32.93	13	7.93	164

Hair Color

Group	Black		Dark Brown		Red Brown		Total
	No.	%	No.	%	No.	%	
Hawaiian Born	106	56.38	82	43.62	—	—	188
Immigrants	118	78.15	32	21.19	1	.66	151
Sedentes	130	83.33	26	16.67	—	—	156

[Continued]

[TABLE 167—*continued*]

OBSERVATIONS ON JAPANESE ADULT MALES

Hair Quantity, Head

Group	Sub-Medium		Medium		Marked		Total
	No.	%	No.	%	No.	%	
Hawaiian Born	6	3.19	175	93.09	7	3.72	188
Immigrants	39	21.91	131	73.60	8	4.49	178
Sedentes	47	28.14	97	58.08	23	13.77	167

Hair Quantity, Upper Cheek

Group	Absent		Sub-Medium		Medium		Total
	No.	%	No.	%	No.	%	
Hawaiian Born	92	48.94	83	44.15	13	6.91	188
Immigrants	101	56.74	75	42.13	2	1.12	178
Sedentes	56	32.75	112	65.50	3	1.75	171

Hair Quantity, Lower Cheek

Group	Absent		Sub-Medium		Medium		Total
	No.	%	No.	%	No.	%	
Hawaiian Born	58	30.85	118	62.77	12	6.38	188
Immigrants	36	20.22	139	78.09	3	1.69	178
Sedentes	70	40.70	97	56.40	5	2.91	172

Hair Quantity, Chin

Group	Absent No.	%	Sub-Medium No.	%	Medium No.	%	Marked No.	%	Total
Hawaiian Born	12	6.38	157	83.51	18	9.57	1	.53	188
Immigrants	9	5.06	159	89.33	10	5.62	—	—	178
Sedentes	15	8.72	145	84.30	12	6.98	—	—	172

Hair Quantity, Moustache

Group	Absent No.	%	Sub-Medium No.	%	Medium No.	%	Total
Hawaiian Born	4	2.13	158	84.04	26	13.83	188
Immigrants	2	1.12	145	81.46	31	17.42	178
Sedentes	4	2.33	153	88.95	15	8.72	172

Hair Quantity, Chest

Group	Absent No.	%	Sub-Medium No.	%	Medium No.	%	Marked No.	%	Total
Hawaiian Born	29	72.50	5	12.50	5	12.50	1	2.50	40
Immigrants	20	86.96	1	4.35	2	8.70	—	—	23
Sedentes	83	73.45	29	25.66	1	.88	—	—	113

[Continued]

[TABLE 167—continued]

OBSERVATIONS ON JAPANESE ADULT MALES

Hair Quantity, Upper Arm

Group	Absent No.	%	Sub-Medium No.	%	Medium No.	%	Marked No.	%	Total
Hawaiian Born	106	75.18	29	20.57	5	3.55	1	.70	141
Immigrants	128	88.28	17	11.72	—		—		145
Sedentes	124	80.00	31	20.00	—		—		155

Hair Quantity, Lower Arm

Group	Absent No.	%	Sub-Medium No.	%	Medium No.	%	Marked No.	%	Total
Hawaiian Born	76	48.72	71	45.51	8	5.13	1	.64	156
Immigrants	117	68.42	52	30.41	2	1.17	—		171
Sedentes	38	22.22	127	74.27	6	3.51	—		171

Hair Quantity, Hand

Group	Absent No.	%	Sub-Medium No.	%	Medium No.	%	Total
Hawaiian Born	116	76.32	29	19.08	7	4.60	152
Immigrants	148	87.06	22	12.94	—		170
Sedentes	153	91.07	15	8.93	—		168

Hair Quantity, Upper Leg

Group	Absent No.	%	Sub-Medium No.	%	Medium No.	%	Total
Hawaiian Born	12	52.17	8	34.78	3	13.04	23
Immigrants	9	75.00	2	16.67	1	8.33	12
Sedentes	49	61.25	30	37.50	1	1.25	80

Hair Quantity, Lower Leg

Group	Absent No.	%	Sub-Medium No.	%	Medium No.	%	Marked No.	%	Total
Hawaiian Born	17	27.42	35	56.45	9	14.52	1	1.61	62
Immigrants	44	62.86	23	32.86	3	4.29	—		70
Sedentes	18	15.93	90	79.65	4	3.54	1	.88	113

Eye Color

Group	Gray Green No.	%	Gray Brown No.	%	Green Brown No.	%	Light Brown and Brown No.	%	Dark Brown No.	%	Black No.	%	Total
Hawaiian Born	—		3	1.60	1	.53	22	11.70	154	81.92	8	4.26	188
Immigrants	2	1.12	4	2.25	1	.56	24	13.48	139	78.09	8	4.49	178
Sedentes	—		12	6.98	13	7.56	24	13.95	116	67.44	7	4.05	172

[Continued]

[TABLE 167—continued]

OBSERVATIONS ON JAPANESE ADULT MALES

Iris

Group	Homogeneous		Rayed		Diffuse		Speckled		Banded		Rayed and Banded		Total
	No.	%	No.	%	No.	%	No.	%	No.	%	No.	%	
Hawaiian Born	157	83.96	20	10.70	4	2.14	2	1.07	3	1.60	1	.53	187
Immigrants	147	82.58	18	10.11	8	4.49	2	1.12	2	1.12	1	.56	178
Sedentes	120	69.77	37	21.51	8	4.65	—		6	3.49	1	.58	172

Sclera

Group	Clear		Yellow		Gray		Bloodshot		Yellow and Bloodshot		Total
	No.	%	No.	%	No.	%	No.	%	No.	%	
Hawaiian Born	155	82.45	5	2.66	5	2.66	20	10.64	3	1.60	188
Immigrants	136	76.40	12	6.74	10	5.62	19	10.67	1	.56	178
Sedentes	153	88.95	11	6.40	1	.58	6	3.49	1	.58	172

Eyefolds

Group	Absent		Present		Total
	No.	%	No.	%	
Hawaiian Born	15	7.98	173	92.02	188
Immigrants	11	6.18	167	93.82	178
Sedentes	42	24.42	130	75.58	172

Epicanthus

Group	Slight		Medium		Marked		Total
	No.	%	No.	%	No.	%	
Hawaiian Born	29	16.86	139	80.81	4	2.33	172
Immigrants	36	22.22	123	75.93	3	1.85	162
Sedentes	61	52.59	50	43.10	5	4.31	116

Median

Group	Slight		Medium		Marked		Total
	No.	%	No.	%	No.	%	
Hawaiian Born	40	25.97	113	73.38	1	.65	154
Immigrants	54	35.29	95	62.09	4	2.61	153
Sedentes	50	46.30	48	44.44	10	9.26	108

Lateral

Group	Slight		Medium		Marked		Total
	No.	%	No.	%	No.	%	
Hawaiian Born	31	20.95	117	79.05	—		148
Immigrants	47	31.76	94	63.51	7	4.73	148
Sedentes	43	44.79	47	48.96	6	6.25	96

[Continued]

[TABLE 167—continued]

OBSERVATIONS ON JAPANESE ADULT MALES

Axis of Eye

Group	Straight No.	Straight %	Up No.	Up %	Down No.	Down %	Total
Hawaiian Born	46	24.47	3	1.60	139	73.94	188
Immigrants	54	30.51	8	4.52	115	64.97	177
Sedentes	55	31.98	19	11.05	98	56.98	172

Palpebral Opening

Group	Wide No.	Wide %	Medium No.	Medium %	Narrow No.	Narrow %	Total
Hawaiian Born	5	2.67	69	36.90	113	60.43	187
Immigrants	4	2.25	59	33.15	115	64.61	178
Sedentes	2	1.16	79	45.93	91	52.91	172

Eyebrow Thickness

Group	Thick No.	Thick %	Medium No.	Medium %	Thin No.	Thin %	Total
Hawaiian Born	38	20.21	142	75.53	8	4.26	188
Immigrants	34	19.10	135	75.84	9	5.06	178
Sedentes	32	18.60	116	67.44	24	13.95	172

Eyebrows

Group	Concurrent Slight No.	%	Concurrent Marked No.	%	Spaced Medium No.	%	Spaced Slight No.	%	Total
Hawaiian Born	—		28	24.14	57	49.14	31	26.72	116
Immigrants	1	.76	25	19.08	73	55.73	32	24.43	131
Sedentes	—		25	17.36	73	50.69	46	31.94	144

Forehead Slope

Group	Marked No.	%	Medium No.	%	Straight No.	%	Total
Hawaiian Born	5	2.66	125	66.49	58	30.85	188
Immigrants	7	3.93	107	60.11	64	35.96	178
Sedentes	4	2.34	128	74.85	39	22.81	171

Forehead Height

Group	Low No.	%	Medium No.	%	High No.	%	Total
Hawaiian Born	31	16.49	139	73.94	18	9.57	188
Immigrants	39	21.91	123	69.10	16	8.99	178
Sedentes	37	21.64	99	57.89	35	20.47	171

[Continued]

[TABLE 167—*continued*]

OBSERVATIONS ON JAPANESE ADULT MALES

Browridges

Group	Marked		Medium		Slight		Total
	No.	%	No.	%	No.	%	
Hawaiian Born	71	37.77	101	53.72	16	8.51	188
Immigrants	71	39.89	82	46.07	25	14.04	178
Sedentes	28	16.37	56	32.75	87	50.88	171

Glabella

Group	Absent		Slight		Medium		Marked		Total
	No.	%	No.	%	No.	%	No.	%	
Hawaiian Born	1	.53	16	8.51	169	89.89	2	1.06	188
Immigrants	—		14	7.87	162	91.01	2	1.12	178
Sedentes	—		78	45.35	88	51.16	6	3.49	172

Temporal Hair

Group	Absent		Slight		Medium		Marked		Total
	No.	%	No.	%	No.	%	No.	%	
Hawaiian Born	42	22.34	52	27.66	89	47.34	5	2.66	188
Immigrants	51	28.65	53	29.78	70	39.33	4	2.25	178
Sedentes	107	62.21	49	28.49	14	8.14	2	1.16	172

Nasal Bridge

Group	Concave		Straight		Convex		Wavy		Concavo-Convex		Total
	No.	%	No.	%	No.	%	No.	%	No.	%	
Hawaiian Born	14	7.45	95	50.53	63	33.51	12	6.38	4	2.13	188
Immigrants	6	3.37	93	52.25	73	41.01	4	2.25	2	1.12	178
Sedentes	16	9.30	88	51.16	52	30.23	13	7.56	3	1.74	172

Nasal Bridge, Height

Group	High		Medium		Low		Total
	No.	%	No.	%	No.	%	
Hawaiian Born	65	34.57	116	61.70	7	3.72	188
Immigrants	54	30.34	111	62.36	13	7.30	178
Sedentes	22	12.79	121	70.35	29	16.86	172

Nasal Root, Height

Group	Depressed		Low		Medium		High		Total
	No.	%	No.	%	No.	%	No.	%	
Hawaiian Born	12	6.38	37	19.68	105	55.85	34	18.08	188
Immigrants	8	4.49	33	18.54	99	55.62	38	21.35	178
Sedentes	22	12.79	78	45.35	61	35.47	11	6.40	172

[Continued]

[TABLE 167—continued]

OBSERVATIONS ON JAPANESE ADULT MALES

Nasal Root, Breadth

Group	Compressed No.	%	Medium No.	%	Wide No.	%	Total
Hawaiian Born	74	39.36	104	55.32	10	5.32	188
Immigrants	61	34.27	97	54.49	20	11.24	178
Sedentes	17	9.88	97	56.40	58	33.72	172

Nasal Tip, Thickness

Group	Thick No.	%	Medium No.	%	Thin No.	%	Total
Hawaiian Born	31	16.49	147	78.19	10	5.32	188
Immigrants	60	33.71	110	61.80	8	4.49	178
Sedentes	76	44.19	92	53.49	4	2.33	172

Nasal Tip, Tilt

Group	Depressed No.	%	Level No.	%	Tilted No.	%	Total
Hawaiian Born	29	15.43	138	73.40	21	11.17	188
Immigrants	35	19.66	130	73.03	13	7.30	178
Sedentes	88	51.16	72	41.86	12	6.98	172

Axis of Nostrils

Group	Antero-Posterior No.	Antero-Posterior %	Oblique No.	Oblique %	Transverse No.	Transverse %	Total
Hawaiian Born	169	90.86	17	9.14	—		186
Immigrants	167	94.89	9	5.11	—		176
Sedentes	136	79.53	34	19.88	1	.58	171

Lip Thickness

Group	Thin No.	Thin %	Medium No.	Medium %	Thick No.	Thick %	Total
Hawaiian Born	22	11.70	139	73.94	27	14.36	188
Immigrants	27	15.17	109	61.24	42	23.60	178
Sedentes	13	7.56	86	50.00	73	42.44	172

Chin

Group	Prominent No.	Prominent %	Medium No.	Medium %	Receding No.	Receding %	Total
Hawaiian Born	61	32.62	79	42.25	47	25.13	187
Immigrants	34	19.10	82	46.07	62	34.83	178
Sedentes	14	8.19	48	28.07	109	63.74	171

[Continued]

[TABLE 167—continued]

OBSERVATIONS ON JAPANESE ADULT MALES

Ear Lobe

Group	Absent No.	%	Separate No.	%	Attached No.	%	Total
Hawaiian Born	9	4.84	45	24.19	132	70.97	186
Immigrants	10	5.65	62	35.03	105	59.32	177
Sedentes	5	2.91	52	30.23	115	66.86	172

Ear Lobe, Size

Group	Small No.	%	Large No.	%	Total
Hawaiian Born	140	79.10	37	20.90	177
Immigrants	116	69.46	51	30.54	167
Sedentes	93	55.69	74	44.31	167

Roll of Helix

Group	One-Third No.	%	Two-Thirds No.	%	Three-Thirds No.	%	Flat No.	%	Total
Hawaiian Born	4	2.15	20	10.75	160	86.02	2	1.08	186
Immigrants	—		12	6.74	166	93.26	—		178
Sedentes	—		34	19.77	138	80.23	—		172

Position of Upper Mesial Incisors

Group	∧		—		V		Total
	No.	%	No.	%	No.	%	
Hawaiian Born	26	14.36	100	55.25	55	30.39	181
Immigrants	14	9.03	84	54.19	57	36.77	155
Sedentes	1	5.56	8	44.44	9	50.00	18

Bite

Group	Under		Edge-Edge		Slightly Over		Marked Over		Total
	No.	%	No.	%	No.	%	No.	%	
Hawaiian Born	9	4.97	36	19.89	129	71.27	7	3.87	181
Immigrants	6	3.95	34	22.37	104	68.42	8	5.26	152
Sedentes	—		1	5.00	17	85.00	2	10.00	20

Musculature

Group	Weak		Medium		Marked		Total
	No.	%	No.	%	No.	%	
Hawaiian Born	20	10.81	130	70.27	35	18.92	185
Immigrants	22	12.50	133	75.57	21	11.93	176
Sedentes	14	8.14	136	79.07	22	12.79	172

TABLE 168

OBSERVATIONS ON JAPANESE ADULT FEMALES

Birthplace

Group	Yamaguchi		Hiroshima		Kyushu Is.		'Other Japan'		Kauai, Niihau		Oahu		Maui, Molokai, Lanai		Hawaii		Total
	No.	%	No.	%	No.	%	No.	%	No.	%	No.	%	No.	%	No.	%	
Hawaiian Born	—		—		—		—		8	8.79	31	34.07	20	21.98	32	35.16	91
Immigrants	25	26.88	29	31.18	19	20.43	20	21.51	—		—		—		—		93
Sedentes	16	17.58	35	38.46	23	25.27	17	18.68	—		—		—		—		91

Father's Birthplace

Group	Yamaguchi		Hiroshima		Kyushu Is.		'Other Japan'		Total
	No.	%	No.	%	No.	%	No.	%	
Hawaiian Born	26	29.89	23	26.44	19	21.84	19	21.84	87
Immigrants	21	24.71	29	34.12	17	20.00	18	21.18	85
Sedentes	16	19.28	31	37.35	20	24.10	16	19.28	83

Mother's Birthplace

Group	Yamaguchi		Hiroshima		Kyushu Is.		'Other Japan'		Total
	No.	%	No.	%	No.	%	No.	%	
Hawaiian Born	25	29.76	25	29.76	17	20.24	17	20.24	84
Immigrants	19	24.05	28	35.44	16	20.25	16	20.25	79
Sedentes	17	20.99	28	34.57	20	24.69	16	19.75	81

Skin Color, Cheek (Von Luschan Scale)

Group	3 No.	%	5 No.	%	6 No.	%	7 No.	%	8 No.	%	9 No.	%	10 No.	%
Hawaiian Born	2	2.20	—		—		—		5	5.49	9	9.89	12	13.19
Immigrants	3	3.23	1	1.08	1	1.08	3	3.23	3	3.23	5	5.38	9	9.68
Sedentes	—		—		—		1	1.12	1	1.12	4	4.49	9	10.11

Group	11 No.	%	12 No.	%	13 No.	%	14 No.	%	15 No.	%	16, 17 No.	%	18 No.	%	Total
Hawaiian Born	22	24.18	14	15.38	18	19.78	6	6.59	—		3	3.30	—		91
Immigrants	11	11.83	17	18.28	18	19.35	15	16.13	2	2.15	5	5.38	—		93
Sedentes	13	14.61	15	16.85	20	22.47	14	15.73	4	4.49	7	7.87	1	1.12	89

Skin Color, Arm (Von Luschan Scale)

Group	3 No.	%	4 No.	%	7 No.	%	8, 9 No.	%	10 No.	%
Hawaiian Born	—		—		5	6.41	37	47.44	27	34.62
Immigrants	2	2.56	1	1.28	16	20.51	30	38.46	19	24.36
Sedentes	3	5.45	—		13	23.64	23	41.82	11	20.00

Group	11 No.	%	12 No.	%	13 No.	%	14 No.	%	16, 17 No.	%	Total
Hawaiian Born	5	6.41	1	1.28	1	1.28	1	1.28	1	1.28	78
Immigrants	8	10.26	2	2.56	—		—		—		78
Sedentes	2	3.64	3	5.45	—		—		—		55

[Continued]

[TABLE 168—*continued*]

OBSERVATIONS ON JAPANESE ADULT FEMALES

Hair Form

Group	Straight No.	%	Low Waves No.	%	Medium Waves No.	%	Total
Hawaiian Born	74	82.22	16	17.78	—		90
Immigrants	81	88.04	11	11.96	—		92
Sedentes	79	86.81	11	12.09	1	1.10	91

Hair Texture

Group	Coarse No.	%	Medium No.	%	Fine No.	%	Total
Hawaiian Born	22	24.44	62	68.89	6	6.67	90
Immigrants	20	21.51	66	70.97	7	7.53	93
Sedentes	20	21.98	64	70.33	7	7.69	91

Hair Color

Group	Black No.	%	Dark Brown No.	%	Red Brown No.	%	Total
Hawaiian Born	50	54.95	41	45.05	—		91
Immigrants	60	69.77	25	29.07	1	1.16	86
Sedentes	47	53.41	40	45.45	1	1.14	88

Hair Quantity, Head

Group	Absent		Sub-Medium		Medium		Marked		Total
	No.	%	No.	%	No.	%	No.	%	
Hawaiian Born	—		—		86	94.51	5	5.49	91
Immigrants	1	1.08	2	2.15	86	92.47	4	4.30	93
Sedentes	1	1.10	3	3.30	77	84.62	10	10.99	91

Hair Quantity, Upper Cheek

Group	Absent		Sub-Medium		Medium		Total
	No.	%	No.	%	No.	%	
Hawaiian Born	88	96.70	2	2.20	1	1.10	91
Immigrants	90	100.00	—		—		90
Sedentes	82	90.11	9	9.89	—		91

Hair Quantity, Lower Arm

Group	Absent		Sub-Medium		Total
	No.	%	No.	%	
Hawaiian Born	64	75.29	21	24.71	85
Immigrants	81	93.10	6	6.90	87
Sedentes	73	80.22	18	19.78	91

[Continued]

[TABLE 168—continued]

OBSERVATIONS ON JAPANESE ADULT FEMALES

Hair Quantity, Lower Leg

Group	Absent No.	%	Sub-Medium No.	%	Medium No.	%	Total
Hawaiian Born	38	66.67	18	31.58	1	1.75	57
Immigrants	63	96.92	2	3.08	—	—	65
Sedentes	47	59.49	32	40.51	—	—	79

Eye Color

Group	Gray No.	%	Gray Brown No.	%	Green Brown No.	%	Light Brown, Brown No.	%	Dark Brown No.	%	Black No.	%	Total
Hawaiian Born	—	—	—	—	—	—	2	2.20	83	91.21	6	6.59	91
Immigrants	—	—	1	1.08	—	—	8	8.60	81	87.10	3	3.23	93
Sedentes	1	1.10	2	2.20	2	2.20	13	14.29	72	79.12	1	1.10	91

Iris

Group	Homogeneous No.	%	Rayed No.	%	Banded No.	%	Total
Hawaiian Born	85	93.41	6	6.59	—	—	91
Immigrants	81	88.04	11	11.96	—	—	92
Sedentes	74	81.32	15	16.48	2	2.20	91

Sclera

Group	Clear		Yellow		Gray		Bloodshot		Yellow and Bloodshot		Total
	No.	%	No.	%	No.	%	No.	%	No.	%	
Hawaiian Born	80	87.91	—		9	9.89	2	2.20	—		91
Immigrants	78	86.67	3	3.33	6	6.67	3	3.33	—		90
Sedentes	84	92.31	—		2	2.20	4	4.40	1	1.10	91

Eyefolds

Group	Absent		Present		Total
	No.	%	No.	%	
Hawaiian Born	9	9.89	82	90.11	91
Immigrants	9	9.68	84	90.32	93
Sedentes	22	24.18	69	75.82	91

Epicanthus

Group	Slight		Medium		Marked		Total
	No.	%	No.	%	No.	%	
Hawaiian Born	21	25.61	61	74.39	—		82
Immigrants	23	28.05	56	68.29	3	3.66	82
Sedentes	35	56.45	26	41.94	1	1.61	62

[Continued]

[TABLE 168—*continued*]

OBSERVATIONS ON JAPANESE ADULT FEMALES

Median

Group	Slight No.	%	Medium No.	%	Marked No.	%	Total
Hawaiian Born	33	44.59	41	55.41	—		74
Immigrants	36	48.00	38	50.67	1	1.33	75
Sedentes	31	53.45	27	46.55	—		58

Lateral

Group	Slight No.	%	Medium No.	%	Marked No.	%	Total
Hawaiian Born	29	42.03	40	57.97	—		69
Immigrants	26	38.24	40	58.82	2	2.94	68
Sedentes	21	46.67	23	51.11	1	2.22	45

Axis of Eye

Group	Straight No.	%	Up No.	%	Down No.	%	Total
Hawaiian Born	18	19.78	2	2.20	71	78.02	91
Immigrants	22	23.66	2	2.15	69	74.19	93
Sedentes	31	34.07	7	7.69	53	58.24	91

Palpebral Opening

Group	Wide No.	%	Medium No.	%	Narrow No.	%	Total
Hawaiian Born	4	4.40	32	35.16	55	60.44	91
Immigrants	5	5.49	32	35.16	54	59.34	91
Sedentes	2	2.20	51	56.04	38	41.76	91

Eyebrow Thickness

Group	Thick No.	%	Medium No.	%	Thin No.	%	Total
Hawaiian Born	5	5.49	73	80.22	13	14.29	91
Immigrants	6	10.71	32	57.14	18	32.14	56
Sedentes	1	1.10	41	45.05	49	53.85	91

Eyebrows

Group	Concurrent Marked No.	%	Concurrent Medium No.	%	Spaced Slight No.	%	Total
Hawaiian Born	29	36.71	—		12	15.19	79
Immigrants	22	27.16	1	1.23	13	16.05	81
Sedentes	23	27.06	—		17	20.00	85

[Continued]

[TABLE 168—*continued*]

OBSERVATIONS ON JAPANESE ADULT FEMALES

Forehead Slope

Group	Medium No.	%	Straight No.	%	Total
Hawaiian Born	49	53.85	42	46.15	91
Immigrants	59	63.44	34	36.56	93
Sedentes	51	56.04	40	43.96	91

Forehead Height

Group	Low No.	%	Medium No.	%	High No.	%	Total
Hawaiian Born	29	31.87	47	51.65	15	16.48	91
Immigrants	21	22.58	59	63.44	13	13.98	93
Sedentes	28	30.77	49	53.85	14	15.38	91

Browridges

Group	Marked No.	%	Medium No.	%	Slight No.	%	Total
Hawaiian Born	—		15	16.48	76	83.52	91
Immigrants	3	3.23	15	16.13	75	80.65	93
Sedentes	—		5	5.49	86	94.51	91

Glabella

Group	Slight		Medium		Marked		Total
	No.	%	No.	%	No.	%	
Hawaiian Born	40	43.96	50	54.95	1	1.10	91
Immigrants	27	29.35	65	70.65	—		92
Sedentes	75	82.42	16	17.58	—		91

Temporal Hair

Group	Absent		Slight		Medium		Marked		Total
	No.	%	No.	%	No.	%	No.	%	
Hawaiian Born	6	6.59	29	31.87	50	54.95	6	6.59	91
Immigrants	16	17.20	31	33.33	38	40.86	8	8.60	93
Sedentes	16	17.58	41	45.05	30	32.97	4	4.40	91

Nasal Bridge

Group	Concave		Straight		Convex		Wavy		Concavo-Convex		Total
	No.	%	No.	%	No.	%	No.	%	No.	%	
Hawaiian Born	13	14.29	41	45.05	27	29.67	2	2.20	8	8.79	91
Immigrants	16	20.78	34	44.16	24	31.17	1	1.30	2	2.60	77
Sedentes	29	31.87	38	41.76	15	16.48	—		9	9.89	91

[Continued]

[TABLE 168—continued]

OBSERVATIONS ON JAPANESE ADULT FEMALES

Nasal Bridge, Height

Group	High No.	%	Medium No.	%	Low No.	%	Total
Hawaiian Born	17	18.68	66	72.53	8	8.79	91
Immigrants	16	19.28	65	78.31	2	2.41	83
Sedentes	4	4.40	57	62.64	30	32.97	91

Nasal Root, Height

Group	Depressed No.	%	Low No.	%	Medium No.	%	High No.	%	Total
Hawaiian Born	6	6.59	23	25.27	49	53.85	13	14.29	91
Immigrants	—		16	17.78	63	70.00	11	12.22	90
Sedentes	10	10.99	50	54.95	25	27.47	6	6.59	91

Nasal Root, Breadth

Group	Compressed No.	%	Medium No.	%	Wide No.	%	Total
Hawaiian Born	27	29.67	53	58.24	11	12.09	91
Immigrants	19	20.43	62	66.67	12	12.90	93
Sedentes	6	6.67	38	42.22	46	51.11	90

Nasal Tip, Thickness

Group	Thick No.	%	Medium No.	%	Thin No.	%	Total
Hawaiian Born	16	17.58	65	71.43	10	10.99	91
Immigrants	21	22.58	66	70.97	6	6.45	93
Sedentes	36	39.56	52	57.14	3	3.30	91

Nasal Tip, Tilt

Group	Depressed No.	%	Level No.	%	Tilted No.	%	Total
Hawaiian Born	8	8.79	62	68.13	21	23.08	91
Immigrants	10	10.99	66	72.53	15	16.48	91
Sedentes	25	27.47	48	52.75	18	19.78	91

Axis of Nostrils

Group	Antero-Posterior No.	%	Oblique No.	%	Transverse No.	%	Total
Hawaiian Born	85	94.44	5	5.56	—		90
Immigrants	85	94.44	5	5.56	—		90
Sedentes	67	73.63	23	25.27	1	1.10	91

[Continued]

[TABLE 168—continued]

OBSERVATIONS ON JAPANESE ADULT FEMALES

Lip Thickness

Group	Thin No.	Thin %	Medium No.	Medium %	Thick No.	Thick %	Total
Hawaiian Born	14	15.38	61	67.03	16	17.58	91
Immigrants	14	15.05	60	64.52	19	20.43	93
Sedentes	7	7.69	52	57.14	32	35.16	91

Chin

Group	Prominent No.	%	Medium No.	%	Receding No.	%	Total
Hawaiian Born	23	25.27	41	45.05	27	29.67	91
Immigrants	23	24.73	36	38.71	34	36.56	93
Sedentes	4	4.40	21	23.08	66	72.53	91

Ear Lobe

Group	Absent No.	%	Separate No.	%	Attached No.	%	Total
Hawaiian Born	1	1.19	16	19.05	67	79.76	84
Immigrants	2	2.17	15	16.30	75	81.52	92
Sedentes	5	5.49	15	16.48	71	78.02	91

Ear Lobe, Size

Group	Small No.	Small %	Large No.	Large %	Total
Hawaiian Born	73	87.95	10	12.05	83
Immigrants	71	78.89	19	21.11	90
Sedentes	62	72.09	24	27.91	86

Roll of Helix

Group	One-Third No.	One-Third %	Two-Thirds No.	Two-Thirds %	Three-Thirds No.	Three-Thirds %	Total
Hawaiian Born	—		5	5.88	80	94.12	85
Immigrants	—		1	1.15	86	98.85	87
Sedentes	1	1.10	9	9.89	81	89.01	91

Position of Upper Mesial Incisors

Group	Λ No.	Λ %	— No.	— %	V No.	V %	Total
Hawaiian Born	12	15.79	34	44.74	30	39.47	76
Immigrants	9	13.24	36	52.94	23	33.82	68
Sedentes	3	23.08	5	38.46	5	38.46	13

[Continued]

[TABLE 168—*continued*]

OBSERVATIONS ON JAPANESE ADULT FEMALES

Bite

Group	Under		Edge-Edge		Slightly Over		Marked Over		Total
	No.	%	No.	%	No.	%	No.	%	
Hawaiian born	3	3.90	14	18.18	57	74.03	3	3.90	77
Immigrants	1	1.41	18	25.35	50	70.42	2	2.82	71
Sedentes	—		1	7.69	12	92.31	—		13

Musculature

Group	Weak		Medium		Total
	No.	%	No.	%	
Hawaiian Born	83	93.26	6	6.74	89
Immigrants	75	88.24	10	11.76	85
Sedentes	91	100.00	—		91